HUMAN FACTORS METHODS

Human Factors Methods
A Practical Guide for Engineering and Design

NEVILLE A. STANTON
PAUL M. SALMON
GUY H. WALKER
CHRIS BABER
DANIEL P. JENKINS
Human Factors Integration Defence Technology Centre

ASHGATE

Published by
Ashgate Publishing Limited
Gower House
Croft Road
Aldershot
Hampshire GU11 3HR
England

Ashgate Publishing Company
Suite 420
101 Cherry Street
Burlington, VT 05401-4405
USA

Ashgate website: http://www.ashgate.com

British Library Cataloguing in Publication Data
Human factors methods: a practical guide for engineering
   and design
   1. Human engineering
   I. Stanton, Neville, 1960–
   620.8'2

Library of Congress Cataloging-in-Publication Data
Human factors methods: a practical guide for engineering and design
   / by Neville A. Stanton ... [et al.].
      p. cm.
   Includes bibliographical references and index.
   ISBN 0-7546-4660-2 (hardback) -- ISBN 0-7546-4661-0 (pbk.)
   1. Human engineering. 2. Design, Industrial. I. Stanton, Neville,
   1960–
   TA166.H795 2005
   620.8'2--dc22

                                                                    2005021087

ISBN 0 7546 4660 2 (hardback)
      0 7546 4661 0 (paperback)

Printed and bound in Great Britain by TJ International Ltd, Padstow, Cornwall.

Contents

List of Figures

List of Tables

Acknowledgements

The Human Factors Integration Defence Technology Centre is a consortium of defence companies and Universities working in co-operation on a series of defence related projects. The consortium is led by Aerosystems International and comprises Birmingham University, Brunel University, Cranfield University, Lockheed Martin, MBDA, SEA and VP Defence.

Aerosystems International	Birmingham University	Brunel University	Cranfield University
Dr David Morris	Dr Chris Baber	Professor Neville Stanton	Dr Don Harris
Dr Karen Lane	Professor Bob Stone	Dr Guy Walker	Lauren Thomas
Stephen Brackley	Dr Theodoros Arvanitis	Daniel Jenkins	Rebecca Stewart
Linda Wells	Dr Huw Gibson	Dr Stephen Gulliver	Andy Farmilo
Kevin Bessell	Richard McMaster	Dr Damian Green	Brian Farmilo
	Dr James Cross	Dr Mark Young	Ray Burcham
	Dr Robert Houghton	Professor Stephen Watts	Geoff Hone
			Steve Smith
			Jacob Mulenga
			Iain McLeod
			Ian Whitworth
			John Huddlestone

Lockheed Martin UK	MBDA Missile Systems	Systems Engineering and Assessment (SEA) Ltd	VP Defence
Mark Linsell	Michael Goom	Pamela Newman	David Hendon
Mick Fuchs	Dr Carol Mason	Clare Borras	
	Georgina Hutchison	Kerry Tatlock	
		Mel Mock	

We are grateful to the Ministry of Defence and David Ferbrache for funding this work, and also to DSTL who have managed the work of the consortium, in particular to Geoff Barrett, Bruce Callander, Colin Corbridge, Roland Edwards, Alan Ellis, Jim Squire and Alison Rogers.

This work from the Human Factors Integration Defence Technology Centre was part-funded by the Human Capability Domain of the UK Ministry of Defence Scientific Research Programme.

Further information on the work and people that comprise the HFI DTC can be found on www.hfidtc.com.

About the Authors

Professor Neville A. Stanton
HFI DTC, BIT Lab, School of Engineering and Design,
Brunel University, Uxbridge, UK.
neville.stanton@brunel.ac.uk

Professor Stanton holds a Chair in Human-Centred Design and has published over 75 international academic journal papers and 10 books on human-centred design. He was a Visiting Fellow of the Department of Design and Environmental Analysis at Cornell University in 1998. In 1998 he was awarded the Institution of Electrical Engineers Divisional Premium Award for a co-authored paper on Engineering Psychology and System Safety. The Ergonomics Society awarded him the prestigious Otto Edholm medal in 2001 for his contribution to basic and applied ergonomics research. Professor Stanton is on the editorial boards of *Ergonomics*, *Theoretical Issues in Ergonomics Science* and the *International Journal of Human Computer Interaction*. Professor Stanton is a Chartered Occupational Psychologist registered with The British Psychological Society, a Fellow of The Ergonomics Society and a Fellow of the RSA. He has a BSc in Occupational Psychology from Hull University, an MPhil in Applied Psychology from Aston University, and a PhD in Human Factors, also from Aston.

Paul M. Salmon
HFI DTC, BIT Lab, School of Engineering and Design,
Brunel University, Uxbridge, UK.
Now at Monash University Accident Research Centre (MUARC),
Victoria 3800, Australia.
paul.salmon@general.monash.edu.au

Paul Salmon is a Human Factors specialist and has a BSc Honours degree in Sports Science and an MSc in Applied Ergonomics, both from the University of Sunderland in the UK. He worked as a Human Factors researcher at Brunel University in the UK between 2001 and 2004, where he was involved in a number of different projects, including ERRORPRED (the development and validation of a human error identification tool for use in the certification of civil flight decks), as well as the HFI DTC (developing novel human factors theory and methods within the military domain). In 2005 Paul began working as a Research Fellow at the Monash University Accident Research Centre (MUARC) in Australia. So far he has been involved in several projects in the area of human error, cognitive work analysis and young driver training. He is also currently working towards a PhD on distributed situation awareness in the road transport domain. Paul has specialist expertise in the fields of human error and situation awareness, and also in the application of structured human factors methods, including human error identification and analysis, situation awareness measurement, task analysis and cognitive task analysis techniques.

Dr Guy H. Walker
*HFI DTC, BIT Lab, School of Engineering and Design, Brunel University,
Uxbridge, UK.
guy.walker@brunel.ac.uk*

Guy Walker read for a BSc Honours degree in Psychology at Southampton University specialising in engineering psychology, statistics and psychophysics. During his undergraduate studies he also undertook work in auditory perception laboratories at Essex University and the Applied Psychology Unit at Cambridge University. After graduating in 1999 he moved to Brunel University, gaining a PhD in Human Factors in 2002. His research focused on driver performance, situational awareness and the role of feedback in vehicles. Since this time Guy has worked for a human factors consultancy on a project funded by the Rail Safety and Standards Board, examining driver behaviour in relation to warning systems and alarms fitted in train cabs. Currently Guy works within the DTC HFI consortium at Brunel University, engaged primarily in work on future C4i systems. He is also author of numerous journal articles and book contributions.

Dr Chris Baber
*HFI DTC, School of Electrical, Electronic and Computer Engineering,
University of Birmingham, Edgbaston, Birmingham, UK
c.baber@bham.ac.uk*

Chris Baber graduated from Keele University with BA (Hons) in Psychology and English in 1987, which led him to read for a PhD in Speech Technology at Aston University. On completion, in 1990, he began working at The University of Birmingham. Originally he taught on the MSc Work Design & Ergonomics course, covering such topics as human-computer interaction, job design and research methods. In 1999, he moved to the Department of Electronic, Electrical and Computer Engineering where, in 2004, he was promoted to Reader in Interactive Systems Design. Chris's research focuses on human interaction with technology, particularly in terms of the use of everyday skills (such as speech or tool-use) to support interaction. This has led to his research team designing, building and evaluating wearable computers to both support everyday activity and collect data in the field. Currently, this work is directed towards crime scene investigation and distributed command and control.

Daniel P. Jenkins
*HFI DTC, BIT Lab, School of Engineering and Design, Brunel University,
Uxbridge, UK.
guy.walker@brunel.ac.uk*

Dan Jenkins graduated in 2004 from Brunel University with MEng (Hons) in Mechanical Engineering and Design. Part of his degree involved designing and developing a system to raise driver situational awareness and reduce lateral collisions. Dan has over two years experience as a Design Engineer in the Automotive Industry, and has worked in a number of roles throughout the world with a strong focus on customer orientated design; design for inclusion; and human factors. He is currently a full-time research fellow within the HFI-DTC consortium and is studying for a PhD related to the project.

Chapter 1

Introduction to Human Factors Methods

Human Factors Integration is concerned with providing a balanced development of both the technical and human aspects of equipment procurement. It provides a process that ensures the application of scientific knowledge about human characteristics through the specification, design and evaluation of systems. (MoD, 2000, p.6)[1]

The purpose of this book is to present a range of Human Factors (HF) methods that can be used in system design and evaluation. It is important to note immediately that our focus is on the design and evaluation of systems, as opposed to specific products, and this sets the tone for the entire book. HF has a broad remit, covering all manner of analysis from human interaction with devices, to the design of tools and machines, to team working, and to various other general aspects of work and organisational design. Of particular interest to the work reflected in this book is the issue of Human Factors Integration (HFI). According to MoD (2000) HFI is concerned with '… providing a balanced development of both the technical and human aspects of equipment procurement. It provides a process that ensures the application of scientific knowledge about human characteristics through the specification, design and evaluation of systems' [MoD, 2000, p.6]. Within the UK Ministry of Defence, the HFI process covers six domains: Manpower, Personnel, Training, Human Factors Engineering, System Safety, and Health Hazards. The HFI process is intended to be seen as an activity that supports attention towards all six domains during the entire system design lifecycle. For the purposes of this book, our attention focuses on the HF methods that can be used to support these domains. In particular, while the primary focus will be on Human Factors Engineering, we cover methods that are essential to System Safety and to Manpower, and that can support Training and Personnel. Issues relating to Health Hazards relate to risk analysis, but also require additional knowledge and techniques outside the scope of this book. The Human-Centred Design of Systems is also covered by the International Standard ISO13407. This emphasises the need to focus on the potential users of systems at all stages in the design and development process in order to ensure that requirements have been adequately defined and that functions are allocated between user and technology appropriately.

Much has been made about the timeliness of HF input into projects, but the appropriateness of the analysis depends on a number of factors, including which stage of design the project is at, how much time and resources are available, the skills of the analyst, access to the end-user population, and what kind of data are required (Stanton and Young, 1999). Stanton and Young (1999) showed that many of the methods they reviewed were flexible with regard to the design stage they could be applied to. Indeed many of the methods could be applied to very early stages of design, such as to concept models and mock-ups. Many methods may be used in a predictive as well as an evaluative manner. This flexibility of application to the various design stages bodes well for HF methods. Other factors that the analyst needs to be aware of when choosing methods are: the accuracy of the methods (particularly where a predictive element is involved), the criteria to be evaluated (such as time, errors, communications, movement, usability, and so on), the acceptability and appropriateness of

---

1   MoD (2000) Human Factors Integration: An Introductory Guide. London: HMSO

the methods (to the people being analysed, the domain context, resources available, and so on), and the cost-benefit of the method(s) and the product(s). Methods form a major part of the HF discipline. For example, the International Encyclopaedia of Human Factors and Ergonomics (Karwowski, 2001) has an entire section devoted to methods and techniques. Many of the other sections of the encyclopaedia also make reference to, if not provide actual examples of, HF methods. In short, the importance of HF methods cannot be overstated. These methods offer the ergonomist a structured approach to the analysis and evaluation of design problems. The ergonomist's approach may be described using the scientist-practitioner model (Stanton, 2005). As a scientist, the ergonomist is:

- extending the work of others;
- testing theories of human-machine performance;
- developing hypotheses;
- questioning everything;
- using rigorous data collection and analysis techniques;
- ensuring repeatability of results;
- disseminating the findings of studies.

As a practitioner, the ergonomist is:

- addressing real-world problems;
- seeking the best compromise under difficult circumstances;
- looking to offer the most cost-effective solution;
- developing demonstrators and prototype solutions;
- analysing and evaluating the effects of change;
- developing benchmarks for best practice;
- communicating findings to interested parties.

According to Stanton (2005) ergonomists will work somewhere between the poles of scientist and practitioner, varying the emphasis of their approach depending upon the problems that they face. Human Factors and Ergonomics methods are useful in the scientist-practitioner model, because of the structure, and potential for repeatability that they offer. There is an implicit guarantee in the use of methods that, provided they are used properly, they will produce certain types of useful products. It has been suggested that Human Factors and Ergonomics methods are a route to making the discipline accessible to all (Diaper, 1989; Wilson, 1995). Despite the rigor offered by methods however, there is still plenty of scope for the role of experience. Stanton and Annett (2000) summarised the most frequently asked questions raised by users of ergonomics methods as follows:

- How deep should the analysis be?
- Which methods of data collection should be used?
- How should the analysis be presented?
- Where is the use of the method appropriate?
- How much time/effort does each method require?
- How much, and what type, of expertise is needed to use the method(s)?
- What tools are there to support the use of the method(s)?
- How reliable and valid is/are the method(s)?

This book will help answer some of those questions.

Annett (2002) questions the relative merits for construct and criterion-referenced validity in the development of ergonomics theory. He distinguishes between construct validity (how acceptable the underlying theory is), predictive validity (the usefulness and efficiency of the approach in predicting the behaviour of an existing or future system), and reliability (the repeatability of the results). Investigating the matter further, Annett identifies a dichotomy of ergonomics methods: analytical methods and evaluative methods. Annett argues that analytical methods (i.e., those methods that help the analyst gain an understanding of the mechanisms underlying the interaction between human and machines) require construct validity, whereas evaluative methods (i.e., those methods that estimate parameters of selected interactions between human and machines) require predictive validity. This distinction is made in Table 1.1.

Table 1.1   Annett's Dichotomy of Ergonomics Methods (adapted from Annett, 2002)

	Analytic	Evaluative
Primary purpose	Understand a system.	Measure a parameter.
Examples	Task analysis, training needs analysis, etc.	Measures of workload, usability, comfort, fatigue, etc.
Construct validity	Based on an acceptable model of the system and how it performs.	Is consistent with theory and other measures of parameter.
Predictive validity	Provides answers to questions, e.g., structure of tasks.	Predicts performance.
Reliability	Data collection conforms to an underlying model.	Results from independent samples agree.

This presents an interesting question for ergonomics; are the methods really mutually exclusive? Some methods appear to have dual roles (i.e., both analytical and evaluative, such as Task Analysis for Error Identification), which implies that they must satisfy both criteria. However, it is plausible, as Baber (2005) argues in terms of evaluation, that the approach taken will influence which of the purposes one might wish to emphasise. The implication is that the way in which one approaches a problem, e.g., along the scientist-practitioner continuum, could well have a bearing on how one employs a method. At first glance (particularly from a 'scientist' perspective) such a 'pragmatic' approach appears highly dubious: if we are selecting methods piecemeal in order to satisfy contextual requirements, how can we be certain that we are producing useful, valid, reliable etc. output? While it may be possible for a method to satisfy three types of validity: construct (i.e., theoretical validity), content (i.e., face validity), and predictive (i.e., criterion-referenced empirical validity), it is not always clear whether this arises from the method itself or from the manner in which it is applied. This means that care needs to be taken before embarking on any application of methods to make sure that one is attempting to use the method in the spirit for which it was originally designed.

Prior to embarking on any kind of intervention (be it an analysis, design or evaluation of a system), an Ergonomist needs to have a strategy for deciding what methods to use in, and how to adapt to, the domain context (Annett, 2005). Determining an appropriate set of methods (because individual methods are rarely used alone) requires some planning and preparation. Stanton and Young (1999) proposed a process model to guide the selection of methods, as shown in Figure 1.1. As Annett (2005) points out, care and skill is required in developing the approach for analysing the problem, formulating the intervention, implementing the intervention, and determining the success of the intervention. Complex systems may require the Ergonomist to have a flexible strategy when approaching the problem. This can mean changing the nature of the analysis and developing a new approach as required. Thus, pilot studies are often helpful in scoping out the problem before a detailed study is undertaken. This may mean that there can be several iterations through the criteria development and methods selection process. Of course, from a practitioner perspective, the time taken to carry out pilot studies might simply be unavailable. However, we would argue that there is no harm in running through one's selection of methods as a form of 'thought-experiment' in order to ascertain what type of output each method is likely to produce, and deciding whether or not to include a method in the battery that will be applied. While it is important not to rely too heavily on a single approach, nor is there any guarantee that simply throwing a lot of methods at a problem will guarantee useful results

.

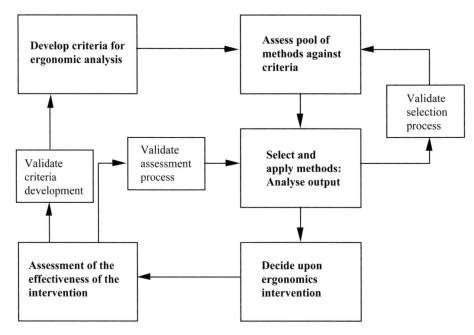

Figure 1.1   Validating the Methods Selection and Ergonomics Intervention Process
(adapted from Stanton and Young, 1999)

As shown in Figure 1.1, method selection is a closed loop process with three feedback loops. The first feedback loop validates the selection of the methods against the selection criteria. The second feedback loop validates the methods against the adequacy of the ergonomic intervention. The third feedback loop validates the initial criteria against the adequacy of the intervention. There could be errors in the development of the initial criteria, the selection of the methods, and the appropriateness of the intervention. Each should be checked. The main stages in the process are identified as: determine criteria (where the criteria for assessment are identified), compare methods against criteria (where the pool of methods are compared for their suitability), application of methods (where the methods are applied)), implementation of ergonomics intervention (where an ergonomics programme is chosen and applied) and evaluation of the effectiveness of the intervention (where the assessment of change brought about by the intervention is assessed).

For this book, a collection of contemporary HF methods were reviewed. The review was conducted over three stages. First, an initial review of existing HF methods and techniques was conducted. Second, a screening process was employed in order to remove any duplicated methods or any methods which require more than paper and pencil to conduct. The reason for this latter criterion was not to disparage any of the various computer-based tools on the market, but to focus on those techniques that the practitioner could use without recourse to specialised equipment. Thirdly, the methods selected for review were analysed using a set of pre-determined criteria. Each stage of the HF methods review is described in more detail below.

Stage 1 – Initial Literature Review of Existing HF Methods

A literature review was conducted in order to create a comprehensive database of existing HF methodologies. The purpose of this literature review was to provide the authors with a comprehensive systematic database of available HF methods and their associated author(s) and source(s). It is intended that the database will be used by HF practitioners who require an appropriate technique for a specific analysis. The database allows the HF practitioner to select the appropriate technique through the subject classification of HF methods (e.g. mental workload assessment techniques, situation awareness measurement techniques, etc.). For example, if an analysis of situation awareness is required, the database can be used to select a number of appropriate methods. The review presented in this book is then used to select the most appropriate method on offer, and also to offer step by step guidance on how to use it.

The literature review was based upon a survey of standard ergonomics textbooks, relevant scientific journals and existing HF method reviews. At this initial stage, none of the HF methods were subjected to any further analysis and were simply recorded by name, author(s) or source(s), and class of method (e.g. Mental Workload Assessment, Human Error Identification, Data Collection, Task Analysis etc.). In order to make the list as comprehensive as possible, any method discovered in the literature was recorded and added to the database. The result of this initial literature review was a database of over 200 HF methods and techniques, including the following categories of technique:

1. Data collection techniques.
2. Task analysis techniques.
3. Cognitive task analysis techniques.
4. Charting techniques.
5. Human error identification (HEI) techniques.
6. Mental workload assessment techniques.
7. Situation awareness measurement techniques.
8. Interface analysis techniques.
9. Design techniques.
10. Performance time prediction/assessment techniques.
11. Team performance analysis techniques.

The HF methods database is presented in Appendix 1 of this book. A description of each technique category is presented in Table 1.3.

Stage 2 – Initial Methods Screening

Before the HF techniques were subjected to further analysis, a screening process was employed in order to remove any techniques that were not suitable for review with respect to their use in the design and evaluation of systems. Techniques were deemed unsuitable for review if they fell into the following categories:
*   Unavailable – The technique should be freely available in the public domain. The techniques covered in this review included only those that were freely available.

- Inapplicable – The applicability of each technique to complex systems was evaluated. Those techniques deemed unsuitable for the use in the design of systems were rejected. In addition, anthropometric, physiological and biomechanical techniques were not reviewed. The reader is referred to Stanton, Hedge, Brookhuis, Salas and Hendrick (2005) for an account of these.
- Duplication – HF techniques are often reiterated and presented in a new format. Any techniques that were very similar to other techniques already chosen for review were rejected.
- Limited use – Often HF techniques are developed and not used by anyone other than the developer. Any techniques that had not been applied in an analysis of some sort were rejected.

As a result of the method screening procedure, a list of 91 HF methods suitable for use in the design and evaluation process was created. This HF design and evaluation methods list was circulated internally within the HFI-DTC research consortium to ensure the suitability and comprehensiveness of the methods chosen for review. The HF methods list was also subject to independent peer scrutiny. The methods review is divided into eleven sections, each section representing a specific category of method or technique. The sequence of the sections and a brief description of their contents are presented in Table 1.3. The eleven sections are intended to represent the different categories of human factors methods and techniques that will be utilised during the design process.

Stage 3 – Methods Review

The 91 HF design and evaluation methods were then analysed using the set of pre-determined criteria outlined in Table 1.2. The criteria were designed not only to establish which of the techniques were the most suitable for use in the design and evaluation of systems, but also to aid the HF practitioner in the selection and use of the appropriate method(s). The output of the analysis is designed to act as a HF methods manual, aiding practitioners in the use of the HF design methods reviewed. The methods reviewed are presented in Table 1.4 to Table 1.14.

Table 1.2   Descriptions of Method Review Criteria

Criteria	*Description of criteria*
Name and acronym	The name of the technique or method and its associated acronym.
Author(s), affiliations(s) and address(es)	The names, affiliations and addresses of the authors are provided to assist with citation and requesting any further help in using the technique.
Background and applications	This section introduces the method, its origins and development, the domain of application of the method and also application areas that it has been used in.
Domain of application	Describes the domain that the technique was originally developed for and applied in.
Procedure and advice	This section describes the procedure for applying the method as well as general points of expert advice.
Flowchart	A flowchart is provided, depicting the methods procedure.
Advantages	Lists the advantages associated with using the method in the design of systems.
Disadvantages	Lists the disadvantages associated with using the method in the design of systems.
Example	An example, or examples, of the application of the method are provided to show the methods output.
Related methods	Any closely related methods are listed, including contributory and similar methods.

Table 1.2 (continued)

Criteria	Description of criteria
Approximate training and application times	Estimates of the training and application times are provided to give the reader an idea of the commitment required when using the technique.
Reliability and validity	Any evidence on the reliability or validity of the method cited.
Tools needed	Describes any additional tools required when using the method.
Bibliography	A bibliography lists recommended further reading on the method and the surrounding topic area

Table 1.3   HF Technique Categories

Method category	Description
Data collection techniques	Data collection techniques are used to collect specific data regarding a system or scenario. According to Stanton (2003) the starting point for designing future systems is a description of a current or analogous system.
Task Analysis techniques	Task analysis techniques are used to represent human performance in a particular task or scenario under analysis. Task analysis techniques break down tasks or scenarios into the required individual task steps, in terms of the required human-machine and human-human interactions.
Cognitive Task analysis techniques	Cognitive task analysis (CTA) techniques are used to describe and represent the unobservable cognitive aspects of task performance. CTA is used to describe the mental processes used by system operators in completing a task or set of tasks.
Charting techniques	Charting techniques are used to depict graphically a task or process using standardised symbols. The output of charting techniques can be used to understand the different task steps involved with a particular scenario, and also to highlight when each task step should occur and which technological aspect of the system interface is required.
HEI/HRA techniques	HEI techniques are used to predict any potential human/operator error that may occur during a man-machine interaction. HRA techniques are used to quantify the probability of error occurrence.
Situation Awareness assessment techniques	Situation Awareness (SA) refers to an operator's knowledge and understanding of the situation that he or she is placed in. According to Endsley (1995a), SA involves a perception of appropriate goals, comprehending their meaning in relation to the task and projecting their future status. SA assessment techniques are used to determine a measurer of operator SA in complex, dynamic systems.
Mental Workload assessment techniques	Mental workload (MWL) represents the proportion of operator resources demanded by a task or set of tasks. A number of MWL assessment techniques exist, which allow the HF practitioner to evaluate the MWL associated with a task or set of tasks.
Team Performance Analysis techniques	Team performance analysis techniques are used to describe, analyse and represent team performance in a particular task or scenario. Various facets of team performance can be evaluated, including communication, decision-making, awareness, workload and co-ordination.
Interface Analysis techniques	Interface analysis techniques are used to assess the interface of a product or systems in terms of usability, error, user-satisfaction and layout.
Design techniques	Design techniques represent techniques that are typically used during the early design lifecycle by design teams, including techniques such as focus groups and scenario-based design.
Performance time prediction techniques	Performance time prediction techniques are used to predict the execution times associated with a task or scenario under analysis.

Data Collection Techniques

Data collection techniques are used to gather specific data regarding the task or scenario under analysis. A total of three data collection techniques are reviewed as shown in Table 1.4.

Table 1.4   Data Collection Techniques

Technique	Author/Source
Interviews	Various
Questionnaires	Various
Observation	Various

Task Analysis Techniques

Task analysis techniques are used to describe and represent the task or scenario under analysis. A total of seven task analysis techniques are reviewed as shown in Table 1.5.

Table 1.5   Task Analysis Techniques

Technique	Author/Source
HTA – Hierarchical Task Analysis	Annett et al (1971)
CPA – Critical Path Analysis	Newell and John (1987); Baber and Mellor (2001)
GOMS – Goals, Operators and Selection Methods	Card, Moran and Newell (1983)
VPA – Verbal Protocol Analysis	Walker (In Press)
Task Decomposition	Kirwan and Ainsworth (1992)
The Sub Goal Template (SGT) Approach	Schraagen, Chipman and Shalin (2003)
Tabular Task Analysis	Kirwan (1994)

Cognitive Task Analysis Techniques

Cognitive task analysis techniques are used to describe and represent the unobservable cognitive processes employed during the performance of the task or scenario under analysis. A total of four cognitive task analysis techniques are reviewed as shown in Table 1.6.

Table 1.6   Cognitive Task Analysis Techniques

Technique	Author/Source
ACTA – Applied Cognitive Task analysis	Militello and Hutton (2000)
Cognitive Walkthrough	Anon
CDM – Critical Decision Method	Klein (2000)
Critical Incident Technique	Flanagan (1954)

Charting Techniques

Charting techniques are used to graphically describe and represent the task or scenario under analysis. A total of six charting techniques are reviewed as shown in Table 1.7.

Table 1.7   Charting Techniques

Technique	Author/Source
Process Charts	Kirwan and Ainsworth (1992)
Operational Sequence Diagrams	Various
DAD – Decision Action Diagram	Kirwan and Ainsworth (1992)
Event Tree analysis	Kirwan and Ainsworth (1992)
Fault Tree analysis	Kirwan and Ainsworth (1992)
Murphy Diagrams	Kirwan (1994)

Human Error Identification (HEI) Techniques

HEI techniques are used to predict or analyse potential errors resulting from an interaction with the system or device under analysis. A total of eleven HEI techniques are reviewed as shown in Table 1.8.

Table 1.8   HEI/HRA Techniques

Technique	Author
CREAM – Cognitive Reliability Error Analysis Method	Hollnagel (1998)
HEART – Human Error Assessment and Reduction Technique	Williams (1986)
HEIST – Human Error Identification In Systems Tool	Kirwan (1994)
HET – Human Error Template	Marshall et al (2003)
Human Error HAZOP	Whalley (1988)
SHERPA – Systematic Human Error Reduction and Prediction Approach	Embrey (1986)
SPEAR - System for Predictive Error Analysis and Reduction	CCPS (1994)
TAFEI – Task Analysis For Error Identification	Baber and Stanton (1996)
THEA – Technique for Human Error Assessment	Pocock et al (2001)
The HERA Framework	Kirwan (1998a, 1998b)
TRACEr - Technique for the Retrospective and Predictive Analysis of Cognitive Errors in Air Traffic Control (ATC)	Shorrock and Kirwan (2000)

Situation Awareness Measurement Techniques

Situation awareness measurement techniques are used to assess the level of SA that an operator possesses during a particular task or scenario. A total of thirteen situation awareness techniques are reviewed as shown in Table 1.9.

Table 1.9   Situation Awareness Measurement Techniques

Method	Author/Source
SA Requirements Analysis	Endsley (1993)
SAGAT – Situation Awareness Global Assessment Technique	Endsley (1995b)
SART – Situation Awareness Rating Technique	Taylor (1990)
SA-SWORD – Subjective Workload Dominance Metric	Vidulich (1989)
SALSA	Hauss and Eyferth (2003)
SACRI – Situation Awareness Control Room Inventory	Hogg et al (1995)
SARS – Situation Awareness Rating Scales	Waag and Houck (1994)
SPAM – Situation-Present Assessment Method	Durso et al (1998)
SASHA_L and SASHA_Q	Jeanott, Kelly and Thompson 2003
SABARS – Situation Awareness Behavioural Rating Scales	Endsley (2000)
MARS	Matthews and Beal (2002)
CARS	McGuinness and Foy (2000)
C-SAS	Dennehy (1997)

MARS = Mission Awareness Rating Scale; C-SAS = Cranfield Situational Awareness Rating Scale; CARS = Crew Awareness Rating Scale; SARS = Situational Awareness Rating Scale.

Mental Workload Assessment Techniques

Mental workload assessment techniques are used to assess the level of demand imposed on an operator by a task or scenario. A total of 15 mental workload assessment techniques are reviewed as shown in Table 1.10.

Table 1.10   Mental Workload Assessment Techniques

Method	Author/Source
Primary Task Performance Measures	Various
Secondary Task Performance Measures	Various
Physiological Measures	Various
Bedford Scale	Roscoe and Ellis (1990)
DRAWS – Defence Research Agency Workload Scale	Farmer et al (1995) Jordan et al (1995)
ISA – Instantaneous Self Assessment Workload	Jordan (1992)
MACE - Malvern Capacity Estimate	Goillau and Kelly (1996)
MCH – Modified Cooper Harper Scale	Cooper and Harper (1969)
NASA TLX – NASA Task Load Index	Hart and Staveland (1988)
SWAT – Subjective Workload Assessment Technique	Reid and Nygeren (1988)
SWORD – Subjective WORkload Dominance Assessment Technique	Vidulich (1989)
Workload Profile Technique	Tsang and Valesquez (1996)
CTLA – Cognitive Task Load Analysis	Neerincx (2003)
Pro-SWAT	Reid and Nygren (1988)
Pro-SWORD	Vidulich (1989)

Team Performance Analysis Techniques

Team performance analysis techniques are used to assess team performance in terms of teamwork and taskwork, behaviours exhibited, communication, workload, awareness, decisions made and team member roles. A total of 13 team performance analysis techniques are reviewed as shown in Table 1.11.

Table 1.11 Team Techniques

Method	Author
BOS – Behavioural Observation Scales	Baker (2005)
Comms Usage Diagram	Watts and Monk (2000)
Co-ordination Demands Analysis	Burke (2005)
Team Decision Requirement Exercise	Klinger and Bianka (2005)
Groupware Task Analysis	Wellie and Van Der Veer (2003)
HTA (T)	Annett (2005)
Questionnaires for Distributed Assessment of Team Mutual Awareness	MacMillan et al (2005)
Social Network Analysis	Driskell and Mullen (2005)
Team Cognitive Task Analysis	Klien (2000)
Team Communications Analysis	Jentsch and Bowers (2005)
Team Task Analysis	Burke (2005)
Team Workload Assessment	Bowers and Jentsch (2004)
TTRAM – Task and Training Requirements Methodology	Swezey et al (2000)

Interface Analysis Techniques

Interface analysis techniques are used to assess a particular interface in terms of usability, user satisfaction, error and interaction time. A total of eleven interface analysis techniques are reviewed as shown in Table 1.12.

Table 1.12 Interface Analysis Techniques

Method	Author/Source
Checklists	Stanton and Young (1999)
Heuristics	Stanton and Young (1999)
Interface Surveys	Kirwan and Ainsworth (1992)
Layout Analysis	Stanton and Young (1999)
Link Analysis	Drury (1990)
QUIS – Questionnaire for User Interface Satisfaction	Chin, Diehl and Norman (1988)
Repertory Grids	Kelly (1955)
SUMI – Software Usability Measurement Inventory	Kirakowski
SUS – System Usability Scale	Stanton and Young (1999)
User Trials	Salvendy (1997)
Walkthrough Analysis	Various

System Design Techniques

System design techniques are used to inform the design process of a system or device. A total of five system design techniques are reviewed in this document as shown in Table 1.13.

Table 1.13   Design Techniques

Method	Author
Allocation of Functions Analysis	Marsden and Kirby (in press)
Focus Groups	Various
Groupware Task Analysis	Van Welie and Van Der Veer (2003)
Mission Analysis	Wilkinson (1992)
TCSD – Task Centred System Design	Greenberg (2003) Clayton and Lewis (1993)

Performance Time Assessment Techniques

Performance time assessment techniques are used to predict or assess the task performance times associated with a particular task or scenario. A total of three performance time assessment techniques are reviewed as shown in Table 1.14.

Table 1.14   Performance Time Assessment Techniques

Method	Author
KLM – Keystroke Level Model	Card, Moran and Newell (1983)
Timeline Analysis	Kirwan and Ainsworth (1992)
CPA – Critical Path Analysis	Baber (2005)

The methods review was conducted in order to specify the HF techniques that are the most suitable for use in the design and evaluation of systems. The output of the methods review also acts as a methods manual. It is intended that analysts will consult this book for advice and guidance on which methods have potential application to their problem, and also how to use the chosen techniques. This book is also useful for enabling analyst(s) to determine which method outputs are required to act as inputs for other chosen method(s) in cases where forms of 'methods integration' are being attempted. For example, a SHERPA analysis can only be conducted upon an initial HTA of the task under analysis, so the two go together, and this interrelation (and many others) are expressed in an HF methods matrix (Table 1.15).

Table 1.15   Example of the Human Factors Methods Matrix

To From	Interview	Obs	HTA	OSD	SHERPA	SAGAT	SA Req	NASA TLX	BOS	Comm Usage	Checklists	Link	Focus Group	KLM
Interviews		C	I	I			I		C	I	C	I	C	
Observation	C		I	I		C	I		I C	I	I C	I C		I C
HTA	C	I		I	I	I	I	I		I	I	I		I
Operator Sequence Diagrams	C	C	C							C		C		
SHERPA			C											
SA Req Analysis	C	C	C			I								
SAGAT			C				C	C						
NASA-Task Load Index						C								
BOS Behavioural Observation Scales	C	C				C		C		C				
Comms Usage Diagram	C	C	C	C					C					
Checklists	C	C	C											
Link Analysis	C	C	C											
Focus Groups	C	C												
KLM	C	C	C											

Key: I = Input source, C = Used in conjunction with.

The Event Analysis of Systemic Teamwork (EAST) methodology is a framework for analysing command and control (C2) activity that arises from the methods matrix. EAST is a unique and powerful integration of a number of individual HF methods. The method has been applied successfully to a range of C2 scenarios across a number of different domains as presented in Table 1.16.

Table 1.16   Domains Examined Using the EAST Methodology

Domain	Scenario
Air Traffic Control National Air Traffic Services	Holding
	Over flight
	Departure
	Approach
	Shift handover
Energy Distribution National Grid Transco	Barking switching operations
	Feckenham switching operations
	Tottenham return to service operations
	Alarm handling operations
Fire Service	Chemical incident at remote farmhouse
	Road traffic accident involving chemical tanker
	Incident Command in a factory fire
Military Aviation A3D	General operation
Navy HMS Dryad	Air threat
	Surface threat
	Sub-surface threat
Police	Car break-in caught on CCTV
	Suspected car break-in
	Assault and mobile phone robbery
Rail (Signalling)	Detachment scenario
	Emergency Possession scenario
	Handback Possession scenario
	Possession scenario

In order to analyse the performance of the EAST methodology and its component methods, a review of the technique was conducted based upon the applications described above. The review of EAST was based upon the same criteria that were used in the HF methods review, and the results of the evaluation are summarised in Table 1.17.

Table 1.17   Summary of EAST Methods Review

Method	Type of method	Related methods	Training time	Application time	Tools needed	Reliability	Validity	Advantages	Disadvantages
Event Analysis of Systemic Teamwork (EAST) (Baber and Stanton 2004)	Team analysis method	Obs HTA CDA OSD CUD SNA CDM Prop Nets	High	High	Video/Audio recording equipment MS Word MS Excel MS Visio AGNA	Med	High	1. EAST offers an extremely exhaustive analysis of the C4i domain in question. 2. EAST is relatively easy to train and apply. The provision of the WESTT and AGNA software packages also reduces application time considerably. 3. The EAST output is extremely useful, offering a number of different analyses and perspectives on the C4i activity in question.	1. Due to its exhaustive nature, EAST is time consuming to apply. 2. Reliability may be questionable in some areas. A large part of the analysis is based upon the analyst's subjective judgement. 3. A large portion of the output is descriptive. Great onus is placed upon the analyst to interpret the results accordingly.
Observation	Data collection	HTA	Low	High	Video/Audio recording equipment MS Word	High	High	1. Acts as the primary input for the EAST methodology. 2. Easy to conduct provided the appropriate planning has been made. 3. Allows the analysts to gain a deeper understanding of the domain and scenario under analysis.	1. Observations are typically time consuming to conduct (including the lengthy data analysis procedure). 2. It is often difficult to gain the required access to the establishment under analysis. 3. There is no guarantee that the required data will be obtained.

Table 1.17 (continued)

Method	Type of method	Related methods	Training time	Application time	Tools needed	Reliability	Validity	Advantages	Disadvantages
Hierarchical Task Analysis (Annett 2004)	Task analysis	Obs	Med	High	Pen and paper MS Notepad	Med	High	1. Easy to learn and apply. 2. Allows the analysts to gain a deeper understanding of the domain and scenario under analysis. 3. Describes the task under analysis in terms of component task steps and operations.	1. Can be difficult and time consuming to conduct for large, complex scenarios. 2. Reliability is questionable. Different analysts may produce different HTA outputs for the same scenario. 3. Provides mainly descriptive rather than analytical information. Also does not cater for the cognitive components of task performance.
Co-ordination demands analysis (CDA) (Burke 2005)	Team analysis	Obs HTA	Low	Med	Pen and paper MS Excel	Low	High	1. Offers an overall rating of co-ordination between team members for each teamwork based task step in the scenario under analysis. 2. Also offers a rating for each teamwork behaviour in the CDA teamwork taxonomy. 3. The technique can be used to identify task-work (individual) and team-work task steps involved in the scenario in question.	1. The CDA procedure can be time consuming and laborious. For each individual task step, seven teamwork behaviours are rated. 2. To ensure validity, SMEs are required. 3. Intra- and inter-analyst reliability may be questionable.

Table 1.17 (continued)

Method	Type of method	Related methods	Training time	Application time	Tools needed	Reliability	Validity	Advantages	Disadvantages
Comms Usage Diagram (CUD) (Watts and Monk 2000)	Comms analysis	HTA SNA Obs	Low	Low - Med	MS Visio	Med	High	1. The output is particularly useful, offering a description of the task under analysis, and also a description of collaborative activity involved, including the order of activity, the communications between agents, the personnel involved, the technology used and its associated advantages and disadvantages, and recommendations regarding the technology used. 2. Useful for highlighting flaws in communication in a particular C4i environment. 3. Quick and easy to learn and apply.	1. For large, complex scenarios involving many agents, the CUD analysis may become time consuming and laborious. 2. Limited guidance is offered to the analyst. As a result, many of the recommendations made (i.e. appropriate technology) are based entirely upon the analyst's subjective judgement. 3. In its present usage the CUD technique only defines the technology used for the source of the communication (the technology at the other end of the communication is not defined).
Social Network Analysis (SNA) (Dekker 2002)	Team analysis	Obs HTA CUD	Low	Low	AGNA	High	High	1. SNA can be used to determine the key agents within a scenario network and also to classify the network type. 2. Additional analysis of the network in question requires minimal effort. Agent sociometric status, centrality and network density are all calculated with minimal effort. 3. SNA is quick and easy to learn and apply.	1. For large, complex networks, it may be difficult to conduct a SNA. Application time is a function of network size, and large networks may incur lengthy application times. 2. It is difficult to collect comprehensive data for an SNA analysis. For example, a network with 10 agents would require 10 observers during data collection (one observer per agent). This is not always possible and so a true analysis of network links is difficult to obtain.

Table 1.17 (continued)

Method	Type of method	Related methods	Training time	Application time	Tools needed	Reliability	Validity	Advantages	Disadvantages
Operation Sequence Diagrams	Charting technique	Obs HTA CDA	Low	High	MS Visio	High	High	1. The OSD output is particularly useful, depicting the activity and agent involved, the flow of information, HTA task steps, the CDA results, the tech-nology used and also time. 2. Particularly suited for the analysis of distributed or collab-orative activity. 3. Extremely flexible, and also easy to learn and apply.	1. Constructing an OSD for C4i activity is often extremely time consuming and laborious. 2. For larger more complex scenarios involving many agents, the OSD output can become cluttered and confusing. 3. In its present usage, the OSD symbols are limited for C4i applications. More symbols may be needed.
Critical Decision Method (CDM) (Klein and Armstrong 2004)	Cognitive Task Analysis	Obs Interviews	High	Med	Audio recording device	Low	Med	1. CDM can be used to elicit specific information regarding the decision-making strategies used in complex systems. 2. The CDM output is useful in analysing the SA requirements for the task under analysis. 3. Once familiar with the procedure, CDM is relatively easy to apply.	1. Dependent upon the analyst's skill and the quality of the participants used. 2. Klein and Armstrong (2004) suggest that retrospective incidents are linked to concerns of data reliability, due to memory degradation. 3. Prior experience of interviewing is essential.

Table 1.17 (continued)

Method	Type of method	Related methods	Training time	Application time	Tools needed	Reliability	Validity	Advantages	Disadvantages
Propositional Networks (Baber and Stanton 2004)	N/A	CDM Content analysis	Low	High	MS Visio	Med	Med	1. The output is extremely useful, highlighting the knowledge required and also when the knowledge is used. Links between knowledge objects are also specified. 2. Useful for analysing agent and shared SA during the scenario under analysis. 3. The technique is relatively easy to learn and apply.	1. Inter- and intra-analyst reliability of the technique is questionable. 2. The quality of the propositional network is dependent upon the initial CDM analysis. 3. Can be time consuming for complex scenarios.

An example of the application of the EAST methodology is contained in the concluding chapter of this book where it is presented as an exhaustive technique. A number of different analyses are conducted and various perspectives on the problem domains under analysis are offered. In its present form, the EAST methodology offers the following analyses of complex socio-technical systems:

- A step-by-step (goals, sub-goals, operations and plans) description of the activity in question.
- A definition of roles within the scenario.
- An analysis of the agent network structure involved (e.g. network type and density).
- A rating of co-ordination between agents for each team-based task step and an overall co-ordination rating.
- An analysis of the current technology used during communications between agents and also recommendations for novel communications technology.
- A description of the task in terms of the flow of information, communications between agents, the activity conducted by each agent involved and a timeline of activity.
- A definition of the key agents involved in the scenario and other structural properties of the social networks.
- A cognitive task analysis of operator decision making during the scenario.
- A definition of the knowledge objects (information, artefacts etc.) required and the knowledge objects used during the scenario.
- A definition of shared knowledge or shared situation awareness during the scenario.

The integration of HF techniques offers numerous possibilities and advantages. In the course of reviewing this body of HF methods it has become apparent that there is limited literature or assistance available for the practitioner wishing to embark on this route, and we hope that the EAST method, and the methods matrix above may help users to add more value to their endeavours, and to better serve the aims of HFI.

Chapter 2

Data Collection Methods

The starting point of any HF analysis will be scoping and definition of expected outcomes, e.g., this might mean defining hypotheses or might mean determining which questions the analysis is intended to answer. Following this stage, effort normally involves collecting specific data regarding the system, activity and personnel that the analysis effort is focused upon. In the design of novel systems, information regarding activity in similar, existing systems is required. This allows the design team to evaluate existing or similar systems in order to determine existing design flaws and problems and also to highlight efficient aspects that may be carried forward into the new design. The question of what constitutes a 'similar' system is worth considering at this juncture. If we concentrate solely in the current generation of systems (with a view to planning the next generation) then it is likely that any design proposals would simply be modifications to current technology or practice. While this might be appropriate in many instances, it does not easily support original design (which might require a break with current systems). An alternative approach is to find systems that reflect some core aspect of current work, and then attempt to analyse the activity within these systems. Thus, in designing novel technology to support newspaper editing, production and layout planning, Bødker (1988) focused on manual versions of the activities, rather than on the contemporary word processing or desktop publishing systems. An obvious reason for doing this is that the technology (particularly at the time of her study) would heavily constrain the activity that people could perform, and these constraints might be appropriate for the limitations of the technology but not supportive of the goals and activity of the people working within the system. In a similar manner, Stanton and Baber (2002), in a study redesigning a medical imaging system, decided to focus their analysis on cytogeneticists using conventional microscopes rather than analysts using the sophisticated imaging equipment. Thus, it can be highly beneficial to look at activity away from the technology for several reasons: (i.) avoiding the problems of technology constraining possible activity; (ii.) allowing appreciation of the fundamental issues relating to the goals of people working with the system (as opposed to understanding the manner in which particular technology needs to be used); (iii.) allowing (often) rapid appreciation of basic needs without the need to fully understand complex technology.

The evaluation of existing, operational systems (e.g. usability, error analysis, task analysis) also requires that specific data regarding task performance in the system under analysis is collected, represented and analysed accordingly. Data collection methods therefore represent the cornerstone of any HF analysis effort. Such methods are used by the HF practitioner to collect specific information regarding the system, activity or artefact under analysis, including the nature of the activity conducted within the system, the individuals performing the activity, the component task steps and their sequence, the technological artefacts used by the system and its personnel in performing the tasks (controls, displays, communication technology etc.), the system environment and also the organisational environment. In terms of Human Factors Integration, therefore, the methods can readily contribute to understanding of Personnel, Training, Human Factors Engineering and System Safety.

The importance of an accurate representation of the system or activity under analysis cannot be underestimated and is a necessary pre-requisite for any further analysis efforts. As we noted above, the starting point for designing future systems is a description of the current or analogous system, and any inaccuracies within the description could potentially hinder the design effort. Data collection methods are used to collect the relevant information that is used to provide this description of the system or activity under analysis. There are a number of different data collection methods available to the HF practitioner, including observation, interviews, questionnaires, analysis of artefacts, usability metrics and the analysis of performance. Often, data collected through the use of these methods can be used as the starting point or input for another HF method, such as human error identification (HEI), task analysis and charting techniques.

The main advantage associated with the application of data collection methods is the high volume and utility of the data that is collected. The analyst(s) using the methods also have a high degree of control over the data collection process and are able to direct the data collection procedure as they see fit. Despite the usefulness of data collection methods, there are a number of potential problems associated with their use. For example, one problem associated with the use of data collection methods such as interviews, observational study and questionnaires is the high level of resource usage incurred, particularly during the design of data collection procedures. For example, the design of interviews and questionnaires is a lengthy process, involving numerous pilot runs and reiterations. In addition to this, large amounts of data are typically collected, and lengthy data analysis procedures are common. For example, analysing the data obtained during observational study efforts is particularly laborious and time consuming, even with the provision of supporting computer software such as Observer™, and can last weeks rather than hours or days. In addition to the high resource usage incurred, data collection methods also require access to the system and personnel under analysis, which is often very difficult and time consuming to obtain. If the data need to be collected during operational scenarios, getting the required personnel to take part in interviews is also difficult, and questionnaires often have very low return rates i.e. typically 10% for a postal questionnaire. Similarly, institutions do not readily agree to personnel being observed whilst at work, and often access is rejected on this basis. A brief description of each of the data collection methods is given below, along with a summary in Table 2.1.

Interviews

Interviews offer a flexible approach to data collection and have consequently been applied for a plethora of different purposes. Interviews can be used to collect a wide variety of data, ranging from user perceptions and reactions, to usability and error related data. There are three types of interview available to the HF practitioner. These are structured interviews, semi-structured and unstructured or open interviews. Typically, participants are interviewed on a one-to-one basis and the interviewer uses pre-determined probe questions to elicit the required information. A number of interview-based methods have been developed, including the critical decision method (CDM; Klein and Armstrong, 2004) and the applied cognitive task analysis technique (ACTA; Militello and Hutton, 2000). Both are semi-structured interview based cognitive task analysis approaches that are used to elicit information regarding operator decision making in complex, dynamic environments.

Questionnaires

Questionnaires offer a very flexible means of quickly collecting large amounts of data from large participant populations. Questionnaires have been used in many forms to collect data regarding numerous issues within HF design and evaluation. Questionnaires can be used to collect information regarding almost anything at all, including usability, user satisfaction, opinions and attitudes. More specifically, questionnaires can be used throughout the design

Table 2.1 Summary of Data Collection Methods

Method	Type of method	Domain	Training time	App time	Related methods	Tools needed	Validation studies	Advantages	Disadvantages
Interviews	Data collection	Generic	Med-high	High	Interviews Critical Decision Method	Pen and paper. Audio recording equipment	Yes	1) Flexible technique that can be used to assess anything from usability to error. 2) Interviewer can direct the analysis. 3) Can be used to elicit data regarding cognitive components of a task.	1) Data analysis is time consuming and laborious. 2) Reliability is difficult to assess. 3) Subject to various sources of bias.
Questionnaires	Data collection	Generic	Low	High	SUMI QUIS SUS	Pen and paper. Video and audio recording equipment	Yes	1) Flexible technique that can be used to assess anything from usability to error. 2) A number of established HF questionnaire methods already exist, such as SUMI and SUS. 3) Easy to use, requiring minimal training.	1) Data analysis is time consuming and laborious. 2) Subject to various sources of bias. 3) Questionnaire development is time consuming and requires a large amount of effort on behalf of the analyst(s).
Observation	Data collection	Generic	Low	High	Acts as an input to various HF methods e.g. HTA	Pen and paper. Video and audio recording equipment	Yes	1) Can be used to elicit specific information regarding decision making in complex environments. 2) Acts as the input to numerous HF methods such as HTA. 3) Suited to the analysis of C4i activity.	1) Data analysis procedure is very time consuming. 2) Coding data is also laborious. 3) Subject to bias.

process to evaluate design concepts and prototypes, to probe user perceptions and reactions and to evaluate existing systems. Established questionnaires such as the system usability scale (SUS), the questionnaire for user interface satisfaction (QUIS) and the software usability measurement inventory (SUMI) are available for practitioners to apply to designs and existing systems. Alternatively, specific questionnaires can be designed and administered during the design process.

Observation

Observation (and observational studies) are used to gather data regarding activity conducted in complex, dynamic systems. In its simplest form, observation involves observing an individual or group of individuals performing work-related activity. A number of different types of observational study exist, such as direct observation, covert observation and participant observation. Observation is attractive due to the volume and utility of the data collected, and also the fact that the data is collected in an operational context. Although at first glance simply observing an operator at work seems to be a very simple approach to employ, it is evident that this is not the case, and that careful planning and execution are required (Stanton 2003). Observational methods also require the provision of technology, such as video and audio recording equipment. The output from an observational analysis is used as the primary input for most HF methods, such as task analysis, error analysis and charting techniques.

Interviews

Background and Applications

Interviews provide the HF practitioner with a flexible means of gathering large amounts of specific information regarding a particular subject. Due to the flexible nature of interviews, they have been used extensively to gather information on a plethora of topics, including system usability, user perceptions, reactions and attitudes, job analysis, cognitive task analysis, error and many more. As well as designing their own interviews, HF practitioners also have a number of specifically designed interview methods at their disposal. For example, the Critical Decision Method (CDM; Klein and Armstrong, 2004) is a cognitive task analysis technique that provides the practitioner with a set of cognitive probes designed to elicit information regarding decision making during a particular scenario (see the relevant section for CDM description). There are three generic interview 'types' typically employed by the HF practitioner. These are structured, semi-structured and unstructured. A brief description of each interview type is given below:

1. *Structured Interview.* In a structured interview, the interviewer probes the participant using a set of pre-defined questions designed to elicit specific information regarding the subject under analysis. The content of the interview (questions and their order) is pre-determined and no scope for further discussion is permitted. Due to their rigid nature, structured interviews are the least popular type of interview. A structured interview is only used when the type of data required is rigidly defined, and no additional data is required.

2. *Semi-structured Interview.* When using a semi-structured interview, a portion of the questions and their order is pre-determined. However, semi-structured interviews are flexible in that the interviewer can direct the focus of the interview and also use further questions that were

not originally part of the planned interview structure. As a result, information surrounding new or unexpected issues is often uncovered during semi-structured interviews. Due to this flexibility, the semi-structured interview is the most commonly applied type of interview.

3. *Unstructured Interview.* When using an unstructured interview, there is no pre-defined structure or questions and the interviewer goes into the interview 'blind' so to speak. This allows the interviewer to explore, on an ad-hoc basis, different aspects of the subject under analysis. Whilst their flexibility is attractive, unstructured interviews are infrequently used, as their unstructured nature may result in crucial information being neglected or ignored.

Focus Group

While many interviews concentrate on one-to-one elicitation of information, group discussions can provide an efficient means of canvassing consensus opinion from several people. Ideally, the focus group would contain around five people with similar backgrounds and the discussion would be managed at a fairly high-level, i.e. rather than asking specific questions, the analyst would introduce topics and facilitate their discussion. A useful text for exploring focus groups is Langford and McDonagh (2002).

Question Types

An interview involves the use of questions or probes designed to elicit information regarding the subject under analysis. An interviewer typically employs three different types of question during the interview process. These are closed questions, open-ended questions, and probing questions. A brief description of each interview question type is presented below:

1. *Closed questions.* Closed questions are used to gather specific information and typically permit yes or no answers. An example of a closed question would be, 'Do you think that system X is usable?'. The question is designed to gather a yes or no response, and the interviewee does not elaborate on his chosen answer.

2. *Open-ended questions.* An open-ended question is used to elicit more than the simple yes/ no information that a closed question gathers. Open-ended questions allow the interviewee to answer in whatever way they wish, and also elaborate on their answer. For example, an open-ended question approach to the topic of system X's usability would be something like, 'What do you think about the usability of system X?'. By allowing the interviewee to elaborate upon answers given, open-ended questions typically gather more pertinent data than closed questions. However, open-ended question data requires more time to analyse than closed question data does, and so closed questions are more commonly used.

3. *Probing question.* A probing question is normally used after an open-ended or closed question to gather more specific data regarding the interviewee's previous answer. Typical examples of a probing question would be, 'Why did you think that system X was not usable?' or 'How did it make you feel when you made that error with the system?'.

Stanton and Young (1999) recommend that interviewers should begin with a specific topic and probe it further until the topic is exhausted; then moving onto a new topic. Stanton and Young (1999) recommend that the interviewer should begin by focusing on a particular topic with an open-ended question, and then once the interviewee has answered, use a probing question to gather further information. A closed question should then be used to gather specific information regarding the topic. This cycle of open, probe and closed question should be maintained throughout the interview. An excellent general text on interview design is Oppenheim (2000).

Domain of Application

Generic.

Procedure and Advice (Semi-Structured Interview)

There are no set rules to adhere to during the construction and conduction of an interview. The following procedure is intended to act as a set of flexible guidelines for the HF practitioner.

Step 1: Define the interview objective
Firstly, before any interview design takes place, the analyst should clearly define the objective of the interview. Without a clearly defined objective, the focus of the interview is unclear and the data gathered during the interview may lack specific content. For example, when interviewing a civil airline pilot for a study into design induced human error on the flight deck, the objective of the interview would be to discover which errors the pilot had made or seen being made in the past, with which part of the interface, and during which task. A clear definition of the interview objectives ensures that the interview questions used are wholly relevant and that the data gathered is of optimum use.

Step 2: Question development
Once the objective of the interview is clear, the development of the questions to be used during the interview can begin. The questions should be developed based upon the overall objective of the interview. In the design induced pilot error case, examples of pertinent questions would be, 'What sort of design induced errors have you made in the past on the flight deck?' This would then be followed by a probing question such as, 'Why do you think you make this error?' or 'What task were you performing when you made this error?' Once all of the relevant questions are developed, they should be put into some sort of coherent order or sequence. The wording of each question should be very clear and concise, and the use of acronyms or confusing terms should be avoided. An interview transcript or data collection sheet should then be created, containing the interview questions and spaces for demographic information (name, age, sex, occupation etc.) and interviewee responses.

Step 3: Piloting the interview
Once the questions have been developed and ordered, the analyst should then perform a pilot or trial run of the interview procedure. This allows any potential problems or discrepancies to be highlighted. Typical pilot interview studies involve submitting the interview to colleagues or even by performing a trial interview with real participants. This process is very useful in shaping the interview into its most efficient form and allows any potential problems in the data collection procedure to be highlighted and eradicated. The analyst is also given an indication of the type of data that the interview may gather, and can change the interview content if appropriate.

Step 4: Redesign interview based upon pilot run
Once the pilot run of the interview is complete, any changes highlighted should be made. This might include the removal of redundant questions, the rewording of existing questions or the addition of new questions.

Step 5: Select appropriate participants

Once the interview has been thoroughly tested and is ready for use, the appropriate participants should be selected. Normally, a representative sample from the population of interest is used. For example, in an analysis of design induced human error on the flight deck, the participant sample would comprise airline pilots with varying levels of experience.

Step 6: Conduct and record the interview

According to Stanton and Young (1999) the interviewee should use a cycle of open-ended, probe and closed questions. The interviewee should persist with one particular topic until it is exhausted, and then move onto a new topic. General guidelines for conducting an interview include that the interviewer is confident and familiar with the topic in question, communicates clearly and establishes a good rapport with the interviewee. The interview should avoid being overbearing, and should not mislead, belittle, embarrass or insult the interviewee. The use of technical jargon or acronyms should also be avoided. It is recommended that the interview be recorded using either audio or visual recording equipment.

Step 7: Transcribe the data

Once the interview is completed, the analyst should proceed to transcribe the data. This involves replaying the initial recording of the interview and transcribing fully everything that is said during the interview, both by the interviewer and the interviewee. This is typically a lengthy and laborious process and requires much patience on behalf of the analyst involved. It might be worth considering paying someone to produce a word-processed transcription, e.g., by recruiting someone from a Temp Agency for a week or two.

Step 8: Data gathering

Once the transcript of the interview is complete, the analyst should analyse the interview transcript, looking for the specific data that was required by the objective of the interview. This is known as the 'expected data'. Once all of the 'expected data' is gathered, the analyst should re-analyse the interview in order to gather any 'unexpected data', that is any extra data (not initially outlined in the objectives) that is unearthed.

Step 9: Data analysis

Finally, the analysts should then analyse the data using appropriate statistical tests, graphs etc. The form of analysis used is dependent upon the aims of the analysis, but typically involves converting the words collected during the interview into numerical form in readiness for statistical analysis. A good interview will *always* involve planning, so that the data is collected with a clear understanding of how subsequent analysis will be performed. In other words it is not sufficient to have piles of handwritten notes following many hours of interviewing, and then no idea what to do with them. A good starting point is to take the transcribed information and then perform some 'content analysis', i.e., divide the transcription into specific concepts. Then one can determine whether the data collected from the interviews can be reduced to some numerical form, e.g., counting the frequency with which certain concepts are mentioned by different individuals, or the frequency with which concepts occur together.

Alternatively, the content of the interview material might not be amenable to reduction to numerical form, and so it is not possible or sensible to consider statistical analysis. In this case, it is common practice to work through the interview material and look for common themes and issues. These can be separated out and (if possible) presented back to the interviewees, using their own words. This can provide quite a powerful means of presenting opinion or understanding. If the interview has been video-taped, then it can be useful to edit the video down in a similar manner, i.e., to select specific themes and use the video of the interviewees to present and support these themes.

Advantages

1. Interviews can be used to gather data regarding a wide range of subjects.
2. Interviews offer a very flexible way of gathering large amounts of data.
3. Potentially the data gathered is very powerful.
4. The interviewer has full control over the interview and can direct the interview in any way.
5. Response data can be treated statistically.
6. A structured interview offers consistency and thoroughness (Stanton and Young, 1999).
7. Interviews have been used extensively in the past for a number of different types of analysis.
8. Specific, structured HF interview methods already exist, such as the Critical Decision Method (Klein and Armstrong, 2004).

Disadvantages

1. The construction and data analysis process ensure that the interview method is a time consuming one.
2. The reliability and validity of the method is difficult to address.
3. Interviews are susceptible to both interviewer and interviewee bias.
4. Transcribing the data is a laborious, time consuming process.
5. Conducting an interview correctly is quite difficult and requires great skill on behalf of the interviewer.
6. The quality of the data gathered is based entirely upon the skill of the interviewer and the quality of the interviewee.

Approximate Training and Application Times

In a study comparing 12 HF methods, Stanton and Young (1999) reported that interviews took the longest to train of all the methods, due to the fact that the method is a refined process requiring a clear understanding on the analyst's behalf. In terms of application times, a normal interview could last anything between 10 and 60 minutes. Kirwan and Ainsworth (1992) recommend that an interview should last a minimum of 20 minutes and a maximum of 40 minutes. Whilst this represents a low application time, the data analysis part of the interview method can be extremely time consuming (e.g. data transcription, data gathering and data analysis). Transcribing the data is a particularly lengthy process. For this reason, the application time for interviews is estimated as very high.

Reliability and Validity

Although the reliability and validity of interview methods is difficult to address, Stanton and Young (1999) report that in a study comparing 12 HF methods, a structured interview method scored poorly in terms of reliability and validity.

Tools Needed

An interview requires a pen and paper and an audio recording device, such as a cassette or mini-disc recorder. A PC with a word processing package such as Microsoft Word™ is also required in order to transcribe the data, and statistical analysis packages such as SPSS™ may be required for data analysis procedures.

Flowchart

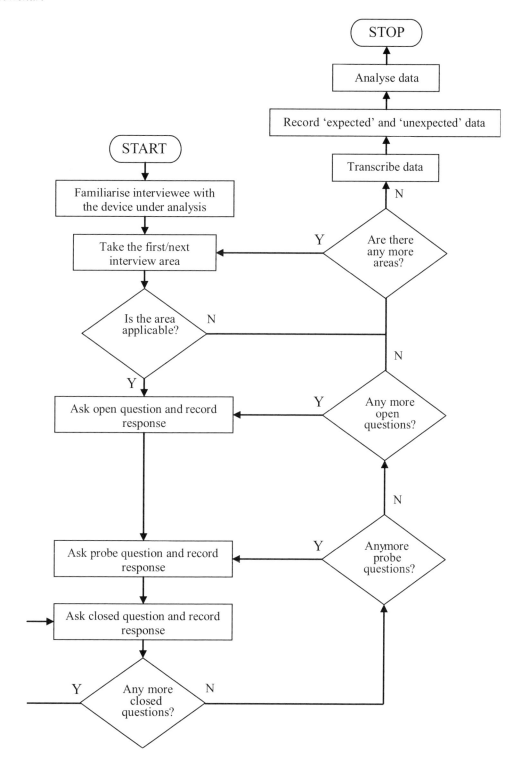

Questionnaires

Background and Applications

Questionnaires offer a very flexible way of quickly collecting large amounts of specific data from a large population sample. Questionnaires have been used in many forms to collect data regarding numerous issues within HF and design, including usability, user satisfaction, error, and user opinions and attitudes. More specifically, they can be used in the design process to evaluate concept and prototypical designs, to probe user perceptions and to evaluate existing system designs. They can also be used in the evaluation process, to evaluate system usability or attitudes towards an operational system. A number of established HF questionnaires already exist, including the system usability scale (SUS), the Questionnaire for User Interface Satisfaction (QUIS) and the Software Usability Measurement Inventory (SUMI). Alternatively, specific questionnaires can be designed and administered based upon the objectives of a particular study. The method description offered here will concentrate on the design of questionnaires, as the procedure used when applying existing questionnaire methods is described in following chapters.

Domain of Application

Generic.

Procedure and Advice

There are no set rules for the design and administration of questionnaires. The following procedure is intended to act as a set of guidelines to consider when constructing a questionnaire.

Step 1: Define study objectives
The first step involves clearly defining the objectives of the study i.e. what information is wanted from the questionnaire data that is gathered. Before any effort is put into the design of the questions, the objectives of the questionnaire must be clearly defined. It is recommended that the analyst should go further than merely describing the goal of the research. For example, when designing a questionnaire in order to gather information on the usability of a system or product, the objectives should contain precise descriptions of different usability problems already encountered and descriptions of the usability problems that are expected. Also, the different tasks involved in the use of the system in question should be defined and the different personnel should be categorised. What the results are supposed to show and what they could show should also be specified as well as the types of questions (closed, multiple choice, open, rating, ranking etc.) to be used. This stage of questionnaire construction is often neglected, and consequently the data obtained normally reflects this (Wilson and Corlett, 1995).

Step 2: Define the population
Once the objectives of the study are clearly defined, the analyst should define the sample population i.e. the participants whom the questionnaire will be administered to. Again, the definition of the participant population should go beyond simply describing an area of personnel, such as 'control room operators' and should be as exhaustive as possible, including defining age groups, different job categories (control room supervisors, operators, management etc.) and different organisations. The sample size should also be determined at this stage. Sample size is dependent upon the scope of the study and also the amount of time and resources available for data analysis.

Step 3: Construct the questionnaire

A questionnaire is typically comprised of four parts: an introduction, participant information section, the information section and an epilogue. The introduction should contain information that informs the participant who you are, what the purpose of the questionnaire is and what the results are going to be used for. One must be careful to avoid putting information in the introduction that may bias the participant in any way. For example, describing the purpose of the questionnaire as 'determining usability problems with existing C4i interfaces' may lead the participant before the questionnaire has begun. The classification part of the questionnaire normally contains multiple-choice questions requesting information about the participant, such as age, sex, occupation and experience. The information part of the questionnaire is the most crucial part, as it contains the questions designed to gather the required information related to the initial objectives. There are numerous categories of questions that can be used in this part of the questionnaire. Which type of question to be used is dependent upon the analysis and the type of data required. Where possible, the type of question used in the information section of the questionnaire should be consistent i.e. if the first few questions are multiple choice, then all of the questions should be kept as multiple choice. The different types of questions available are displayed in Table 2.2. Each question used in the questionnaire should be short in length, worded clearly and concisely, using relevant language. Data analysis should be considered when constructing the questionnaire. For instance, if there is little time available for the data analysis process, then the use of open-ended questions should be avoided, as they are time consuming to collate and analyse. If time is limited, then closed questions should be used, as they offer specific data that is quick to collate and analyse. The size of the questionnaire is also of importance. Too large and participants will not complete the questionnaire, yet a very small questionnaire may seem worthless and could suffer the same fate. Optimum questionnaire length is dependent upon the participant population, but it is generally recommended that questionnaires should be no longer than two pages (Wilson and Corlett, 1995).

Step 4: Piloting the questionnaire

Wilson and Corlett (1995) recommend that once the questionnaire construction stage is complete, a pilot run of the questionnaire is required. This is a crucial part of the questionnaire design process, yet it is often neglected by HF practitioners due to various factors, such as time and financial constraints. During this step, the questionnaire is evaluated by its potential user population, domain experts and also by other HF practitioners. This allows any problems with the questionnaire to be removed before the critical administration phase. Typically, numerous problems are encountered during the piloting stage, such as errors within the questionnaire, redundant questions and questions that the participants simply do not understand or find confusing. Wilson and Corlett (1995) recommend that the pilot stage should comprise the following three stages:

1. *Individual criticism.* The questionnaire should be administered to several colleagues who are experienced in questionnaire construction, administration and analysis. Colleagues should be encouraged to offer criticisms of the questionnaire.

2. *Depth interviewing.* Once the individual criticisms have been attended to and any changes have been made, the questionnaire should be administered to a small sample of the intended population. Once they have completed the questionnaire, the participants should be subjected to an interview regarding the answers that they provided. This allows the analyst to ensure that the questions were fully understood and that the correct (required) data is obtained.

3. *Large sample administration.* The redesigned questionnaire should then be administered to a large sample of the intended population. This allows the analyst to ensure that the correct data is being collected and also that sufficient time is available to analyse the data. Worthless questions can also be highlighted during this stage. The likely response rate can also be predicted based upon the returned questionnaires in this stage.

Table 2.2   Types of Questions Used in Questionnaire Design

Type of Question	Example question	When to use
Multiple choice	On approximately how many occasions have you witnessed an error being committed with this system? (0-5, 6-10, 11-15, 16-20, More than 20)	When the participant is required to choose a specific response.
Rating scales	I found the system unnecessarily complex. (Strongly Agree (5), Agree (4), Not sure (3), Disagree (2), Strongly Disagree (1))	When subjective data regarding participant opinions is required.
Paired Associates (Bipolar alternatives)	Which of the two tasks A + B subjected you to more mental workload? (A or B)	When two alternatives are available to choose from.
Ranking	Rank, on a scale of 1 (Very Poor Usability) to 10 (Excellent Usability) the usability of the device.	When a numerical rating is required.
Open-ended questions	What did you think of the system's usability?	When data regarding participants own opinions about a certain subject is required i.e. subjects compose their own answers.
Closed questions	Which of the following errors have you committed or witnessed whilst using the existing system? (Action omitted, action on wrong interface element, action mistimed, action repeated, action too little, action too much)	When the participant is required to choose a specific response.
Filter questions	Have you ever committed an error whilst using the current system interface? (Yes or No, if Yes, go to question 10, if No, go to question 15)	To determine whether participant has specific knowledge or experience. To guide participant past redundant questions.

Step 5: Questionnaire administration

Once the questionnaire has been successfully piloted, it is ready to be administered. Exactly how the questionnaire is administered is dependent upon the aims and objectives of the analysis, and also the target population. For example, if the target population can be gathered together at a certain time and place, then the questionnaire could be administered at this time, with the analyst(s) present. This ensures that the questionnaires are completed. However, gathering the target population in one place at the same time can be problematic and so questionnaires are often administered by post. Although this is quick and cheap, requiring little input from the analyst(s), the response rate is very low, typically 10%. Procedures to address poor responses rates are available, such as offering payment on completion, the use of encouraging letters, offering a donation to charity upon return, contacting non-respondents by telephone and sending shortened versions of the initial questionnaire to non-respondents. All these methods have been shown in the past to improve response rates, but almost all involve substantial extra cost.

Step 6: Data analysis
Once all (or a sufficient amount) of the questionnaires have been returned or collected, the data analysis process should begin. This is a lengthy process, the exact time required being dependent upon a number of factors (e.g. number of question items, sample size, required statistical techniques and data reduction). Questionnaire data is normally computerised and analysed statistically.

Step 7: Follow-up phase
Once the data is analysed sufficiently and conclusions are drawn, the participants who completed the questionnaire should be informed regarding the outcome of the study. This might include a thank you letter and an associated information pack containing a summary of the research findings.

Advantages

1. Questionnaires offer a very flexible way of collecting large volumes of data from large participant samples.
2. When the questionnaire is properly designed, the data analysis phase should be quick and very straightforward.
3. Very few resources are required once the questionnaire has been designed.
4. A number of HF questionnaires already exist (QUIS, SUMI, SUS etc), allowing the analyst to choose the most appropriate for the study purposes. This also removes the time associated with the design of the questionnaire. Also, results can be compared with past results obtained using the same questionnaire.
5. Very easy to administer to large numbers of participants.
6. Skilled questionnaire designers can use the questions to direct the data collection.

Disadvantages

1. Designing, piloting, administering and analysing a questionnaire is time consuming.
2. Reliability and validity of questionnaires is questionable.
3. The questionnaire design process is taxing, requiring great skill on the analyst's behalf.
4. Typically, response rates are low e.g. around 10% for postal questionnaires.
5. The answers provided in questionnaires are often rushed and non-committal.
6. Questionnaires are prone to a number of different biases, such as prestige bias.
7. Questionnaires can offer a limited output.

Flowchart

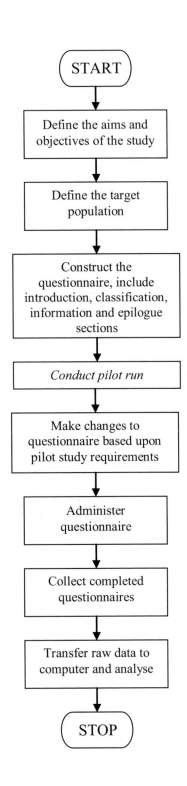

Example

Marshall, Stanton, Young, Salmon, Harris, Demagalski, Waldmann and Dekker (2003) conducted a study designed to investigate the prediction of design induced error on civil flight decks. The human error template (HET) method was developed and used to predict potential design induced errors on the flight deck of aircraft X during the flight task, 'Land aircraft X at New Orleans airport using the Autoland system'. In order to validate the error predictions made, a database of error occurrence for the flight task under analysis was required. A questionnaire was developed based upon the results of an initial study using the SHERPA (Embrey, 1986) method to predict design induced error during the flight task under analysis. The questionnaire was based upon the errors identified using the SHERPA method, and included a question for each error identified. Each question was worded to ask respondents whether they had ever made the error in question or whether they knew anyone else who had made the error. The questionnaire contained 73 questions in total. A total of 500 questionnaires were sent out to civil airline pilots and 46 (9.2%) were completed and returned (Marshall et al, 2003). An extract of the questionnaire is presented below (Source: Marshall et al, 2003).

Aircraft pilot error questionnaire extract

The questionnaire aims to establish mistakes or errors that you have made or that you know have been made when completing approach and landing. For the most part, it is assumed that the task is carried out using the Flight Control Unit for most of the task. We are hoping to identify the errors that are made as a result of the design of the flight deck, what are termed 'Design Induced Errors'.

Position: _____

Total Flying Hours : _____

Hours on Aircraft Type: _____

This questionnaire has been divided broadly into sections based upon the action being completed. In order to be able to obtain the results that we need, the questionnaire may appear overly simplistic or repetitive but this is necessary for us to break down the possible problems into very small steps that correspond to the specific pieces of equipment or automation modes being used.

Some of the questions may seem to be highly unlikely events that have not been done as far as you are aware but please read and bypass these as you need to.

Next to each statement, there are two boxes labelled 'Me' and 'Other'. If it is something that you have done personally then please tick 'Me'. If you know of colleagues who have made the same error, then please tick 'Other'. If applicable, please tick both boxes.

Q	Error	Me	Other
	Failed to check the speed brake setting at any time	☐	☐
	Intended to check the speed brake setting and checked something else by mistake	☐	☐
	Checked the speed brake position and misread it	☐	☐
	Assumed that the lever was in the correct position and later found that it was in the wrong position	☐	☐
	Set the speed brake at the wrong time (early or late)	☐	☐
	Failed to set the speed brake (at all) when required	☐	☐
	Moved the flap lever instead of the speed brake lever when intended to apply the speed brake	☐	☐

Q	Error	Me	Other
	Started entering an indicated air speed on the Flight Control Unit and found that it was in MACH mode or vice versa	☐	☐
	Misread the speed on the Primary Flight Display	☐	☐
	Failed to check airspeed when required to	☐	☐
	Initially, dialled in an incorrect airspeed on the Flight Control Unit by turning the knob in the wrong direction	☐	☐
	Found it hard to locate the speed change knob on the Flight Control Unit	☐	☐
	Having entered the desired airspeed, pushed or pulled the switch in the opposite way to the one that you wanted	☐	☐
	Adjusted the heading knob instead of the speed knob	☐	☐
	Found the Flight Control Unit too poorly lit at night to be able to complete actions easily	☐	☐
	Found that the speed selector knob is easily turned too little or too much i.e. speed is set too fast/slow	☐	☐
	Turned any other knob when intending to change speed	☐	☐
	Entered an airspeed value and accepted it but it was different to the desired value	☐	☐

Q	Error	Me	Other
	Failed to check that the aircraft had established itself on the localiser when it should have been checked	☐	☐
	Misread the localiser on the ILS	☐	☐
	If not on localiser, started to turn in wrong direction to re-establish localiser	☐	☐
	Incorrectly adjusted heading knob to regain localiser and activated the change	☐	☐
	Adjusted the speed knob by mistake when intending to change heading	☐	☐
	Turned heading knob in the wrong direction but realised before activating it	☐	☐
	Pulled the knob when you meant to push it and vice versa	☐	☐

Q	Error	Me	Other
	Misread the glideslope on the ILS	☐	☐
	Failed to monitor the glideslope and found that the aircraft had not intercepted it	☐	☐

Q	Error	Me	Other
	Adjusted the speed knob by mistake when intending to change heading	☐	☐
	Turned heading knob in the wrong direction but realised before activating it	☐	☐
	Turned the knob too little or too much	☐	☐
	Entered a heading on the Flight Control Unit and failed to activate it at the appropriate time (SEE EQ NOTE 1)	☐	☐

Q	Error	Me	Other
	Misread the altitude on the Primary Flight Display	☐	☐
	Maintained the wrong altitude	☐	☐
	Entered the wrong altitude on the Flight Control Unit but realised before activating it	☐	☐
	Entered the wrong altitude on the Flight Control Unit and activated it	☐	☐
	Not monitored the altitude at the necessary time	☐	☐
	Entered an incorrect altitude because the 100/1000 feet knob wasn't clicked over	☐	☐
	Believed that you were descending in FPA and found that you were in fact in V/S mode or vice versa	☐	☐
	Having entered the desired altitude, pushed or pulled the switch in the opposite way to the one that you wanted	☐	☐

If you would like to tell us anything about the questionnaire or you feel that we have missed out some essential design induced errors, please feel free to add them below and continue on another sheet if necessary.

Please continue on another sheet if necessary

If you would be interested in the results of this questionnaire then please put the address or e-mail address below that you would like the Executive Summary sent to.

_____

_____

I would be interested in taking part on the expert panel of aircraft X pilots ☐

Thank you very much for taking the time to complete this questionnaire.

Related Methods

There are numerous questionnaire methods available to the HF practitioner. Different types of questionnaires include rating scale questionnaires, paired comparison questionnaires and ranking questionnaires. A number of established questionnaire methods exist, such as SUMI, QUIS and the system usability scale (SUS).

Approximate Training and Application Times

Wilson and Corlett (1995) suggest that questionnaire design is more of an art than a science. Practice makes perfect, and practitioners normally need to make numerous attempts at questionnaire design before becoming proficient at the process (see Openheim, 2000). Similarly, although the application time associated with questionnaires is at first glance minimal (i.e. the completion phase), when one considers the time expended in the construction and data analysis phases, it is apparent that the total application time is high.

Reliability and Validity

The reliability and validity of questionnaire methods is questionable. Questionnaire methods are prone to a number of biases and often suffer from 'social desirability' whereby the participants are merely 'giving the analyst(s) what they want'. Questionnaire answers are also often rushed and non-committal. In a study comparing 12 HF methods, Stanton and Young (1999) report that questionnaires demonstrated an acceptable level of inter-rater reliability, but unacceptable levels of intra-rater reliability and validity.

Tools Needed

Questionnaires are normally paper based and completed using pen and paper. Questionnaire design normally requires a PC, along with a word processing package such as Microsoft Word™. In the analysis of questionnaire data, a spreadsheet package such as Microsoft Excel™ is required, and a statistical software package such as SPSS™ is also required to treat the data statistically.

Observation

Background and Applications

Observational methods are used to gather data regarding the physical and verbal aspects of a task or scenario. These include tasks catered for by the system, the individuals performing the tasks, the tasks themselves (task steps and sequence), errors made, communications between individuals, the technology used by the system in conducting the tasks (controls, displays, communication technology etc.), the system environment and the organisational environment. Observation has been extensively used, and typically forms the starting point of an analysis effort. The most obvious and widely used form of observational technique is direct observation, whereby an analyst records visually a particular task or scenario. However, a number of different forms of observation exist, including direct observation but also participant observation and remote observation. Drury (1990) suggests that there are five different types of information that can be elicited from observational methods. These are the sequence of activities, duration of activities, frequency of activities, fraction of time spent in states, and spatial movement. As well as physical (or visually recorded) data, verbal data is also recorded, in particular verbal interactions between the agents involved in the scenario under analysis. Observational methods can be used at any stage of the design process in order to gather information regarding existing or proposed designs.

Domain of Application

Generic.

Procedure and Advice

There is no set procedure for carrying out an observational analysis. The procedure would normally be determined by the nature and scope of analysis required. A typical observational analysis procedure can be split into the following three phases: the observation design stage, the observation application stage and the data analysis stage. The following procedure provides the analyst with a general set of guidelines for conducting a 'direct' type observation.

Step 1: Define the objective of the analysis
The first step in observational analysis involves clearly defining the aims and objectives of the observation. This should include determining which product or system is under analysis, in which environment the observation will take place, which user groups will be observed, what type of scenarios will be observed and what data is required. Each point should be clearly defined and stated before the process continues.

Step 2: Define the scenario(s)
Once the aims and objectives of the analysis are clearly defined, the scenario(s) to be observed should be defined and described further. For example, when conducting an observational analysis of control room operation, the type of scenario required should be clearly defined. Normally, the analyst(s) have a particular type of scenario in mind. For example, operator interaction and performance under emergency situations may be the focus of the analysis. The exact nature of the required scenario(s) should be clearly defined by the observation team. It is recommended that a HTA is then conducted for the task or scenario under analysis.

Step 3: Observation plan
Once the aim of the analysis is defined and also the type of scenario to be observed is determined, the analysis team should proceed to plan the observation. The analysis team should consider what they are hoping to observe, what they are observing, and how they are going to observe it Depending upon the nature of the observation, access to the system in question should be gained first. This may involve holding meetings with the organisation or establishment in question, and is typically a lengthy process. Any recording tools should be defined and also the length of observations should be determined. Placement of video and audio recording equipment should also be considered. To make things easier, a walkthrough of the system/environment/scenario under analysis is recommended. This allows the analyst(s) to become familiar with the task in terms of activity conducted, the time taken, location and also the system under analysis.

Step 4: Pilot observation
In any observational study a pilot or practice observation is crucial. This allows the analysis team to assess any problems with the data collection, such as noise interference or problems with the

recording equipment. The quality of data collected can also be tested as well as any effects upon task performance that may result from the presence of observers. If major problems are encountered, the observation may have to be re-designed. Steps 1 to 4 should be repeated until the analysis team are happy that the quality of the data collected will be sufficient for their study requirements.

Step 5: Conduct observation
Once the observation has been designed, the team should proceed with the observation(s). Typically, data is recorded visually using video and audio recording equipment. An observation transcript is also created during the observation. An example of an observation transcript is presented in Table 2.3. Observation length and timing is dependent upon the scope and requirements of the analysis and also the scenario(s) under analysis. The observation should end only when the required data is collected.

Step 6: Data analysis
Once the observation is complete, the data analysis procedure begins. Typically, the starting point of the analysis phase involves typing up the observation notes or transcript made during the observation. This is a very time-consuming process but is crucial to the analysis. Depending upon the analysis requirements, the team should then proceed to analyse the data in the format that is required, such as frequency of tasks, verbal interactions, and sequence of tasks. When analysing visual data, typically user behaviours are coded into specific groups. The software package Observer™ is typically used to aid the analyst in this process.

Step 7: Further analysis
Once the initial process of transcribing and coding the observational data is complete, further analysis of the data begins. Depending upon the nature of the analysis, observation data is used to inform a number of different HF analyses, such as task analysis, error analysis and communications analysis. Typically, observational data is used to develop a task analysis (e.g. HTA) of the task or scenario under analysis.

Step 8: Participant feedback
Once the data has been analysed and conclusions have been drawn, the participants involved should be provided with feedback of some sort. This could be in the form of a feedback session or a letter to each participant. The type of feedback used is determined by the analysis team.

Example

An observational analysis of an energy distribution scenario was conducted as part of an analysis of C4i activity in the energy distribution domain. Three observers observed a switching scenario basic maintenance to substation equipment. There were three main parties involved in the work, two at different substations and one on overhead lines working in between the two sites. The data collected during the observation was then used as the input for an analysis of the scenario using the event analysis of systemic teamwork (EAST; Baber and Stanton, 2004) methodology. This involved analysing the observation data using the following HF methods:

- Hierarchical task analysis
- Co-ordination demands analysis
- Operator sequence diagram
- Social network analysis
- Comms usage diagram
- Critical decision method
- Propositional networks.

Table 2.3 **Extract From Observation Transcript of Energy Distribution Scenario** (Salmon, Stanton, Walker, McMaster and Green, 2005)

Time	Process	Comms	Location	Notes
09:54	GA & DW engage in general pre-amble about the forthcoming switching ops. Considering asking the Operations Centre in Wokingham to switch out SGT1A1B early so that SGT5 can be done at the same time?	Person to person	Barking 275Kv switch-house	
10:15	Wokingham call Barking ask if they still want isolation – GA confirms yes.	Telephone		
10:19	Switching phone rings throughout building. NOC? Wants 132Kv busbar opened [GA].	Green Telephone		
10:40	SGT1A1B waiting to be handed over to NOC. Delay.			
10:40	Wokingham report to Barking 275 [GA] complication with EDF. EDF want to reselect circuits at the last minute at another substation due to planned shutdown of SGT1A.	Telephone		Wokingham contact EDF to confirm switching (as they did with Barking 275 at 10:15). EDF report a problem. Wokingham pass this onto Barking 275.
10:53	GA and DW discuss EDF problem. Can DW reconfigure circuits in Barking West (33Kv)?	Person to person		
10:53	GA contact Wokingham. Confusion as to what circuits need reconfiguring and who can do it. GA talks to DW at the same time. Decided that DW can reconfigure circuits. Wokingham give GA name and phone number of EDF contact.	GA/DW Person to Person, Wokingham Telephone		This is an unplanned measure – now need to go to Barking West 33Kv to reconfigure local electricity supply circuits.
10:58	GA and DW discuss plans for Barking West 33. Discuss who owns what, safety rules etc. Also discuss and decide order of subsequent site visits (might have to go to Barking West 33 twice).			
11:04	GA & DW waiting to travel to Barking West.			

Flowchart

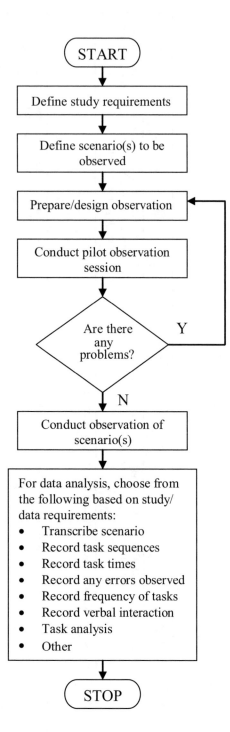

Advantages

1. Observational data provides a 'real life' insight into the activity performed in complex systems.
2. Various data can be elicited from an observational study, including task sequences, task analysis, error data, task times, verbal interaction and task performance.
3. Observation has been used extensively in a wide range of domains.
4. Observation provides objective information.
5. Detailed physical task performance data is recorded, including social interactions and any environmental task influences (Kirwan and Ainsworth, 1992).
6. Observation analysis can be used to highlight problems with existing operational systems. It can be used in this way to inform the design of new systems or devices.
7. Specific Scenarios are observed in their real-world setting.
8. Observation is typically the starting point in any HF analysis effort, and observational data is used as the input into numerous HF analyses methods, such as human error identification techniques (SHERPA), task analysis (HTA), communications analysis (Comms Usage Diagrams), and charting techniques (operator sequence diagrams).

Disadvantages

1. Observational methods are intrusive to task performance.
2. Observation data is prone to various biases. Knowing that they are being watched tends to elicit new and different behaviours in participants. For example, when observing control room operators, they may perform exactly as their procedures say they should. However, when not being observed, the same control room operators may perform completely differently, using short cuts and behaviours that are not stated in their procedures. This may be due to the fact that the operators do not wish to be caught bending the rules in any way i.e. bypassing a certain procedure.
3. Observational methods are time consuming in their application, particularly the data analysis procedure. Kirwan and Ainsworth (1992) suggest that when conducting the transcription process, one hour of recorded audio data takes on analyst approximately eight hours to transcribe.
4. Cognitive aspects of the task under analysis are not elicited using observational methods. Verbal protocol analysis is more suited for collecting data on the cognitive aspects of task performance.
5. An observational study can be both difficult and expensive to set up and conduct. Gaining access to the required establishment is often extremely difficult and very time consuming. Observational methods are also costly, as they require the use of expensive recording equipment (digital video camera, audio recording devices).
6. Causality is a problem. Errors can be observed and recorded during an observation but why the errors occur may not always be clear.
7. The analyst has only a limited level of experimental control.
8. In most cases, a team of analysts is required to perform an observation study. It is often difficult to acquire a suitable team with sufficient experience in conducting observational studies.

Related Methods

There are a number of different observational methods, including indirect observation, participant observation and remote observation. The data derived from observational methods is used as the input to a plethora of HF methods, including task analysis, cognitive task analysis, charting and human error identification techniques.

Approximate Training and Application Times

Whilst the training time for an observational analysis is low (Stanton and Young, 1999), the application time is typically high. The data analysis phase in particular is extremely time consuming. Kirwan and Ainsworth (1992) suggest that, during the transcription process, one hour of audio recorded data would take approximately eight hours to transcribe.

Reliability and Validity

Observational analysis is beset by a number of problems that can potentially affect the reliability and validity of the method. According to Baber and Stanton (1996) problems with causality, bias (in a number of forms), construct validity, external validity and internal validity can all arise unless the correct precautions are taken. Whilst observational methods possess a high level of face validity (Drury 1990) and ecological validity (Baber and Stanton, 1996), analyst or participant bias can adversely affect their reliability and validity.

Tools Needed

For a thorough observational analysis, the appropriate visual and audio recording equipment is necessary. Simplistic observational studies can be conducted using pen and paper only, however, for observations in complex, dynamic systems, more sophisticated equipment is required, such as video and audio recording equipment. For the data analysis purposes, a PC with the Observer™ software is required.

Chapter 3

Task Analysis Methods

Whilst data collection techniques are used to collect specific data regarding the activity performed in complex systems, task analysis methods describe and represent it. Another well established (and used) group of HF methods, task analysis helps the analyst to understand and represent human and system performance in a particular task or scenario. Task analysis involves identifying tasks, collecting task data, analysing the data so that tasks are understood, and then producing a documented representation of the analysed tasks (Annett, Duncan and Stammers, 1971). According to Diaper and Stanton (2004) there are, or at least have been, over 100 task analysis methods described in the literature. Typical task analysis methods are used for understanding the required human-machine and human-human interactions and for breaking down tasks or scenarios into component task steps or physical operations. According to Kirwan and Ainsworth (1992) task analysis can be defined as the study of what an operator (or team of operators) is required to do (their actions and cognitive processes) in order to achieve system goals.

The use of task analysis methods is widespread, with applications in a range of domains, including military operations, aviation (Marshall et al, 2003), air traffic control, driving (Walker, Stanton and Young, 2001), public technology (Stanton and Stevenage, 1999), product design and nuclear petro-chemical domains to name a few. According to Annett (2004) a survey of defence task analysis studies demonstrated its use in system procurement, manpower analysis, interface design, operability assessment and training specification. Diaper (2004) suggests that task analysis is possibly the most powerful technique available to HCI practitioners, and it has potential applications at each stage in the system design and development process. Stanton (2004) also suggests that task analysis is the central method for the design and analysis of system performance, involved in everything from design concept to system development and operation. Stanton (2004) also highlights the role of task analysis in task allocation, procedure design, training design and interface design.

A task analysis of the task(s) and system under analysis is the next logical step after the data collection process. Specific data is used to conduct a task analysis, allowing the task to be described in terms of the individual task steps required, the technology used in completing the task (controls, displays etc.) and the sequence of the task steps involved. The task description offered by task analysis methods is then typically used as the input to further analysis methods, such as human error identification (HEI) techniques and process charting techniques. For example, the systematic human error reduction and prediction approach (SHERPA; Embrey 1986) and human error template (HET; Marshall et al 2003) are both human error identification techniques that are applied to the bottom level task steps identified in a hierarchical task analysis (HTA). In doing so, the task under analysis can be scrutinised to identify potential errors that might occur during the performance of that task. Similarly, an operations sequence diagram (OSD) is another example of a method that is based upon an initial task analysis of the task or process in question.

The popularity of task analysis methods is a direct function of their usefulness and flexibility. Typically, a task analysis of some sort is required in any HF analysis effort, be it usability evaluation, error identification or performance evaluation. Task analysis outputs are particularly useful, providing a step-by-step description of the activity under analysis. Also, analysts using task analysis approaches often develop a (required) deep understanding of the activity under analysis.

Task analysis methods, however, are not without their flaws. The resource usage incurred when using such approaches is often considerable. The data collection phase is time consuming and often requires the provision of video and audio recording equipment. Such techniques are also typically time consuming in their application, and many reiterations are needed before an accurate representation of the activity under analysis is produced. Task analysis methods are also affected by several reliability issues, as different analysts may produce entirely different representations of the same activity. Similarly, analysts may produce different representations of the same activity on different occasions.

There are a number of different approaches to task analysis available to the HF practitioner, including hierarchical task analysis (HTA), tabular task analysis (TTA), verbal protocol analysis (VPA), goals, operators, methods and selection rules (GOMS) and the sub-goal template (SGT) method. A brief summary description of the task analysis methods reviewed is given below.

The most commonly used and well-known task analysis method is hierarchical task analysis (HTA; Annett, 2004). HTA involves breaking down the task under analysis into a nested hierarchy of goals, operations and plans. GOMS (Card, Moran and Newell, 1983) attempts to define the user's goals, decompose these goals into sub-goals and demonstrate how the goals are achieved through user interaction. Verbal protocol analysis (VPA) is used to derive the processes, cognitive and physical, that an individual uses to perform a task. VPA involves creating a written transcript of operator behaviour as they perform the task under analysis. Task decomposition (Kirwan and Ainsworth, 1992) can be used to create a detailed task description using specific categories to exhaustively describe actions, goals, controls, error potential and time constraints. The sub-goal template (SGT) method is a development of HTA that is used to specify information requirements to system designers. The output of the SGT method provides a re-description of HTA for the task(s) under analysis in terms of information handling operations (IHOs), SGT task elements and the associated information requirements.

Task analysis methods have evolved in response to increased levels of complexity and the increased use of teams within work settings. A wide variety of task analysis procedures now exist, including techniques designed to consider the cognitive aspects of decision making and activity in complex systems (Cognitive task analysis) and also collaborative or team-based activity (Team task analysis). Cognitive task analysis techniques, such as the critical decision method (CDM; Klein and Armstrong, 2004), and applied cognitive task analysis (ACTA; Militello and Hutton 2000) use probe interview techniques in order to analyse, understand and represent the unobservable cognitive processes associated with tasks or work. Team task analysis (TTA) techniques attempt to describe the process of work across teams or distributed systems. A summary of the task analysis methods reviewed is presented in Table 3.1.

Hierarchical Task Analysis (HTA)

Background and Applications

Hierarchical task analysis (HTA; Annett 2004) is the most popular task analysis method and has become perhaps the most widely used of all HF methods available. Originally developed in response to the need for greater understanding of cognitive tasks (Annett 2004), HTA involves describing the activity under analysis in terms of a hierarchy of goals, sub-goals, operations and plans. The end result is an exhaustive description of task activity. One of the main reasons for the enduring popularity of the method is its flexibility, and scope for further analysis that it offers to the HF practitioner.

Table 3.1   Summary of Task Analysis Methods

Method	Type of method	Domain	Training time	App time	Related methods	Tools needed	Validation studies	Advantages	Disadvantages
HTA – Hierarchical Task Analysis	Task analysis	Generic	Med	Med	HEI Task analysis	Pen and paper	Yes	1) HTA output feeds into numerous HF techniques. 2) Has been used extensively in a variety of domains. 3) Provides an accurate description of task activity.	1) Provides mainly descriptive information. 2) Cannot cater for the cognitive components of task performance. 3) Can be time consuming to conduct for large, complex tasks.
GOMS – Goals, Operators, Methods and Selection Rules	Task analysis	HCI	Med-High	Med-High	NGOMSL CMN-GOMS KLM CPM-GOMS	Pen and paper	Yes No outside of HCI	1) Provides a hierarchical description of task activity.	1) May be difficult to learn and apply for non-HCI practitioners. 2) Time consuming in its application. 3) Remains invalidated outside of HCI (SEE AQ NOTE 2) domain.
VPA – Verbal Protocol Analysis	Task analysis	Generic	Low	High	Walk-through analysis	Audio recording equipment Observer software PC	Yes	1) Rich data source. 2) Verbalisations can give a genuine insight into cognitive processes. 3) Easy to conduct, providing the correct equipment is used.	1) The data analysis process is very time consuming and laborious. 2) It is often difficult to verbalise cognitive behaviour. 3) Verbalisations intrude upon primary task performance.

Table 3.1 (continued)

Method	Type of method	Domain	Training time	App time	Related methods	Tools needed	Validation studies	Advantages	Disadvantages
Task Decomposition	Task analysis	Generic	High	High	HTA Observation Interviews Questionnaire Walkthrough	Pen and paper Video recording equipment	No	1) A very flexible method, allowing the analyst(s) to direct the analysis as they wish. 2) Potentially very exhaustive. 3) Can cater for numerous aspects of the interface under analysis including error, usability, interaction time etc.	1) Very time consuming and laborious to conduct properly.
The Sub-Goal Template Method	Task analysis	Generic	Med	High	HTA	Pen and paper	No	1) The output is very useful. Information requirements for the task under analysis are specified.	1) Techniques required further testing regarding reliability and validity. 2) Can be time consuming in its application.
Tabular Task Analysis	Task analysis	Generic	Low	High	HTA Interface surveys Task decomposition	Pen and paper	No	1) A very flexible method, allowing the analyst(s) to direct the analysis as they wish. 2) Can cater for numerous aspects of the interface under analysis. Potentially very exhaustive.	1) Time consuming to conduct properly. 2) Used infrequently.

The majority of HF analysis methods either require an initial HTA of the task under analysis as their input, or at least are made significantly easier through the provision of a HTA. HTA acts as an input into numerous HF analyses methods, such as human error identification (HEI), allocation of function, workload assessment, interface design and evaluation and many more. In a review of ergonomics texts, Stanton (2004) highlights at least twelve additional applications to which HTA has been put, including interface design and evaluation, training, allocation of functions, job description, work organisation, manual design, job aid design, error prediction and analysis, team task analysis, workload assessment and procedure design. Consequently, HTA has been applied across a wide spectrum of domains, including the process control and power generation industries (Annett 2004), emergency services, military applications (Kirwan and Ainsworth, 1992; Ainsworth and Marshall, 1998/2000), civil aviation (Marshall et al, 2003), driving (Walker, Stanton and Young, 2001) public technology (Stanton and Stevenage, 1998) and retail (Shepherd 2001) to name but a few.

Domain of Application

HTA was originally developed for the chemical processing and power generation industries (Annett, 2004). However the method is generic and can be applied in any domain.

Procedure and Advice

Step 1: Define task under analysis
The first step in conducting a HTA is to clearly define the task(s) under analysis. As well as identifying the task under analysis, the purpose of the task analysis effort should also be defined. For example, Marshall et al (2003) conducted a HTA of a civil aircraft landing task in order to predict design induced error for the flight task in question.

Step 2: Data collection process
Once the task under analysis is clearly defined, specific data regarding the task should be collected. The data collected during this process is used to inform the development of the HTA. Data regarding the task steps involved, the technology used, interaction between man and machine and team members, decision making and task constraints should be collected. There are a number of ways to collect this data, including observations, interviews with SMEs, questionnaires, and walkthroughs. The methods used are dependent upon the analysis effort and the various constraints imposed, such as time and access constraints. Once sufficient data regarding the task under analysis is collected, the development of the HTA should begin.

Step 3: Determine the overall goal of the task
The overall goal of the task under analysis should first be specified at the top of the hierarchy i.e. 'Land aircraft X at New Orleans Airport using the autoland system' (Marshall et al, 2003), 'Boil kettle', or 'Listen to in-car entertainment' (Stanton and Young, 1999).

Step 4: Determine task sub-goals
Once the overall task goal has been specified, the next step is to break this overall goal down into meaningful sub-goals (usually four or five but this is not rigid), which together form the tasks required to achieve the overall goal. In the task, 'Land aircraft X at New Orleans Airport using the autoland system' (Marshall et al, 2003), the overall goal of landing the aircraft was broken down into the sub-goals, 'Set up for approach', 'Line up aircraft for runway' and 'Prepare aircraft for landing'. In a HTA of a Ford in-car radio (Stanton and Young, 1999) the overall task goal, 'Listen

to in-car entertainment', was broken down into the following sub-goals, 'Check unit status', 'Press on/off button', 'Listen to the radio', 'Listen to cassette', and 'Adjust audio preferences'.

Step 5: Sub-goal decomposition
Next, the analyst should break down the sub-goals identified during step four into further sub-goals and operations, according to the task step in question. This process should go on until an appropriate operation is reached. The bottom level of any branch in a HTA should always be an operation. Whilst everything above an operation specifies goals, operations actually say what needs to be done. Therefore operations are actions to be made by an agent in order to achieve the associated goal. For example, in the HTA of the flight task 'Land aircraft X at New Orleans Airport using the autoland system' (Marshall et al, 2003), the sub-goal 'Reduce airspeed to 210 Knots' is broken down into the following operations: 'Check current airspeed' and 'Dial the Speed/MACH selector knob to enter 210 on the IAS/MACH display'.

Step 6: Plans analysis
Once all of the sub-goals and operations have been fully described, the plans need to be added. Plans dictate how the goals are achieved. A simple plan would say Do 1, then 2, and then 3. Once the plan is completed, the agent returns to the super-ordinate level. Plans do not have to be linear and exist in many forms, such as Do 1, or 2 and 3. The different types of plans used are presented in Table 3.2. The output of a HTA can either be a tree diagram (see Figure 3.1) or a tabular diagram (see Table 3.3).

Table 3.2   Example HTA Plans

Plan	Example
Linear	Do 1 then 2 then 3
Non-linear	Do 1, 2 and 3 in any order
Simultaneous	Do 1, then 2 and 3 at the same time
Branching	Do 1, if X present then do 2 then 3, if X is not present then EXIT
Cyclical	Do 1 then 2 then 3 and repeat until X
Selection	Do 1 then 2 or 3

Advantages

1. HTA requires minimal training and is easy to implement.
2. The output of a HTA is extremely useful and forms the input for numerous HF analyses, such as error analysis, interface design and evaluation and allocation of function analysis.
3. HTA is an extremely flexible method that can be applied in any domain for a variety of purposes.
4. Quick to use in most instances.
5. The output provides a comprehensive description of the task under analysis.
6. HTA has been used extensively in a wide range of contexts.
7. Conducting an HTA gives the user a great insight into the task under analysis.
8. HTA is an excellent method to use when requiring a task description for further analysis. If performed correctly, the HTA should depict everything that needs to be done in order to complete the task in question.
9. The method is generic and can be applied to any task in any domain.
10. Tasks can be analysed to any required level of detail, depending on the purpose.

Disadvantages

1. Provides mainly descriptive information rather than analytical information.
2. HTA contains little that can be used directly to provide design solutions.
3. HTA does not cater for the cognitive components of the task under analysis.
4. The method may become laborious and time consuming to conduct for large, complex tasks.
5. The initial data collection phase is time consuming and requires the analyst to be competent in a variety of HF methods, such as interviews, observations and questionnaires.
6. The reliability of the method may be questionable in some instances. For example, for the same task, different analysts may produce very different task descriptions.
7. Conducting a HTA is more of an art than a science, and much practice is required before an analyst becomes proficient in the application of the method.
8. An adequate software version of the method has yet to emerge.

Related Methods

HTA is widely used in HF and often forms the first step in a number of analyses, such as HEI, HRA and mental workload assessment. In a review of ergonomics texts, Stanton (2004b) highlights at least twelve additional applications to which HTA has been put, including interface design and evaluation, training, allocation of functions, job description, work organisation, manual design, job aid design, error prediction and analysis, team task analysis, workload assessment and procedure design. As a result HTA is perhaps the most commonly used HF method and is typically used as the start point or basis of any HF analysis.

Approximate Training and Application Times

According to Annett (2004), a study by Patrick, Gregov and Halliday (2000) gave students a few hours' training with not entirely satisfactory results on the analysis of a very simple task, although performance improved with further training. A survey by Ainsworth and Marshall (1998/2000) found that the more experienced practitioners produced more complete and acceptable analyses. Stanton and Young (1999) report that the training and application time for HTA is substantial. The application time associated with HTA is dependent upon the size and complexity of the task under analysis. For large, complex tasks, the application time for HTA would be high.

Reliability and Validity

According to Annett (2004), the reliability and validity of HTA is not easily assessed. From a comparison of twelve HF methods, Stanton and Young (1999) reported that the method achieved an acceptable level of validity but a poor level of reliability. The reliability of the method is certainly questionable. It seems that different analysts, with different experience may produce entirely different analyses for the same task (intra-analyst reliability). Similarly, the same analyst may produce different analyses on different occasions for the same task (inter-analyst reliability).

Tools Needed

HTA can be carried out using pencil and paper only. The HTA output can be developed and presented in a number of software applications, such as Microsoft Visio, Microsoft Word and Microsoft Excel. A number of HTA software tools also exist, such as the C@STTA HTA tool.

Example

An example HTA for the task 'boil kettle' is presented in Figure 3.1. The same HTA is presented in tabular format in Table 3.3. This is typically the starting point in the training process of the method, and is presented in order to depict a simplistic example of the methods output. An extract of the HTA for the flight task 'Land aircraft X at New Orleans using the autoland system' is presented in Figure 3.2.

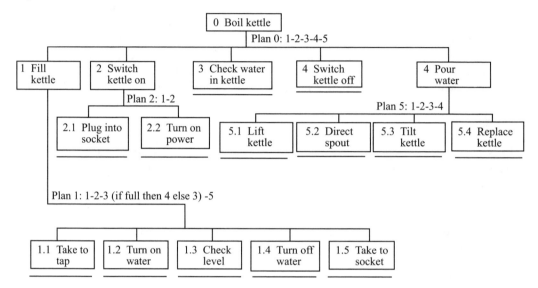

Figure 3.1   HTA of the Task 'Boil Kettle'

Table 3.3   Tabular HTA for the Boil Kettle Task

0. Boil kettle Plan 0: Do 1 then 2 then 3 then 4 then 5
1. Fill kettle Plan 1: Do 1 then 2 then 3 (if full then 4 else 3) then 5

Take to tap
    Turn on water
    Check level
    Turn off water
    Take to socket

2. Switch kettle on Plan 2: Do 1 then 2
2.1 Plug into socket   2.2 Turn on power
3. Check water in kettle
4. Switch kettle off
5. Pour water Plan 5: Do 1 then 2 then 3

5.1 Lift kettle
    5.2 Direct spout
    5.3 Tilt kettle
    5.4 Replace kettle

Flowchart

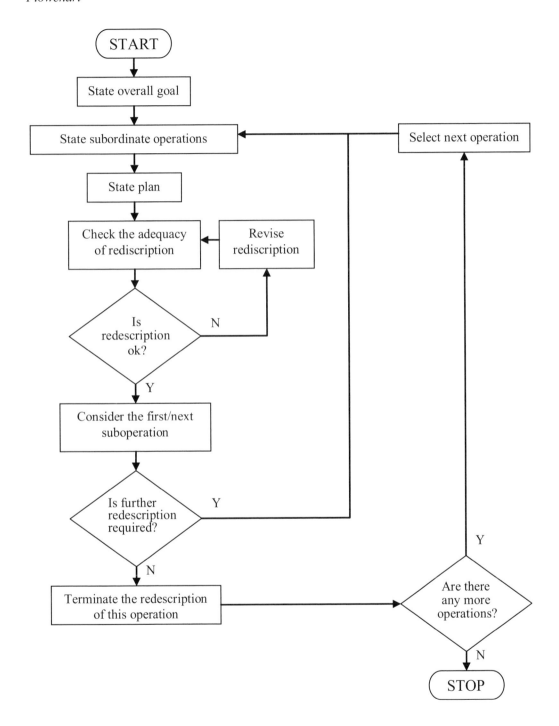

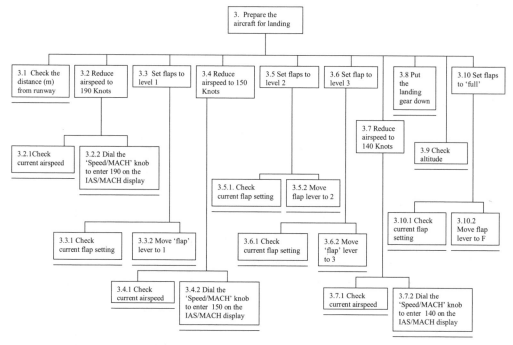

Figure 3.2   HTA Extract for the Landing Task 'Land Aircraft X at New Orleans Using the Autoland System (Source: Marshall et al, 2003)

Goals, Operators, Methods and Selection Rules (GOMS)

Background and Applications

The Goals, Operators, Methods and Selection Rules (GOMS; Card, Moran and Newell, 1983) method is part of a family of human computer interaction (HCI) based techniques that is used to provide a description of human performance in terms of user goals, operators, methods and selection rules. GOMS attempts to define the user's goals, decompose these goals into sub-goals and demonstrate how the goals are achieved through user interaction. GOMS can be used to provide a description of how a user performs a task, to predict performance times and to predict human learning. Whilst the GOMS methods are most commonly used for the evaluation of existing designs or systems, it is also feasible that they could be used to inform the design process, particularly to determine the impact of a design concept on the user. Within the GOMS family, there are four techniques: NGOMSL, the keystroke level model (KLM), CMN-GOMS, and CPM-GOMS. The GOMS methods are based upon the assumption that the user's interaction with a computer is similar to solving problems. Problems are broken down into sub-problems, which are then broken down further and so on. The GOMS method focuses upon four basic components of human interaction, goals, operators, methods and selection rules. These components are described below.

1. *Goals*. Represent exactly what the user wishes to achieve through the interaction. Goals are decomposed until an appropriate stopping point is reached.
2. *Operators*. The motor or cognitive actions that the user performs during the interaction. The goals are achieved through performing the operators.

3. *Methods*. Describe the user's procedures for accomplishing the goals in terms of operators and sub-goals. Often there are more than one set of methods available to the user.
4. *Selection Rules*. When there is more than one method for achieving a goal available to a user, selection rules highlight which of the available methods should be used.

Domain of Application

HCI.

Procedure and Advice

Step 1: Define the user's top-level goals
Firstly, the analyst should describe the user's top-level goals. Kieras (2003) suggests that the top-level goals should be described at a very high level. This ensures that any methods are not left out of the analysis.

Step 2: Goal decomposition
Once the top-level goal or set of goals has been specified, the next step is to break down the top-level goal into a set of sub-goals.

Step 3: Determine and describe operators
Operators are actions executed by the user to achieve a goal or sub-goal. The next phase of a GOMS analysis involves describing the operators required for the achievement of the sub-goals specified during step 2. Each high level operator should be replaced with another goal/method set until the analysis is broken down to the level desired by the analyst (Kieras, 2003).

Step 4: Determine and describe methods
Methods describe the procedures or set of procedures used to achieve the goal (Kirwan and Ainsworth, 1992). In the next phase of the GOMS analysis, the analyst should describe each set of methods that the user could use to achieve the task. Often there are a number of different methods available to the user and the analyst is encouraged to include all possible methods.

Step 5: Describe selection rules
If there is more than one method of achieving a goal, then the analyst should determine selection rules for the goal. Selection rules predict which of the available methods will be used by the user to achieve the goal.

Advantages

1. GOMS can be used to provide a hierarchical description of task activity.
2. The methods part of a GOMS analysis allows the analyst to describe a number of different potential task routes.
3. GOMS analysis can aid designers in choosing between systems, as performance and learning times can be specified.
4. GOMS has been applied extensively in the past and has a wealth of associated validation evidence.

Disadvantages

1. GOMS is a difficult method to apply. Far simpler task analysis methods are available.
2. GOMS can be time consuming to apply.
3. The GOMS method appears to be restricted to HCI. As it was developed specifically for use in HCI, most of the language is HCI orientated. Reported use of GOMS outside of the HCI domain is limited.
4. A high level of training and practice would be required.
5. GOMS analysis is limited as it only models error-free, expert performance.
6. Context is not taken into consideration.
7. The GOMS methods remain largely invalidated outside of HCI.

Related Methods

There are four main techniques within the GOMS family. These are NGOMSL, KLM, CMN-GOMS and CPM-GOMS.

Approximate Training and Application Times

For non-HCI experienced practitioners, it is expected that the training time would be medium to high. The application time associated with the GOMS method is dependent upon the size and complexity of the task under analysis. For large, complex tasks involving many operators and methods, the application time for GOMS would be very high. However, for small, simplistic tasks the application time would be minimal.

Reliability and Validity

Within the HCI domain, the GOMS method has been validated extensively. According to Salvendy (1997), Card et al (1983) reported that for a text-editing task, the GOMS method predicted the user's methods 80-90% of the time and also the user's operators 80-90% of the time. However, evidence of the validation of the GOMS method in applications outside of the HCI domain is limited.

Tools Needed

GOMS can be conducted using pen and paper. Access to the system, programme or device under analysis is also required.

Flowchart

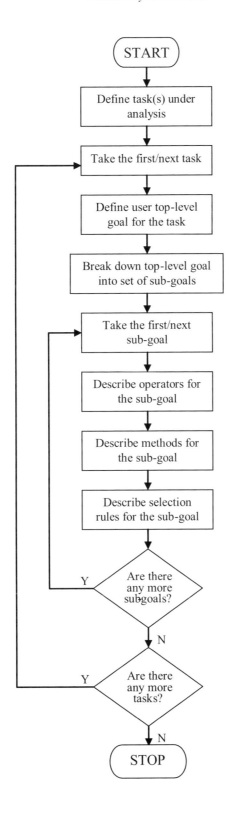

Verbal Protocol Analysis (VPA)

Background and Applications

Verbal protocol analysis (VPA) is used to derive descriptions of the processes, cognitive and physical, that an individual uses to perform a task. VPA involves creating a written transcript of operator behaviour as they perform the task or scenario under analysis. The transcript is based upon the operator 'thinking aloud' as they conduct the task under analysis. VPA has been used extensively as a means of gaining an insight into the cognitive aspects of complex behaviours. Walker (2004) reports the use of VPA in areas such as heavy industry (Bainbridge 1974), Internet usability (Hess 1999) and driving (Walker, Stanton and Young 2001).

Domain of Application

Generic.

Procedure and Advice

The following procedure is adapted from Walker (2004).

Step 1: Define scenario under analysis
Firstly, the scenario under analysis should be clearly defined. It is recommended that a HTA is used to describe the task under analysis.

Step 2: Instruct/train the participant
Once the scenario is clearly defined, the participant should be briefed regarding what is required of them during the analysis. What they should report verbally is clarified here. According to Walker (2004) it is particularly important that the participant is informed that they should continue talking even when what they are saying does not appear to make much sense. A small demonstration should also be given to the participant at this stage. A practice run may also be undertaken, although this is not always necessary.

Step 3: Begin scenario and record data
The participant should begin to perform the scenario under analysis. The whole scenario should be audio recorded (at least) by the analyst. It is also recommended that a video recording be made.

Step 4: Verbalisation of transcript
Once collected, the data should be transcribed into a written form. An excel spreadsheet is normally used. This aspect of VPA is particularly time consuming and laborious.

Step 5: Encode verbalisations
The verbal transcript (written form) should then be categorised or coded. Depending upon the requirements of the analysis, the data is coded into one of the following five categories; words, word senses, phrases, sentences or themes. The encoding scheme chosen should then be encoded according to a rationale determined by the aims of the analysis. Walker (2004) suggests that this involves attempting to ground the encoding scheme according to some established theory or approach, such as mental workload or situation awareness. The analyst should also develop a set of written instructions for the encoding scheme. These instructions should be strictly adhered to and

constantly referred to during the encoding process (Walker 2004). Once the encoding type, framework and instructions are completed, the analyst should proceed to encode the data. Various computer software packages are available to aid the analyst with this process, such as General Enquirer.

Step 6: Devise other data columns
Once the encoding is complete, the analyst should devise any 'other' data columns. This allows the analyst to note any mitigating circumstances that may have affected the verbal transcript.

Step 7: Establish inter and intra-rater reliability
Reliability of the encoding scheme then has to be established (Walker 2004). In VPA, reliability is established through reproducibility i.e. independent raters need to encode previous analyses.

Step 8: Perform pilot study
The protocol analysis procedure should now be tested within the context of a small pilot study. This will demonstrate whether the verbal data collected is useful, whether the encoding system works, and whether inter and intra-rater reliability are satisfactory. Any problems highlighted through the pilot study should be refined before the analyst conducts the VPA for real.

Step 9: Analyse structure of encoding
Finally, the analyst can analyse the results from the VPA. During any VPA analysis the responses given in each encoding category require summing, and this is achieved simply by adding up the frequency of occurrence noted in each category. Walker (In Press) suggests a more fine-grained analysis, the structure of encodings can be analysed contingent upon events that have been noted in the 'other data' column(s) of the worksheet, or in light of other data that have been collected simultaneously.

Example

The following example is a VPA taken from Walker (2004). This digital video image (Figure 3.3) is taken from the study reported by Walker, Stanton, and Young (2001) and shows how the Protocol Analysis was performed with normal drivers. The driver in Figure 3.3 is providing a concurrent verbal protocol whilst being simultaneously videoed. The driver's verbalisations and other data gained from the visual scene are transcribed into the data sheet in Figure 3.4. Figure 3.4 illustrates the 2-second incremental time index, the actual verbalisations provided by the driver's verbal commentary, the encoding categories, the events column and the protocol structure. In this study three encoding groups were defined: behaviour, cognitive processes, and feedback. The behaviour group defined the verbalisations as referring to the driver's own behaviour (OB), behaviour of the vehicle (BC), behaviour of the road environment (RE), and behaviour of other traffic (OT). The cognitive processes group was subdivided into perception (PC), comprehension (CM), projection (PR), and action execution (AC). The feedback category offered an opportunity for vehicle feedback to be further categorised according to whether it referred to system or control dynamics (SD or CD), or vehicle instruments (IN). The cognitive processes and feedback encoding categories were couched in relevant theories in order to establish a conceptual framework. The events column was for noting road events from the simultaneous video log, and the protocol structure was colour coded according to the road type being travelled upon. In this case the shade corresponds to a motorway, and would permit further analysis of the structure of encoding contingent upon road type. The section frequency counts simply sum the frequency of encoding for each category for that particular road section.

Figure 3.3   Digital Audio/Video Recording of Protocol Analysis Scenario

Advantages

1. Verbal protocol analysis provides a rich data source.
2. Protocol analysis is particularly effective when used to analyse sequences of activities.
3. Verbalisations can provide a genuine insight into cognitive processes.
4. Domain experts can provide excellent verbal data.
5. Verbal protocol analysis has been used extensively in a wide variety of domains.
6. Simple to conduct with the right equipment.

Disadvantages

1. Data analysis (encoding) can become extremely laborious and time consuming.
2. Verbal Protocol Analysis is a very time consuming method to apply (data collection and data analysis).
3. It is difficult to verbalise cognitive behaviour. Researchers have been cautioned in the past for relying on verbal protocol data (Militello and Hutton 2000).
4. Verbal commentary can sometimes serve to change the nature of the task.
5. Complex tasks involving high demand can often lead to a reduced quantity of verbalisations (Walker, 2004).
6. Strict procedure is often not adhered to fully.
7. VPA is prone to bias on the participant's behalf.

TIME (mm:ss)	VERBALIZATIONS	OB	BC	RE	OT	PC	CM	PR	AC	SD	CD	IN	EVENTS
		BEHAV				COG				F/B			
01:34	70mph, 5th gear		1			1					1	1	Glances at gear lever
01:36	2800 rpm		1			1						1	
01:38	that's quite smooth		1				1						
01:40	he's slowing down				1	1							Other car crossing from lane 3 over
01:42	don't know what's wrong with him	1			1		1						to hard shoulder in front of driver
01:44													
01:46													
01:48													
01:50													
01:52													
01:54													
01:56													
01:58													
02:00													
02:02													
02:04	it's all clear ahead				1	1							
02:06													
02:08	chap behind has eased off a bit luckily				1	1	1						
02:10													
02:12	make my intention clear that I'm going right	1							1				Indicating right
02:14	so I'll stick to the right side of this slip lane	1		1			1						
02:16													
02:18													
02:20	bit worried about overtaking him	1			1		1						Passing other vehicle
02:22													
02:24													
02:26													
Section Frequency Counts		**4**	**3**	**1**	**5**	**5**	**5**	**0**	**1**	**0**	**1**	**2**	
02:28													
02:30													

Figure 3.4   Transcription and Encoding Sheet

Related Methods

Verbal protocol analysis is related to observational techniques such as walkthroughs and direct observation. Task analysis methods such as HTA are often used in constructing the scenario under analysis. VPA is also used for various purposes, including situation awareness measurement, mental workload assessment and task analysis.

Approximate Training and Application Times

Although the method is very easy to train, the VPA procedure is time consuming to implement. According to Walker (2004) if transcribed and encoded by hand, 20 minutes of verbal transcript data at around 130 words per minute can take between 6 to 8 hours to transcribe and encode.

Reliability and Validity

Walker (2004) reports that the reliability of the method is reassuringly good. For example, Walker, Stanton and Young (2001) used two independent raters and established inter-rater reliability at Rho=0.9 for rater 1 and Rho=0.7 for rater 2. Intra-rater reliability during the same study was also high, being in the region of Rho=0.95.

Tools Needed

A VPA can be conducted using pen and paper, a digital audio recording device and a video recorder if required. The device or system under analysis is also required. For the data analysis part of VPA, Microsoft Excel is normally required, although this can be done using pen and paper. A number of software packages can also be used by the analyst, including Observer, General Enquirer, TextQuest and Wordstation.

Task Decomposition

Background and Applications

Kirwan and Ainsworth (1992) describe the task decomposition methodology that can be used to gather detailed information regarding a particular task or scenario. Task decomposition involves describing the task or activity under analysis and then using specific task-related information to decompose the task in terms of specific statements regarding the task. The task can be decomposed to describe a variety of task-related features, including the devices and interface components used, the time taken, errors made, feedback and decisions required. The categories used to decompose the task steps should be chosen by the analyst based on the requirements of the analysis. There are numerous decomposition categories that can be used and new categories can be developed if required by the analysis. According to Kirwan and Ainsworth (1992), Miller (1953) was the first practitioner to use the task decomposition method. Miller (1953) recommended that each task step should be decomposed around the following categories:

1. Description.
2. Subtask.
3. Cues initiating action.
4. Controls used.
5. Decisions.
6. Typical errors.
7. Response.
8. Criterion of acceptable performance.
9. Feedback.

However, further decomposition categories have since been defined (e.g. Kirwan and Ainsworth, 1992). It is recommended that the analyst develops a set of decomposition categories based upon the analysis requirements.

Domain of Application

Generic.

Procedure and Advice

Step 1: Hierarchical task analysis
The first step in a task decomposition analysis involves creating an initial description of the task or scenario under analysis. It is recommended that a HTA is conducted for this purpose, as a goal driven, step-by-step description of the task is particularly useful when conducting a task decomposition analysis.

Step 2: Create task descriptions
Once an initial HTA for the task under analysis has been conducted, the analyst should create a set of clear task descriptions for each of the different task steps. These descriptions can be derived from the HTA developed during step 1. The task description should give the analyst enough information to determine exactly what has to be done to complete each task element. The detail of the task descriptions should be determined by the requirements of the analysis.

Step 3: Choose decomposition categories
Once a sufficient description of each task step is created, the analyst should choose the appropriate decomposition categories. Kirwan and Ainsworth (1992) suggest that there are three types of decomposition categories: descriptive, organisation-specific and modelling. Table 3.4 presents a taxonomy of descriptive decomposition categories that have been used in various studies (Source: Kirwan and Ainsworth, 1992).

Table 3.4   Task Decomposition Categories (Source: Kirwan and Ainsworth, 1992)

Description of task	Task difficulty
Description	Task criticality
Type of activity/behaviour	Amount of attention required
Task/action verb	Performance on the task
Function/purpose	Performance
Sequence of activity	Time taken
Requirements for undertaking task	Required speed
Initiating cue/event	Required accuracy
Information	Criterion of response adequacy
Skills/training required	Other activities
Personnel requirements/manning	Subtasks
Hardware features	Communications
Location	Co-ordination requirements
Controls used	Concurrent tasks
Displays used	Outputs from the task
Critical values	Output
Job aids required	Feedback
Nature of the task	Consequences/problems
Actions required	Likely/typical errors
Decisions required	Errors made/problems
Responses required	Error consequences
Complexity/task complexity	Adverse conditions/hazards

Step 4: Information collection
Once the decomposition categories have been chosen, the analyst should create a data collection pro-forma for each decomposition category. The analyst should then work through each decomposition category, recording task descriptions and gathering the additional information required for each of

the decomposition headings. To gather this information, Kirwan and Ainsworth (1992) suggest that there are many possible methods to use, including observation, system documentation, procedures, training manuals and discussions with system personnel and designers. Interviews, questionnaires, VPA and walkthrough analysis can also be used.

Step 5: Construct task decomposition
The analyst should then put data collected into a task decomposition output table. The table should comprise all of the decomposition categories chosen for the analysis. The amount of detail included in the table is also determined by the scope of the analysis.

Advantages

1. Task decomposition is a very flexible approach. In selecting which decomposition categories to use, the analyst can determine the direction and focus of the analysis.
2. A task decomposition analysis has the potential to provide a very comprehensive analysis of a particular task.
3. Task decomposition techniques are easy to learn and use.
4. The method is generic and can be used in any domain.
5. Task decomposition provides a much more detailed description of tasks than traditional task analysis methods do.
6. As the analyst has control over the decomposition categories used, potentially any aspect of a task can be evaluated. In particular, the method could be adapted to assess the cognitive components associated with tasks (goals, decisions, SA).

Disadvantages

1. As the task analysis method is potentially so exhaustive, it is a very time consuming method to apply and analyse. The HTA only serves to add to the high application time. Furthermore, obtaining information about the tasks (observation, interview etc) creates even more work for the analyst.
2. Task decomposition can be laborious to perform, involving observations, interviews etc.

Example

A task decomposition analysis was performed on the landing task, 'Land aircraft X at New Orleans using the Autoland system' (Marshall et al, 2003). The purpose of the analysis was to ascertain how suitable the task decomposition method was for the prediction of design induced error on civil flight decks. A HTA of the flight task was constructed (Figure 3.5) and a task decomposition analysis was performed. An extract of the analysis is presented in Table 3.5. Data collection included the following tasks:

1. Walkthrough of the flight task.
2. Questionnaire administered to aircraft X pilots.
3. Consultation with training manuals.
4. Performing the flight task in aircraft simulator
5. Interview with aircraft X pilot.

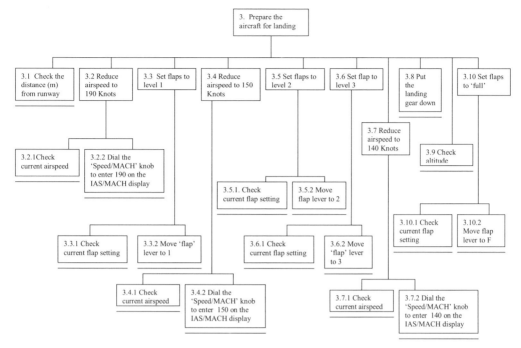

Figure 3.5   Extract of HTA 'Land Aircraft X at New Orleans Using the Autoland System'
(Source: Marshall et al, 2003)

Table 3.5   Extract of Task Decomposition Analysis for Flight Task 'Land Aircraft X at New Orleans Using the Autoland System'

Task step description 3.2.2 Dial the speed/MACH knob to enter 190 knots on the IAS/MACH display	Complexity Medium. The task involves a number of checks in quick succession and also the use of the Speed/MACH knob, which is very similar to the HDG/Track knob
Initiating cue/event: Check that the distance from the runway is 15 miles	Difficulty: Low
Displays used: Captain's Primary Flight display IAS/MACH window (Flight control unit) Captain's navigation display	Criticality: High. The task is performed in order to reduce the aircraft's speed so that the descent and approach can begin
Controls used: IAS/MACH Knob	Feedback provided: Speed/MACH window displays current airspeed value. CPFD displays airspeed
Actions required: Check distance from runway on CPFD Dial in 190 using the IAS/MACH display Check IAS/MACH window for speed value	Probable errors: a) Using the wrong knob i.e. the HDG/Track knob b) Failing to check the distance from runway c) Failing to check current airspeed d) Dialling in the wrong speed value e) Fail to enter new airspeed
Decisions required: Is distance from runway 15 miles or under? Is airspeed over/under 190knots? Have you dialled in the correct airspeed (190Knots)? Has the aircraft slowed down to 190knots?	Error consequences: a) Aircraft will change heading to 190 b) Aircraft may be too close or too far way from the runway c) Aircraft travelling at the wrong airspeed d) Aircraft may be travelling too fast for the approach

Related Methods

The task decomposition method relies on a number of data collection techniques for its input. The initial task description required is normally provided by conducting a HTA for the task under analysis. Data collection for the task decomposition analysis can involve any number of HF methods, including observational methods, interviews, walkthrough analysis and questionnaires.

Approximate Training and Application Times

As a number of methods are used within a task decomposition analysis, the training time associated with the method is high. Not only would an inexperienced practitioner require training in the task decomposition method itself (which incidentally would be minimal), but they would also require training in HTA and any methods that would be used in the data collection part of the analysis. Also, due to the exhaustive nature of a task decomposition analysis, the associated application time is also very high. Kirwan and Ainsworth (1992) suggest that task decomposition can be a lengthy process and that its main disadvantage is the huge amount of time associated with collecting the required information.

Reliability and Validity

At present, no data regarding the reliability and validity of the method is offered in the literature. It is apparent that such a method may suffer from reliability problems, as a large portion of the analysis is based upon the analyst's subjective judgement.

Tools Needed

The tools needed for a task decomposition analysis are determined by the scope of the analysis and the techniques used for the data collection process. Task decomposition can be conducted using just pen and paper. However, it is recommended that for the data collection process, visual and audio recording equipment would be required. The system under analysis is also required in some form, either in mock-up, prototype or operational form.

Flowchart

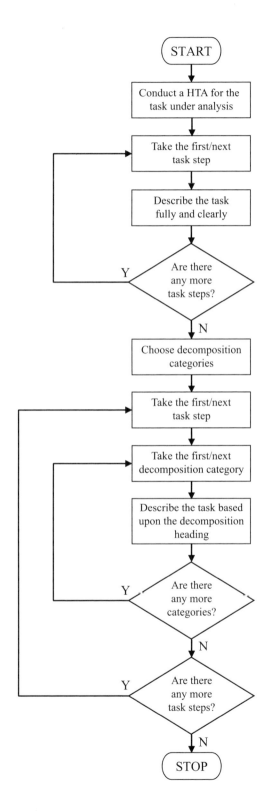

The Sub-Goal Template Method (SGT)

Background and Application

The SGT method was initially devised as a means of re-describing the output of HTA, in order to specify the relevant information requirements for the task or system under analysis (Ormerod, 2000). Although the method was originally designed for use in the process control industries, Ormerod and Shepherd (2003) describe a generic adaptation that can be used in any domain. The method itself involves re-describing a HTA for the task(s) under analysis in terms of information handling operations (IHOs), SGT task elements, and the associated information requirements. The SGT task elements used are presented in Table 3.6.

Table 3.6   SGT Task Elements (Source: Ormerod, 2000)

Code	Label	Information requirements
Action elements		
A1	Prepare equipment	Indication of alternative operating states, feedback that equipment is set to required state
A2	Activate	Feedback that the action has been effective
A3	Adjust	Possible operational states, feedback confirming actual state
A4	De-activate	Feedback that the action has been effective
Communication elements		
C1	Read	Indication of item
C2	Write	Location of record for storage and retrieval
C3	Wait for instruction	Projected wait time, contact point
C4	Receive instruction	Channel for confirmation
C5	Instruct or give data	Feedback for receipt
C6	Remember	Prompt for operator-supplied value
C7	Retrieve	Location of information for retrieval
Monitoring elements		
M1	Monitor to detect deviance	Listing of relevant items to monitor, normal parameters for comparison
M2	Monitor to anticipate change	Listing of relevant items to monitor, anticipated level
M3	Monitor rate of change	Listing of relevant items to monitor, template against which to compared observed parameters
M4	Inspect plant and equipment	Access to symptoms, templates for comparison with acceptable tolerances if necessary
Decision-making elements		
D1	Diagnose problems	Information to support trained strategy
D2	Plan adjustments	Planning information from typical scenarios
D3	Locate containment	Sample points enabling problem bracketing between a clean input and a contaminated output
D4	Judge adjustment	Target indicator, adjustment values
Exchange elements		
E1	Enter from discrete	Item position and delineation, advance descriptors, choice recovery
E2	Enter from continuous range	Choice indicator, range/category delineation, advance descriptors, end of range, range recovery
E3	Extract from discrete range	Information structure (e.g. criticality, weight, frequency structuring), feedback on current choice
E4	Extract from continuous range	Available range; information structure (e.g. criticality, weight, frequency structuring), feedback on current choices

Table 3.6 (continued)

Navigation elements		
N1	Locate a given information set	Organisation structure cues (e.g. screen set/menu hierarchy, catalogue etc.), choice descriptor conventions, current location, location relative to start, selection indicator
N2	Move to a given location	Layout structure cues (e.g. screen position, menu selection, icon, etc.), current position, position relative to information coordinates, movement indicator
N3	Browse an information set	Information (e.g. screen/menu hierarchy, catalogue etc.), organisation cues, information scope, choice points, current location, location relative to start, selection indicator

Ormerod and Shepherd (2003) describe a modified set of task elements, presented in Table 3.7.

Table 3.7   Modified SGT Task Elements (Source: Ormerod and Shepherd 2003)

SGT	Task elements	Context for assigning SGT and task element	Information requirements
Act		Perform as part of a procedure or subsequent to a decision made about changing the system	Action points and order; Current, alternative, and target states; preconditions, outcomes, dependencies, halting, recovery indicators
	A1 Activate	Make subunit operational: switch from off to on	Temporal/stage progression, outcome activation level
	A2 Adjust	Regulate the rate of operation of a unit maintaining 'on' state	Rate of state of change
	A3 Deactivate	Make subunit non-operational: switch from on to off	Cessation descriptor
Exchange		To fulfil a recording requirement. To obtain or deliver operating value	Indication of item to be exchanged, channel for confirmation
	E1 Enter	Record a value in a specified location	Information range (continuous, discrete)
	E2 Extract	Obtain a value of a specified parameter	Location of record for storage and retrieval; prompt for operator
Navigate		To move an informational state for exchange, action or monitoring	System/state structure, current relative location
	N1 Locate	Find the location of a target value or control	Target information, end location relative to start
	N2 Move	Go to a given location and search it	Target location, directional descriptor
	N3 Explore	Browse through a set of locations and values	Current/next/previous item categories
Monitor		To be aware of system states that determine need for navigation, exchange and action	Relevant items to monitor; record of when actions were taken; elapsed time from action to the present.
	M1 Monitor to detect deviance	Routinely compare system state against target state to determine need for action	Normal parameters for comparison
	M2 Monitor to anticipate cue	Compare system state against target state to determine readiness for known action	Anticipated level
	Monitor transition	Routinely compare state of change during state transition	Template against which to compare observed parameters.

Domain of Application

The SGT method was originally developed for use in the process control industries.

Procedure and Advice

Step 1: Define the task(s) under analysis
The first step in a SGT analysis involves defining the task(s) or scenario under analysis. The analyst(s) should specify the task(s) that are to be subjected to the SGT analysis. A task or scenario list should be created, including the task, system, environment and personnel involved.

Step 2: Collect specific data regarding the task(s) under analysis
Once the task under analysis is defined, the data that will inform the development of the HTA should be collected. Specific data regarding the task should be collected, including task steps involved, task sequence, technology used, personnel involved, and communications made. There are a number of ways available to collect this data, including observations, interviews, and questionnaires. It is recommended that a combination of observation of the task under analysis and interviews with the personnel involved should be used when conducting a task analysis.

Step 3: Conduct a HTA for the task under analysis
Once sufficient regarding the task under analysis is collected, a HTA for the task under analysis should be conducted.

Step 4: Assign SGT to HTA sub goals
Each bottom level task from the HTA should then be assigned a SGT. SGT sequencing elements are presented as an example in Table 3.8.

Step 5: Specify sequence
The order in which the tasks should be carried out is specified next using the SGT sequencing elements presented in Table 3.8.

Table 3.8   SGT Sequencing Elements (Source: Ormerod, 2000)

Code	Label	Syntax
S1	Fixed	S1 then X
S2	Choice/contingent	S2 if Z then X if not Z then Y
S3	Parallel	S3 then do together X and Y
S4	Free	S4 In any order X and Y

Step 6: Specify information requirements
Once a SGT has been assigned to each bottom level operation in the HTA and the appropriate sequence of the operations has been derived, the information requirements should be derived. Each SGT has its own associated information requirements, and so this involves merely looking up the relevant SGT's and extracting the appropriate information requirements.

Advantages

1. The SGT method can be used to provide a full information requirements specification to system designers.
2. The method is based upon the widely used HTA method.
3. Once the initial concepts are grasped, the method is easy to apply

Disadvantages

1. There are no data offered regarding the reliability and validity of the method.
2. The initial requirement of a HTA for the task/system under analysis creates further work for the analyst(s).
3. Further categories of SGT may require development, depending upon the system under analysis.
4. One might argue that the output of a HTA would suffice.

Flowchart

Related Methods

The SGT method uses HTA as its primary input.

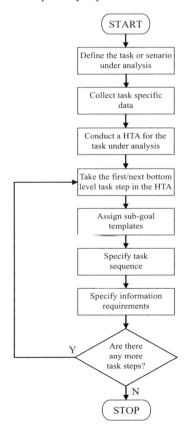

Approximate Training and Application Times

Training time for the SGT method is estimated to be medium to high. The analyst is required to fully understand how HTA works and then to grasp the SGT method. It is estimated that this may take a couple of days' training. The application is also estimated to be considerable, although this is dependent upon the size of the task(s) under analysis. For large, complex tasks it is estimated that the SGT application time is high. For small, simple tasks and those tasks where a HTA is already constructed, the application time is estimated to be low.

Reliability and Validity

No data regarding the reliability and validity of the SGT method are available in the literature.

Tools Needed

The SGT method can be conducted using pen and paper. Ormerod (2000) suggests that the method would be more usable and easier to execute if it were computerised. A computer version of the SGT method was compared to a paper-based version (Ormerod, Richardson and Shepherd, 1998). Participants using the computer version solved more problems correctly at first attempt and also made fewer errors (Ormerod, 2000).

Tabular Task Analysis (TTA)

Background and Applications

Tabular task analysis (TTA; Kirwan 1994) can be used to analyse a particular task or scenario in terms of the required task steps and the interface used. A TTA takes each bottom level task step from a HTA and analyses specific aspects of the task step, such as displays and controls used, potential errors, time constraints, feedback, triggering events etc. The content and focus of the TTA is dependent upon the nature of the analysis required. For example, if the purpose of the TTA is to evaluate the error potential of the task(s) under analysis, then the columns used will be based upon errors, their causes and their consequences.

Domain of Application

Generic.

Procedure and Advice

Step 1: Define the task(s) under analysis
The first step in a TTA involves defining the task or scenario under analysis. The analyst firstly should specify the task(s) that are to be subjected to the TTA. A task or scenario list should be created, including the task, system, environment and personnel involved.

Step 2: Collect specific data regarding the task(s) under analysis
Once the task under analysis is defined, the data that will inform the development of the TTA should be collected. Specific data regarding the task should be collected, including task steps involved, task sequence, technology used, personnel involved, and communications made. There are a number

of ways available to collect this data, including observations, interviews, and questionnaires. It is recommended that a combination of observation of the task under analysis and interviews with the personnel involved should be used when conducting a TTA.

Step 3: Conduct a HTA for the task under analysis
Once sufficient data regarding the task under analysis is collected, an initial task description should be created. For this purpose it is recommended that HTA is used. The data collected during step 2 should be used as the primary input to the HTA.

Step 4: Convert HTA into tabular format
Once an initial HTA for the task under analysis has been conducted, the analyst should put the HTA into a tabular format. Each bottom level task step should be placed in a column running down the left hand side of the table. An example of an initial TTA is presented in Table 3.9.

Table 3.9   Extract of Initial TTA

Task No.	Task description	Controls & Displays used	Required action	Feedback	Possible errors	Error consequences	Error remedies
3.2.1	Check current airspeed						
3.2.2	Dial in 190 Knots using the speed/MACH selector knob						
3.3.1	Check current flap setting						
3.3.2	Set the flap lever to level '3'						

Step 5: Choose task analysis categories
Next the analyst should select the appropriate categories and enter them into the TTA. The selection of categories is dependent upon the nature of the analysis. The example in this case was used to investigate the potential for design induced error on the flightdeck, and so the categories used are based upon error identification and analysis.

Step 6: Complete TTA table
Once the categories are chosen, the analyst should complete the columns in the TTA for each task. How this is achieved is not a strictly defined process. A number of methods can be used, such as walkthrough analysis, heuristic evaluation, observations or interviews with SMEs. Typically, the TTA is based upon the analyst's subjective judgement.

Advantages

1. TTA is a flexible method, allowing any factors associated with the task to be assessed.

2. A TTA analysis has the potential to provide a very comprehensive analysis of a particular task or scenario.
3. Easy to learn and use.
4. The method is generic and can be used in any domain.
5. TTA provides a much more detailed description of tasks than traditional task analysis methods do.
6. As the analyst has control over the TTA categories used, potentially any aspect of a task can be evaluated.
7. Potentially exhaustive, if the correct categories are used.

Disadvantages

1. As the TTA is potentially so exhaustive, it is a very time consuming method to apply. The initial data collection phase and the development of a HTA for the task under analysis also add considerably to the overall application time.
2. Data regarding the reliability and validity of the method is not available in the literature. It is logical to assume that the method may suffer from problems surrounding the reliability of the data produced.
3. A HTA for the task under analysis may suffice in most cases.

Example

A TTA was performed on the landing task, 'Land aircraft X at New Orleans using the autoland system' (Marshall et al, 2003). The purpose of the analysis was to ascertain how suitable the TTA method was for the prediction of design induced error on civil flight decks. A HTA of the flight task was constructed (Figure 3.6) and a TTA analysis was performed (Table 3.10). Data collection included the following:

1. Walkthrough of the flight task.
2. Questionnaire administered to aircraft X pilots.
3. Consultation with training manuals.
4. Performing the flight task in aircraft simulator.
5. Interview with aircraft X pilot.

Related Methods

TTA is a task analysis method of which there are many. The TTA method relies on a number of data collection techniques for its input. The initial task description required is normally provided by conducting a HTA for the task under analysis. Data collection for the TTA can involve any number of HF methods, including observational methods, interviews, walkthrough analysis and questionnaires. The TTA method is very similar to the task decomposition method (Kirwan and Ainsworth, 1992).

Training and Application Times

The training time for the TTA method is minimal, provided the analyst in question is competent in the use of HTA. The application time is considerably longer. It is estimated that each task step in a HTA requires up to ten minutes for further analysis. Thus, for large, complex tasks the TTA application time is estimated to be high. A TTA for the flight task 'Land aircraft X at New Orleans using the autoland system', which consisted of 32 bottom level task steps took around four hours to complete.

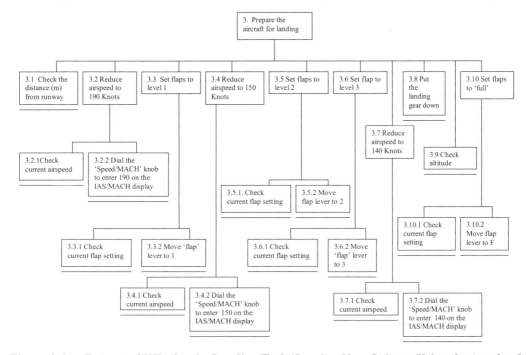

Figure 3.6   Extract of HTA for the Landing Task 'Land at New Orleans Using the Autoland System' (Source: Marshall et al, 2003)

Table 3.10   Extract of TTA Analysis for Flight Task 'Land at New Orleans Using the Autoland System'

Task No.	Task description	Controls/Displays used	Required action	Feedback	Possible errors
3.2.1	Check current airspeed	Captains primary flight display Speed/Mach window	Visual check		Misread Check wrong display Fail to check
3.2.2	Dial in 190 Knots using the speed/MACH selector knob	Speed/Mach selector knob Speed/Mach window Captain's primary flight display	Rotate Speed/Mach knob to enter 190 Visual check of speed/Mach window	Speed change in speed/Mach window and on CPFD Aircraft changes speed	Dial in wrong speed Use the wrong knob e.g. heading knob
3.3.1	Check current flap setting	Flap lever Flap display	Visual check		Misread Check wrong display Fail to check
3.3.2	Set the flap lever to level '3'	Flap lever Flap display	Move flap lever to '3' setting	Flaps change Aircraft lifts and slows	Set flaps to wrong setting

Flowchart

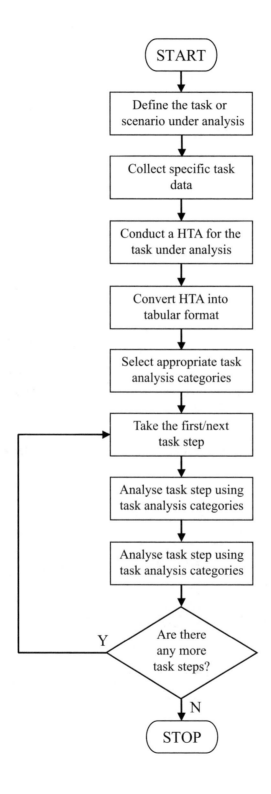

Chapter 4

Cognitive Task Analysis Methods

In contrast to traditional task analysis methods, which provide a physical description of the activity performed within complex systems, cognitive task analysis (CTA) methods are used to determine and describe the cognitive processes used by agents. Agents performing activity in today's complex systems face increasing demands upon their cognitive skills and resources. As system complexity increases, so agents require training in specific cognitive skills and processes in order to keep up. System designers require an analysis of the cognitive skills and demands associated with the operation of these systems in order to propose design concepts, allocate tasks, develop training procedures and work processes, and to evaluate performance. Traditional task analysis method outputs can be used to develop physical, step-by-step descriptions of agent activity during task performance. Whilst this is useful, it does not explicitly consider the cognitive processes associated with the activity. For some analysts, the detail provided by traditional task analysis can be used as the basis for consideration of more 'cognitive' aspects, e.g., the 'plans' in HTA could be taken to reflect the manner in which information is used to guide activity. However, it can be argued that assuming an equivalence between mental processes and the information needed to guide physical tasks can often lead to misunderstanding cognition (or at least requires a view of 'cognition' which is so restricted as to be at odds with what the term usually means).

The past three decades has seen the emergence of cognitive task analysis (CTA), and a number of methods now exist that can be used to determine, describe and analyse the cognitive processes employed during task performance. According to Schraagen, Chipman and Shalin (2000) CTA represents an extension of traditional task analysis methods used to describe the knowledge, thought processes and goal structures underlying observable task performance. Militello and Hutton (2000) describe CTA methods as those that focus upon describing and representing the cognitive elements that underlie goal generation, decision-making and judgements. CTA outputs are used, amongst other things for interface design and evaluation, the design of procedures and processes, allocation of functions, the design and evaluation of training procedures and interventions, and the evaluation of individual and team performance within complex systems.

Flanagan (1954) first probed the decisions and actions made by pilots in near accidents using the critical incident technique (CIT). However, the term 'Cognitive Task Analysis' did not appear until the early 1980s when it began to be used in research texts. According to Hollnagel (2003) the term was first used in 1981 to describe approaches to the understanding of the cognitive activities required in man-machine systems. Since then, the focus on the cognitive processes employed by system operators has increased, and CTA applications are now on the increase, particularly in complex, dynamic environments such as those seen in the nuclear power, defence and emergency services domains. Various CTA methods have been subject to widespread use over the past two decades, with applications in a number of domains, such as fire fighting (Militello and Hutton, 2000), aviation (O'Hare, Wiggins, Williams and Wong, 2000), emergency services (O'Hare et al, 2000), command and control (Salmon, Stanton, Walker and Green, 2004), military operations (Klein, 2000), naval maintenance (Schaafstal and Schraagen, 2000) and even white-water rafting (O'Hare et al, 2000). Consequently, there are a great number of CTA approaches available. The

Cognitive Task Analysis Resource Website (www.ctaresource.com) lists over 100 CTA related techniques designed to evaluate and describe the cognitive aspects of task performance. According to Roth, Patterson and Mumaw (2002) there are three different approaches under which cognitive task analyses can be grouped. The first approach involves analysing the domain in question in terms of goals and functions, in order to determine the cognitive demands imposed by the tasks performed. The second approach involves the use of empirical techniques, such as observation and interview methods, in order to determine how the users perform the task(s) under analysis, allowing a specification of the knowledge requirements and strategies involved. The third and more recent approach involves developing computer models that can be used to simulate the cognitive activities required during the task under analysis. It is beyond the scope of this book to review all of the CTA methods available to the HF practitioner. Rather, a review of selected approaches based upon popularity and previous applications is presented. A brief description of the CTA approaches reviewed is presented below.

The cognitive work analysis framework (Vicente, 1999) is currently receiving the most attention from the HF community. The CWA approach was originally developed at the Risø National Laboratory in Denmark (Rasmussen, Pejtersen and Goodstein, 1994) and offers a comprehensive framework for the design, evaluation and analysis of complex socio-technical systems. Rather than offer a description of the activity performed within a particular system, the CWA framework provides methods that can be used to develop an in-depth analysis of the constraints that shape agent activity within the system. The CWA framework comprises five different phases; work domain analysis, control task analysis, strategies analysis, social organization and co-operation analysis and worker competencies analysis. The critical decision method (Klein and Armstrong, 2004) is a semi-structured interview approach that uses pre-defined probes to elicit information regarding expert decision making during complex activity. The CDM procedure is perhaps the most commonly used CTA technique, and has been used in a wide variety of domains. Applied cognitive task analysis (Millitello and Hutton, 2000) offers a toolkit of semi-structured interview methods that can be used to analyse the cognitive demands associated with a particular task or scenario. The cognitive walkthrough method is used to evaluate interface usability. Based upon traditional design walkthrough methods and a theory of exploratory learning (Polson and Lewis), the method focuses upon the usability particularly from an ease of learning perspective. Finally, the critical incident technique (Flanagan, 1954) is a semi-structured interview approach that uses a series of probes designed to elicit information regarding pilot decision making during non-routine tasks.

CTA methods are useful in evaluating individual and team performance, in that they offer an analysis of cognitive processes surrounding decisions made and choices taken. This allows the HF practitioner to develop guidelines for effective performance and decision making in complex environments. The main problem associated with the use of cognitive task analysis methods is the considerable amount of resource required. CTA methods are commonly based upon interview and observational data, and therefore require considerable time and effort to conduct. Access to SMEs is also required, as is great skill on the analyst's behalf. CTA methods are also criticised for their reliance upon the recall of events or incidents from the past. Klein and Armstrong (2004) suggests that methods which analyse retrospective incidents are associated with concerns of data reliability due to memory degradation. These issues and more are addressed below. A summary of the CTA methods reviewed is presented in Table 4.1.

Table 4.1   Summary of Cognitive Task Analysis Methods

Method	Type of method	Domain	Training time	App time	Related methods	Tools needed	Validation studies	Advantages	Disadvantages
ACTA	Cog task analysis	Generic	Med-high	High	Interviews Critical Decision Method	Pen and paper Audio recording equipment	Yes	1) Requires fewer resources than traditional cognitive task analysis methods. 2) Provides the analyst with a set of probes.	1) Great skill is required on behalf of the analyst for the method to achieve its full potential. 2) Consistency/reliability of the method is questionable. 3) Time consuming in its application.
Cognitive Walkthrough	Cog task analysis	Generic	High	High	HTA	Pen and paper Video and audio recording equipment	Yes	1) Has a sound theoretical underpinning (Normans Action Execution model). 2) Offers a very useful output.	1) Requires further validity and reliability testing. 2) Time consuming in application. 3) Great skill is required on behalf of the analyst for the method to achieve its full potential.
Cognitive Work Analysis	Cog task analysis	Generic	High	High	Abstraction hierarchy Decision ladder Information flow maps SRK framework Interviews Observation	Pen and paper Video and audio recording equipment	Yes	1) Extremely flexible approach that can be used for a number of different purposes. 2) Has been used extensively in a number of different domains for the design, development, representation and evaluation of systems and technologies. 3) Based on sound underpinning theory.	1) CWA analyses are typically resource intensive. 2) Only limited guidance is given to analysts, and the methods within the framework may be difficult to grasp for novice analysts. 3) The latter phases of the framework have previously received only limited attention.

Table 4.1 (continued)

Critical Decision Method	Cog task analysis	Generic	Med-High	High	Critical Incident Technique	Pen and paper Audio recording equipment	Yes	1) Can be used to elicit specific information regarding decision making in complex environments. 2) Seems suited to C4i analysis. 3) Various cognitive probes are provided.	1) Reliability is questionable. 2) There are numerous problems associated with recalling past events, such as memory degradation. 3) Great skill is required on behalf of the analyst for the method to achieve its full potential.
Critical Incident Technique	Cog task analysis	Generic	Med-High	High	Critical Decision Method	Pen and paper Audio recording equipment	Yes	1) Can be used to elicit specific information regarding decision making in complex environments. 2) Seems suited to C4i analysis.	1) Reliability is questionable. 2) There are numerous problems associated with recalling past events, such as memory degradation. 3) Great skill is required on behalf of the analyst for the method to achieve its full potential.

Cognitive Work Analysis (CWA)

Background and Applications

Cognitive Work Analysis (Vicente, 1999) offers a comprehensive framework for the design, development and analysis of complex socio-technical systems. CWA was originally developed at the Risø National Laboratory in Denmark (Rasmussen, Pejtersen and Goodstein, 1994) and offers a framework of methods that are used to develop an in-depth analysis of the constraints that shape activity within complex systems.

The CWA approach can be used to describe the functional properties of the work domain under analysis, the nature of the tasks that are conducted within the system, the roles of the different actors residing within the system, and the cognitive skills and strategies that they use to conduct activity within the system. The CWA framework comprises five different phases; work domain analysis, control task analysis, strategies analysis, social organization and co-operation analysis and worker competencies analysis. Rather than offer a prescribed methodology for analysing complex systems, the CWA framework instead acts as a toolkit of methods that can be used either individually or in combination with one another, depending upon the analysis needs.

The different methods within the CWA framework have been used for a plethora of different purposes, including system modelling (Chin, Sanderson and Watson, 1999), system design (Bisantz, Roth, Brickman, Gosbee, Hettinger and McKinney, 2003, Rasmussen et al, 1994), process design (Olsson and Lee, 1994) training needs analysis (Naikar and Sanderson, 1999), training design and evaluation, interface design and evaluation (Dinadis and Vicente, 1999, Salmon, Stanton, Walker and Green, 2004), information requirements specification (Stoner, Wiese and Lee, 2003), tender evaluation (Naikar and Sanderson, 2001), team design (Naikar, Pearce, Drumm and Sanderson, 2003) and error management training design (Naikar and Saunders, 2003). Despite its origin within the nuclear power domain, the CWA applications referred to above have taken place in a wide range of different domains, including naval, military, aviation, driving and health care domains.

Domain of Application

The CWA framework was originally developed for the nuclear power domain, however the generic nature of the methods within the framework allow it to be applied in a wide range of domains.

Procedure and Advice

It is especially difficult to prescribe a strict procedure for the CWA framework. The methods used are loosely defined and the CWA phases employed are dependent entirely on the nature of the analysis in question. For example, work domain analysis is commonly used for interface design and evaluation purposes, but it can also be used for training design and evaluation. It would also be beyond the scope of this review to describe the procedure fully. The following procedure is intended to act as a broad set of guidelines for each of the phases defined by the CWA framework.

Step 1: Define nature of analysis
The first step in a CWA is to clearly define the purpose of the analysis. Exactly what the aims of the analysis are should be clearly specified, so that the correct CWA phases are employed. For example, the intended output may be a set of training requirements, a novel interface design concept, or a task analysis for a particular system.

Step 2: Select appropriate CWA phases and methods
Once the nature and desired outputs of the analysis are clearly defined, the analysis team should spend considerable time and effort selecting the most appropriate CWA phases and methods to be employed during the analysis. For example, when using the framework for the design of a novel interface, it may be that only the work domain analysis component is required. Conduct steps 3–8 as appropriate

Step 3: Work domain analysis
The work domain analysis phase involves describing or modelling the system in which the activity under analysis takes place. A work domain analysis is used to identify the functional purpose and structure of the work domain in terms of the overall system goals, the processes adopted and the artefacts used within the system. In modelling a system in this way, the system constraints that modify activity within are specified. The abstraction decomposition space (ADS) is used for the work domain analysis component of CWA. In constructing the ADS, a number of data collection procedures may be used, including interviews with SMEs, observational study of activity within the system under analysis, walkthrough analysis and consultation with appropriate documentation, such as standard operating procedures. An ADS template is presented in Figure 4.1. The ADS is comprised of an abstraction hierarchy and a decomposition hierarchy, and offers a 2-dimensional representation of the system in question (Vicente, 1999). Each cell in the ADS provides a different representation of the same work system. For example, the top left cell in the ADS represents the purpose of the entire system whilst the bottom right cell represents the physical form of the individual components that comprise the system (Vicente, 1999). The abstraction hierarchy consists of five levels of abstraction, ranging from the most abstract level of purposes to the most concrete level of form (Vicente 1999). A description of each of the five abstraction hierarchy levels is given below (Vicente 1999).

1. Functional purpose – The overall meaning of the system and its purpose in the world, e.g. system goals at a high level;
2. Abstract function – General and symbolic level of the system, e.g. descriptions in mass or energy terms to convey flow through the system;
3. Generalised function – Generalised processes of the system that reflects behavioural structure, e.g. diagram of information flow and feedback loops;
4. Physical function – Specific processes related to sets of interacting components, e.g. specific sub-systems, such as electrical or mechanical; and
5. Physical form – Static, spatial, description of specific objects in the system in purely physical terms, e.g. a picture or mimic of the components.

The decomposition hierarchy (the top row in the abstraction-decomposition space) comprises five levels of resolution, ranging from the coarsest level of total system to the finest level of component (Vicente, 1999). According to Vicente (1999) each of the five levels represents a different level of granularity with respect to the system in question and moving from left to right across the decomposition hierarchy is the equivalent of zooming into the system, as each level provides a more detailed representation of the system in question. The ADS also employs structural means-ends relationships in order to link the different representations of the system within the ADS. This means that every node in the ADS should be the end that is achieved by all of the nodes below it, and also the means that can be used to achieve all of the nodes above it.

Decompo-sition / Abstraction	Total System	Subsystem	Function Unit	Subassembly	Component
Functional Purpose	Purpose of the entire system				
Abstract Function			WHY?		
Generalised Function			WHAT?		
Physical Function			HOW?		
Physical Form					Material form of individual components

Figure 4.1   Abstraction Decomposition Space Template

Step 4: Conduct control task analysis
The control task analysis phase involves the identification of the control tasks that are performed within the system under analysis. A control task analysis is used to determine what tasks are undertaken within the system under analysis, regardless of how they are undertaken or who undertakes them. Decision ladders are used for the control task analysis component of CWA. The decision ladder is presented in Figure 4.2.

Step 5: Conduct strategies analysis
The strategies analysis phase involves identifying and representing the strategies that actors within the system under analysis employ when conducting the control tasks identified during the control task analysis phase. Information flow maps are used for the strategies analysis component of CWA.

Step 6: Conduct social organization and co-operation analysis
The social organization and co-operation analysis phase of a CWA involves identifying exactly how the control tasks are distributed between agents and artefacts within the system. The social organization and co-operation analysis component of CWA uses the abstraction decomposition space, decision ladders and information flow maps developed during the preceding phases for this purpose.

The fifth and final stage of a CWA involves identifying the cognitive skills required for control task performance in the system under analysis. Worker competencies analysis uses Rasmussen's Skill, Rule, Knowledge (SRK) framework in order to classify the cognitive activities employed by agents during control task performance.

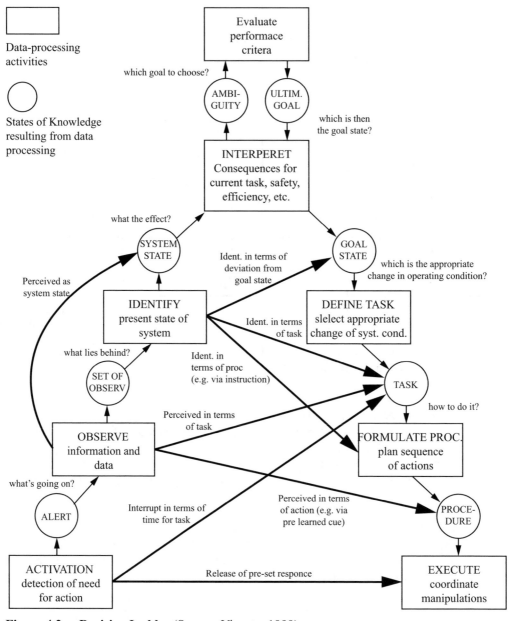

Figure 4.2   Decision Ladder (Source: Vicente, 1999)

Example

Salmon, Stanton, Walker and Green (2004) used the work domain analysis component of CWA to identify the information requirements for a command, control, communication, computers and intelligence (C4i) system knowledge Wall display interface. Salmon and colleagues used the abstraction-decomposition space in a slightly different manner to other practitioners in that, rather than describe the system or work domain with the abstraction-decomposition space, they used each cell in the abstraction-decomposition space to specify the information that should be presented by the knowledge wall display. Based upon a knowledge wall display taxonomy developed from a review of knowledge wall type displays, Salmon et al (2004) created an abstraction-decomposition space using the following levels of decomposition.

1. *Total System*. The overall C4i system.
2. *Sub-System*. The C4i system consists of three sub-systems, gold command, silver command, and bronze command.
3. *Function Unit*. Own forces on the battlefield. Represents the different forces comprising the allied forces e.g. foot soldier units, air, sea etc.
4. *Sub-Assembly*. Different teams of agents on the battlefield (friendly and enemy forces).
5. *Component*. Individual and artefacts within the teams (friendly and enemy forces) e.g. individual troops, weapons, tanks etc.

The knowledge wall abstraction decomposition space is presented in Figure 4.3.

Decomposition / Abstraction	Total System	Subsystem	Function Unit	Subassembly	Component
Functional Purpose	Overall Mission Goals	Command level mission goals	Unit mission goals	Team mission goals	Agent mission goals
Abstract Function	Mission Plans Projected course of action Planned responses Mission planning info	Gold, silver and bronze command mission plans Planned responses Mission planning information	Mission plans Tactical overlays Planned responses	Mission plans Tactical overlays Planned responses Projected paths (enemy and own forces)	Mission plans Tactical overlays Mission plans for individual agents Projected paths (enemy and own forces)
Generalised Function	Course of action	Sub-system capability	Unit capability	Team capability	Agent capability
Physical Function	Current mission status Mission summaries	Current mission status Mission summaries	Current mission status Unit Mission summaries	Current mission status Team status Mission summaries	Current mission status Agent status Mission summaries
Physical Form	Global view of battlespace	Location of sub-system	Location of unit	Location of team	Location of agents

'Drill Down' Capability →

Figure 4.3   Abstraction Decomposition Space for Military Knowledge Wall Display (Source: Salmon et al, 2004)

In conclusion, Salmon et al (2004) identified the following categories of information that the military knowledge wall display should present to gold commanders:

- Global view of the battlespace with drill down capability (Overall battlespace to individual agents).
- Overall mission goals (command level, units, teams and individual agents).
- Mission planning information (command level, units, teams and individual agents).
- Capability (System, sub-system, unit, team and agents).
- Current mission status (System, sub-system, unit, team and agents).
- Overall mission summaries (System, sub-system, unit, team and agents).
- Location – (System, sub-system, unit, team and agents).

Advantages

1. The CWA framework offers a comprehensive framework for the design and analysis of complex systems.
2. The CWA framework is based on sound underpinning theory.
3. The CWA framework is extremely flexible and can be applied for a number of different purposes.
4. The diversity of the different methods within the framework ensure comprehensiveness.
5. The methods within the framework are extremely useful. The abstraction-decompositions space in particular can be used for a wide range of purposes.
6. CWA can be applied in a number of different domains.

Disadvantages

1. The methods within the framework are complex and practitioners may require considerable training in their application.
2. The CWA methods are extremely time consuming to apply.
3. Some of the methods within the framework are still in their infancy and there is only limited published guidance available on their usage.
4. Reliability of the methods may be questionable.
5. CWA outputs can be large and unwieldy and difficult to present.

Related Methods

The CWA approach does not explicitly define the methods for each of the different CWA phases. Vicente (1999) describes the following approaches for the CWA framework: the abstraction-decomposition space (work domain analysis), decision-ladders (control task analysis), information flow maps (strategies analysis) and the SRK framework (worker competencies analysis).

Training and Application Times

The methods used within the CWA framework are complex and there is also limited practical guidance available on their application. The training time associated with the CWA framework is therefore high, particularly if all phases of the framework are to be undertaken. Due to the exhaustive nature of the CWA framework and the methods used, the application time is also considerable. Naikar and Sanderson (2001) report that a work domain analysis of the airborne early warning and control (AEW&C; Naikar and Sanderson, 2001) system took around six months to complete.

Reliability and Validity

The reliability and validity of the CWA framework is difficult to assess. The flexibility and diversity of the methods used ensure that reliability is impossible to address, although it is apparent that the reliability of the approaches used may be questionable.

Tools Needed

At their simplest, the CWA phases can be applied using pen and paper only. However, typically interviews and observational study are required, and so audio and video recorded equipment may be needed. CWA outputs are also typically large and require software support in their construction. For example, Microsoft Visio is particularly useful in construction of abstraction-decomposition spaces.

Applied Cognitive Task Analysis (ACTA)

Background and Applications

Applied Cognitive Task Analysis (ACTA, Militello and Hutton, 2000) offers a toolkit of interview methods that can be used to analyse the cognitive demands associated with a particular task or scenario. Originally used in the fire fighting domain, ACTA was developed as part of a Navy Personnel Research and Development Centre funded project as a solution to the inaccessibility and difficulty associated with the application of existing cognitive task analysis type methods (Militello and Hutton, 2000). The overall goal of the project was to develop and evaluate techniques that would allow system designers to extract the critical cognitive elements of a particular task. The ACTA approach was designed so that no training in cognitive psychology is required to use it (Militello and Hutton, 2000). According to Militello and Hutton (2000) ACTA outputs are typically used to aid system design. The ACTA procedure comprises the following:

Task diagram interview
The task diagram interview is used to provide the analyst with an in-depth overview of the task under analysis. During the task diagram interview, the analyst highlights those elements of the task that are cognitively challenging.

Knowledge audit interview
The knowledge audit interview is used to highlight those parts of the task under analysis where expertise is required. Once examples of expertise are highlighted, the SME is probed for specific examples within the context of the task.

Simulation interview
The simulation interview is used to probe the cognitive processes used by the SME during the task under analysis.

Cognitive demands table
The cognitive demands table is used to integrate the data obtained from the task diagram, knowledge audit and simulation interviews.

Domain of Application

Generic.

Procedure and Advice

Step 1: Define the task under analysis
The first part of an ACTA analysis is to select and define the task or scenario under analysis. This is dependent upon the nature and focus of the analysis.

Step 2: Select appropriate participant(s)
Once the scenario under analysis is defined, the analyst(s) should proceed to identify an appropriate SME or set of SMEs. Typically, operators of the system under analysis are used.

Step 3: Task observation
In order to prepare for the ACTA data collection phase, it is recommended that the analyst(s) involved observe the task or scenario under analysis. If an observation is not possible, a walkthrough of the task may suffice. This allows the analyst to fully understand the task and the participant's role during task performance.

Step 4: Task diagram interview
The purpose of the task diagram interview is to elicit a broad overview of the task under analysis in order to focus the knowledge audit and simulation interview parts of the analysis. Once the task diagram interview is complete, the analyst should have created a diagram representing the component task steps involved and those task steps that require the most cognitive skill. According to Militello and Hutton (2000) the SME should first be asked to decompose the task into relevant task steps. The analyst should use questions like, 'Think about what you do when you (perform the task under analysis.' 'Can you break this task down into less than six, but more than three steps?' (Militello and Hutton, 2000). Once the task is broken down into a number of separate task steps, the SME should then be asked to identify which of the task steps require cognitive skills. Militello and Hutton (2000) define cognitive skills as judgements, assessments, problem solving and thinking skills.

Step 5: Knowledge audit
Next, the analyst should proceed with the knowledge audit interview. This allows the analyst to identify instances during the task under analysis where expertise is used and also what sort of expertise is used. The knowledge audit interview is based upon the following knowledge categories that characterise expertise (Militello and Hutton, 2000):

- Diagnosing and Predicting.
- Situation Awareness.
- Perceptual skills.
- Developing and knowing when to apply tricks of the trade.
- Improvising.
- Meta-cognition.
- Recognising anomalies.
- Compensating for equipment limitations.

Once a probe has been administered, the analyst should then query the SME for specific examples of critical cues and decision-making strategies. Potential errors should then be discussed. The list of knowledge audit probes is presented below (Source: Militello and Hutton 2000).

Basic Probes

- *Past and Future*: Is there a time when you walked into the middle of a situation and knew exactly how things got there and where they were headed?
- *Big Picture*: Can you give me an example of what is important about the big picture for this task? What are the major elements you have to know and keep track of?
- *Noticing*: Have you had experiences where part of a situation just 'popped' out at you; where you noticed things going on that others didn't catch? What is an example?
- *Job Smarts*: When you do this task, are there ways of working smart or accomplishing more with less – that you have found especially useful?
- *Opportunities/Improvising*: Can you think of an example when you have improvised in this task or noticed an opportunity to do something better?
- *Self-Monitoring*: Can you think of a time when you realised that you would need to change the way you were performing in order to get the job done?

Optional Probes

- *Anomalies*: Can you describe an instance when you spotted a deviation from the norm, or knew something was amiss?
- *Equipment difficulties*: Have there been times when the equipment pointed in one direction but your own judgement told you to do something else? Or when you had to rely on experience to avoid being led astray by the equipment?

Step 6: Simulation interview
The simulation interview allows the analyst to determine the cognitive processes involved during the task under analysis. The SME is presented with a typical scenario. Once the scenario is completed, the analyst should prompt the SME to recall any major events, including decisions and judgements that occurred during the scenario. Each event or task step in the scenario should be probed for situation awareness, actions, critical cues, potential errors and surrounding events. Militello and Hutton (2000) present the following set of simulation interview probes:

For each major event, elicit the following information:

- As the (job you are investigating) in this scenario, what actions, if any, would you take at this point in time?
- What do you think is going on here? What is your assessment of the situation at this point in time?
- What pieces of information led you to this situation assessment and these actions?
- What errors would an inexperienced person be likely to make in this situation?

Any information elicited here should be recorded in a simulation interview table. An example simulation interview table is shown in Table 4.2.

Table 4.2   Example Simulation Interview Table (Source: Militello and Hutton, 2000)

Events	Actions	Assessment	Critical Cues	Potential errors
On scene arrival	Account for people (names) Ask neighbours Must knock on or knock down to make sure people aren't there	It's a cold night, need to find place for people who have been evacuated	Night time Cold > 15° Dead space Add on floor Poor materials, metal girders Common attic in whole building	Not keeping track of people (could be looking for people who are not there)
Initial attack	Watch for signs of building collapse If signs of building collapse, evacuate and throw water on it from outside	Faulty construction, building may collapse	Signs of building collapse include: What walls are doing: cracking What floors are doing: groaning What metal girders are doing: clicking, popping Cable in old buildings hold walls together	Ventilating the attic, this draws the fire up and spreads it through the pipes and electrical system

Step 7: Construct cognitive demands table

Once the knowledge audit and simulation interview are completed, it is recommended that a cognitive demands table is used to integrate the data collected (Militello and Hutton, 2000). This table is used to help the analyst focus on the most important aspects of the data obtained. The analyst should prepare the cognitive demands table based upon the goals of the particular project involved. An example of a cognitive demands table is shown in Table 4.3 (Militello and Hutton, 2000).

Table 4.3   Example Cognitive Demands Table (Source: Militello and Hutton, 2000)

Difficult cognitive element	Why difficult?	Common errors	Cues and strategies used
Knowing where to search after an explosion	Novices may not be trained in dealing with explosions. Other training suggests you should start at the source and work outward	Novice would be likely to start at the source of the explosion. Starting at the source is a rule of thumb for most other kinds of incidents	Start where you are most likely to find victims, keeping in mind safety considerations Refer to material data sheets to determine where dangerous chemicals are likely to be Consider the type of structure and where victims are likely to be Consider the likelihood of further explosions. Keep in mind the safety of your crew
Finding victims in a burning building	There are lots of distracting noises. If you are nervous or tired, your own breathing makes it hard to hear anything else	Novices sometimes don't recognise their own breathing sounds; they mistakenly think they hear a victim breathing	Both you and your partner stop, hold your breath and listen Listen for crying, victims talking to themselves, victims knocking things over etc.

Flowchart

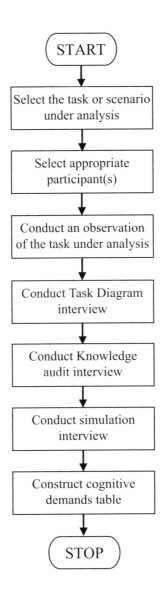

Advantages

1. The method offers a structured approach to cognitive task analysis.
2. The use of three different interview approaches ensures the comprehensiveness of the method.
3. Analysts using the method do not require training in cognitive psychology.
4. Militello and Hutton (2000) reported that in a usability questionnaire focusing on the use of the ACTA method, ratings were very positive. The data indicated that participants found the ACTA method easy to use and flexible, and that the output of the interviews was clear and the knowledge representations to be useful.
5. Probes and questions are provided for the analyst, facilitating relevant data extraction.

Disadvantages

1. The quality of data obtained is very much dependent upon the skill of the analyst involved and also the quality of the SMEs used.
2. The reliability of such a method is questionable.
3. The method appears to be time consuming in its application. In a validation study (Militello and Hutton, 2000) participants using the ACTA method were given three hours to perform the interviews and four hours to analyse the data.
4. The training time for the ACTA method is also considerable. Militello and Hutton (2000) gave participants an initial two-hour workshop introducing cognitive task analysis and then a six-hour workshop on the ACTA method.
5. The analysis of the data appears to be a laborious process.
6. As with most cognitive task analysis techniques, ACTA requires further validation. At the moment there is little evidence of validation studies associated with the ACTA method.
7. It is often difficult to gain sufficient access to appropriate SMEs for the task under analysis.

Related Methods

The ACTA method is an interview-based cognitive task analysis technique. There are other interview-based cognitive task analysis approaches, such as the critical decision method (Klein and Armstrong, 2004). The ACTA method also employs various data collection techniques, such as walkthrough and observation.

Approximate Training and Application Times

In a validation study (Militello and Hutton, 2000), participants were given eight hours of training, consisting of a two-hour introduction to cognitive task analysis and a six-hour workshop on the ACTA techniques. In the same study, the total application times for each participant was seven hours, consisting of three hours applying the interviews and four hours analysing the data.

Reliability and Validity

Militello and Hutton (2000) suggest that there are no well-established metrics that exist in order to establish the reliability and validity of cognitive task analysis methods. However, a number of attempts were made to establish the reliability and validity of the ACTA method. In terms of validity, three questions were addressed:

1. Does the information gathered address cognitive issues?
2. Does the information gathered deal with experience based knowledge as opposed to classroom-based knowledge?
3. Do the instructional materials generated contain accurate information that is important for novices to learn?

Each item in the cognitive demands table was examined for its cognitive content. The analysis indicated that 93% of the items were related to cognitive issues. To establish the level of experience based knowledge elicited, participants were asked to subjectively rate the proportion of information that only highly experienced SMEs would know. In the fire fighting study, the average was 95% and in the EW study, the average was 90%. The importance of the instructional materials generated was validated via domain experts rating the importance and accuracy of the data elicited. The findings indicated that the instructional materials generated in the study contained important information for novices (70% fire fighting, 95% EW). The reliability of the ACTA method was assessed by determining whether the participants using the methods generated similar information. It was established that participants using the ACTA method were able to consistently elicit relevant cognitive information.

Tools Needed

ACTA can be applied using pen and paper only, providing the analyst has access to the ACTA probes required during the knowledge audit and simulation interviews. An audio recording device may also be useful to aid the recording and analysis of the data.

Cognitive Walkthrough

Background and Applications

The cognitive walkthrough method is used to evaluate user interface usability. The main driver behind the development of the method was the goal to provide a theoretically based design methodology that could be used in actual design and development situations (Polson, Lewis, Rieman and Wharton, 1992). The main criticism of existing walkthrough methods suggests that they are actually unusable in actual design situations (Polson et al 1992). Based upon traditional design walkthrough methods and a theory of exploratory learning (Polson and Lewis), the method focuses upon the usability of an interface, in particular the ease of learning associated with the interface. The procedure comprises a set of criteria that the analyst uses to evaluate each task and the interface under analysis against. These criteria focus on the cognitive processes required to perform the task (Polson et al 1992). The cognitive walkthrough process involves the analyst 'walking' through each user action involved in a task step. The analyst then considers each criterion and the effect the interface has upon the user's interactions with the device (goals and actions). The criteria used in the cognitive walkthrough method are presented below: (Source: Polson et al 1992). Each task step or action is analysed separately using these criteria.

Goal structure for a step
- Correct goals: What are the appropriate goals for this point in the interaction? Describe as for initial goals.
- Mismatch with likely goals: What percentage of users will not have these goals, based on the analysis at the end of the previous step. Based on that analysis, will all users have the goal at this point, or may some users have dropped it or failed to form it. Also check the analysis at the end of the previous step to see if there are any unwanted goals, not appropriate for this step that will be formed or retained by some users. (% 0 25 50 75 100).

Choosing and executing the action
- Correct action at this step?
- Availability: Is it obvious that the correct action is a possible choice here? If not, what percentage of users might miss it?
- Label: What label or description is associated with the correct action?

- Link of label to action: If there is a label or description associated with the correct action, is it obvious, and is it clearly linked with this action? If not, what percentage of users might have trouble?
- Link of label to goal: If there is a label or description associated with the correct action, is it obvious, and is it clearly linked with this action? If not, what percentage of users might have trouble?
- No label: If there is no label associated with the correct action, how will users relate this action to a current goal? What percentage might have trouble doing so?
- Wrong choices: Are there other actions that might seem appropriate to some current goal? If so, what are they, and what percentage of users might choose one of these?
- Time out: If there is a time out in the interface at this step does it allow time for the user to select the appropriate action? How many users might have trouble?
- Hard to do: Is there anything physically tricky about executing the action? If so, what percentage of users will have trouble?

Modification of goal structure
- Assume the correct action has been taken. What is the system's response?
- Quit or backup: Will users see that they have made progress towards some current goal? What will indicate this to them? What percentage of users will not see progress and try to quit or backup? (% 0 25 50 75 100)
- Accomplished goals: List all current goals that have been accomplished. Is it obvious from the system response that each has been accomplished? If not, indicate for each how many users will not realise it is complete.
- Incomplete goals that look accomplished: Are there any current goals that have not been accomplished, but might appear to have been based upon the system response? What might indicate this? List any such goals and the percentage of users who will think that they have actually been accomplished.
- 'And-then' structures: Is there an 'and-then' structure, and does one of its sub-goals appear to be complete? If the sub-goal is similar to the super-goal, estimate how many users may prematurely terminate the 'and-then' structure.
- New goals in response to prompts: Does the system response contain a prompt or cue that suggests any new goal or goals? If so, describe the goals. If the prompt is unclear, indicate the percentage of users who will not form these goals.
- Other new goals: Are there any other new goals that users will form given their current goals, the state of the interface, and their background knowledge? Why? If so, describe the goals, and indicate how many users will form them. NOTE these goals may or may not be appropriate, so forming them may be bad or good.

Domain of Application

Generic. Although originally developed for use in the software engineering domain, it is apparent that the method could be used to evaluate an interface in any domain.

Procedure and Advice

The cognitive walkthrough procedure comprises two phases, the preparation phase and the evaluation phase. The preparation phase involves selecting the set of tasks to analyse and determining the task sequence. The evaluation phase involves the analysis of the interaction between the user and the interface, using the criteria outlined above (adapted from Polson et al, 1992).

Step 1: Select tasks to be analysed
Firstly, the analyst should select the set of tasks that are to be the focus of the analysis. In order to ensure that the user interface in question is subjected to a thorough examination, an exhaustive set of tasks should be used. However, if time is limited, then the analyst should try to select a set of tasks that are as representative of the tasks that can be performed with the interface under analysis as possible.

Step 2: Create task descriptions
Each task selected by the analyst must be described fully from the point of the user. Although there are a number of ways of doing this, it is recommended that a HTA describing the general operation of the user interface under analysis is used. An exhaustive HTA should provide a description of each task identified during step 1.

Step 3: Determine the correct sequence of actions
For each of the selected tasks, the appropriate sequence of actions required to complete the task must be specified. Again, it is recommended that the analyst uses the HTA for this purpose.

Step 4: Identify user population
Next, the analyst should determine the potential users of the interface under analysis. A list of user groups should be created.

Step 5: Describe the user's initial goals
The final part of the cognitive walkthrough analysis preparation phase involves identifying and recording the user's initial goals. The analyst should record what goals the user has at the start of the task. This is based upon the analyst's subjective judgement. Again, it is recommended that the HTA output is used to generate the goals required for this step of the analysis.

Step 6: Analyse the interaction between user and interface
The second and final phase of the cognitive walkthrough procedure, the evaluation phase, involves analysing the interaction between the user and the interface under analysis. To do this, the analyst should 'walk' through each task, applying the criteria outlined above as they go along. The cognitive walkthrough evaluation concentrates on three key aspects of the user interface interaction (Polson et al 1992):

- The relationship between the required goals and the goals that the user actually has.
- The problems in selecting and executing an action.
- Changing goals due to action execution and system response.

The analyst should record the results for each task step. This can be done via video, audio or pen and paper techniques.

Advantages

1. The cognitive walkthrough method presents a structured approach to user interface analysis.

2. The method is used early in the design lifecycle of an interface. This allows any design flaws highlighted in the analysis to be eradicated.
3. Designed to be used by non-cognitive psychology professionals.
4. The cognitive walkthrough method is based upon sound underpinning theory, including Norman's model of action execution.
5. Easy to learn and apply.
6. The output from a cognitive walkthrough analysis appears to be very useful.

Disadvantages

1. The cognitive walkthrough method is limited to cater only for ease of learning of an interface.
2. Requires validation.
3. May be time consuming for more complex tasks.
4. A large part of the analysis is based upon analyst subjective judgement. For example, the percentage estimates used with the walkthrough criteria require a 'best guess'. As a result, the reliability of the method may be questionable.
5. Cognitive walkthrough requires access to the personnel involved in the task(s) under analysis.

Related Methods

The cognitive walkthrough method is a development of traditional design walkthrough methods (Polson et al, 1992). HTA or tabular task analysis could also be used when applying cognitive walkthrough method in order to provide a description of the task under analysis.

Approximate Training and Application Times

No data regarding the training and application time for the method are offered by the authors. It is estimated that the training time for the method would be quite high. It is also estimated that the application time for the method would be high, particularly for large, complex tasks.

Reliability and Validity

Lewis, Polson, Wharton and Rieman (1990) reported that in a cognitive walkthrough analysis of four answering machine interfaces about half of the actual observed errors were identified. More critically, the false alarm rate (errors predicted in the cognitive walkthrough analysis but not observed) was extremely high, at almost 75%. In a study on voicemail directory, Polson et al (1992) reported that half of all observed errors were picked up in the cognitive walkthrough analysis. It is apparent that the cognitive walkthrough method requires further testing in terms of reliability and validity.

Tools Needed

The cognitive walkthrough method can be applied using pen and paper only. The analyst would also require the walkthrough criteria sections 1, 2 and 3 and the cognitive walkthrough start up sheet. For larger analyses, the analyst may wish to record the process using video or audio recording equipment. The device or interface under analysis is also required.

Flowchart

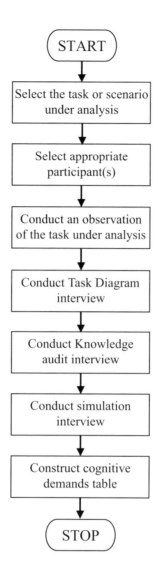

Example

The following example is an extract of a cognitive walkthrough analysis of a phone system task presented in Polson et al (1992).

Task – Forward all my calls to 492 1234.

Task list
1. Pick up the handset
2. Press ##7
3. Hang up the handset

4.   Pick up the handset
5.   Press **7
6.   Press 1234
7.   Hang up the handset

Goals:
75% of users will have FORWARD ALL CALLS TO 492 1234 (Goal)
                        PICK UP HANDSET (Sub-goal)
                        and then SPECIFY FORWARDING (Sub-goal)

25% of users will have FORWARD ALL CALLS TO 492 1234
                        PICK UP HANDSET
                        and then CLEAR FORWARDING
                        and then SPECIFY FORWARDING

Analysis of ACTION 1: Pick up the handset
Correct goals
FORWARD ALL CALLS TO 492 1234
                        PICK UP HANDSET
                        and then CLEAR FORWARDING
                        and then SPECIFY FORWARDING

75% of the users would therefore be expected to have a goal mismatch at this step, due to the required clear forwarding sub-goal that is required but not formed (Polson et al 1992).

Critical Decision Method (CDM)

Background and Applications

The Critical Decision Method (CDM; Klein and Armstrong, 2004) is a semi-structured interview technique that uses cognitive probes in order to elicit information regarding expert decision making. According to the authors, the method can serve to provide knowledge engineering for expert system development, identify training requirements, generate training materials and evaluate the task performance impact of expert systems (Klein, Calderwood and MacGregor, 1989). The method is an extension of the Critical Incident Technique (Flanagan, 1954) and was developed in order to study the naturalistic decision-making strategies of experienced personnel. The CDM procedure is perhaps the most commonly used cognitive task analysis method and has been applied in a number of domains, including the fire service (Baber et al, 2004), military and paramedics (Klein, Calderwood and MacGregor, 1989), air traffic control, civil energy distribution (Salmon et al, 2005), naval warfare, rail, and even white water rafting (O'Hare et al, 2000).

Domain of Application

Generic.

Procedure and Advice

Step 1: Define the task or scenario under analysis
The first part of a CDM analysis is to define the incident that is to be analysed. CDM normally focuses on non-routine incidents, such as emergency incidents, or highly challenging incidents. If the scenario under analysis is not already specified, the analyst(s) may identify an appropriate incident via interview with an appropriate SME, by asking them to describe a recent highly challenging (i.e. high workload) or non-routine incident in which they were involved. The interviewee involved in the CDM analysis should be the primary decision maker in the chosen incident.

Step 2: Select CDM probes
The CDM method works by probing SMEs using specific probes designed to elicit pertinent information regarding the decision-making process during key points in the incident under analysis. In order to ensure that the output is compliant with the original aims of the analysis, an appropriate set of CDM probes should be defined prior to the analysis. The probes used are dependent upon the aims of the analysis and the domain in which the incident is embedded. Alternatively, if there are no adequate probes available, the analyst(s) can develop novel probes based upon the analysis needs. A set of CDM probes defined by O'Hare et al (2000) are presented in Table 4.4.

Step 3: Select appropriate participant
Once the scenario under analysis and the probes to be used are defined, an appropriate participant or set of participants should be identified. The SMEs used are typically the primary decision maker in the task or scenario under analysis.

Step 4: Gather and record account of the incident
The CDM procedure can be applied to an incident observed by the analyst or to a retrospective incident described by the participant. If the CDM analysis is based upon an observed incident, then this step involves firstly observing the incident and then recording an account of the incident. Otherwise, the incident can be described retrospectively from memory by the participant. The analyst should ask the SME for a description of the incident in question, from its starting point to its end point.

Step 5: Construct incident timeline
The next step in the CDM analysis is to construct a timeline of the incident described in step 4. The aim of this is to give the analyst(s) a clear picture of the incident and its associated events, including when each event occurred and what the duration of each event was. According to Klein, Calderwood and MacGregor (1989) the events included in the timeline should encompass any physical events, such as alarms sounding, and also 'mental' events, such as the thoughts and perceptions of the interviewee during the incident.

Step 6: Define scenario phases
Once the analyst has a clear understanding of the incident under analysis, the incident should be divided into key phases or decision points. It is recommended that this is done in conjunction with the SME. Normally, the incident is divided into four or five key phases.

Step 7: Use CDM probes to query participant decision making
For each incident phase, the analyst should probe the SME using the CDM probes selected during step 2 of the procedure. The probes are used in an unstructured interview format in order to gather

pertinent information regarding the SME's decision making during each incident phase. The interview should be recorded using an audio recording device such as a mini-disc recorder.

Step 8: Transcribe interview data
Once the interview is complete, the data should be transcribed accordingly.

Step 9: Construct CDM tables
Finally, a CDM output table for each scenario phase should be constructed. This involves simply presenting the CDM probes and the associated SME answers in an output table. The CDM output tables for an energy distribution scenario are presented in Table 4.5 through to Table 4.8.

Advantages

1. The CDM analysis procedure can be used to elicit specific information regarding the decision-making strategies used by agents in complex, dynamic systems.
2. The method is normally quick in application.
3. Once familiar with the method, CDM is relatively easy to apply.
4. The CDM is a popular procedure and has been applied in a number of domains.
5. The CDM output can be used to construct propositional networks which describe the knowledge or SA objects required during the scenario under analysis.

Disadvantages

1. The reliability of such a method is questionable. Klein and Armstrong (2004) suggest that methods that analyse retrospective incidents are associated with concerns of data reliability, due to evidence of memory degradation.
2. The data obtained is highly dependent upon the skill of the analyst conducting the CDM interview and also the quality of the participant used.
3. A high level of expertise and training is required in order to use the CDM to its maximum effect (Klein and Armstrong, 2004).
4. The CDM relies upon interviewee verbal reports in order to reconstruct incidents. How far a verbal report accurately represents the cognitive processes of the decision maker is questionable. Facts could be easily misrepresented by the participants involved.
5. It is often difficult to gain sufficient access to appropriate SMEs in order to conduct a CDM analysis.

Example

The following example is taken from a CDM analysis that was conducted in order to analyse C4i activity in the civil energy distribution domain (Salmon et al, 2005). The scenario under analysis involved the switching out of three circuits at three substations. Circuit SGT5 was being switched out for the installation of a new transformer for the nearby channel tunnel rail link and SGT1A and 1B were being switched out for substation maintenance. For the CDM analysis, the control room operator co-ordinating the activity and the senior authorised person (SAP) at the substation who conducted the activity were interviewed. The set of CDM probes used are presented in Table 4.4. The scenario was divided into four key phases:

1. First issue of instructions.

2. Deal with switching requests.
3. Perform isolation.
4. Report back to network operations centre.

Flowchart

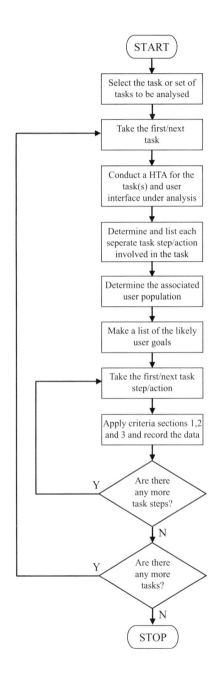

The CDM output is presented in Table 4.5 through to Table 4.8.

Table 4.4   CDM Probes

Goal Specification	What were your specific goals at the various decision points?
Cue Identification	What features were you looking for when you formulated your decision? How did you know that you needed to make the decision? How did you know when to make the decision?
Expectancy	Were you expecting to make this sort of decision during the course of the event? Describe how this affected your decision-making process.
Conceptual	Are there any situations in which your decision would have turned out differently? Describe the nature of these situations and the characteristics that would have changed the outcome of your decision.
Influence of uncertainty	At any stage, were you uncertain about either the reliability or the relevance of the information that you had available? At any stage, were you uncertain about the appropriateness of the decision?
Information integration	What was the most important piece of information that you used to formulate the decision?
Situation Awareness	What information did you have available to you at the time of the decision?
Situation Assessment	Did you use all of the information available to you when formulating the decision? Was there any additional information that you might have used to assist in the formulation of the decision?
Options	Were there any other alternatives available to you other than the decision you made?
Decision blocking – stress	Was their any stage during the decision-making process in which you found it difficult to process and integrate the information available? Describe precisely the nature of the situation.
Basis of choice	Do you think that you could develop a rule, based on your experience, which could assist another person to make the same decision successfully? Why/Why not?
Analogy/ generalisation	Were you at any time reminded of previous experiences in which a similar decision was made? Were you at any time reminded of previous experiences in which a different decision was made?

Related Methods

The CDM is an extension of the critical incident technique (Flanagan, 1954). The CDM is also closely related to other interview based cognitive task analysis (CTA) methods, in that it uses probes to elicit data regarding task performance from participants. Other similar CTA methods include ACTA (Militello and Hutton, 2000) and cognitive walkthrough analysis (Polson et al, 1992). CDM is also used in conjunction with propositional networks to identify the knowledge objects required during performance of a particular task.

Approximate Training and Application Times

Klein and Armstrong (2004) report that the training time associated with the CDM would be high. Experience in interviews with SMEs is required, and also a grasp of cognitive psychology. The application time for the CDM is medium. The CDM interview takes between 1-2 hours, and the transcription process takes approximately 1-2 hours.

Table 4.5   Phase 1: First Issue of Instructions

Goal Specification	Establish what isolation the SAP at Barking is looking for. Depends on gear?
Cue identification	Don't Believe It (DBI) alarm is unusual – faulty contact (not open or closed) questionable data from site checking rating of earth switches (may be not fully rated for circuit current – so additional earths may be required). Check that SAP is happy with instructions as not normal.
Expectancy	Decision expected by DBI is not common.
Conceptual Model	Recognised instruction but not stated in WE1000 – as there are not too many front and rear shutters metal clad switch gear.
Uncertainty	Confirm from field about planned instruction – make sure that SAP is happy with the instruction.
Information	Reference to front and rear busbars.
Situation Awareness	WE1000 procedure. Metal clad switchgear. Barking SGT1A/1B substation screen. SAP at Barking.
Situation Assessment	Ask colleagues if need to.
Options	No alternatives.
Stress	N/A
Choice	WE1000 – need to remove what does not apply. Could add front and rear busbar procedures.
Analogy	Best practice guide for metal clad EMS switching.

Table 4.6   Phase 2: Deal with Switching Requests

Goal Specification	Obtain confirmation from NOC that planned isolation is still required.
Cue identification	Approaching time for planned isolation. Switching phone rings throughout building. Airblast circuit breakers (accompanied by sirens) can be heard to operate remotely (more so in Barking 275 than Barking C 132).
Expectancy	Yes – routine planned work according to fixed procedures.
Conceptual Model	Wokingham have performed remote isolations already. Circuit configured ready for local isolation.
Uncertainty	Physical verification of apparatus always required (DBI – don't believe it).
Information	Proceduralised information from NOC – circuit, location, time, actions required etc. Switching log.
Situation Awareness	Switching log. Physical status of apparatus. Planning documentation. Visual or verbal information from substation personnel.
Situation Assessment	Planning documentation used only occasionally.
Options	Refusal of switching request. Additional conditions to switching request.
Stress	Some time pressure.
Choice	Yes – highly proceduralised anyway.
Analogy	Yes – routine activity.

Reliability and Validity

Both intra- and inter-analyst reliability of the CDM approach is questionable. It is apparent that such an approach may elicit different data from similar incidents when applied by different analysts on

separate participants. Klein and Armstrong (2004) suggest that there are also concerns associated
with the reliability of the CDM due to evidence of memory degradation.

Table 4.7   Phase 3: Perform Isolation

Goal Specification	Ensure it is safe to perform local isolation. Confirm circuits/equipment to be operated.
Cue identification	Telecontrol displays/circuit loadings. Equipment labels. Equipment displays. Other temporary notices.
Expectancy	Equipment configured according to planned circuit switching. Equipment will function correctly.
Conceptual Model	Layout/type/characteristics of circuit. Circuit loadings/balance. Function of equipment.
Uncertainty	Will equipment physically work as expected (will something jam etc.)? Other work being carried out by other parties (e.g. EDF).
Information	Switching log. Visual and verbal information from those undertaking the work.
Situation Awareness	Physical information from apparatus and telecontrol displays.
Situation Assessment	All information used.
Options	Inform NOC that isolation cannot be performed/other aspects of switching instructions cannot be carried out.
Stress	Some time pressure. Possibly some difficulties in operating or physically handling the equipment.
Choice	Yes – proceduralised within equipment types. Occasional non-routine activities required to cope with unusual/unfamiliar equipment, or equipment not owned by NGT.
Analogy	Yes – often. Except in cases with unfamiliar equipment.

Table 4.8   Phase 4: Report Back to Network Operations Centre

Goal Specification	Inform NOC of isolation status.
Cue identification	Switching telephone. NOC operator answers.
Expectancy	NOC accepts.
Conceptual Model	Manner in which circuit is now isolated. Form of procedures.
Uncertainty	No – possibly further instructions, possibly mismatches local situation and remote displays in NOC.
Information	Switching log.
Situation Awareness	Verbal information from NOC. Switching log.
Situation Assessment	Yes – all information used.
Options	No (raise or add on further requests etc. to the same call?).
Stress	No.
Choice	Yes – highly proceduralised.
Analogy	Yes – frequently performed activity.

Tools Needed

When conducting a CDM analysis, pen and paper could be sufficient. However, to ensure that data collection is comprehensive, it is recommended that video or audio recording equipment is used. A set of relevant CDM probes, such as those presented in Table 4.4 are also required. The type of probes used is dependent upon the focus of the analysis.

Critical Incident Technique (CIT)

Background and Applications

Critical incident technique (CIT; Flanagan, 1954) is an interview method that is used to retrospectively analyse operator decision making. The method was first used to analyse aircraft incidents that 'almost' led to accidents and has since been used extensively and redeveloped in the form of CDM (Klein and Armstrong, 2004). The CIT involves the use of semi-structured interviews to facilitate operator recall of critical events or incidents, including the actions and decisions made by themselves and colleagues and the reasons why they made them. The analyst uses a set of probes designed to elicit pertinent information surrounding the participant's decision making during the scenario under analysis. A set of probes used by Flanagan (1954) are presented below:

- Describe what led up to the situation.
- Exactly what did the person do or not do that was especially effective or ineffective.
- What was the outcome or result of this action?
- Why was this action effective or what more effective action might have been expected?

Domain of Application

Generic. Although the method was originally developed for use in analysing pilot decision making in non-routine (e.g. near miss) incidents, the method can be applied in any domain.

Procedure and Advice

Step 1: Select the incident to be analysed
The first part of a CIT analysis is to select the incident or group of incidents that are to be analysed. Depending upon the purpose of the analysis, the type of incident may already be selected. CIT normally focuses on non-routine incidents, such as emergency scenarios, or highly challenging incidents. If the type of incident is not already known, CIT analysts may select the incident via interview with system personnel, probing the interviewee for recent high risk, highly challenging, emergency situations. The interviewee involved in the CIT analysis should be the primary decision maker in the chosen incident. CIT can also be conducted on groups of operators.

Step 2: Gather and record account of the incident
Next the interviewee(s) should be asked to provide a description of the incident in question, from its starting point (i.e. alarm sounding) to its end point (i.e. when the incident was classed as 'under control').

Step 3: Construct incident timeline
The next step in the CIT analysis is to construct an accurate timeline of the incident under analysis. The aim of this is to give the analysts a clear picture of the incident and its associated events, including when each event occurred and what the duration of each event was. According to Klein, Calderwood and MacGregor (1989) the events included in the timeline should encompass any physical events, such as alarms sounding, and also 'mental' events, such as the thoughts and perceptions of the interviewee during the incident.

Step 4: Select required incident aspects
Once the analyst has an accurate description of the incident, the next step is to select specific incident points that are to be analysed further. The points selected are dependent upon the nature and focus of the analysis. For example, if the analysis is focusing upon team communication, then aspects of the incident involving team communication should be selected.

Step 5: Probe selected incident points
Each incident aspect selected in step 4 should be analysed further using a set of specific probes. The probes used are dependent upon the aims of the analysis and the domain in which the incident is embedded. The analyst should develop specific probes before the analysis begins. In an analysis of team communication, the analyst would use probes such as 'Why did you communicate with team member B at this point?', 'How did you communicate with team member B?', 'Was there any miscommunication at this point?' etc.

Advantages

1. The CIT can be used to elicit specific information regarding decision making in complex systems.
2. Once learned, the method requires relatively little effort to apply.
3. The incidents which the method concentrates on have already occurred, removing the need for time consuming incident observations.
4. Has been used extensively in a number of domains and has the potential to be used anywhere.
5. CIT is a very flexible method.
6. High face validity (Kirwan and Ainsworth, 1992).

Disadvantages

1. The reliability of such a method is questionable. Klein (2004) suggests that methods that analyse retrospective incidents are associated with concerns of data reliability, due to evidence of memory degradation.
2. A high level of expertise in interview methods is required.
3. After the fact data collection has a number of concerns associated with it. Such as degradation, correlation with performance etc.
4. Relies upon the accurate recall of events.
5. Operators may not wish to recall events or incidents in which their performance is under scrutiny.
6. The data obtained is dependent upon the skill of the analyst and also the quality of the SMEs used.
7. The original CIT probes are dated and the method has effectively been replaced by the CDM.

Related Methods

CIT was the first interview-based method designed to focus upon past events or incidents. A number of methods have since been developed as a result of the CIT, such as the critical decision method (Klein 2003).

Flowchart

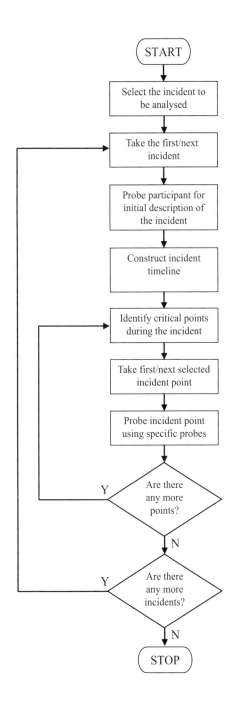

Approximate Training and Application Times

Provided the analyst is experienced in interview methods, the training time for CIT is minimal. However, for analysts with no interview experience, the training time would be high. Application time for the CIT is typically low, although for complex incidents involving multiple agents, the application time could increase considerably.

Reliability and Validity

The reliability of the CIT is questionable. There are concerns over inter- and intra-analyst reliability when using such methods. Klein (2004) suggests that there are concerns associated with the reliability of the CDM (similar method) due to evidence of memory degradation. Also, recalled events may be correlated with performance and also subject to bias.

Tools Needed

CIT can be conducted using pen and paper. It is recommended however, that the analysis is recorded using video and audio recording equipment.

Chapter 5

Process Charting Methods

Process charting methods are used to represent activity or processes in a graphical format. According to Kirwan and Ainsworth (1992) the first attempt to chart a work process was conducted by Gilbreth and Gilbreth in the 1920s. Process charting methods have since been used in a number of different domains to provide graphical representations of tasks or sequences of activity. Process charting methods use standardised symbols to depict task sequences or processes and are used because they are easier to understand than text descriptions (Kirwan and Ainsworth, 1992). The charting of work processes is also a useful way of highlighting essential task components and requirements. Process chart outputs are extremely useful as they convey a number of different features associated with the activity under analysis, including a breakdown of the component task steps involved, the sequential flow of the tasks, the temporal aspects of the activity, an indication of collaboration between different agents during the tasks, a breakdown of who performs what component task steps and also what technological artefacts are used to perform the activity. Charting techniques therefore represent both the human and system elements involved in the performance of a certain task or scenario (Kirwan and Ainsworth, 1992).

Charting techniques are particularly useful for representing team-based or distributed tasks, which are often exhibited in command and control systems. A process chart type analysis allows the specification of what tasks are conducted by what team member or technological component. A number of variations on process charting methods exist, including techniques used to represent operator decisions (DAD), and the causes of hardware and human failures (Fault tree analysis, Murphy diagrams). Process charting methods have been used in a variety of domains in order to understand, evaluate and represent the human and system aspects of a task, including the nuclear petro-chemical domains, aviation, maritime, railway and air traffic control. Sanders and McCormick (1992) suggest that operation sequence diagrams (OSDs) are developed during the design of complex systems in order to develop a detailed understanding of the tasks involved in systems operation. In fact the process of developing the OSD may be more important than the actual outcome itself. A brief description of the process charting methods reviewed is given below.

Process charts are probably the simplest form of charting method, consisting of a single, vertical flow line which links up the sequence of activities that are performed in order to complete the task under analysis successfully. Operation sequence diagrams are based on this basic principle, and are used to graphically describe the interaction between individuals and/or teams in relation to the performance of activities within a system or task. The output of an OSD graphically depicts a task process, including the tasks performed and the interaction between operators over time, using standardised symbols.

Event tree analysis is a task analysis method that uses tree like diagrams to represent the various possible outcomes associated with operator task steps in a scenario. Fault trees are used to depict system failures and their causes. A fault tree is a tree-like diagram, which defines the failure event and displays the possible causes in terms of hardware failure or human error (Kirwan and Ainsworth, 1992).

Decision Action Diagrams (DADs) are used to depict the process of a scenario through a system in terms of the decisions required and actions to be performed by the operator in conducting the task or scenario under analysis. Murphy Diagrams (Pew et al, 1981; cited in Kirwan, 1992a) are also used to graphically describe errors and their causes (proximal and distal). A summary of the charting methods reviewed is presented in Table 5.1.

Table 5.1   Summary of Charting Methods

Method	Type of method	Domain	Training time	App time	Related methods	Tools needed	Validation studies	Advantages	Disadvantages
Process Charts	Charting method	Generic	Low	Med	HTA Observation Interviews	Pen and paper Microsoft Visio Video and audio recording equipment	No	1) Can be used to graphically depict a task or scenario sequence. 2) Can be used to represent man and machine tasks. 3) Easy to learn and use.	1) For large, complex tasks, the process chart may become too large and unwieldy. Also may be time consuming to conduct. 2) Some of the process chart symbols are irrelevant to C4i. 3) Only models error-free performance.
Operator Sequence Diagrams	Charting method	Generic	Low	Med	HTA Observation Interviews	Pen and paper Microsoft Visio Video and audio recording equipment	No	1) Can be used to graphically depict a task or scenario sequence. 2) Can be used to represent man and machine tasks. 3) Seems to be suited for use in analysing C4i or team-based tasks.	1) For large, complex tasks, the OSD may become too large and unwieldy. Also may be time consuming to conduct. 2) Laborious to construct.
Event Tree Analysis	Charting method	Generic	Low	Med	HTA Observation Interviews	Pen and paper Microsoft Visio Video and audio recording equipment	No	1) Can be used to graphically depict a task or scenario sequence. 2) Can be used to represent man and machine tasks.	1) For large, complex tasks, the event tree may become too large and unwieldy. Also may be time consuming to conduct. 2) Some of the chart symbols are irrelevant to C4i. 3) Only models error-free performance.
DAD – Decision Action Diagrams	Charting method	Generic	Low	Med	HTA Observation Interviews	Pen and paper Microsoft Visio Video and audio recording equipment	No	1) Can be used to graphically depict a task or scenario sequence. 2) Can be used to represent man and machine tasks. 3) Can be used to analyse decision making in a task or scenario.	1) For large, complex tasks, the DAD may become too large and unwieldy. Also may be time consuming to conduct.
Fault Tree Analysis	Charting method	Generic	Low	Med	HTA Observation Interviews	Pen and paper Microsoft Visio Video and audio recording equipment	No	1) Can be used to graphically depict a task or scenario sequence. 2) Can be used to represent man and machine tasks. 3) Offers an analysis of error events.	1) For large, complex tasks, the fault tree may become too large and unwieldy. Also may be time consuming to conduct. 2) Only used retrospectively.
Murphy Diagrams	Charting method	Generic	Low	Med	HTA Observation Interviews	Pen and paper Microsoft Visio Video and audio recording equipment	No	1) Offers an analysis of task performance and potential errors made. 2) Has a sound theoretical underpinning. 3) Potentially exhaustive	1) For large, complex tasks, the Murphy diagram may become too large and unwieldy. Also may be time consuming to conduct. 2) Only used retrospectively.

Process Charts

Background and Applications

Process charts offer a systematic approach to describing and representing a task or scenario that is easy to follow and understand (Kirwan and Ainsworth, 1992). Process charts are used to graphically represent separate steps or events that occur during the performance of a task. Process charts were originally used to show the path of a product through its manufacturing process i.e. the construction of an automobile. Since the original use of process charts, however, there have been many variations in their use. Variations of the process chart methodology include operation sequence process charts, which show a chronological sequence of operations and actions that are employed during a particular process, and also various forms of resource chart, which has separate columns for the operator, the equipment used and also the material. In its simplest form, a process chart consists of a single, vertical flow line which links up the sequence of activities that are performed in order to complete the task under analysis successfully. A set of typical process chart symbols are presented below in Figure 5.1 (source: Kirwan and Ainsworth, 1992).

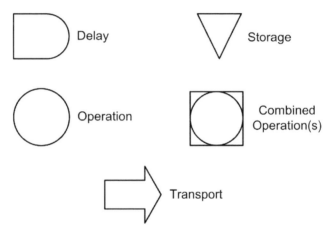

Figure 5.1   Generic Process Chart Symbols (Source: Kirwan and Ainsworth, 1992)

Once completed, a process chart depicts the task in a single, top down flow line, which represents a sequence of task steps or activities. Time taken for each task step or activity can also be recorded and added to the process chart.

Domain of Application

Generic.

Procedure and Advice

The symbols should be linked together in a vertical chart depicting the key stages in the task or process under analysis.

Step 1: Data collection

In order to construct a process chart, the analyst(s) must first obtain sufficient data regarding the scenario under analysis. It is recommended that the analyst(s) uses various forms of data collection in this phase, including observations, interviews, questionnaires and walkthrough analyses. The type and amount of data collected in step 1 is dependent upon the analysis requirements.

Step 2: Create task list

Firstly, the analyst should create a comprehensive list of the task steps involved in the scenario under analysis. These should then be put into a chronological order. A HTA for the task or process under analysis may be useful here, as it provides the analyst with a thorough description of the activity under analysis.

Step 3: Task step classification

Next, the analyst needs to classify each task step into one of the process chart behaviours; Operation, Transportation, Storage, Inspection, Delay or combined operation. To do this, the analyst should take each task step and classify it as one of the process chart symbols employed. This is typically based upon the analyst's subjective judgement, although consultation with appropriate SMEs can also be used.

Step 4: Create the process chart

Once all of the task steps are classified into the appropriate symbol categories, the process chart can be constructed. This involves linking each operation, transportation, storage, inspection, delay or combined operation in a vertical chart. Each task step should be placed in the order that they would occur when performing the task. Alongside the task steps symbol, another column should be placed, describing the task step fully.

Advantages

1. Process charts are useful in that they depict the flow and structure of actions involved in the task under analysis.
2. Process charts are simple to learn and construct.
3. They have the potential to be applied to any domain.
4. Process charts allow the analyst to observe how a task is undertaken.
5. Process charts can also display task time information.
6. Process charts can represent both operator and system tasks (Kirwan and Ainsworth, 1992).
7. Process charts provide the analyst with a simple, graphical representation of the task or scenario under analysis.

Disadvantages

1. For large tasks, a process chart may become large and unwieldy.
2. When using process charts for complex, large tasks, chart construction will become very time consuming. Also, complex tasks require complex process charts.
3. The process chart symbols are somewhat limited.
4. Process charts do not take into account error, modelling only error-free performance.
5. Only a very limited amount of information can be represented in a process chart.
6. Process charts do not represent the cognitive processes employed during task performance.
7. Process charts only offer descriptive information.

Related Methods

The process chart method belongs to a family of charting or network methods. Other charting/networking methods include input-output diagrams, functional flow diagrams, information flow diagrams, Murphy diagrams, critical path analysis, petri nets and signal flow graphs (Kirwan and Ainsworth, 1992).

Approximate Training and Application Times

The training time for such a method should be low, representing the amount of time it takes for the analyst to become familiar with the process chart symbols. Application time is dependent upon the size and complexity of the task under analysis. For small, simple tasks, the application time would be very low. For larger, more complex tasks, the application time would be high.

Reliability and Validity

No data regarding the reliability and validity of the method are available in the literature.

Example

The following example is a process chart analysis of the landing task, 'Land aircraft at New Orleans airport using the autoland system' (Marshall et al, 2003). A process chart analysis was conducted in order to assess the feasibility of applying process chart type analysis in the aviation domain. Initially, a HTA was developed for the landing task, based upon an interview with an aircraft pilot, a video demonstration of the landing task and a walkthrough of the task using Microsoft flight simulator 2000. The HTA is presented in list form below. A simplistic process chart was then constructed, using the process chart symbols presented in Figure 5.2.

1.1.1 Check the current speed brake setting
1.1.2 Move the speed brake lever to 'full' position
1.2.1 Check that the auto-pilot is in IAS mode
1.2.2 Check the current airspeed
1.2.3 Dial the speed/Mach knob to enter 210 on the IAS/MACH display
2.1 Check the localiser position on the HSI display
2.2.1 Adjust heading +
2.2.2 Adjust heading -
2.3 Check the glideslope indicator
2.4 Maintain current altitude
2.5 Press 'APP' button to engage the approach system
2.6.1 Check that the 'APP' light is on
2.6.2 Check that the 'HDG' light is on
2.6.3 Check that the 'ALT' light is off
3.1 Check the current distance from runway on the captain's primary flight display
3.2.1 Check the current airspeed
3.2.2 Dial the speed/Mach knob to enter 190 on the IAS/MACH display
3.3.1 Check the current flap setting
3.3.2 Move the flap lever to setting '1'
3.4.1 Check the current airspeed
3.4.2 Dial the speed/Mach knob to enter 150 on the IAS/MACH display
3.5.1 Check the current flap setting
3.5.2 Move the flap lever to setting '2'
3.6.1 Check the current flap setting
3.6.2 Move the flap lever to setting '3'
3.7.1 Check the current airspeed
3.7.2 Dial the speed/Mach knob to enter 140 on the IAS/MACH display
3.8 Put the landing gear down

3.9 Check altitude
3.3.1 Check the current flap setting
3.3.2 Move the flap lever to 'FULL' setting.

Flowchart

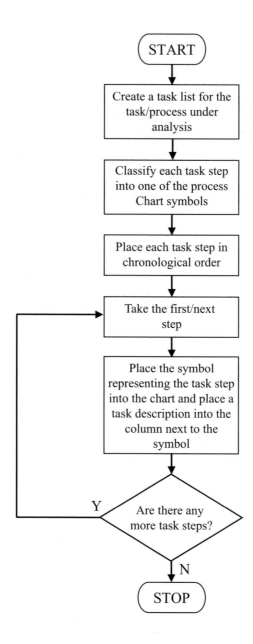

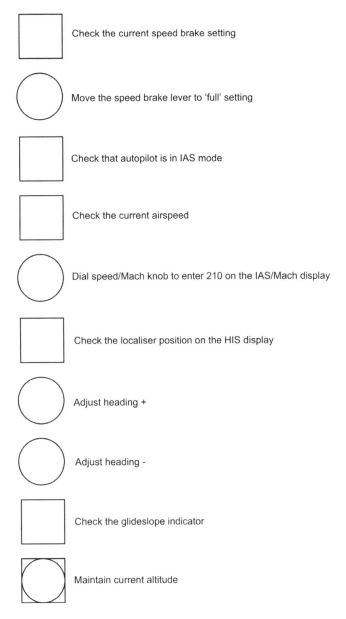

Figure 5.2   Extract of Process Chart for the Landing Task 'Land at New Orleans Using the Autoland System' (Source: Marshall et al, 2003)

Operation Sequence Diagrams (OSD)

Background and Applications

Operation Sequence Diagrams (OSD) are used to graphically describe the activity and interaction between teams of agents within a network. According to Kirwan and Ainsworth (1992), the original purpose of OSD analysis was to represent complex multi-person tasks. The output of an OSD graphically depicts the task process, including the tasks performed and the interaction between operators over time, using standardised symbols. There are various forms of OSDs, ranging from a simple flow diagram representing task order, to more complex OSDs which account for team interaction and communication. OSDs have recently been used by the authors for the analysis of command and control in a number of domains, including the fire service, naval warfare, aviation, energy distribution, air traffic control and rail domains.

Domain of Application

The method was originally used in the nuclear power and chemical process industries. However, the method is generic and can be applied in any domain.

Procedure and Advice

Step 1: Define the task(s) under analysis
The first step in an OSD analysis is to define the task(s) or scenario(s) under analysis. The task(s) or scenario(s) should be defined clearly, including the activity and agents involved.

Step 2: Data collection
In order to construct an OSD, the analyst(s) must obtain specific data regarding the task or scenario under analysis. It is recommended that the analyst(s) use various forms of data collection in this phase. Observational study should be used to observe the task (or similar types of task) under analysis. Interviews with personnel involved in the task (or similar tasks) should also be conducted. The type and amount of data collected in step 2 is dependent upon the analysis requirements. The more exhaustive the analysis is intended to be, the more data collection methods should be employed.

Step 3: Describe the task or scenario using HTA
Once the data collection phase is completed, a detailed task analysis should be conducted for the scenario under analysis. The type of task analysis is determined by the analyst(s), and in some cases, a task list will suffice. However, it is recommended that a HTA is conducted for the task under analysis.

Step 4: Construct the OSD diagram
Once the task has been described adequately, the construction of the OSD can begin. The process begins with the construction of an OSD template. The template should include the title of the task or scenario under analysis, a timeline, and a row for each agent involved in the task. An OSD template used during the analysis of C4i activity in the civil energy distribution domain is presented in Figure 5.3 (Salmon et al, 2004). In order to construct the OSD, it is recommended that the analyst walks through the HTA of the task under analysis, creating the OSD in conjunction. The OSD symbols used to analyse C4i activity by the authors is presented in Figure 5.4. The symbols involved in a particular task step should be linked by directional arrows, in order to represent the flow of activity during the scenario. Each symbol in the OSD should contain the corresponding task step number from the HTA of the scenario. The artefacts used during the communications should also be annotated onto the OSD.

Step 5: Overlay additional analyses results
One of the endearing features of the OSD method is that additional analysis results can easily be added to the OSD. According to the analysis requirements, additional task features can also be

annotated onto the OSD. For example, in the analysis of C4i activity in a variety of domains, the authors annotated co-ordination values (from a co-ordination demands analysis) between team members for each task step onto the OSD.

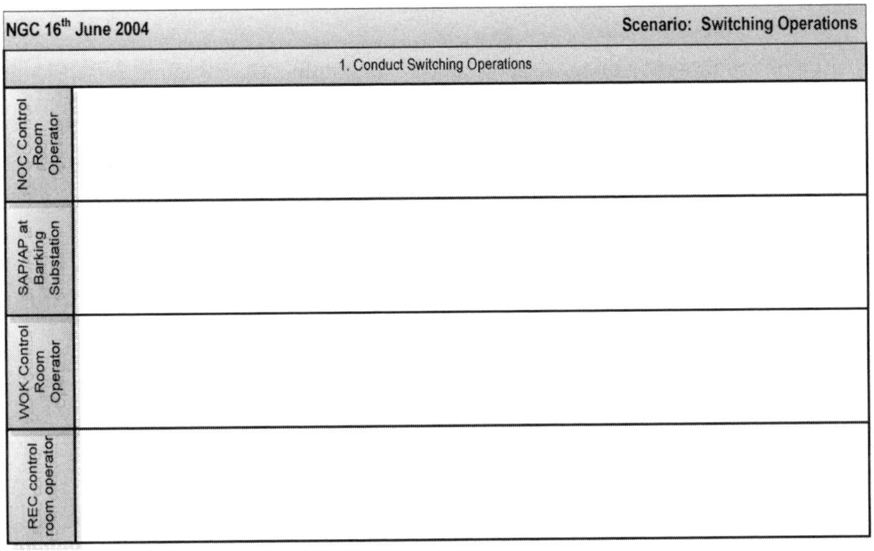

Figure 5.3   **Example OSD Template**

Step 6: Calculate operation loading figures

From the OSD, operational loading figures are calculated for each agent involved in the scenario under analysis. Operational loading figures are calculated for each OSD operator or symbol used e.g. operation, receive, delay, decision, transport, and combined operations. The operational loading figures refer to the frequency in which each agent was involved in the operator in question during the scenario.

Advantages

1. The OSD provides an exhaustive analysis of the task in question. The flow of the task is represented in terms of activity and information, the type of activity and the agents involved are specified, a timeline of the activity, the communications between agents involved in the task, the technology used and also a rating of total co-ordination for each teamwork activity is also provided. The method's flexibility also permits the analyst(s) to add further analysis outputs onto the OSD, adding to its exhaustiveness.
2. An OSD is particularly useful for analysing and representing distributed teamwork or collaborated activity.
3. OSDs are useful for demonstrating the relationship between tasks, technology and team members.
4. High face validity (Kirwan and Ainsworth, 1992).
5. OSDs have been used extensively in the past and have been applied in a variety of domains.
6. A number of different analyses can be overlaid onto an OSD of a particular task. For example, Baber et al (2004) add the corresponding HTA task step numbers and co-ordination demands analysis results to OSDs of C4i activity.
7. The OSD method is very flexible and can be modified to suit the analysis needs.

8. The WESTT software package can be used to automate a large portion of the OSD procedure.
9. Despite its exhaustive nature, the OSD method requires only minimal training.

Disadvantages

1. The application time for an OSD analysis is lengthy. Constructing an OSD for large, complex tasks can be extremely time consuming and the initial data collection adds further time to the analysis.
2. The construction of large, complex OSDs is also quite a laborious and taxing process.
3. OSDs can become cluttered and confusing (Kirwan and Ainsworth, 1992).
4. The output of OSDs can become large and unwieldy.
5. The present OSD symbols are limited for certain applications (e.g. C4i scenarios).
6. The reliability of the method is questionable. Different analysts may interpret the OSD symbols differently.

Related Methods

Various types of OSD exist, including temporal operational sequence diagrams, partitioned operational sequence diagrams and spatial operational sequence diagrams (Kirwan and Ainsworth, 1992). During the OSD data collection phase, traditional data collection procedures such as observational study and interviews are typically employed. Task analysis methods such as HTA are also used to provide the input for the OSD. Timeline analysis may also be used in order to construct an appropriate timeline for the task or scenario under analysis. Additional analyses results can also be annotated onto an OSD, such as co-ordination demands analysis (CDA) and comms usage diagram. The OSD method has also recently been integrated with a number of other methods (HTA, observation, co-ordination demands analysis, comms usage diagram, social network analysis and propositional networks) to form the event analysis of systemic teamwork (EAST) methodology (Baber et al, 2004), which has been used by the authors to analyse C4i activity in a number of domains.

Approximate Training and Application Times

No data regarding the training and application time associated with the OSD method are available in the literature. However, it is apparent that the training time for such a technique would be minimal. The application time for the method is very high, including the initial data collection phase of interviews and observational analysis and also the construction of an appropriate HTA for the task under analysis. The construction of the OSD in particular is a very time-consuming process. A typical OSD normally can take up to one week to construct.

Reliability and Validity

According to Kirwan and Ainsworth, OSD methods possess a high degree of face validity. The intra-analyst reliability of the method may be suspect, as different analysts may interpret the OSD symbols differently.

Tools Needed

When conducting an OSD analysis, pen and paper could be sufficient. However, to ensure that data collection is comprehensive, it is recommended that video or audio recording devices are used in conjunction with the pen and paper. For the construction of the OSD, it is recommended that a suitable drawing package, such as Microsoft Visio™ is used. The WESTT software package (Houghton et al., 2005) can also be used to automate a large portion of the OSD procedure. WESTT constructs the OSD based upon an input of observational data for the scenario under analysis.

Example

The OSD method has recently been used by the authors in the analysis of C4i activity in the fire service (Baber et al, 2004), naval warfare, aviation, energy distribution, air traffic control and rail domains. The following example is an extract of an OSD from a railway maintenance scenario (Salmon, Stanton, Walker, McMaster and Green, 2005). The task involved the switching out of three circuits at three substations. Observational data from the substation (SAP) and the network operations centre (NOC) control room was used to conduct a HTA of the switching scenario. A HTA was then created, which acted as the primary input into the OSD diagram. Total co-ordination values for each teamwork task step (from a co-ordination demands analysis – see Chapter 9) were also annotated onto the OSD. The glossary for the OSD is presented in Figure 5.4. An extract of the HTA for the corresponding energy distribution task is presented in Figure 5.5. The corresponding extract of the OSD is presented in Figure 5.6. The operational loading figures are presented in Table 5.2.

Table 5.2   Operational Loading Results

Agent	Operation	Receive	Transport	Decision	Delay	Total
NOC	98	40				138
SAP	223	21	19		1	264
WOK	40	10				50
REC	15	14				29

The operational loading analysis indicates that the senior authorised person (SAP) at the substation has the highest loading in terms of operations, transport, and delay whilst the network operations centre (NOC) operator has the highest loading in terms of receipt of information. This provides an indication of the nature of the roles involved in the scenario. The NOC operator's role is one of information distribution (giving and receiving) indicated by the high receive operator loading, whilst the majority of the work is conducted by the SAP, indicated by the high operation and transport loading figures.

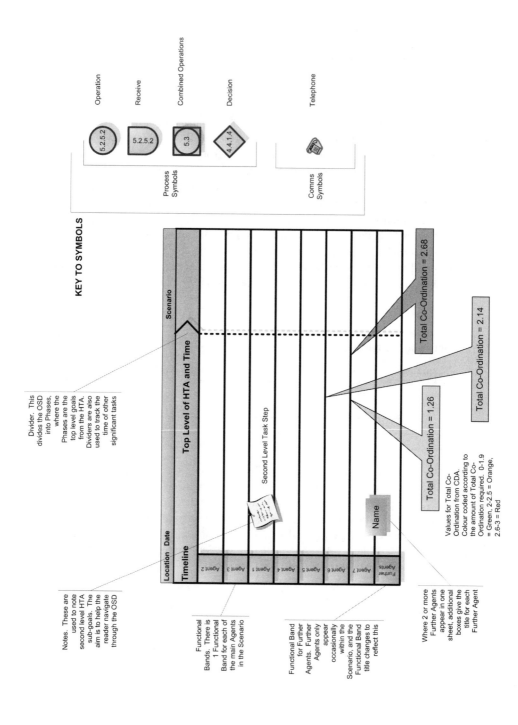

Figure 5.4 OSD Glossary (Source: Salmon et al, 2004)

0. Co-ordinate and carry out switching operations on circuits SGT5. SGT1A and 1B at Bark s/s (*Plan 0. Do 1 then 2 then 3, EXIT*)

1. Prepare for switching operations (*Plan 1. Do 1.1, then 1.2, then 1.3, then 1.4, then 1.5, then 1.6, then 1.7, then 1.8, then 1.9,then 1.10 EXIT*)

   1.1. Agree SSC (Plan 1.1. Do 1.1.1, then 1.1.2, then 1.1.3, then 1.1.4, then 1.1.5, EXIT)

      1.1.1. (WOK) Use phone to Contact NOC

      1.1.2. (WOK + NOC) Exchange identities

      1.1.3. (WOK + NOC) Agree SSC documentation

      1.1.4. (WOK+NOC) Agree SSC and time (Plan 1.1.4. Do 1.1.4.1, then 1.1.4.2, EXIT)

         1.1.4.1. (NOC) Agree SSC with WOK

         1.1.4.2. (NOC) Agree time with WOK

      1.1.5. (NOC) Record and enter details (Plan 1.1.5. Do 1.1.5.1, then 1.1.5.2, EXIT)

         1.1.5.1. Record details on log sheet

         1.1.5.2. Enter details into worksafe

   1.2. (NOC) Request remote isolation (Plan 1.2. Do 1.2.1, then 1.2.2, then 1.2.3,then 1.2.4, EXIT)

      1.2.1. (NOC) Ask WOK for isolators to be opened remotely

      1.2.2. (WOK) Perform remote isolation

      1.2.3. (NOC) Check Barking s/s screen

      1.2.4. (WOK + NOC) End communications

   1.3. Gather information on outage at transformer 5 at Bark s/s (Plan 1.3. Do 1.3.1, then 1.3.2, then 1.3.3, then 1.3.4, EXIT)

      1.3.1. (NOC) Use phone to contact SAP at Bark

Figure 5.5   Extract of HTA for NGT Switching Scenario (Source: Salmon et al, 2004)

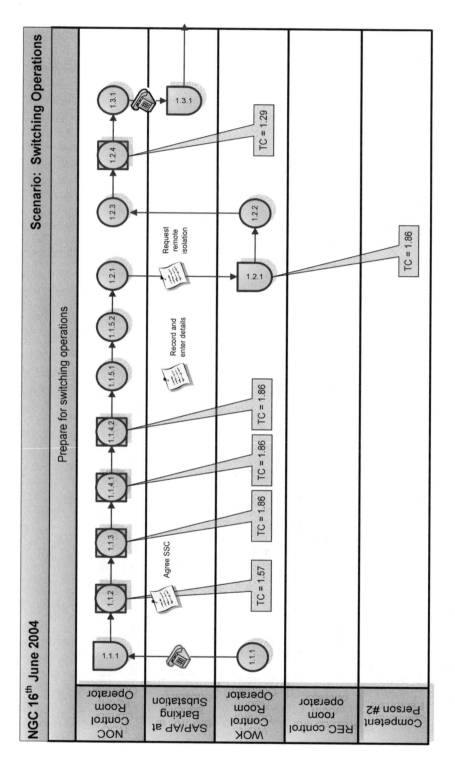

Figure 5.6 Extract of OSD for NGT Switching Scenario (Source: Salmon et al, 2004)

Flowchart

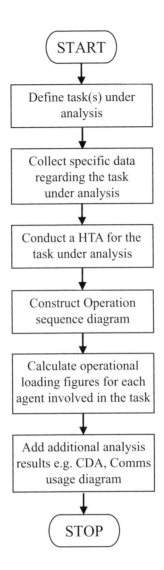

Event Tree Analysis (ETA)

Background and Applications

Event tree analysis is a task analysis method that uses tree-like diagrams to represent possible outcomes associated with operator tasks steps in a scenario. Originally used in system reliability analysis (Kirwan and Ainsworth, 1992), event tree analysis can also be applied to human operations to investigate possible actions and their consequences. A typical event tree output comprises a tree-like diagram consisting of nodes (representing task steps) and exit lines (representing the possible outcomes). Typically, success and failure outcomes are used, but for more complex analyses, multiple outcomes can be represented (Kirwan and Ainsworth, 1992). Event tree analysis can be used to depict task sequences and their possible outcomes, to identify error potential within a system and to model team-based tasks.

Domain of Application

Event tree analysis was originally applied in the nuclear power and chemical processing domains. However, the method is generic and could feasibly be applied in any domain.

Procedure and Advice

Step 1: Define scenario(s) under analysis
Firstly, the scenario(s) under analysis should be clearly defined. Event tree analysis can be used to analyse activity in existing systems or system design concepts. The task under analysis should be clearly defined.

Step 2: Data collection phase
The next step involves collecting the data required to construct the event tree diagram. If the event tree analysis is focused upon an operational system, then data regarding the scenario under analysis should be collected. It is recommended that traditional HF data collection methods, such as observational study, interviews and questionnaires, are used for this purpose. However, if the analysis is based upon a design concept, then storyboards can be used to depict the scenario(s) under analysis.

Step 3: Draw up task list
Once the scenario under analysis is defined clearly and sufficient data is collected, a comprehensive task list should be created. The component task steps required for effective task performance should be specified in sequence. This initial task list should be representative of standard error-free performance of the task or scenario under analysis. It may be useful to consult with SMEs during this process.

Step 4: Determine possible actions for each task step
Once the task list is created, the analyst should then describe every possible action associated with each task step in the task list. It may be useful to consult with SMEs during this process. Each task step should be broken down into the human or system operations required and any controls or interface elements used should also be noted. Every possible action associated with each task step should be recorded.

Step 5: Determine consequences associated with each possible action
Next, the analyst should take each action specified in step 4 and record the associated consequences.

Step 6: Construct event tree
Once steps 4 and 5 are complete, the analyst can begin to construct the event tree diagram. The event tree should depict all possible actions and their associated consequences.

Advantages

1. Event tree analysis can be used to highlight a sequence of tasks steps and their associated consequences.
2. Event tree analysis can be used to highlight error potential and error paths throughout a system.
3. The method can be used in the early design life cycle to highlight task steps that may become problematic (multiple associated response options) and also those task steps that have highly critical consequences.

4. If used correctly, the method could potentially depict anything that could possibly go wrong in a system.
5. Event tree analysis is a relatively easy method that requires little training.
6. Event tree analysis has been used extensively in PSA/HRA.

Disadvantages

1. For large, complex tasks, the event tree diagram can become very large and complex.
2. Can be time consuming in its application.
3. Task steps are often not explained in the output.

Example

An extract of an event tree analysis is presented in Figure 5.7. An event tree was constructed for the landing task, 'Land A320 at New Orleans using the autoland system' in order to investigate the use of event tree analysis for predicting design induced pilot error (Marshall et al, 2003).

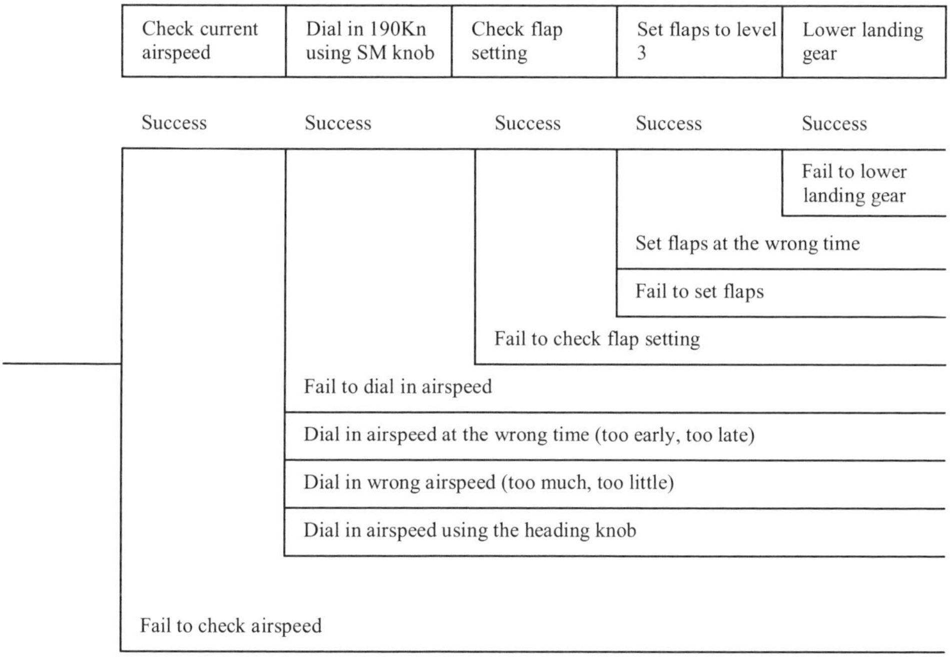

Figure 5.7   Extract of Event Tree Diagram for the Flight Task 'Land at New Orleans Using the Autoland System' (Source: Marshall et al, 2003)

Related Methods

According to Kirwan and Ainsworth (1992) there are a number of variations of the original event tree analysis method, including operator action event tree analysis (OATS), and human reliability analysis event tree analysis (HRAET). Event trees are also similar to fault tree analysis and operator sequence diagrams.

Flowchart

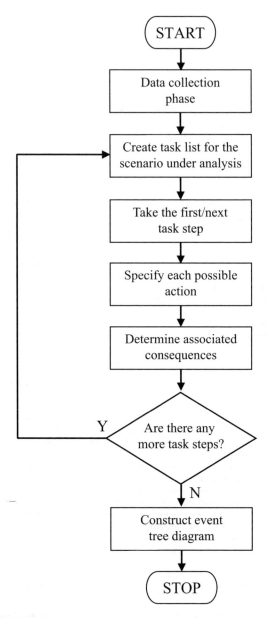

Reliability and Validity

No data regarding the reliability and validity of the event tree method are available.

Tools Needed

An event tree diagram can be conducted using pen and paper. If the event tree is based on an existing system, then observational study may be used for data collection purposes, which requires video and audio recording equipment and a PC.

Decision Action Diagrams (DAD)

Background and Applications

Decision Action Diagrams (DADs), also known as information flow diagrams (Kirwan and Ainsworth, 1992) are used to graphically depict a scenario process in terms of the decisions required and actions to be performed by the operator involved in the activity. Decisions are represented by diamonds and each decision option available to the system operator is represented by exit lines. In their simplest form, the decision options are usually 'Yes' or 'No', however depending upon the complexity of the task and system, multiple options can also be represented. The DAD output diagram should display all of the possible outcomes at each task step in a process. DAD analysis can be used to evaluate existing systems or to inform the design of system's and procedures.

Domain of Application

Event tree analysis was originally applied in the nuclear power and chemical processing domains. However, the method is generic and could feasibly be applied in any domain.

Procedure and Advice

Step 1: Define the task or scenario under analysis
Firstly, the scenario(s) under analysis should be clearly defined. DAD analysis can be used to analyse activity in existing systems or system design concepts.

Step 2: Data collection
In order to construct a DAD, the analyst(s) must obtain sufficient data regarding the task or scenario under analysis. It is recommended that traditional HF data collection methods, such as observational study, interviews and questionnaires, are used for this purpose. However, if the analysis is based upon a design concept, then storyboards can be used to depict the scenario(s) under analysis.

Step 3: Conduct a task analysis
Once the data collection phase is completed, a detailed task analysis should be conducted for the scenario under analysis. The type of task analysis is determined by the analyst(s), and in some cases, a task list will suffice. However, it is recommended that when constructing a DAD, a HTA for the scenario under analysis is conducted.

Step 4: Construct DAD
Once the task or scenario under analysis is fully understood, the DAD can be constructed. This process should begin with the first decision available to the operator of the system. Each possible outcome or action associated with the decision should be represented with an exit line from the decision diamond. Each resultant action and outcome for each of the possible decision exit lines should then be specified. This process should be repeated for each task step until all of the possible decision outcomes for each task have been exhausted.

Advantages

1. A DAD can be used to depict the possible options that an operator faces during each task step in a scenario. This information can be used to inform the design of the system or procedures i.e. task steps that have multiple options associated with them can be redesigned.
2. DADs are relatively easy to construct and require little training.
3. DADs could potentially be used for error prediction purposes.

Disadvantages

1. In their current form, DADs do not cater for the cognitive component of task decisions.
2. It would be very difficult to model parallel activity using DADs.
3. DADs do not cater for processes involving teams. Constructing a team DAD would appear to be extremely difficult.
4. It appears that a HTA for the task or scenario under analysis would be sufficient. A DAD output is very similar to the plans depicted in a HTA.
5. For large, complex tasks, the DAD would be difficult and time consuming to construct.
6. The initial data collection phase involved in the DAD procedure adds a considerable amount of time to the analysis.
7. Reliability and validity data for the method is sparse.

Related Methods

DADs are also known as information flow charts (Kirwan and Ainsworth, 1992). The DAD method is related to other process chart methods such as operation sequence diagrams and also task analysis methods such as HTA. When conducting a DAD type analysis, a number of data collection techniques are used, such as observational study and interviews. A task analysis (e.g. HTA) of the task/scenario under analysis may also be required.

Approximate Training and Application Times

No data regarding the training and application times associated with DADs are available in the literature. It is estimated that the training time for DADs would be minimal or low. The application time associated with the DAD method is dependent upon the task and system under analysis. For complex scenarios with multiple options available to the operator involved, the application time would be high. For more simple linear tasks, the application time would be very low. The data collection phase of the DAD procedure adds considerable time, particularly when observational analysis is used.

Reliability and Validity

No data regarding the reliability and validity of the DAD method are available.

Tools Needed

Once the initial data collection is complete, the DAD method can be conducted using pen and paper, although it may be more suitable to use a drawing package such as Microsoft Visio. The tools required for the data collection phase are dependent upon the methods used. Typically, observational study is used, which would require video and audio recording equipment and a PC.

Flowchart

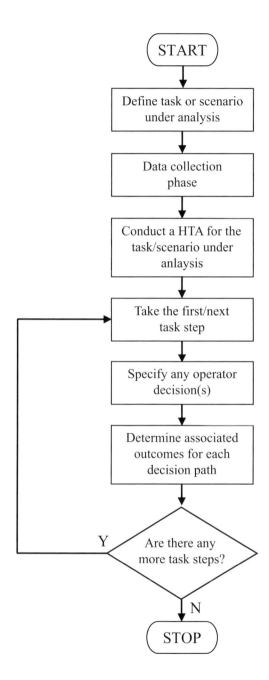

Example

The following example (Figure 5.8) is a DAD taken from Kirwan and Ainsworth (1992).

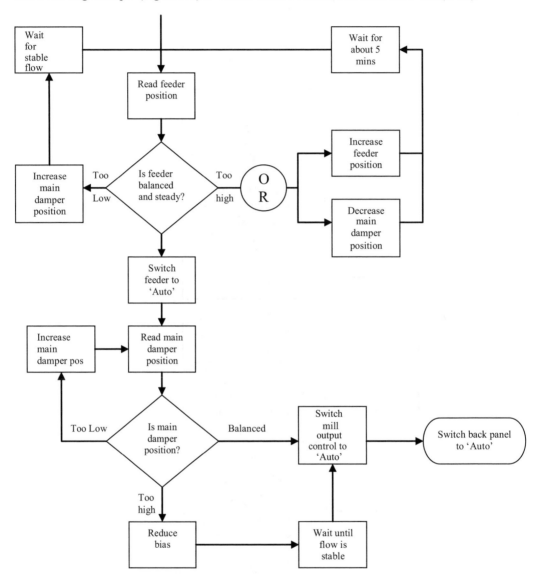

Figure 5.8   Decision-Action Diagram (Adapted from Kirwan and Ainsworth, 1992)

Fault Trees

Background and Application

Fault trees are used to graphically represent system failures and their causes. A fault tree is a tree-like diagram, which defines the failure event and displays the possible causes in terms of hardware failure or human error (Kirwan and Ainsworth, 1992). Fault tree analysis was originally developed for the analysis of complex systems in the aerospace and defence industries (Kirwan and Ainsworth, 1992) and they are now used extensively in probabilistic safety assessment (PSA). Although typically used to evaluate events retrospectively, fault trees can be used at any stage in the system life cycle to predict failure events and their causes. Typically, the failure event or top event (Kirwan and Ainsworth, 1992) is placed at the top of the fault tree, and the contributing events are placed below. The fault tree is held together by AND and OR gates, which link contributory events together. An AND gate is used when more than one event causes a failure i.e. when multiple contributory factors are involved. The events placed directly underneath an AND gate must occur together for the failure event above to occur. An OR gate is used when the failure event could be caused by more than one contributory event in isolation, but not together. The event above the OR gate may occur if any one of the events below the OR gate occurs. Fault tree analysis can be used for the retrospective analysis of incidents or for the prediction of failure in a particular scenario.

Domain of Application

Fault tree analysis was originally applied in the nuclear power and chemical processing domains. However the method is generic and could potentially be applied in any domain.

Procedure and Advice

Step 1: Define failure event
The failure or event under analysis should be defined first. This may be either an actual event that has occurred (retrospective incident analysis) or an imaginary event (predictive analysis). This event then becomes the top event in the fault tree.

Step 2: Determine causes of failure event
Once the failure event has been defined, the contributory causes associated with the event should be defined. The nature of the causes analysed is dependent upon the focus of the analysis. Typically, human error and hardware failures are considered (Kirwan and Ainsworth, 1992).

Step 3: AND/OR classification
Once the cause(s) of the failure event are defined, the analysis proceeds with the AND or OR causal classification phase. Each contributory cause identified during step 2 of the analysis should be classified as either an AND or an OR event. If two or more contributory events contribute to the failure event, then they are classified as AND events. If two or more contributory events are responsible for the failure even when they occur separately, then they are classified as OR events.
        Steps 2 and 3 should be repeated until each of the initial causal events and associated causes are investigated and described fully.

Step 4: Construct fault tree diagram
Once all events and their causes have been defined fully, they should be put into the fault tree diagram. The fault tree should begin with the main failure or top event at the top of the diagram with its associated causes linked underneath as AND/OR events. Then, the causes of these events should be linked underneath as AND/OR events. The diagram should continue until all events and causes are exhausted fully.

Example

The following example (Figure 5.9) is taken from Kirwan (1994) from a brake failure scenario model.

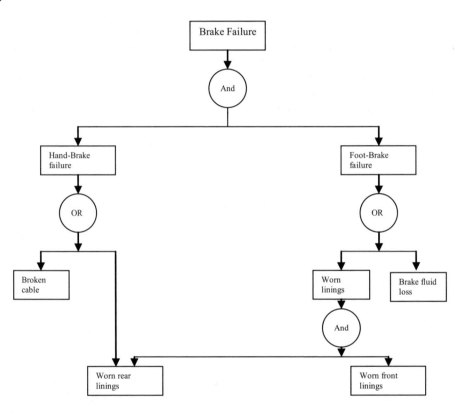

Figure 5.9   Fault Tree for Brake Failure Scenario

Flowchart

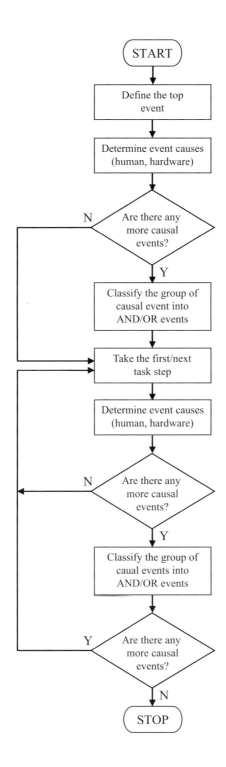

Advantages

1. Fault trees are useful in that they define possible failure events and associated causes. This is especially useful when looking at failure events with multiple causes.
2. Fault tree type analysis has been used extensively in PSA.
3. Could potentially be used both predictively and retrospectively.
4. Although most commonly used in the analysis of nuclear power plant events, the method is generic and can be applied in any domain.
5. Fault trees can be used to highlight potential weak points in a system design concept (Kirwan and Ainsworth, 1992).
6. The method could be particularly useful in modelling team-based errors, where a failure event is caused by multiple events distributed across a team of personnel.

Disadvantages

1. When used in the analysis of large, complex systems, fault trees can be complex, difficult and time consuming to construct. It is apparent that fault tree diagrams can quickly become large and complicated.
2. To utilise the method quantitatively, a high level of training may be required (Kirwan and Ainsworth, 1992).
3. The use of fault trees as a predictive tool remains largely unexplored.
4. There is little evidence of their use outside of the nuclear power domain.

Related Methods

The fault tree method is often used with event tree analysis (Kirwan and Ainsworth, 1992). Fault trees are similar to many other charting methods, including cause-consequence charts, DADs and event trees.

Approximate Training and Application Times

No data regarding the training and application times associated with fault tree analysis are available in the literature. It is estimated that the training time for fault trees would be low. The application time associated with the fault tree method is dependent upon the task and system under analysis. For complex failure scenarios, the application time would be high. For more simple failure events, the application time would be very low.

Reliability and Validity

No data regarding the reliability and validity of the DAD method are available

Tools Needed

Fault tree analysis can be conducted using pen and paper. If the analysis were based upon an existing system, an observational study of the failure event under analysis would be useful. This would require video and audio recording equipment. It is also recommended that when constructing fault tree diagrams, a drawing package such as Microsoft Visio be used.

Murphy Diagrams

Murphy diagrams (Pew, Miller and Feehrer, 1981; cited in Kirwan, 1992a) were originally used for the retrospective examination of errors in process control rooms. Murphy diagrams are based on the notion that 'if anything can go wrong, it will go wrong' (Kirwan and Ainsworth, 1992). The method is very similar to fault tree analysis in that errors or failures are analysed in terms of their potential causes. Murphy diagrams use the following eight behaviour categories:

1. Activation/Detection;
2. Observation and data collection;
3. Identification of system state;
4. Interpretation of situation;
5. Task definition/selection of goal state;
6. Evaluation of alternative strategies;
7. Procedure selection; and
8. Procedure execution.

The Murphy diagram begins with the top event being split into success and failure nodes. The analyst begins by describing the failure event under analysis. Next the 'failure' outcome is specified and the sources of the error that have an immediate effect are defined. These are called the proximal sources of error. The analyst then takes each proximal error source and breaks it down further so that the causes of the proximal error sources are defined. These proximal error causes are termed the distal causes. For example, if the failure was 'procedure incorrectly executed', the proximal sources could be 'wrong switches chosen', 'switches incorrectly operated' or 'switches not operated'. The distal sources for 'wrong switches chosen' could then be further broken down into 'deficiencies in placement of switches', 'inherent confusability in switch design' or 'training deficiency' (Kirwan and Ainsworth, 1992). The Murphy diagram method is typically used for the retrospective analysis of failure events.

Domain of Application

Nuclear power and chemical process industries.

Procedure and Advice

Step 1: Define task/scenario under analysis
The first step in a Murphy Diagram analysis is to define the task or scenario under analysis. Although typically used in the retrospective analysis of incidents, it is feasible that the method could be used proactively to predict potential failure events and their causes.

Step 2: Data collection
If the analysis is retrospective, then data regarding the incident under analysis should be collected. This may involve the interviews with the actors involved in the scenario, or a walkthrough of the event. If the analysis is proactive, and concerns an event that has not yet happened, then walkthroughs of the events should be used.

Step 3: Define error events
Once sufficient data regarding the event under analysis is collected, the analysis begins with the definition of the first error. The analyst(s) should define the error as clearly as possible.

Step 4: Classify error activity into decision-making category
Once the error event under analysis is described, the activity leading up to the error should be classified into one of the eight decision-making process categories.

Step 5: Determine error consequence and causes
Once the error is described and classified, the analyst(s) should determine the consequences of the error event and also determine possible consequences associated with the error. The error causes should be explored fully, with proximal and distal sources described.

Step 6: Construct Murphy diagram
Once the consequences, proximal and distal sources have been explored fully, the Murphy diagram for the error in question should be constructed.

Step 7: Propose design remedies
For the purpose of error prediction in the design of systems, it is recommended that the Murphy diagram be extended to include an error or design remedy column. The analyst(s) should use this column to propose design remedies for the identified errors, based upon the causes identified.

Advantages

1. Easy method to use and learn, requiring little training.
2. Murphy diagrams present a useful way for the analyst to identify a number of different possible causes for a specific error or event.
3. High documentability.
4. Each task step failure is exhaustively described, including proximal and distal sources.
5. The method has the potential to be applied to team-based tasks, depicting teamwork and failures with multiple team-based causes.
6. Murphy diagrams use very little resources (low cost, time spent etc.).
7. Although developed for the retrospective analysis of error, it is feasible that the method could be used proactively.

Disadvantages

1. Its use as a predictive tool remains largely unexplored.
2. Could become large and unwieldy for large, complex tasks.
3. There is little guidance for the analyst.
4. Consistency of the method can be questioned.
5. Design remedies are based entirely upon the analyst's subjective judgement.
6. Dated method that appears to be little used.

Example

A Murphy diagram analysis was conducted for the flight task 'Land aircraft X at New Orleans using the autoland System'. An extract of the analysis is presented in Figure 5.10.

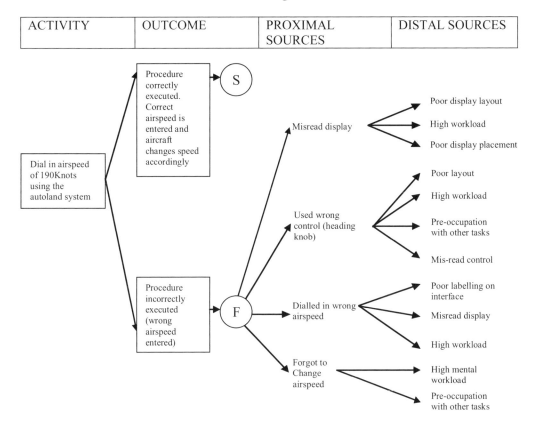

Figure 5.10   Murphy Diagram for the Flight Task 'Land Aircraft X at New Orleans Using the Autoland System'

Related Methods

Murphy diagrams are very similar to fault tree and event tree analysis in that they depict failure events and their causes.

Approximate Training and Application Times

The training time for the method would be minimal. The application time would depend upon the task or scenario under analysis. For error incidences with multiple causes and consequences, the application time would be high.

Reliability and Validity

No data regarding the reliability and validity of Murphy diagrams are available in the literature.

Tools Needed

The method can be conducted using pen and paper. It is recommended that a drawing package such as Microsoft Visio be used to construct the Murphy diagram outputs.

Chapter 6

Human Error Identification Methods

Human error is a complex construct that has received considerable attention from the HF community. Human error has been consistently identified as a contributory factor in a high proportion of incidents in complex, dynamic systems. For example, within the civil aviation domain, recent research indicates that human or pilot error is the major cause of all commercial aviation incidents (McFadden and Towell, 1999). Within the rail transport domain, human error was identified as a contributory cause of almost half of all collisions occurring on the UK's rail network between 2002 and 2003 (Lawton and Ward, 2005). In the health-care domain, the US Institute of Medicine estimates that between 44,000 and 88,000 people die as a result of medical errors (Helmreich, 2000) and it has also been estimated that human or driver error contributes to as much as 75% of roadway crashes (Medina, Lee, Wierwille and Hanowski, 2004). Although human error has been investigated since the advent of the discipline, research into the construct only increased around the late 1970s and early 1980s in response to a number of high profile catastrophes in which human error was implicated. Major incidents such as the Three Mile Island, Chernobyl and Bhopal disasters, and the Tenerife and Papa India air disasters (to name only a few) were all attributed, in part, to human error. As a result, it began to receive considerable attention from the HF community and also the general public, and has been investigated in a number of different domains ever since, including the military and civil aviation domain (Shappell and Wiegmann, 2000, Marshall et al, 2003), road transport (Reason, Manstead, Stradd, Baxter and Campbell, 1990), nuclear power and petro-chemical reprocessing (Kirwan, 1992a, 1992b, 1998a, 1998b, 1999), the military, medicine, air traffic control (Shorrock and Kirwan, 1999), and even the space travel domain (Nelson et al, 1998).

Human error is formally defined as 'All those occasions in which a planned sequence of mental or physical activities fails to achieve its intended outcome, and when these failures cannot be attributed to the intervention of some chance agency' (Reason, 1990). Further classifications of human error have also been proposed, such as the slips (and lapses), mistakes and violations taxonomy proposed by Reason (1990). For a complete description of error classifications and error theory the reader is referred to Reason (1990).

The prediction of human error in complex systems was widely investigated in response to the Three Mile Island, Chernobyl and Bhopal disasters. Human Error Identification (HEI) or error prediction methods are used to identify potential errors that may arise as a result of man-machine interactions in complex systems. The prediction of human error is used within complex, dynamic systems in order to identify the nature of potential human or operator errors and the causal factors, recovery strategies and consequences associated with them. Information derived from HEI analyses is then typically used to propose remedial measures designed to eradicate the potential errors identified. HEI works on the premise that an understanding of an individual's work task and the characteristics of the technology being used permits the analyst to indicate potential errors that may arise from the resulting interaction (Stanton and Baber, 1996a). HEI methods can be used either during the design process to highlight potential design induced error, or to evaluate error potential in existing systems. These are typically conducted on a task analysis of the activity under analysis. The output of HEI methods usually describes potential errors, their consequences, recovery potential, probability, criticality and offers associated design remedies or error reduction strategies. HEI approaches can be broadly categorised into two groups, qualitative and quantitative techniques. Qualitative approaches are used to determine the nature of errors that might occur within a particular system, whilst quantitative approaches are used to provide a numerical probability of error occurrence within a particular system. There is a broad range of HEI approaches available to the HEI practitioner, ranging from simplistic external error mode taxonomy based approaches to more sophisticated human performance simulation methods. The methods reviewed can be further categorised into the following types:

1. Taxonomy-based methods;
2. Error identifier methods;
3. Error quantification methods;

In order to familiarise the reader with the different HEI methods available, a brief overview of them is presented below.

Taxonomy-based HEI methods use external error mode taxonomies and typically involve the application of these error modes to a task analysis of the activity in question. Methods such as SHERPA (Embrey, 1986), HET (Marshall et al, 2003), TRACEr (Shorrock and Kirwan, 2000), and CREAM (Hollnagel, 1998) all use domain specific external error mode taxonomies designed to aid the analyst in identifying potential errors. Taxonomic approaches to HEI are typically the most successful in terms of sensitivity and are the quickest and simplest to apply, and with only limited resource usage. However, these methods also place a great amount of dependence upon the judgement of the analyst and as a result there are concerns associated with the reliability of the error predictions made. Different analysts often make different predictions for the same task using the same method (inter-analyst reliability). Similarly, the same analyst may make different judgements on different occasions (intra-analyst reliability). A brief description of the taxonomy-based HEI methods considered in the review is provided below.

The systematic human error reduction and prediction approach (SHERPA; Embrey, 1986) uses a behavioural classification linked to an external error mode taxonomy (action, retrieval, check, selection and information communication errors) to identify potential errors associated with human activity. The SHERPA method works by indicating which error modes are credible for each bottom level task step in a HTA. The analyst classifies a task step into a behaviour and then determines whether any of the associated error modes are credible. For each credible error the analyst describes the error, determines the consequences, error recovery, probability and criticality. Finally, design remedies are proposed for each error identified.

The human error template (HET; Marshall et al, 2003) method was developed for the certification of civil flight deck technology and is a checklist approach that is applied to each bottom level task step in a HTA of the task under analysis. The HET method works by indicating which of the HET error modes are credible for each task step, based upon analyst subjective judgement. The analyst applies each of the HET error modes to the task step in question and determines whether any of the modes produce credible errors or not. The HET error taxonomy consists of twelve error modes that were selected based upon a study of actual pilot error incidence and existing error modes used in contemporary HEI methods. For each credible error (i.e. those judged by the analyst to be possible) the analyst should give a description of the form that the error would take, such as, 'pilot dials in the airspeed value using the wrong knob'. The associated error consequences, likelihood of occurrence, and criticality in relation to the task under analysis are then specified. Finally, a pass or fail rating is assigned to the interface element in question.

HAZOP (Kletz, 1974) is a well-established engineering approach that was developed in the late 1960s by ICI (Swann and Preston, 1995) for use in process design audit and engineering risk assessment (Kirwan, 1992a). HAZOP involves a team of analysts applying guidewords, such as 'Not Done', 'More than' or 'Later than' to each step in a process in order to identify potential problems that may occur. Human Error HAZOP uses a set of human error guidewords (Whalley, 1988) to identify potential human error. These guidewords are applied to each step in a HTA to determine any credible errors. For each credible error, a description of the error is offered and the associated causes, consequences and recovery steps are specified. Finally, design remedies for each of the errors identified are proposed.

The technique for the retrospective analysis of cognitive errors (TRACEr; Shorrock and Kirwan, 2002) was developed specifically for use in the air traffic control (ATC) domain, and can be used either proactively to predict error or retrospectively to analyse errors that have occurred. TRACEr uses a series of decision flow diagrams and comprises the following eight error classification schemes: Task Error, Information, Performance Shaping Factors (PSFs), External Error Modes (EEMs), Internal Error Modes (IEMs), Psychological Error Mechanisms (PEMs), Error detection and Error Correction.

The system for predictive error analysis and reduction (SPEAR; CCPS; 1993) is another taxonomic approach to HEI that is similar to the SHERPA approach described above. SPEAR uses an error taxonomy consisting of action, checking, retrieval, transmission, selection and planning errors and operates on a HTA of the task under analysis. The analyst considers a series of performance-shaping factors for each bottom level task step and determines whether or not any credible errors could occur. For each credible error, a description of it, its consequences and any error reduction measures are provided.

The Cognitive Reliability and Error Analysis Method (CREAM; Hollnagel, 1998) is a recently developed human reliability analysis technique that can be used either predictively or retrospectively. CREAM uses a model of cognition, the Contextual Control Model (COCOM), which focuses on the dynamics of skilled behaviour as it relates to task performance in work domains. CREAM also uses an error taxonomy containing phenotypes (error modes) and genotypes (error causes). CREAM also uses common performance conditions (CPCs) to account for context.

Error identifier HEI methods, such as HEIST and THEA use a series of error identifier prompts or questions linked to external error modes to aid the analyst in identifying potential human error. Examples of typical error identifier prompts include, 'could the operator fail to carry out the act in time?', 'could the operator carry out the task too early?' and 'could the operator carry out the task inadequately?' (Kirwan, 1994). The error identifier prompts are normally linked to external error modes and remedial measures. Whilst these methods attempt to remove the reliability problems associated with taxonomic-based approaches, they add considerable time to the analysis, as each error identifier prompt must be considered. A brief description of the error identifier-based methods considered in this review is presented below.

The Human Error Identification in Systems Tool (HEIST; Kirwan 1994) uses a set of error identifier prompts designed to aid the analyst in the identification of potential errors. There are eight sets of error identifier prompts including Activation/Detection, Observation/Data collection, Identification of system state, Interpretation, Evaluation, Goal Selection/Task Definition, Procedure selection and Procedure execution. The analyst applies each error identifier prompt to each task step in a HTA and determines whether any of the errors are credible or not. Each error identifier prompt has a set of linked error modes. For each credible error, the analyst records the system causes, the psychological error mechanism and any error reduction guidelines.

The Technique for Human Error Assessment (THEA; Pocock et al., 2001) is a highly structured approach that employs cognitive error analysis based upon Norman's (1988) model of action execution. THEA uses a scenario analysis to consider context and then employs a series of questions in a checklist style approach based upon goals, plans, performing actions and perception/evaluation/interpretation.

Error quantification methods are used to determine the numerical probability of error occurrence. Identified errors are assigned a numerical probability value that represents their associated probability of occurrence. Performance Shaping factors (PSFs) are typically used to aid the analyst in the identification of potential errors. Error quantification methods, such as JHEDI and HEART are typically used in probabilistic safety assessments (PSA) of nuclear processing plants. For example, Kirwan (1999) reports the use of JHEDI in a HRA (Human Reliability Analysis) risk assessment for the BNFL Thermal Oxide Reprocessing Plant at Sellafield, and also the use of HEART in a HRA risk assessment of the Sizewell B pressurised water reactor. The main advantage of error quantification approaches lies in the numerical probability of error occurrence that they offer. However, error quantification approaches are typically difficult to use and may require some knowledge of PSA and mathematical procedures. Doubts also remain over the consistency of such approaches.

The human error assessment and reduction technique (HEART; Williams, 1986) attempts to predict and quantify the likelihood of human error or failure within complex systems. The analyst begins by classifying the task under analysis into one of the HEART generic categories, such as 'totally familiar, performed at speed with no real idea of the likely consequences'. Each HEART generic category has a human error probability associated with it. The analyst then identifies any error producing conditions (EPCs) associated with the task. Each EPC has an associated HEART effect. Examples of HEART EPCs include 'Shortage of time available for error detection and correction', and 'No obvious means of reversing an unintended action'. Once EPCs have been assigned, the analyst calculates the assessed proportion of effect of each EPC (between 0 and 1). Finally an error probability value is derived, and remedial measures are proposed.

A more recent development within HEI is to use a toolkit of different HEI methods in order to maximise the coverage of the error analysis activity. The HERA framework is a prototype multiple method or 'toolkit' approach to human error identification that was developed by Kirwan (1998a, 1998b). In response to a review of HEI methods, Kirwan (1998b) suggested that the best approach would be for practitioners to utilise a framework type approach to HEI, whereby a mixture of independent HRA/HEI tools would be used under one framework. Consequently Kirwan (1998b) proposed the Human Error and Recovery Assessment (HERA) approach, which was developed for the UK nuclear power and reprocessing industry. Whilst the technique has yet to be applied, it is offered in this review as a representation of the form that a HEI 'toolkit' or framework approach may take, and a nascent example of methods integration.

Task Analysis for Error Identification (TAFEI; Baber and Stanton, 1996) combines HTA with State Space Diagrams (SSDs) in order to predict illegal actions associated with the operation of a system or device. In conducting a TAFEI analysis, plans from a HTA of the task under analysis are mapped onto SSDs for the device in question and a TAFEI diagram is produced. The TAFEI diagram is then used to highlight any illegal transitions, or the possibility of entering into erroneous system states that might arise from task activity. Remedial measures or strategies are then proposed for each of the illegal transitions identified.

In terms of performance, the literature consistently suggests that SHERPA is the most promising of the HEI methods available to the HF practitioner. Kirwan (1992b) conducted a comparative study of six HEI methods and reported that SHERPA achieved the highest overall rankings in this respect. In conclusion, Kirwan (1992b) recommended that a combination of expert judgement together with SHERPA would be the best approach to HEI. Other studies have also produced encouraging reliability and validity data for SHERPA (Baber and Stanton, 1996, 2001; Stanton and Stevenage, 2000). In a more recent comparative study of HEI methods, Kirwan (1998b) used 14 criteria to evaluate 38 HEI methods. In conclusion it was reported that of the 38 methods, only nine are available in the public domain and are of practical use, SHERPA included (Kirwan, 1998b).

In general, the main problem surrounding the application of HEI methods is related to their validation. There have only been a limited number of HEI validation studies reported in the literature (Williams, 1989; Whalley and Kirwan, 1989; Kirwan, 1992a, 1992b, 1998a, 1998b, Kennedy, 1995; Baber and Stanton, 1996, 2002; Stanton and Stevenage, 2000). Considering the number of HEI methods available and the importance of their use, this represents a very limited set of validation studies. Problems such as resource usage (e.g. financial and time costs) and also access to systems under analysis often affect attempts at validation. As a result validation is often assumed, rather than tested.

Stanton (2002) suggests that HEI methods suffer from two further problems. The first of these problems relates to the lack of representation of the external environment or objects. This is contrary to a growing movement towards various ecological or distributed notions of cognition. Secondly, HEI methods place a great amount of dependence upon the judgement of the analyst. Quite often the application of so-called 'Performance Shaping Factors' is carried out in a largely subjective, sometimes quite arbitrary manner. This subjectivity can only weaken confidence in any error predictions that arise. A summary of the HEI methods reviewed is presented in Table 6.1.

Systematic Human Error Reduction and Prediction Approach (SHERPA)

Background and Applications

The systematic human error reduction and prediction approach (SHERPA; Embrey, 1986) was originally developed for use in the nuclear reprocessing industry and is probably the most commonly used HEI approach, with further applications in a number of domains, including aviation (Salmon, Stanton, Young, Harris, Demagalski, Marshall, Waldmann and Dekker, 2002, 2003a and b), public technology (Baber and Stanton, 1996, Stanton and Stevenage, 1998), and even in-car radio-cassette machines (Stanton and Young, 1999). SHERPA comprises of an error mode taxonomy linked to a behavioural taxonomy and is applied to a HTA of the task or scenario under analysis in order to predict potential human or design induced error. As well as being the most commonly used of the various HEI methods available, according to the literature it is also the most successful in terms of accuracy of error predictions.

Domain of Application

Despite being developed originally for use in the process industries, the SHERPA behaviour and error taxonomy is generic and can be applied in any domain involving human activity.

Procedure and Advice

Step 1: Hierarchical task analysis (HTA)
The first step in a SHERPA analysis involves describing the task or scenario under analysis. For this purpose, a HTA of the task or scenario under analysis is normally conducted. The SHERPA method works by indicating which of the errors from the SHERPA error taxonomy are credible at each bottom level task step in a HTA of the task under analysis. A number of data collection techniques may be used in order to gather the information required for the HTA, such as interviews with SMEs and observations of the task under analysis.

Step 2: Task classification
Next, the analyst should take the first (or next) bottom level task step in the HTA and classify it according to the SHERPA behaviour taxonomy, which is presented below (Source: Stanton 2005).

Table 6.1 Summary of HEI Methods

Method	Type of method	Domain	Training time	App time	Related methods	Tools needed	Validation studies	Advantages	Disadvantages
SHERPA – Systematic Human Error Reduction and Prediction Approach	HEI	Nuclear Power Generic	Low	Med	HTA	Pen and paper System diagrams	Yes	1) Encouraging reliability and validity data. 2) Probably the best HEI method available. 3) Has been used extensively in a number of domains and is quick to learn and easy to use.	1) Can be tedious and time consuming for large, complex tasks. 2) Extra work may be required in conducting an appropriate HTA.
HET – Human Error Template	HEI	Aviation Generic	Low	Med	HTA	Pen and paper System diagrams	Yes	1) Very easy to use, requiring very little training. 2) Taxonomy is based upon an analysis of pilot error occurrence. 3) Taxonomy is generic.	1) Can be tedious and time consuming for large, complex tasks. 2) Extra work may be required in conducting an appropriate HTA.
TRACEr - Technique for the Retrospective and Predictive Analysis of Cognitive Error	HEI HRA	ATC	Med	High	HTA	Pen and paper System diagrams	No	1) Appears to be a very comprehensive approach to error prediction and error analysis, including IEM, PEM, EEM and PSF analysis. 2) Based upon sound scientific theory, integrating Wickens (1992) model of information processing into its model of ATC. 3) Can be used predictively and retrospectively.	1) Appears complex for a taxonomic error identification tool. 2) No validation evidence.
TAFEI – Task Analysis For Error Identification	HEI	Generic	Med	Med	HTA SSD	Pen and paper System diagrams	Yes	1) Uses HTA and SSDs to highlight illegal interactions. 2) Structured and thorough procedure. 3) Sound theoretical underpinning.	1) Can be tedious and time consuming for large, complex tasks. 2) Extra work may be required in conducting an appropriate HTA. 3) It may be difficult to get hold of SSDs for the system under analysis.

Table 6.1 (continued)

Method	Type of method	Domain	Training time	App time	Related methods	Tools needed	Validation studies	Advantages	Disadvantages
Human Error HAZOP	HEI	Nuclear Power	Low	Med	HAZOP HTA	Pen and paper System diagrams	Yes	1) Very easy to use, requiring very little training. 2) Generic error taxonomy.	1) Can be tedious and time consuming for large, complex tasks. 2) Extra work may be required in conducting an appropriate HTA.
THEA – Technique for Human Error Assessment	HEI	Design Generic	Low	Med	HTA	Pen and paper System diagrams	No	1) Uses error identifier prompts to aid the analyst in the identification of error. 2) Highly structured procedure. 3) Each error question has associated consequences and design remedies.	1) High resource usage. 2) No error modes are used, making it difficult to interpret which errors could occur. 3) Limited usage.
HEIST – Human Error Identification in Systems Tool	HEI	Nuclear Power	Low	Med	HTA	Pen and paper System diagrams	No	1) Uses error identifier prompts to aid the analyst in the identification of error. 2) Each error question has associated consequences and design remedies.	1) High resource usage. 2) Limited usage.
The HERA framework	HEI HRA	Generic	High	High	HTA HEIST JHEDI	Pen and paper System diagrams	No	1) Exhaustive method, covers all aspects of error. 2) Employs a methods toolkit approach, ensuring comprehensiveness.	1) Time consuming in its application. 2) No evidence of usage available. 3) High training and application times.
SPEAR – System for Predictive Error Analysis and Reduction	HEI	Nuclear Power	Low	Med	SHERPA HTA	Pen and paper System diagrams	No	1) Easy to use and learn. 2) Analyst can choose specific taxonomy.	1) Almost exactly the same as SHERPA. 2) Limited use. 3) No validation evidence available.

Table 6.1 (continued)

Method	Type of method	Domain	Training time	App time	Related methods	Tools needed	Validation studies	Advantages	Disadvantages
HEART – Human Error Assessment and Reduction Technique	HEI Quantification	Nuclear Power	Low	Med	HTA	Pen and paper System diagrams	Yes	1) Offers a quantitative analysis of potential error. 2) Considers PSFs. 3) Quick and easy to use.	1) Doubts over consistency of the method. 2) Limited guidance given to the analyst. 3) Further validation required.
CREAM – Cognitive Reliability Analysis Method	HEI HRA	Generic	High	High	HTA	Pen and paper System diagrams	Yes	1) Potentially very comprehensive. 2) Has been used both predictively and retrospectively.	1) Time consuming both to train and apply. 2) Limited use. 3) Overcomplicated.

- Action (e.g., pressing a button, pulling a switch, opening a door)
- Retrieval (e.g., getting information from a screen or manual)
- Checking (e.g., conducting a procedural check)
- Selection (e.g., choosing one alternative over another)
- Information communication (e.g., talking to another party).

Step 3: Human error identification (HEI)
The analyst then uses the associated error mode taxonomy and domain expertise to determine any credible error modes for the task in question. For each credible error (i.e. those judged by the analyst to be possible) the analyst should give a description of the form that the error would take, such as, 'pilot dials in wrong airspeed'. The SHERPA error mode taxonomy is presented in Figure 6.1.

Step 4: Consequence analysis
The next step involves determining and describing the consequences associated with the errors identified in step 3. The analyst should consider the consequences associated with each credible error and provide clear descriptions of the consequences in relation to the task under analysis.

Step 5: Recovery analysis
Next, the analyst should determine the recovery potential of the identified error. If there is a later task step in the HTA at which the error could be recovered, it is entered here. If there is no recovery step then 'None' is entered.

Step 6: Ordinal probability analysis
Once the consequence and recovery potential of the error have been identified, the analyst should rate the probability of the error occurring. An ordinal probability scale of low, medium or high is typically used. If the error has not occurred previously then a low (L) probability is assigned. If the error has occurred on previous occasions then a medium (M) probability is assigned. Finally, if the error has occurred on frequent occasions, a high (H) probability is assigned.

Step 7: Criticality analysis
Next, the analyst rates the criticality of the error in question. A scale of low, medium and high is also used to rate error criticality. Normally, if the error would lead to a critical incident (in relation to the task in question) then it is rated as a highly critical error.

Action Errors
A1 – Operation too long/short
A2 – Operation mistimed
A3 – Operation in wrong direction
A4 – Operation too little/much
A5 – Misalign
A6 – Right operation on wrong object
A7 – Wrong operation on right object
A8 – Operation omitted
A9 – Operation incomplete
A10 – Wrong operation on wrong object
Checking Errors
C1 – Check omitted
C2 – Check incomplete
C3 – Right check on wrong object

C4 – Wrong check on right object
C5 – Check mistimed
C6 – Wrong check on wrong object
Retrieval Errors
R1 – Information not obtained
R2 – Wrong information obtained
R3 – Information retrieval incomplete
Communication Errors
I1 – Information not communicated
I2 – Wrong information communicated
I3 – Information communication
Selection Errors
S1 – Selection omitted
S2 – Wrong selection made

Figure 6.1   SHERPA External Error Mode Taxonomy

Step 8: Remedy analysis
The final stage in the process is to propose error reduction strategies. Normally, remedial measures comprise suggested changes to the design of the process or system. According to Stanton (2005), remedial measures are normally proposed under the following four categories:

1. Equipment (e.g. redesign or modification of existing equipment);
2. Training (e.g. changes in training provided);
3. Procedures (e.g. provision of new, or redesign of old, procedures); and
4. Organisational (e.g. changes in organisational policy or culture).

Advantages

1. The SHERPA method offers a structured and comprehensive approach to the prediction of human error.
2. The SHERPA taxonomy prompts the analyst for potential errors.
3. According to the HF literature, SHERPA is the most promising HEI technique available. SHERPA has been applied in a number of domains with considerable success. There is also a wealth of encouraging validity and reliability data available.
4. SHERPA is quick to apply compared to other HEI methods.
5. SHERPA is also easy to learn and apply, requiring minimal training.
6. The method is exhaustive, offering error reduction strategies in addition to predicted errors, associated consequences, probability of occurrence, criticality and potential recovery steps.
7. The SHERPA error taxonomy is generic, allowing the method to be used in a number of different domains.

Disadvantages

1. Can be tedious and time consuming for large, complex tasks.
2. The initial HTA adds additional time to the analysis.
3. SHERPA only considers errors at the 'sharp end' of system operation. The method does not consider system or organisational errors.
4. Does not model cognitive components of error mechanisms.

5. Some predicted errors and remedies are unlikely or lack credibility, thus posing a false economy (Stanton, 2005).
6. Current taxonomy lacks generalisability (Stanton, 2005).

Example

The following example is a SHERPA analysis of VCR programming task (Baber and Stanton, 1996). The HTA for the VCR programming task is presented in Figure 6.2. The SHERPA output for the VCR programming task is presented in Table 6.2.

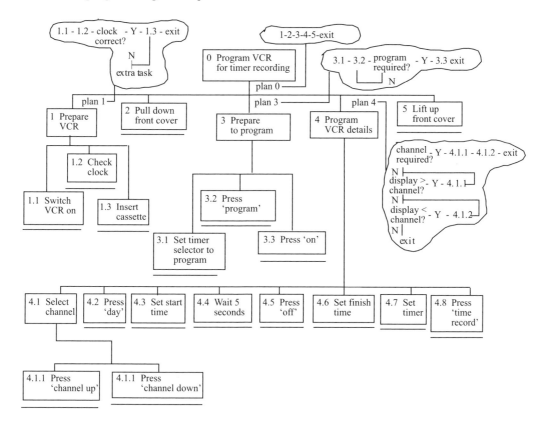

Figure 6.2   HTA of VCR Programming Task (Source: Baber and Stanton, 1996)

The SHERPA analysis of the VCR programming indicated that there were six basic error types that may arise during the VCR programming task. These are presented below:

- Failing to check that the VCR clock is correct.
- Failing to insert a cassette.
- Failing to select the programme number.
- Failing to wait.
- Failing to enter programming information correctly.
- Failing to press the confirmatory buttons.

Table 6.2   SHERPA Output for the VCR Programming Task (Source: Baber and Stanton, 1996)

Task Step	Error Mode	Error Description	Consequence	Recovery	P	C	Remedial Strategy
1.1	A8	Fail to switch VCR on	Cannot proceed	Immediate	L		Press of any button to switch VCR on
1.2	C1	Omit to check clock	VCR Clock time may be incorrect	None	L	!	Automatic clock setting and adjust via radio transmitter
	C2	Incomplete check					
1.3	A3	Insert cassette wrong way around	Damage to VCR Cannot record	Immediate	L	!	Strengthen mechanism On-screen prompt
	A8	Fail to insert cassette		Task 3	L		
2	A8	Fail to pull down front cover	Cannot proceed	Immediate	L		Remove cover to programming
3.1	S1	Fail move timer selector	Cannot proceed	Immediate	L		Separate timer selector from programming function
3.2	A8	Fail to press PROGRAM	Cannot proceed	Immediate	L		Remove this task step from sequence
3.3	A8	Fail to press ON button	Cannot proceed	Immediate	L		Label button START TIME
4.1.1	A8	Fail to press UP button	Wrong channel selected	None	M	!	Enter channel number directly from keypad
4.1.2	A8	Fail to press DOWN button	Wrong channel selected	None	M	!	Enter channel number directly from keypad
4.2	A8	Fail to press DAY button	Wrong day selected	None	M	!	Present day via a calendar
4.3	I1	No time entered	No programme recorded	None	L	!	Dial time in via analogue clock Dial time in via analogue clock
	I2	Wrong time entered	Wrong programme recorded	None	L	!	
4.4	A1	Fail to wait	Start time not set	Task 4.5	L		Remove need to wait
4.5	A8	Fail to press OFF button	Cannot set finish time				Label button FINISH TIME
4.6	I1	No time entered	No programme recorded	None	L	!	Dial time in via analogue clock Dial time in via analogue clock
	I2	Wrong time entered	Wrong programme recorded	None	L	!	
4.7	A8	Fail to set timer	No programme recorded	None	L	!	Separate timer selector from programming function
4.8	A8	Fail to press TIME RECORD button	No programme recorded	None	L	!	Remove this task step from sequence
5	A8	Fail to lift up front cover	Cover left down	Immediate	L		Remove cover to programming

Related Methods

The initial data collection for SHERPA might involve a number of data collection techniques, including interviews, observation and walkthroughs. A HTA of the task or scenario under analysis is typically used as the input to a SHERPA analysis. The taxonomic approach to error prediction employed by the SHERPA method is similar to a number of other HEI approaches, such as HET (Marshall et al, 2003), Human Error HAZOP (Kirwan and Ainsworth, 1992) and TRACEr (Shorrock and Kirwan, 2002).

Approximate Training and Application Times

In order to evaluate the reliability, validity and trainability of various methods, Stanton and Young (1998) compared SHERPA to 11 other HF methods. Based on the application of the method to the operation of an in-car radio-cassette machine, Stanton and Young (1998) reported training times of around three hours (this is doubled if training in Hierarchical Task Analysis is included). It took an average of two hours and forty minutes for people to evaluate the radio-cassette machine using SHERPA. In a study comparing the performance of SHERPA, Human Error HAZOP, HEIST and HET when used to predict design induced pilot error, Salmon et al (2002) reported that participants achieved acceptable performance with the SHERPA method after only two hours of training.

Flowchart

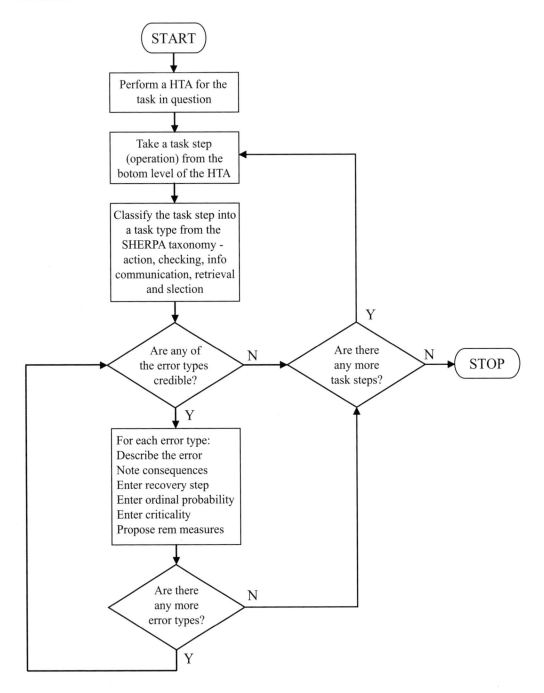

Reliability and Validity

There is a wealth of promising validation data associated with the SHERPA method. Kirwan (1992) reported that SHERPA was the most highly rated of five human error prediction methods by expert users. Baber and Stanton (1996) reported a concurrent validity statistic of 0.8 and a reliability statistic of 0.9 in the application of SHERPA by two expert users to prediction of errors on a ticket vending machine. Stanton and Stevenage (1998) reported a concurrent validity statistic of 0.74 and a reliability statistic of 0.65 in the application of SHERPA by 25 novice users to prediction of errors on a confectionery vending machine. According to Stanton and Young (1999) SHERPA achieved a concurrent validity statistic of 0.2 and a reliability statistic of 0.4 when used by eight novices to predict errors on an in-car radio-cassette machine task. According to Harris et al (in press) SHERPA achieved acceptable performance in terms of reliability and validity when used by novice analysts to predict pilot error on a civil aviation flight scenario. The reliability and validity of the SHERPA method is highly dependent upon the expertise of the analyst and the complexity of the device being analysed.

Tools Needed

SHERPA can be conducted using pen and paper. The device under analysis or at least photographs of the interface under analysis are also required.

Human Error Template (HET)

Background and Applications

The human error template (HET; Marshall et al 2003) method was developed by the ErrorPred consortium specifically for use in the certification of civil flight deck technology. Along with a distinct shortage of HEI methods developed specifically for the civil aviation domain, the impetus for HET came from a US Federal Aviation Administration (FAA) report entitled 'The Interfaces between Flight crews and Modern Flight Deck Systems' (Federal Aviation Administration, 1996), which identified many major design deficiencies and shortcomings in the design process of modern commercial airliner flight decks. The report made criticisms of the flight deck interfaces, identifying problems in many systems including pilots' autoflight mode awareness/indication; energy awareness; position/terrain awareness; confusing and unclear display symbology and nomenclature; a lack of consistency in FMS interfaces and conventions, and poor compatibility between flight deck systems. The FAA Human Factors Team also made many criticisms of the flight deck design process. For example, the report identified a lack of human factors expertise on design teams, which also had a lack of authority over the design decisions made. There was too much emphasis on the physical ergonomics of the flight deck, and not enough on the cognitive ergonomics. Fifty-one specific recommendations came out of the report. The most important in terms of the ErrorPred project were the following:

- 'The FAA should require the evaluation of flight deck designs for susceptibility to design-induced flightcrew errors and the consequences of those errors as part of the type certification process.'
- 'The FAA should establish regulatory and associated material to require the use of a flight deck certification review process that addresses human performance considerations.'

The HET method is a simple error template and works as a checklist. The HET template is applied to each bottom level task step in a HTA of the task under analysis. The analyst uses the HET EEM and subjective judgement to determine credible errors for each task step. The HET error taxonomy consists of twelve error modes that were selected based upon a review of actual pilot error incidence, the EEM taxonomies used in contemporary HEI methods and the responses to a questionnaire on design induced pilot error. The HET EEMs are as follows:

- Fail to execute
- Task execution incomplete
- Task executed in the wrong direction
- Wrong task executed
- Task repeated
- Task executed on the wrong interface element
- Task executed too early
- Task executed too late
- Task executed too much
- Task executed too little
- Misread information
- Other.

        For each credible error (i.e. those judged by the analyst to be possible) the analyst should give a description of the form that the error would take, such as, 'pilot dials in the airspeed value using the wrong knob'. Next, the analyst has to determine the outcome or consequence associated with the error e.g. Aircraft stays at current speed and does not slow down for approach. Finally, the analyst then has to determine the likelihood of the error (low, medium or high) and the criticality of the error (low, medium or high). If the error is assigned a high rating for both likelihood and criticality, the aspect of the interface involved in the task step is then rated as a 'fail', meaning that it is not suitable for certification.

Domain of Application

The HET method was developed specifically for the aviation domain and is intended for use in the certification of flight deck technology. However, the HET EEM taxonomy is generic, allowing the method to be applied in any domain.

Procedure and Advice

Step 1: Hierarchical task analysis (HTA)
The first step in a HET analysis is to conduct a HTA of the task or scenario under analysis. The HET method works by indicating which of the errors from the HET error taxonomy are credible at each bottom level task step in a HTA of the task under analysis. A number of data collection techniques may be used in order to gather the information required for the HTA, such as interviews with SMEs and observations of the task under analysis.

Step 2: Human error identification
In order to identify potential errors, the analyst takes each bottom level task step from the HTA and considers the credibility of each of the HET EEMs. Any EEMs that are deemed credible by the analyst are recorded and analysed further. At this stage, the analyst ticks each credible EEM and provides a description of the form that the error will take.

Step 3: Consequence analysis
Once a credible error is identified and described, the analyst should then consider and describe the consequence(s) of the error. The analyst should consider the consequences associated with each credible error and provide clear descriptions of the consequences in relation to the task under analysis.

Step 4: Ordinal probability analysis
Next, the analyst should provide an estimate of the probability of the error occurring, based upon subjective judgement. An ordinal probability value is entered as low, medium or high. If the analyst feels that chances of the error occurring are very small, then a low (L) probability is assigned. If the analyst thinks that the error may occur and has knowledge of the error occurring on previous occasions then a medium (M) probability is assigned. Finally, if the analyst thinks that the error would occur frequently, then a high (H) probability is assigned.

Step 5: Criticality analysis
Next, the criticality of the error is rated. Error criticality is rated as low, medium or high. If the error would lead to a serious incident (this would have to be defined clearly before the analysis) then it is labelled as high. Typically a high criticality would be associated with error consequences that would lead to substantial damage to the aircraft, injury to crew and passengers, or complete failure of the flight task under analysis. If the error has consequences that still have a distinct effect on the task, such as heading the wrong way or losing a large amount of height or speed, then criticality is labelled as medium. If the error would have minimal consequences that are easily recoverable, such as a small loss of speed or height, then criticality is labelled as low.

Step 6: Interface analysis
The final step in a HET analysis involves determining whether or not the interface under analysis passes the certification procedure. The analyst assigns a 'pass' or 'fail' rating to the interface under analysis (dependent upon the task step) based upon the associated error probability and criticality ratings. If a high probability and a high criticality were assigned previously, then the interface in question is classed as a 'fail'. Any other combination of probability and criticality and the interface in question is classed as a 'pass'.

Advantages

1. The HET methodology is quick, simple to learn and use and requires very little training.
2. HET utilises a comprehensive error mode taxonomy based upon existing HEI EEM taxonomies, actual pilot error incidence data and pilot error case studies.
3. HET is easily auditable as it comes in the form of an error pro-forma.
4. The HET taxonomy prompts the analyst for potential errors.
5. Encouraging reliability and validity data (Marshall et al, 2003, Salmon et al, 2003).
6. Although the error modes in the HET EEM taxonomy were developed specifically for the aviation domain, they are generic, ensuring that the HET method can potentially be used in a wide range of different domains, such as command and control, ATC, and nuclear reprocessing.

Disadvantages

1. For large, complex tasks a HET analysis may become tedious.

2. Extra work is involved if HTA not already available.
3. HET does not deal with the cognitive component of errors.
4. HET only considers errors at the 'sharp end' of system operation. The method does not consider system or organisational errors.

Flowchart

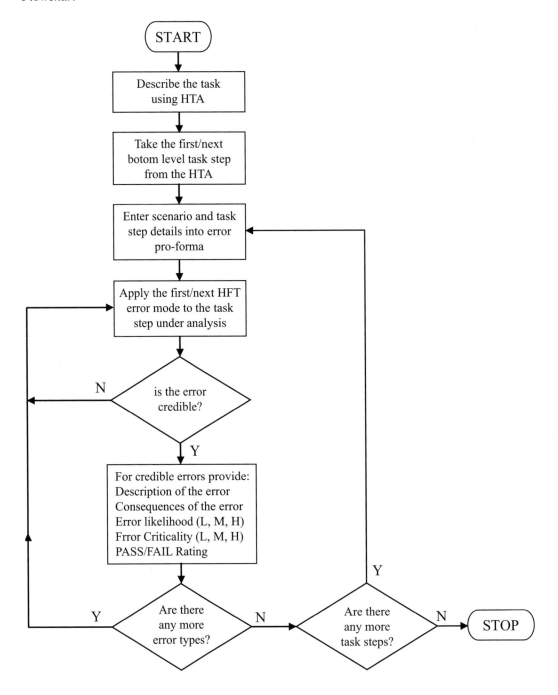

Example

A HET analysis was conducted on the flight task 'Land aircraft X at New Orleans using the autoland system' (Marshall et al, Salmon et al, 2003). Initially, a HTA was developed for the flight task, using data obtained from interviews with SMEs, a video demonstration of the flight task and also a walkthrough of the flight task using Microsoft flight simulator. An extract of the HTA for the flight task is presented in Figure 6.3. An extract of the HET analysis for the flight task is presented in Table 6.3.

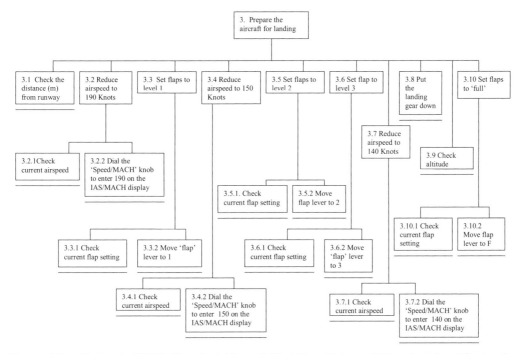

Figure 6.3   Extract of HTA 'Land at Aircraft X at New Orleans Using Autoland System'

Related Methods

HET uses an EEM taxonomy to identify potential design induced error. There are many taxonomic-based HEI approaches available that have been developed for a variety of domains, including SHERPA, CREAM and TRACEr. A HET analysis also requires an initial HTA (or some other specific task description) to be performed for the task in question. The data used in the development of the HTA may be collected through the application of a number of different techniques, including observational study, interviews and walkthrough analysis.

Approximate Training and Application Times

In HET validation studies Marshall et al (2003) reported that with non-human factors professionals, the approximate training time for the HET methodology is around 90 minutes. Application time varies dependent upon the scenario under analysis. Marshall et al (2003) reported a mean application time of 62 minutes based upon an analysis of the flight task, 'Land aircraft X at New Orleans using the autoland system'. The HTA for the New Orleans flight task had 32 bottom level task steps.

Table 6.3　　Example of HET Output

Scenario: Land A320 at New Orleans using the Autoland system			Task step: 3.4.2 Dial the 'Speed/MACH; knob to enter 150 on IAS/MACH display								
Error Mode		**Description**	**Outcome**	Likelihood			Criticality			**PASS**	**FAIL**
				H	**M**	**L**	**H**	**M**	**L**		
Fail to execute											
Task execution incomplete											
Task executed in wrong direction	✓	Pilot turns the Speed/MACH knob the wrong way	Plane speeds up instead of slowing down	✓			✓			✓	
Wrong task executed											
Task repeated											
Task executed on wrong interface element	✓	Pilot dials using the HDG knob instead	Plane changes course and not speed	✓			✓				✓
Task executed too early											
Task executed too late											
Task executed too much	✓	Pilot turns the Speed/MACH knob too much	Plane slows down too much	✓			✓			✓	
Task executed too little	✓	Pilot turns the Speed/MACH knob too little	Plane does not slow down enough/Too fast for approach	✓			✓			✓	
Misread information											
Other											

Reliability and Validity

Salmon et al (2003) reported sensitivity index ratings between 0.7 and 0.8 for subjects using the HET methodology to predict potential design induced pilot errors for the flight task 'Land aircraft X at New Orleans using the autoland system'. These figures represent a high level of accuracy of the error predictions made by participants using the HET method (the closer to 1 the more accurate the error predictions are). Furthermore, it was reported that subjects using the HET method achieved higher SI ratings than subjects using SHERPA, Human Error HAZOP and HEIST to predict errors for the same task (Salmon et al, 2003).

Tools Needed

HET can be carried out using the HET error Pro-forma, a HTA of the task under analysis, functional diagrams of the interface under analysis, a pen and paper. In the example HET analysis described above, subjects were provided with an error pro-forma, a HTA of the flight task, diagrams of the auto-pilot panel, the captain's primary flight display, the flap lever, the landing gear lever, the speed brake, the attitude indicator and an overview of the A320 cockpit (Marshall et al, 2003).

Technique for the Retrospective and Predictive Analysis of Cognitive Errors (TRACEr)

Background and Applications

The Technique for the Retrospective and Predictive Analysis of Cognitive Errors (TRACEr; Shorrock and Kirwan, 2000) is a HEI technique that was developed specifically for use in the air traffic control (ATC) domain, as part of the human error in European air traffic management

(HERA) project (Isaac, Shorrock and Kirwan, 2002). Under the HERA project, the authors were required to develop a human error incidence analysis method that conformed to the following criteria (Isaac, Shorrock and Kirwan, 2002).

1. The method should be flowchart based for ease of use;
2. The method should utilise a set of inter-related taxonomies (EEMs, IEMs, PEMs, PSFs, Tasks and Information and equipment);
3. The method must be able to deal with chains of events and errors;
4. The PSF taxonomy should be hierarchical and may need a deeper set of organisational causal factor descriptors;
5. The method must be comprehensive, accounting for situation awareness, signal detection theory and control theory; and
6. The method must be able to account for maintenance errors, latent errors, violations and errors of commission.

TRACEr can be used both predictively and retrospectively and is based upon a literature review of a number of domains, including experimental and applied psychology, human factors and communication theory (Isaac, Shorrock and Kirwan, 2002). TRACEr uses a series of decision flow diagrams and comprises eight taxonomies or error classification schemes: Task Error, Information, Performance Shaping Factors (PSFs), External Error Modes (EEMs), Internal Error Modes (IEMs), Psychological Error Mechanisms (PEMs), Error detection and error correction.

Domain of Application

TRACEr was originally developed for the ATC domain. However, the method has since been applied in the rail domain and it is feasible that the method could be applied in any domain.

Procedure and Advice (Predictive Analysis)

Step 1: Hierarchical task analysis (HTA)
The first step in a TRACEr analysis involves describing the task or scenario under analysis. For this purpose, a HTA of the task or scenario is normally conducted. The TRACEr method is typically applied to a HTA of the task or scenario under analysis. A number of data collection techniques may be used in order to gather the information required for the HTA, such as interviews with SMEs and observations of the task under analysis.

Step 2: PSF and EEM consideration
The analyst takes the first bottom level task step from the HTA and considers each of the TRACEr PSFs for the task step in question. The purpose of this is to identify any environmental or situational factors that could influence the controllers' performance during the task step in question. Once the analyst has considered all of the relevant PSFs, the EEMs are considered for the task step under analysis. Based upon subjective judgement, the analyst determines whether any of the TRACEr EEMs are credible for the task step in question. The TRACer EEM taxonomy is presented in Table 6.4. If there are any credible errors, the analyst proceeds to step 3. If there are no errors deemed credible, then the analyst goes back to the HTA and takes the next task step.

Step 3: IEM classification
For any credible errors, the analyst then determines which of the internal error modes (IEMs) are associated with the error. IEMs describe which cognitive function failed or could fail (Shorrock and Kirwan, 2000). Examples of TRACEr IEMs include *Late detection, misidentification, hearback error, forget previous actions, prospective memory failure, misrecall stored information and misprojection.*

Table 6.4   TRACEr's External Error Mode Taxonomy

Selection and Quality	Timing and Sequence	Communication
Omission	Action too long	Unclear info transmitted
Action too much	Action too short	Unclear info recorded
Action too little	Action too early	Info not sought/obtained
Action in wrong direction	Action too late	Info not transmitted
Wrong action on right object	Action repeated	Info not recorded
Right action on wrong object	Mis-ordering	Incomplete info transmitted
Wrong action on wrong object		Incomplete info recorded
Extraneous act		Incorrect info transmitted
		Incorrect info recorded

Step 4: PEM classification
Next, the analyst has to determine the psychological cause or 'psychological error mechanism' (PEM) behind the error. Examples of TRACEr PEMs include *insufficient learning, expectation bias, false assumption, perceptual confusion, memory block, vigilance failure and distraction.*

Step 5: Error recovery
Finally, once the error analyst has described the error and determined the EEM, IEMs and PEMs, error recovery steps for each error should be offered. This is based upon the analyst's subjective judgement.

Procedure and Advice (Retrospective Analysis)

Step 1: Analyse incident into 'error events'
Firstly, the analyst has to classify the task steps into error events i.e. the task steps in which an error was produced. This is based upon the analyst's subjective judgement.

Step 2: Task error classification
The analyst then takes the first/next error from the error events list and classifies it into a task error from the task error taxonomy. The task error taxonomy contains thirteen categories describing controller errors. Examples of task error categories include 'radar monitoring error', 'co-ordination error' and 'flight progress strip use error' (Shorrock and Kirwan, 2000).

Step 3: IEM information classification
Next the analyst has to determine the internal error mode (IEM) associated with the error. IEMs describe which cognitive function failed or could fail (Shorrock and Kirwan, 2000). Examples of TRACEr IEMs include *late detection, misidentification, hearback error, forget previous actions, prospective memory failure, misrecall stored information and misprojection.* When using TRACEr retrospectively, the analyst also has to use the *information* taxonomy to describe the 'subject matter' of the error i.e. what information did the controller misperceive? The information terms used are

related directly to the IEMs in the IEM taxonomy. The information taxonomy is important as it forms the basis of error reduction within the TRACEr method.

Step 4: PEM classification
The analyst then has to determine the 'psychological cause' or psychological error mechanism (PEM) behind the error. Example TRACEr PEMs include *Insufficient learning, expectation bias, false assumption, perceptual confusion, memory block, vigilance failure and distraction.*

Step 5: PSF classification
Performance shaping factors are factors that influenced or have the potential to have influenced the operator's performance. The analyst uses the PSF taxonomy to select any PSFs that were evident in the production of the error under analysis. TRACEr's PSF taxonomy contains both PSF categories and keywords. Examples of TRACEr PSF categories and associated keywords are presented in Table 6.5.

Table 6.5   Extract From TRACEr's PSF Taxonomy

PSF Category	Example PSF keyword
Traffic and Airspace	Traffic complexity
Pilot/controller communications	RT Workload
Procedures	Accuracy
Training and experience	Task familiarity
Workplace design, HMI and equipment factors	Radar display
Ambient environment	Noise
Personal factors	Alertness/fatigue
Social and team factors	Handover/takeover
Organisational factors	Conditions of work

Step 6: Error detection and error correction
Unique to retrospective TRACEr applications, the error detection and correction stage provides the analyst with a set of error detection keywords. Four questions are used to prompt the analyst in the identification and selection of error detection keywords (Source: Shorrock and Kirwan, 2000).

1. How did the controller become aware of the error? (e.g. action feedback, inner feedback, outcome feedback);
2. What was the feedback medium? (e.g. radio, radar display);
3. Did any factors, internal or external to the controller, improve or degrade the detection of the error?; and
4. What was the separation status at the time of error detection?

Once the analyst has identified the error detection features, the error correction or reduction should also be determined. TRACEr uses the following questions to prompt the analyst in error correction/ reduction classification (Source: Shorrock and Kirwan, 2000).

1. What did the controller do to correct the error? (e.g. reversal or direct correction, automated correction);
2. How did the controller correct the error? (e.g. turn or climb);
3. Did any factors, internal or external to the controller, improve or degrade the detection of the error?; and
4. What was the separation status at the time of the error correction?

Once the analyst has completes step 6, the next error should be analysed. Alternatively, if there are no more 'error events' then the analysis is complete.

Flowchart (Predictive Analysis)

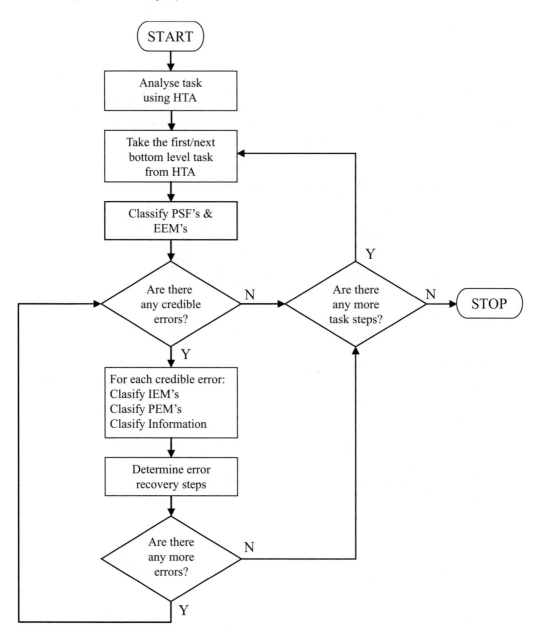

Flowchart (Retrospective Analysis)

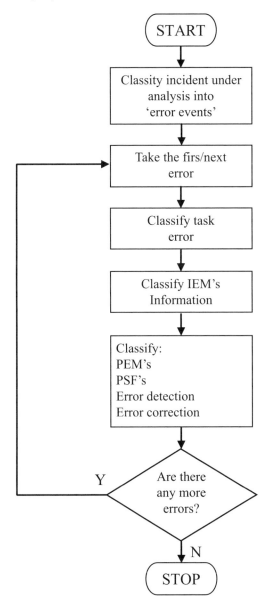

Advantages

1. TRACEr method appears to be a very comprehensive approach to error prediction and error analysis, including IEM, PEM, EEM and PSF analysis.
2. TRACEr is based upon sound scientific theory, integrating Wickens (1992) model of information processing into its model of ATC.
3. In a prototype study (Shorrock, 1997), a participant questionnaire highlighted comprehensiveness, structure, acceptability of results and usability as strong points of the method (Shorrock and Kirwan, 2000).

4. TRACEr has proved successful in analysing errors from AIRPROX reports and providing error reduction strategies.
5. Developed specifically for ATC, based upon previous ATC incidents and interviews with ATC controllers.
6. The method considers PSFs within the system that may have contributed to the errors identified.

Disadvantages

1. The TRACEr method appears unnecessarily overcomplicated. A prototype study (Shorrock, 1997) highlighted a number of areas of confusion in participant use of the different categories (Shorrock and Kirwan, 2000). Much simpler error analysis methods exist, such as SHERPA and HET.
2. No validation evidence or studies using TRACEr.
3. For complex tasks, a TRACEr analysis may become laborious and large.
4. A TRACEr analysis typically incurs high resource usage. In a participant questionnaire used in the prototype study (Shorrock, 1997) resource usage (time and expertise) was the most commonly reported area of concern (Shorrock and Kirwan, 2000).
5. Training time would be extremely high for such a method and a sound understanding of psychology would be required in order to use the method effectively.
6. Extra work involved if HTA not already available.
7. Existing methods using similar EEM taxonomies appear to be far simpler and much quicker to apply (SHERPA, HET etc.).

Example

For an example TRACEr analysis, the reader is referred to Shorrock and Kirwan (2000).

Related Methods

TRACEr is a taxonomy-based approach to HEI. A number of error taxonomy methods exist, such as SHERPA, CREAM and HET. When applying TRACEr (both predictively and retrospectively) an HTA for the task/scenario under analysis is required.

Approximate Training and Application Times

No data regarding training and application times for the TRACEr method are presented in the literature. It is estimated that both the training and application times for TRACEr would be high.

Reliability and Validity

There are no data available regarding the reliability and validity of the TRACEr method. According to the authors (Shorrock and Kirwan, 2000) such a study is being planned. In a small study analysing error incidences from AIRPROX reports (Shorrock and Kirwan, 2000) it was reported, via a participant questionnaire, that the TRACEr method's strengths are its comprehensiveness, structure, acceptability of results and usability.

Tools Needed

TRACEr analyses can be carried out using pen and paper. PEM, EEM, IEM, PSF taxonomy lists are also required. A HTA for the task under analysis is also required.

Task Analysis for Error Identification (TAFEI)

Background and Applications

Task Analysis for Error Identification (TAFEI) is a method that enables people to predict errors with device use by modelling the interaction between the user and the device under analysis. It assumes that people use devices in a purposeful manner, such that the interaction may be described as a 'cooperative endeavour', and it is by this process that problems arise. Furthermore, the method makes the assumption that actions are constrained by the state of the product at any particular point in the interaction, and that the device offers information to the user about its functionality. Thus, the interaction between users and devices progresses through a sequence of states. At each state, the user selects the action most relevant to their goal, based on the System Image.

       The foundation for the approach is based on general systems theory. This theory is potentially useful in addressing the interaction between sub-components in systems (i.e., the human and the device). It also assumes a hierarchical order of system components, i.e., all structures and functions are ordered by their relation to other structures and functions, and any particular object or event is comprised of lesser objects and events. Information regarding the status of the machine is received by the human part of the system through sensory and perceptual processes and converted to physical activity in the form of input to the machine. The input modifies the internal state of the machine and feedback is provided to the human in the form of output. Of particular interest here is the boundary between humans and machines, as this is where errors become apparent. It is believed that it is essential for a method of error prediction to examine explicitly the nature of the interaction.

       The theory draws upon the ideas of scripts and schema. It can be imagined that a person approaching a ticket-vending machine might draw upon a 'vending machine' or a 'ticket kiosk' script when using a ticket machine. From one script, the user might expect the first action to be 'Insert Money', but from the other script, the user might expect the first action to be 'Select Item'. The success, or failure, of the interaction would depend on how closely they were able to determine a match between the script and the actual operation of the machine. The role of the comparator is vital in this interaction. If it detects differences from the expected states, then it is able to modify the routines. Failure to detect any differences is likely to result in errors. Following Bartlett's (1932) lead, the notion of schema is assumed to reflect a person's '... effort after meaning' (Bartlett, 1932), arising from the active processing (by the person) of a given stimulus. This active processing involves combining prior knowledge with information contained in the stimulus. While schema theory is not without its critics (see Brewer, 2000 for a review), the notion of an active processing of stimuli clearly has resonance with a proposal for rewritable routines. The reader might feel that there are similarities between the notion of rewritable routines and some of the research on mental models that was popular in the 1980s. Recent developments in the theory underpinning TAFEI by the authors have distinguished between global prototypical routines (i.e., a repertoire of stereotypical responses that allow people to perform repetitive and mundane activities with little or no conscious effort) and local, state-specific routines (i.e., responses that are developed only for a specific state of the system). The interesting part of the theory is the proposed relationship between global and local routines. It is our contention that these routines are analogous to global and local variables in computer programming code. In the same manner as a local variable in programming code, a local routine is overwritten (or rewritable in TAFEI terms) once the user has moved beyond the specific state for which it was developed. See Baber and Stanton (2002) for a more detailed discussion of the theory.

Examples of applications of TAFEI include prediction of errors in boiling kettles (Baber and Stanton, 1994; Stanton and Baber, 1998), comparison of word processing packages (Stanton and Baber, 1996b; Baber and Stanton, 1999), withdrawing cash from automatic teller machines (Burford, 1993), medical applications (Baber and Stanton, 1999; Yamaoka and Baber, 2000), recording on tape-to-tape machines (Baber and Stanton, 1994), programming a menu on cookers (Crawford, Taylor and Po, 2000), programming video-cassette recorders (Baber and Stanton, 1994; Stanton and Baber, 1998), operating radio-cassette machines (Stanton and Young, 1999), recalling a phone number on mobile phones (Baber and Stanton, 2002), buying a rail ticket on the ticket machines on the London Underground (Baber and Stanton, 1996), and operating high-voltage switchgear in substations (Glendon and McKenna, 1995).

Domain of Application

Public technology and product design.

Procedure and Advice

Step 1: Construct HTA
Firstly, Hierarchical Task Analysis (HTA – see Annett in this volume) is performed to model the human side of the interaction. Of course, one could employ any method to describe human activity. However, HTA suits this purpose for the following reasons:

1. it is related to Goals and Tasks;
2. it is directed at a specific goal;
3. it allows consideration of task sequences (through 'plans').

As will become apparent, TAFEI focuses on a sequence of tasks aimed at reaching a specific goal.

For illustrative purposes of how to conduct the method, a simple, manually-operated electric kettle is used. The first step in a TAFEI analysis is to obtain an appropriate HTA for the device, as shown in Figure 6.4. As TAFEI is best applied to scenario analyses, it is wise to consider just one specific goal, as described by the HTA (e.g., a specific, closed-loop task of interest) rather than the whole design. Once this goal has been selected, the analysis proceeds to constructing State-Space Diagrams (SSDs) for device operation.

Step 2: Construct SSDs
Next, State-Space Diagrams (SSDs) are constructed to represent the behaviour of the artefact. A SSD essentially consists of a series of states that the device passes from a starting state to the goal state. For each series of states, there will be a current state, and a set of possible exits to other states. At a basic level, the current state might be 'off', with the exit condition 'switch on' taking the device to the state 'on'. Thus, when the device is 'off' it is 'waiting to…' an action (or set of actions) that will take it to the state 'on'. It is very important to have, on completing the SSD, an exhaustive set of states for the device under analysis. Numbered plans from the HTA are then mapped onto the SSD, indicating which human actions take the device from one state to another. Thus the plans are mapped onto the state transitions (if a transition is activated by the machine, this

is also indicated on the SSD, using the letter 'M' on the TAFEI diagram). This results in a TAFEI diagram, as shown in Figure 6.5. Potential state-dependent hazards have also been identified.

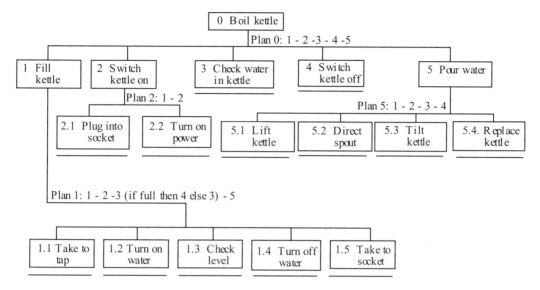

Figure 6.4   Hierarchical Task Analysis

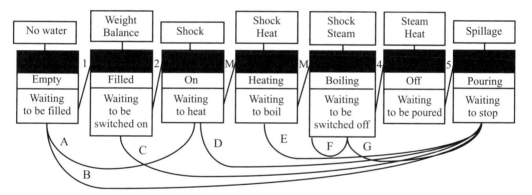

Figure 6.5   State-space TAFEI Diagram

Step 3: Create transition matrix
Finally, a transition matrix is devised to display state transitions during device use. TAFEI aims to assist the design of artefacts by illustrating when a state transition is possible but undesirable (i.e., illegal). Making all illegal transitions impossible should facilitate the cooperative endeavour of device use.

All possible states are entered as headers on a matrix – see Table 6.6. The cells represent state transitions (e.g., the cell at row 1, column 2 represents the transition between state 1 and state 2), and are then filled in one of three ways. If a transition is deemed impossible (i.e., you simply cannot go from this state to that one), a '–' is entered into the cell. If a transition is deemed possible and desirable (i.e., it progresses the user towards the goal state – a correct action), this is a legal transition and "L" is entered into the cell. If, however, a transition is both possible but undesirable (a deviation from the intended path – an error), this is termed illegal and the cell is filled with an 'I'. The idea behind TAFEI is that usability may be improved by making all illegal transitions (errors) impossible, thereby limiting the user to only performing desirable actions. It is up to the analyst to conceive of design solutions to achieve this.

Table 6.6   Transition Matrix

		TO STATE						
		Empty	Filled	On	Heating	Boiling	Off	Pouring
FROM STATE	Empty	---------	L (1)	I (A)	---------	---------	---------	I (B)
	Filled		---------	L (2)	---------	---------	---------	I (C)
	On			---------	L (M)	---------	---------	I (D)
	Heating					L (M)	---------	I (E)
	Boiling					I (F)	L (4)	I (G)
	Off							L (5)
	Pouring							

The states are normally numbered, but in this example the text description is used. The character "L" denotes all of the error-free transitions and the character 'I' denotes all of the errors. Each error has an associated character (i.e., A to G), for the purposes of this example and so that it can be described in Table 6.7.

Table 6.7   Error Descriptions and Design Solutions

Error	Transition	Error description	Design solution
A	1 to 3	Switch empty kettle on	Transparent kettle walls and/or link to water supply
B	1 to 7	Pour empty kettle	Transparent kettle walls and/or link to water supply
C	2 to 7	Pour cold water	Constant hot water or auto heat when kettle placed on base after filling
D	3 to 7	Pour kettle before boiled	Kettle status indicator showing water temperature
E	4 to 7	Pour kettle before boiled	Kettle status indicator showing water temperature
F	5 to 5	Fail to turn off boiling kettle	Auto cut-off switch when kettle boiling
G	5 to 7	Pour boiling water before turning kettle off	Auto cut-off switch when kettle boiling

Obviously the design solutions in table two are just illustrative and would need to be formally assessed for their feasibility and cost.

What TAFEI does best is enable the analysis to model the interaction between human action and system states. This can be used to identify potential errors and consider the task flow in a goal-oriented scenario. Potential conflicts and contradictions in task flow should come to light. For example, in a study of medical imaging equipment design, Baber and Stanton (1999) identified disruptions in task flow that made the device difficult to use. TAFEI enabled the design to be modified and led to the development of a better task flow. This process of analytical prototyping is key to the use of TAFEI in designing new systems. Obviously, TAFEI can also be used to evaluate existing systems. There is a potential problem that the number of states that a device can be in could overwhelm the analyst. Our experience suggests that there are two possible approaches. First, only analyse goal-oriented task scenarios. The process is pointless without a goal and HTA can help focus the analysis. Second, the analysis can be nested at various levels in the task hierarchy, revealing more and more detail. This can make each level of analysis relatively self-contained and not overwhelming. The final piece of advice is to start with a small project and build up from that position.

Example

The following example of TAFEI was used to analyse the task of programming a video-cassette recorder. The task analysis, state-space diagrams and transition matrix are all presented. First of all the task analysis is performed to describe human activity, as shown in Figure 6.6.

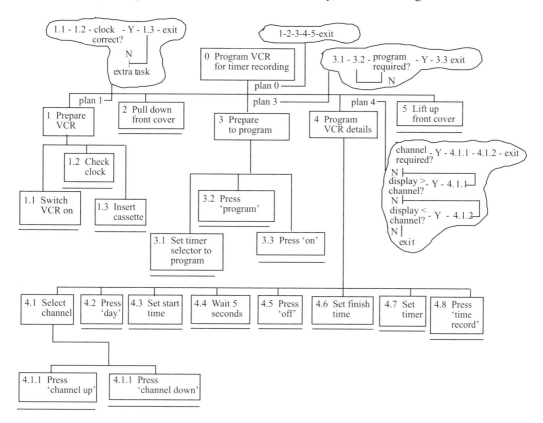

Figure 6.6   HTA of VCR Programming Task

Next, the state-space diagrams are drawn as shown in Figure 6.7.

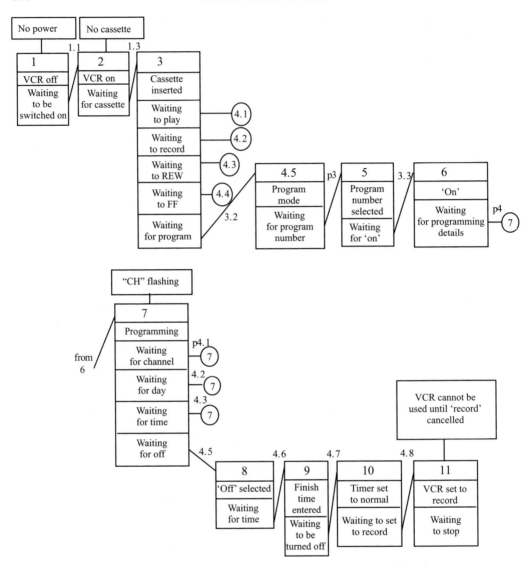

Figure 6.7   The TAFEI Description

From the TAFEI diagram, a transition matrix is compiled and each transition is scrutinised, as presented in Figure 6.8.

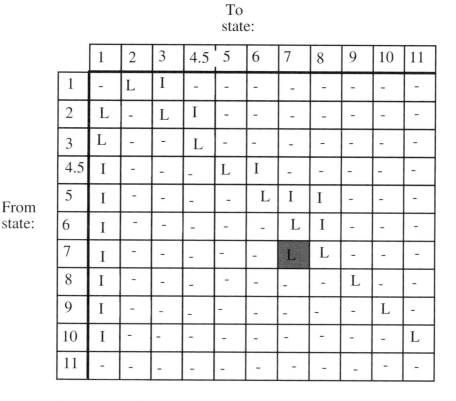

To state:

From state:	1	2	3	4.5	5	6	7	8	9	10	11
1	-	L	I	-	-	-	-	-	-	-	-
2	L	-	L	I	-	-	-	-	-	-	-
3	L	-	-	L	-	-	-	-	-	-	-
4.5	I	-	-	-	L	I	-	-	-	-	-
5	I	-	-	-	-	L	I	I	-	-	-
6	I	-	-	-	-	-	L	I	-	-	-
7	I	-	-	-	-	-	L	L	-	-	-
8	I	-	-	-	-	-	-	-	L	-	-
9	I	-	-	-	-	-	-	-	-	L	-
10	I	-	-	-	-	-	-	-	-	-	L
11	-	-	-	-	-	-	-	-	-	-	-

Figure 6.8   The Transition Matrix

Thirteen of the transitions defined as 'illegal', these can be reduced to a subset of six basic error types:

1. Switch VCR off inadvertently.
2. Insert cassette into machine when switched off.
3. Programme without cassette inserted.
4. Fail to Select programme number.
5. Fail to wait for 'on' light.
6. Fail to enter programming information.

In addition, one legal transition has been highlighted because it requires a recursive activity to be performed. These activities seem to be particularly prone to errors of omission. These predictions then serve as a basis for the designer to address the re-design of the VCR. A number of illegal transitions could be dealt with fairly easily by considering the use of modes in the operation of the device, such as switching off the VCR without stopping the tape and pressing play without inserting the tape.

Related Methods

TAFEI is related to HTA for a description of human activity. Like SHERPA, it is used to predict human error with artefacts. Kirwan and colleagues recommend that multiple human error identification methods can be used to improve the predictive validity of the methods. This is based on the premise that one method may identify an error that another one misses. Therefore using SHERPA and TAFEI may be better than using either alone. It has been found that multiple analysts similarly improve performance of a method. This is based on the premise that one analyst may identify an error that another one misses. Therefore using SHERPA or TAFEI with multiple analysts may perform better than one analyst with SHERPA or TAFEI.

Advantages

1. Structured and thorough procedure.
2. Sound theoretical underpinning.
3. Flexible, generic, methodology.
4. TAFEI can include error reduction proposals.
5. TAFEI appears to be relatively simple to apply.
6. 'TAFEI represents a flexible, generic method for identifying human errors which can be used for the design of anything from kettles to computer systems' (Baber and Stanton, 1994).

Disadvantages

1. Not a rapid method, as HTA and SSD are prerequisites. Kirwan (1998) suggested that TAFEI is a resource intensive method and that the transition matrix and State Space diagrams may rapidly become unwieldy for even moderately complex systems.
2. Requires some skill to perform effectively.
3. Limited to goal-directed behaviour.
4. TAFEI may be difficult to learn and also time consuming to train.
5. It may also be difficult to acquire or construct the SSDs required for a TAFEI analysis. A recent study investigated the use of TAFEI for evaluating design induced pilot error and found that SSDs do not exist for Boeing and Airbus aircraft.

Approximate Training and Application Times

Stanton and Young (1998, 1999) report that observational techniques are relatively quick to train and apply. For example, in their study of radio-cassette machines, training in the TAFEI method took approximately three hours. Application of the method by recently trained people took approximately three hours in the radio-cassette study to predict the errors.

Reliability and Validity

There are some studies that report on the reliability and validity of TAFEI for both expert and novice analysts.

Tools Needed

TAFEI is a pen and paper based tool. There is currently no software available to undertake TAFEI, although there are software packages to support HTA.

Table 6.8   Reliability and Validity Data for TAFEI

	Novices*1	Experts*2
Reliability	r = 0.67	r = 0.9
Validity	SI = 0.79	SI = 0.9

Note:
*1, taken from **Stanton and Baber** (2002) *Design Studies*.

*2, taken from **Baber and Stanton** (1996) *Applied Ergonomics*.

Flowchart

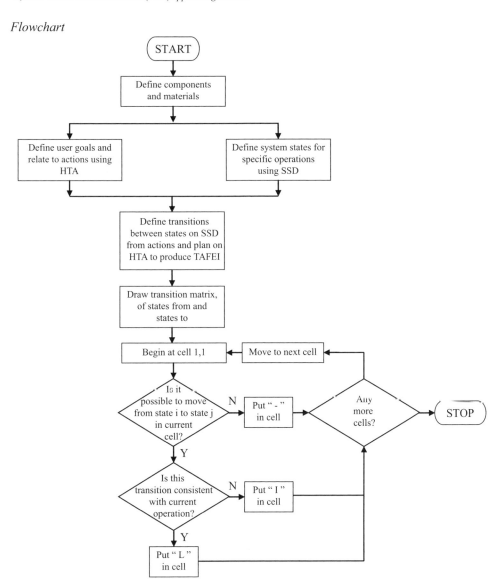

Human Error HAZOP

Background and Applications

The HAZOP (Hazard and Operability study) method was first developed by ICI in the late 1960s in order to investigate the safety or operability of a plant or operation (Swann and Preston 1995) and has been used extensively in the nuclear power and chemical process industries. HAZOP (Kletz, 1974) is a well-established engineering approach that was developed for use in process design audit and engineering risk assessment (Kirwan 1992a). Originally applied to engineering diagrams (Kirwan and Ainsworth 1992) the HAZOP method involves the analyst applying guidewords, such as Not done, More than or Later than, to each step in a process in order to identify potential problems that may occur. When conducting a HAZOP type analysis, a HAZOP team is assembled, usually consisting of operators, design staff, human factors specialists and engineers. The HAZOP leader (who should be extensively experienced in HAZOP type analyses) guides the team through an investigation of the system design using the HAZOP 'deviation' guidewords. The HAZOP team consider guidewords for each step in a process to identify what may go wrong. The guidewords are proposed and the leader then asks the team to consider the problem in the following fashion (Source: Swann and Preston, 1995):

1. Which section of the plant is being considered?
2. What is the deviation and what does it mean?
3. How can it happen and what is the cause of the deviation?
4. If it cannot happen, move onto the next deviation.
5. If it can happen, are there any significant consequences?
6. If there are not, move onto the next guideword.
7. If there are any consequences, what features are included in the plant to deal with these consequences?
8. If the HAZOP team believes that the consequences have not been adequately covered by the proposed design, then solutions and actions are considered.

Applying guide words like this in a systematic way ensures that all of the possible deviations are considered. Typically, the efficiency of the actual HAZOP analysis is largely dependent upon the HAZOP team. There are a number of different variations of HAZOP style approaches, such as CHAZOP (Swann and Preston, 1995) and SCHAZOP (Kennedy and Kirwan, 1998). A HEI- based approach emerged in the form of the Human Error HAZOP method, which was developed for the analysis of human error issues (Kirwan and Ainsworth 1992). In the development of another HEI tool (PHECA) Whalley (1988) also created a set of human factors based guidewords, which are more applicable to human error. These Human Error guidewords are presented in Table 6.9. The error guidewords are applied to each bottom level task step in the HTA to determine any credible errors (i.e. those judged by the subject matter expert to be possible). Once the analyst has recorded a description of the error, the consequences, cause and recovery path of the error are also recorded. Finally, the analyst then identifies any design improvements that could potentially be used to remedy the error.

Domain of Application

HAZOP was originally developed for the nuclear power and chemical processing industries. However, it is feasible that the method could be applied in any domain involving human activity.

Table 6.9   Human Error HAZOP Guidewords

	Repeated
Less Than	Sooner Than
More Than	Later Than
As Well As	Mis-ordered
Other Than	Part Of

Procedure and Advice (Human Error HAZOP)

Step 1: Assembly of HAZOP team
The most important part of any HAZOP analysis is assembling the correct HAZOP team (Swann and Preston, 1995). The HAZOP team needs to possess the right combination of skills and experience in order to make the analysis efficient. The HAZOP team leader should be experienced in HAZOP type analysis so that the team can be guided effectively. For a human error HAZOP analysis of a nuclear petro-chemical plant, it is recommended that the team be comprised of the following personnel.

* HAZOP team leader.
* Human Factors Specialist(s).
* Human Reliability Analysis (HRA)/Human Error Identification (HEI) Specialist.
* Project engineer.
* Process engineer.
* Operating team leader.
* Control room operator(s).
* Data recorder.

Step 2: Hierarchical task analysis (HTA)
Next, an exhaustive description of task and system under analysis should be created. There are a number of task analysis techniques that can be used for this purpose. It is recommended that a HTA of the task under analysis is conducted. The human error HAZOP method works by indicating which of the errors from the HAZOP EEM taxonomy are credible at each bottom level task step in a HTA of the task under analysis. A number of data collection techniques may be used in order to gather the information required for the HTA, such as interviews with SMEs and observations of the task under analysis.

Step 3: Guideword consideration
The HAZOP team takes the first/next bottom level task step from the HTA and considers each of the associated HAZOP guidewords for the task step under analysis. This involves discussing whether the guideword could have any effect on the task step or not and also what type of error would result. If any of the guidewords are deemed credible by the HAZOP team, then they move onto step 4.

Step 4: Error description
For any credible guidewords, the HAZOP team should provide a description of the form that the resultant error would take e.g. operator fails to check current steam pressure setting. The error description should be clear and concise.

Step 5: Consequence analysis
Once the HAZOP team have described the potential error, its consequence should be determined. The consequence of the error should be described clearly e.g. Operator fails to comprehend high steam pressure setting.

Step 6: Cause analysis
Next, the HAZOP team should determine the cause(s) of the potential error. The cause analysis is crucial to the remedy or error reduction part of the HAZOP analysis. Any causes associated with the identified error should be described clearly.

Step 7: Recovery path analysis
In the recovery path analysis, any recovery paths that the operator might potentially take after the described error has occurred to avoid the associated consequences are recorded. The recovery path for an error will typically be another task step in the HTA or a description of a recovery step.

Step 8: Error remedy
Finally, the HAZOP team proposes any design or operational remedies that could be implemented in order to reduce the chances of the error occurring. This is based upon subjective analyst judgement and domain expertise.

Advantages

1. A correctly conducted HAZOP analysis has the potential to highlight all of the possible errors that could occur in the system.
2. HAZOP has been used emphatically in many domains. HAZOP style methods have received wide acceptance by both the process industries and the regulatory authorities (Andrews and Moss, 1993).
3. Since a team of experts is used, the method should be more accurate and comprehensive than other 'single analyst' methods. Using a team of analysts should ensure that no potential errors are missed and also remove the occurrence of non-credible errors.
4. Easy to learn and use.
5. Whalley's (1988) guidewords are generic, allowing the method to be applied to a number of different domains.
6. The HAZOP method only considers errors at the 'sharp-end' of system operation. System and organisation errors are not catered for by a HAZOP analysis.

Disadvantages

1. The method can be extremely time consuming in its application. Typical HAZOP analyses can take up to several weeks to be completed.
2. The method requires a mixed team made up of operators, human factors specialists, designers, engineers etc. Building such a team and ensuring that they can all be brought together at the same time is often a difficult task.
3. HAZOP analysis generates huge amounts of information that has to be recorded and analysed.
4. Laborious.
5. Disagreement and personality clashes within the HAZOP team may be a problem.
6. The guidewords used are either limited or specific to nuclear petro-chemical industry.
7. The human error HAZOP guidewords lack comprehensiveness (Salmon et al, 2002).

Flowchart

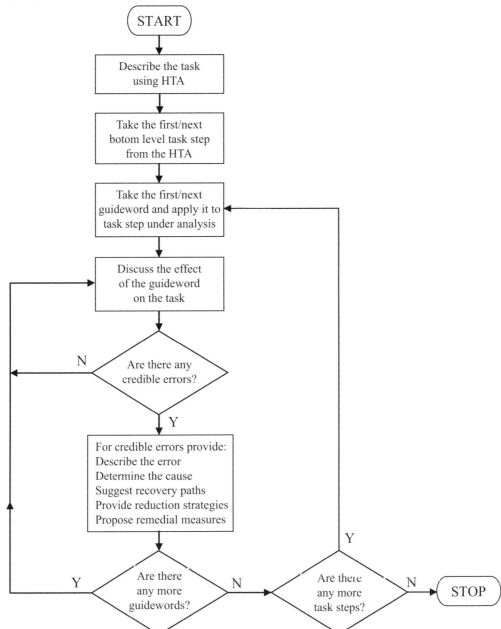

Example

A human error HAZOP analysis was conducted for the flight task 'Land aircraft X at New Orleans using the autoland system' (Marshall et al, 2003). An extract of the HTA for the flight task is presented in Figure 6.9. An extract of the human error HAZOP analysis for the flight task is presented in Table 6.10.

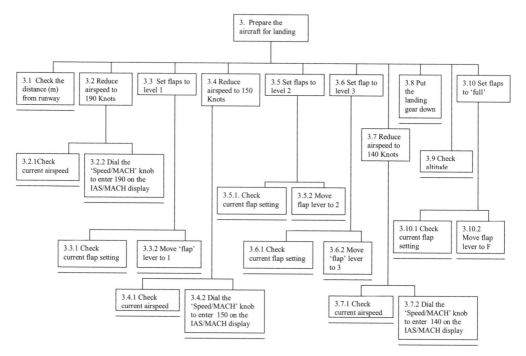

Figure 6.9   Extract of HTA of Task 'Land A320 at New Orleans using the Autoland System'

Related Methods

A number of variations of the HAZOP method exist, such as human error HAZOP (Kirwan and Ainsworth, 1992), CHAZOP (Swann and Preston, 1995) and SCHAZOP (Kennedy and Kirwan, 1998). HAZOP type analyses are typically conducted on a HTA of the task under analysis. Engineering diagrams, flow-sheets, operating instructions and plant layouts are also typically required (Kirwan and Ainsworth, 1992). Human Error HAZOP is a taxonomy-based HEI method, of which there are many, including SHERPA, CREAM and HET.

Approximate Training and Application Times

Whilst the HAZOP method appears to be quick to train, Swann and Preston (1995) report that studies on the duration of the HAZOP analysis process have been conducted, with the conclusion that a thorough HAZOP analysis carried out correctly would take over five years for a typical processing plant. This is clearly a worst-case scenario and impractical. More realistically, Swann and Preston (1995) report that ICI benchmarking shows that a typical HAZOP analysis would require about 40 meetings lasting approximately three hours each.

Table 6.10 Extract of Human Error HAZOP Analysis of Task 'Land A320 at New Orleans Using the Autoland System

Task Step	Guideword	Error	Consequence	Cause	Recovery	Design Improvements
3.1 Check the distance from runway	Later than	Pilot checks the distance from the runway later than he should	Plane may be travelling too fast for that stage of the approach and also may have the wrong level of flap	Pilot inadequacy Pilot is preoccupied with another landing task	3.9	Auditory distance countdown inside 25N miles
3.2.1 Check current airspeed	Not done	Pilot fails to check current airspeed	Pilot changes airspeed wrongly i.e. may actually increase airspeed	Pilot is pre-occupied with other landing tasks	3.4.1	Auditory speed updates Bigger, more apparent speedo
	Mis-ordered	Pilot checks the current airspeed after he has altered the flaps	Plane may be travelling too fast for that level of flap or that leg of the approach	Pilot inadequacy Pilot is preoccupied with other landing tasks	3.4.1	Design flaps so each level can only be set within certain speed level windows
3.2.2 Dial the speed/mach knob to enter 190	Not done	Pilot fails to enter new airspeed	Plane may be travelling too fast for the approach	Pilot is pre-occupied with other landing tasks	3.4.2	Auditory reminder that the plane is travelling too fast e.g. overspeed display
	Less than	Pilot does not turn the Speed/Mach knob enough	The planes speed is not reduced enough and the plane may be travelling too fast for the approach	Poor control design Pilot inadequacy	3.4.2	One full turn for 1 knot Improved control feedback
	More than	Pilot turns the Speed/MACH knob too much	The planes speed is reduced too much and so the plane is travelling too slow for the approach	Poor control design Pilot inadequacy	3.4.2	Improved control feedback
	Sooner than	Pilot reduces the planes speed too early	The plane slows down too early	Pilot is preoccupied with other landing tasks Pilot inadequacy	3.4.2	Plane is travelling too slow auditory warning
	Other than	Pilot reduces the planes using the wrong knob e.g. HDG knob	Plane does not slow down to desired speed and takes on a heading of 190	Pilot is preoccupied with other landing tasks Pilot inadequacy	3.4.2	Clearer labelling of controls Overspeed auditory warning
3.3.1 Check the current flap setting	Not done	Pilot fails to check the current flap setting	The pilot does not comprehend the current flap setting	Pilot is preoccupied with other landing tasks Pilot inadequacy	3.4.2	Bigger/improved flap display/control Auditory flap setting reminders

Reliability and Validity

The HAZOP type approach has been used emphatically over the last four decades in process control environments. However (Kennedy, 1997) reports that it has not been subjected to rigorous academic scrutiny (Kennedy and Kirwan, 1998). In a recent study (Stanton et al, 2003) reported that in a comparison of four HEI methods (HET, Human Error HAZOP, HEIST, SHERPA) when used to predict potential design induced pilot error, subjects using the human error HAZOP method achieved acceptable sensitivity in their error predictions (mean sensitivity index 0.62). Furthermore, only those subjects using the HET methodology performed better.

Tools Needed

HAZOP analyses can be carried out using pen and paper. Engineering diagrams are also normally required. The EEM taxonomy is also required for the human error HAZOP variation. A HTA for the task under analysis is also required.

Technique for Human Error Assessment (THEA)

Background and Applications

The Technique for Human Error Assessment (THEA; Pocock, Harrison, Wright and Johnson, 2001) was developed to aid designers and engineers in the identification of potential user interaction problems in the early stages of interface design. The impetus for the development of THEA was the requirement for a HEI tool that could be used effectively and easily by non-HF specialists. To that end, it is suggested by the creators that the technique is more suggestive and also much easier to apply than typical HRA methods. The technique itself is a structured approach to HEI, and is based upon Norman's model of action execution (Norman, 1988). Similar to HEIST (Kirwan, 1994) THEA uses a series of questions in a checklist style approach based upon goals, plans, performing actions and perception/evaluation/interpretation. THEA also utilises a scenario-based analysis, whereby the analyst exhaustively describes the scenario under analysis before any error analysis is performed.

Domain of Application

Generic.

Procedure and Advice

Step 1: System description
Initially, a THEA analysis requires a formal description of the system and task or scenario under analysis. This system description should include details regarding the specification of the system's functionality and interface and also if and how it interacts with any other systems (Pocock, Harrison, Wright and Fields, 1997).

Step 2: Scenario description
Next, the analyst should provide a description of the type of scenario under analysis. The authors have developed a scenario template that assists the analyst in developing the scenario description. The scenario description is conducted in order to give the analyst a thorough description of the

scenario under analysis, including information such as actions and any contextual factors which may provide error potential. The scenario description template is presented in Table 6.11.

Step 3: Task description
A description of the tasks that the operator or user would perform in the scenario is also required. This should describe goals, plans and intended actions. It is recommended that a HTA of the task under analysis is conducted for this purpose.

Step 4: Goal decomposition
The HTA developed for step 3 of the THEA analysis should be used for step 4, which involves decomposing the task goals into operations.

Table 6.11   A Template for Describing Scenarios (Source: Pocock, Harrison, Wright and Fields, 1997)

AGENTS
The human agents involved and their organisations
The roles played by the humans, together with their goals and responsibilities
RATIONALE
Why is this scenario and interesting or useful one to have picked?
SITUATION AND ENVIRONMENT
The physical situation in which the scenario takes place
External and environmental triggers, problems and events that occur in this scenario
TASK CONTEXT
What tasks are performed?
Which procedures exist, and will they be followed as prescribed?
SYSTEM CONTEXT
What devices and technology are involved?
What usability problems might participants have?
What effects can users have?
ACTION
How are the tasks carried out in context?
How do the activities overlap?
Which goals do actions correspond to?
EXCEPTIONAL CIRCUMSTANCES
How might the scenario evolve differently, either as a result of uncertainty in the environment or because of variations in agents, situation, design options, system and task context?
ASSUMPTIONS
What, if any, assumptions have been made that will affect this scenario?

Step 5: Error analysis
Next, the analyst has to identify and explain any human error that may arise during task performance. THEA provides a structured questionnaire or checklist style approach in order to aid the analyst in identifying any possible errors. The analyst simply asks questions (from THEA) about the scenario under analysis in order to identify potential errors. For any credible errors, the analyst should record the error, its causes and its consequences. Then questions are normally asked about each goal or task in the HTA, or alternatively, the analyst can select parts of the HTA where problems are anticipated. The THEA error analysis questions are comprised of the following four categories:

1. Goals;
2. Plans;

3. Performing Actions; and
4. Perception, Interpretation and evaluation.

Examples of the THEA error analysis questions for each of the four categories are presented in Table 6.12.

Table 6.12   Example THEA Error Analysis Questions (Source: Pocock, Harrison, Wright and Fields, 2001)

Questions	Consequences	Design Issues
Goals		
G1 – Are items triggered by stimuli in the interface, environment, or task?	If not, goals (and the tasks that achieve them) may be lost, forgotten or not activated, resulting in omission errors.	Are triggers clear and meaningful? Does the user need to remember all of the goals?
G2 – Does the user interface 'evoke' or 'suggest' goals?	If not, goals may not be activated, resulting in omission errors. If the interface does 'suggest' goals, they may not always be the right ones, resulting in the wrong goal being addressed.	e.g. graphical display of flight plan shows pre-determined goals as well as current progress.
Plans		
P1 – Can actions be selected in situ, or is pre-planning required?	If the correct action can only be taken by planning in advance, then the cognitive work may be harder. However, when possible, planning ahead often leads to less error-prone behaviour and fewer blind alleys.	
P2 – Are there well practised and pre-determined plans?	If a plan isn't well known or practised then it may be prone to being forgotten or remembered incorrectly. If plans aren't pre-determined, and must be constructed by the user, then their success depends heavily on the user possessing enough knowledge about their goals and the interface to construct a plan. If pre-determined plans do exist and are familiar, then they might be followed inappropriately, not taking account of the peculiarities of the current context.	
Performing actions		
A1 – Is there physical or mental difficulty in executing the actions?	Difficult, complex or fiddly actions are prone to being carried out incorrectly.	
A2 – Are some actions made unavailable at certain times?		
Perception, Interpretation and evaluation		
I1 – Are changes in the system resulting from user action clearly perceivable?	If there is no feedback that an action has been taken, the user may repeat actions, with potentially undesirable effects.	
I2 – Are the effects of user actions perceivable immediately?	If feedback is delayed, the user may become confused about the system state, potentially leading up to a supplemental (perhaps inappropriate) action being taken.	

Step 6: Design implications/recommendations

Once the analyst has identified any potential errors, the final step of the THEA analysis is to offer any design remedies for each error identified. This is based primarily upon the analyst's subjective judgement. However, the design issues section of the THEA questions also prompt the analyst for design remedies.

Advantages

1. THEA offers a structured approach to HEI.
2. The THEA technique is easy to learn and use and can be used by non-human factors professionals.
3. As it is recommended that THEA be used very early in the system life cycle, potential interface problems can be identified and eradicated very early in the design process.
4. THEA error prompt questions are based on sound underpinning theory (Norman's action execution model).
5. THEA's error prompt questions aid the analyst in the identification of potential errors.
6. According to the creators of the method, THEA is more suggestive and easier to apply than typical HRA methods (Pocock, Harrison, Wright and Fields, 1997).
7. Each error question has associated consequences and design issues to aid the analyst.
8. THEA appears to be a generic technique, allowing it to be applied in any domain.

Disadvantages

1. Although error questions prompt the analyst for potential errors, THEA does not use any error modes and so the analyst may be unclear on the types of errors that may occur. HEIST (Kirwan, 1994) however, uses error prompt questions linked with an error mode taxonomy, which seems to be a much sounder approach.
2. THEA is very resource intensive, particularly with respect to time taken to complete an analysis.
3. Error consequences and design issues provided by THEA are generic and limited.
4. At the moment, there appears to be no validation evidence associated with THEA.
5. HTA, task decomposition and scenario description create additional work for the analyst.
6. For a technique that is supposed to be usable by non-human factors professionals, the terminology used in the error analysis questions section is confusing and hard to decipher. This could cause problems for non-human factors professionals.

Flowchart

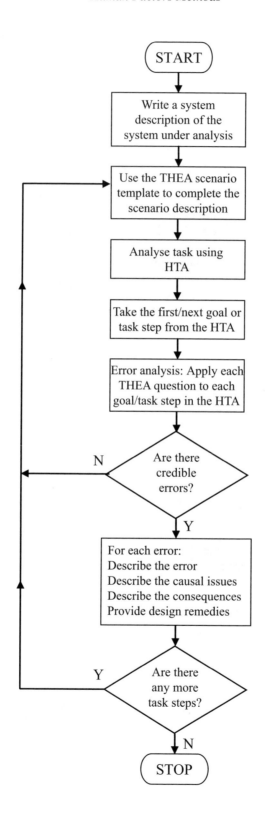

Example

The following example (Table 6.13, Figure 6.10 and Table 6.14) is a THEA analysis of a video recorder programming task (Pocock, Harrison, Wright and Fields, 2001).

Table 6.13   Scenario Details

SCENARIO NAME: Programming a video recorder to make a weekly recording
ROOT GOAL: Record a weekly TV programme
SCENARIO SUB-GOAL: Setting the recording date
ANALYST(S) NAME(S) & DATE:
AGENTS: A single user interfacing with a domestic video cassette recorder (VCR) via a remote control unit (RCU)
RATIONALE: The goal of programming this particular VCR is quite challenging. Successful programming is not certain
SITUATION & ENVIRONMENT: A domestic user wishes to make a recording of a television programme which occurs on a particular channel at the same time each week. The user is not very technologically aware and has not programmed this VCR previously. A reference handbook is not available, but there is no time pressure to set the machine – recording is not due to commence until tomorrow
TASK CONTEXT: The user must perform the correct tasks to set the VCR to record a television programme on three consecutive Monday evenings from 6pm-7pm on Channel 3. Today is Sunday
SYSTEM CONTEXT: The user has a RCU containing navigation keys used in conjunction with programming the VCR as well as normal VCR playback operation. The RCU has 4 scrolling buttons, indicating left, right, up, down. Other buttons relevant to programming are labelled OK and I
ACTIONS: The user is required to enter a recording date into the VCR via the RCU using the buttons listed above. The actions appear in the order specified by the task decomposition
EXCEPTIONAL CIRCUMSTANCES: None
ASSUMPTIONS: None

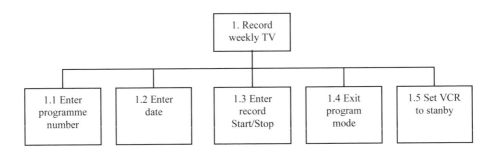

Figure 6.10   Video Recorder HTA (adapted from Pocock, Harrison, Wright and Fields, 1997)

Table 6.14   Error Analysis Questionnaire (Source: Pocock, Harrison, Wright and Fields, 1997)

SCENARIO NAME: Programming a video recorder to make a weekly recording			
TASK BEING ANALYSED: Setting the recording date			
ANALYST(S) NAME(S) AND DATE			
QUESTION	CAUSAL ISSUES	CONSEQUENCES	DESIGN ISSUES
GOALS, TRIGGERING, INITIATION			
G1 – Is the task triggered by stimuli in the interface, environment or the task itself?	Yes. (The presence of an 'enter date' prompt is likely to trigger the user to input the date at this point)		
G2 – Does the UI 'evoke' or 'suggest' goals?	N/A. (The UI does not per se, strictly evoke or suggest the goal of entering the date)		
G3 – Do goals come into conflict?	There are no discernible goal conflicts		
G4 – Can the goal be satisfied without all its sub-goals being achieved?	NO. The associated sub-goal on this page of setting the DAILY/WEEKLY function may be overlooked. Once the date is entered, pressing the right cursor key on the RCU will enter the next 'ENTER HOUR' setting	Failure to set the DAILY/WEEKLY option. Once the ENTER HOUR screen is entered, the DAILY/ WEEKLY option is no longer available	Suggest addition of an interlock so that the daily/weekly option cannot be bypassed
PLANS			
P1 – Can actions be selected in-situ, or is pre-planning required?	True. (Entering the date can be done 'on-the-fly'. No planning is required)		
P2 – Are there well practised and pre-determined plans?	N/A. (A pre-determined plan, as such, does not exist, but the user should possess enough knowledge to know what to do at this step)		
P3 – Are there plans or actions that are similar? Are some used more often than others?	There are no similar or more frequently used plans or actions associated with this task		
P4 – Is there feedback to allow the user to determine that the task is proceeding successfully towards the goal, and according to plan?	Yes. (As the user enters digits into the date field via the RCU, they are echoed back on screen)	Task is proceeding satisfactorily towards the goal of setting the date, although the date being entered is not necessarily correct.	(See A1)
PERFORMING ACTIONS			
A1 – Is there physical or mental difficulty in performing the task?	Yes. The absence of any cues for how to enter the correct date format makes this task harder to perform	The user may try to enter the year or month instead of the day. Additionally, the user may try to add a single figure date, instead of preceding the digit with a zero	Have an explanatory text box under the field or, better still, default today's date in the date field
A2 – Are some actions made unavailable at certain times?	No. (The only actions required of the user is to enter two digits into the blank field)		
A3 – Is the correct action dependent on the current mode?	No. (The operator is operating in a single programming mode)		

A4 – Are additional actions required to make the right controls and information available at the right time?	Yes. The date field is presented blank. If the user does not know the date for recording (or today's date), the user must know to press the 'down' cursor key on the RCU to make today's date visible	The user may be unable to enter the date, or the date must be obtained from an external source. Also, if the user presses either the left or right cursor key, the 'enter date' screen is exited	Default current date into field Prevent user from exiting 'enter date' screen before an entry is made (e.g. software lock-in)
PERCEPTION, INTERPRETATION AND EVALUATION			
I1 – Are changes to the system resulting from user action clearly perceivable?	Yes. (Via on-screen changes to the date field)		
I2 – Are effects of such user actions perceivable immediately?	Yes. (Digit echoing of RCU key presses is immediate)		
I3 – Are changes to the system resulting from autonomous system actions clearly perceivable?	N/A. (The VCR performs no autonomous actions)		
I4 – Are the effects of such autonomous system actions perceivable immediately?	N/A		
I5 – Does the task involve monitoring, vigilance, or spells of continuous attention?	No. (There is no monitoring or continuous attention requirements on the user)		
I6 – Can the user determine relevant information about the state of the system from the total information provided?	NO. User cannot determine current date without knowing about the 'down' cursor key. Also, if date of recording is known, user may not know about the need to enter two digits	If user doesn't know today's date, and only knows that, say, Wednesday, is when you want the recordings to commence, then the user is stuck	As A1
I7 – Is complex reasoning, calculation, or decision making involved?	No		
I8 – If the user is interfacing with a moded system, is the correct interpretation dependent on the current mode?	N/A	It is not considered likely that the date field will be confused with another entry field e.g. hour	

Related Methods

THEA is one of a number of HEI techniques. THEA is very similar to HEIST (Kirwan, 1994) in that it uses error prompt questions to aid the analysis. A THEA analysis should be conducted on an initial HTA of the task under analysis.

Approximate Training and Application Times

Although no training and application time is offered in the literature, it is apparent that the amount of training time would be minimal. The application time, however, would be high, especially for large, complex tasks.

Reliability and Validity

No data regarding reliability and validity are offered by the authors.

Tools Needed

To conduct a THEA analysis, pen and paper is required. The analyst would also require functional diagrams of the system/interface under analysis and the THEA error analysis questions.

Human Error Identification in Systems Tool (HEIST)

Background and Applications

The Human Error Identification in Systems Tool (HEIST; Kirwan, 1994) is based upon a series of tables containing questions or 'error identifier prompts' surrounding external error modes (EEM), performance shaping factors (PSF) and psychological error mechanisms (PEM). When using HEIST, the analyst identifies errors through applying the error identifier prompt questions to all of the tasks involved in the task or scenario under analysis. The questions link EEMs (type of error) to relevant PSFs. All EEMs are then linked to PEMs (psychological error-mechanisms). The method comprises eight HEIST tables, each containing a series of pre-defined error-identifier questions linked to external error modes (EEMs), associated causes (system cause or psychological error mechanism) and error reduction guidelines. The HEIST tables and questions are based upon the Skill, Rule and Knowledge (SRK) framework (Rasmussen at al, 1981) i.e. Activation/Detection, Observation/Data collection, Identification of system state, Interpretation, Evaluation, Goal selection/Task definition, Procedure selection and Procedure execution. These error prompt questions are designed to prompt the analyst for potential errors. Each of the error identifying prompts are PSF-based questions which are coded to indicate one of six PSFs. These performance shaping factors are Time (T), Interface (I), Training/Experience (E), Procedures (P), Task organisation (O), and Task Complexity (C). The analyst classifies the task step under analysis into one of the HEIST behaviours and then applies the associated error prompts to the task step and determines whether any of the proposed errors are credible or not. For each credible error, the analyst then records the system cause or PEM and error reduction guidelines (both of which are provided in the HEIST tables) and also the error consequence. Although it can be used as a stand-alone method, HEIST is also used as part of the HERA 'toolkit' methodology (Kirwan, 1998b) as a back-up check for any of the errors identified.

Domain of Application

Nuclear power and chemical process industries. However, it is feasible that the HEIST technique can be applied in any domain.

Procedure and Advice

Step 1: Hierarchical task analysis (HTA)
The HEIST procedure begins with the development of a HTA of the task or scenario under analysis. A number of data collection techniques may be used in order to gather the information required for the HTA, such as interviews with SMEs and observations of the task under analysis.

Step 2: Task step classification
The analyst takes the first task step from the HTA and classifies it into one or more of the eight HEIST behaviours (Activation/Detection, Observation/Data collection, Identification of system state, Interpretation, Evaluation, Goal selection/Task definition, Procedure selection and Procedure

execution). For example, the task step 'Pilot dials in airspeed of 190 using the speed/MACH selector knob' would be classified as procedure execution. This part of the HEIST analysis is based entirely upon analyst subjective judgement.

Step 3: Error analysis
Next, the analyst takes the appropriate HEIST table and applies each of the error identifier prompts to the task step under analysis. Based upon subjective judgement, the analyst should determine whether or not any of the associated errors could occur during the task step under analysis. If the analyst deems an error to be credible, then the error should be described and the EEM, system cause and PEM should be determined from the HEIST table.

Step 4: Error reduction analysis
For each credible error, the analyst should select the appropriate error reduction guidelines from the HEIST table. Each HEIST error prompt has an associated set of error reduction guidelines. Whilst it is recommended that the analyst should use these, it is also possible for analysts to propose their own design remedies based upon domain knowledge.

Advantages

1. As HEIST uses error identifier prompts the technique has the potential to be very exhaustive.
2. Error identifier prompts aid the analyst in error identification.
3. Once a credible error has been identified, the HEIST tables provide the EEMs, PEMs and error reduction guidelines.
4. The technique is easy to use and learn, and requires only minimal training.
5. HEIST offers a structured approach to error identification.
6. Considers PSFs and PEMs.

Disadvantages

1. The use of error identifier prompts ensure that HEIST is time consuming in its application.
2. The need for an initial HTA creates further work for HEIST analysts.
3. Although the HEIST tables provide error reduction guidelines, these are generic and do not offer specific design remedies e.g. ergonomic design of equipment and good system feedback.
4. A HEIST analysis requires human factors/psychology professionals.
5. No validation evidence is available for the HEIST.
6. There is only limited evidence of HEIST applications in the literature.
7. Many of the error identifier prompts used by HEIST are repetitive.
8. Salmon et al (2002) reported that HEIST performed poorly when used to predict potential design induced error on the flight task 'Land aircraft at New Orleans using the autoland system'. Out of the four methods HET, SHERPA, Human Error HAZOP and HEIST, subjects using HEIST achieved the lowest error prediction accuracy.

Example

A HEIST analysis was conducted on the flight task 'Land A320 at New Orleans using the autoland system' in order to investigate the potential use of the HEIST approach for predicting design induced pilot error on civil flight decks (Salmon et al, 2002, 2003). An extract of the HTA for the flight task is presented in Figure 6.11. An extract of the HEIST analysis is presented in Table 6.15.

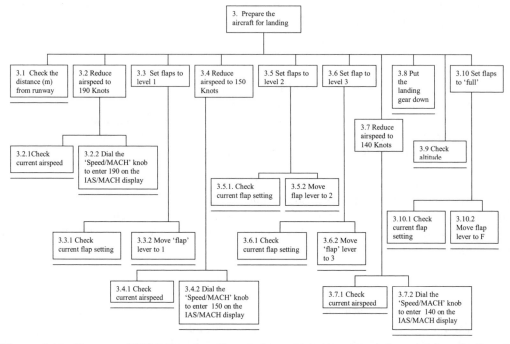

Figure 6.11   Extract of HTA 'Land at New Orleans Using Autoland System' (Marshall et al, 2003)

Table 6.15   Extract of HEIST Analysis of the Task 'Land at New Orleans Using Autoland System' (Salmon et al, 2003)

Task step	Error code	EEM	Description	PEM System cause	Consequence	Error reduction guidelines
3.2.2	PEP3	Action on wrong object	Pilot alters the airspeed using the wrong knob e.g. heading knob	Topographic misorientation Mistakes alternatives Similarity matching	The airspeed is not altered and the heading will change to the value entered	Ergonomic design of controls and displays Training Clear labelling
3.2.2	PEP4	Wrong action	Pilot enters the wrong airspeed	Similarity matching Recognition failure Stereotype takeover Misperception Intrusion	Airspeed will change to the wrong airspeed	Training Ergonomic procedures with checking facilities Prompt system feedback

Flowchart

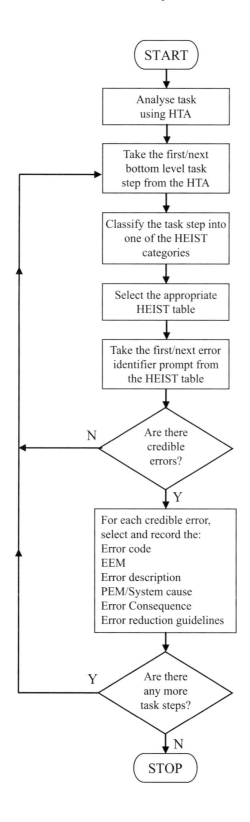

Related Methods

A HEIST analysis is typically conducted on a HTA of the task under analysis. The use of error identifier prompts is similar to the approach used by THEA (Pocock et al, 2001). HEIST is also used as a back-up check when using the HERA toolkit approach to HEI (Kirwan 1998b).

Approximate Training and Application Times

Although no training and application time is offered in the literature, it is apparent that the amount of training required would be minimal, providing the analyst in question has some experience of human factors and psychology. The application time is dependent upon the size and complexity of the task under analysis. However, it is generally recommended that the application time for a typical HEIST analysis would be medium to high, due to the use of the error identifier prompts. When using HEIST to predict potential design induced pilot error, Marshall et al (2003) reported that the average training time for participants using the HEIST technique was 90 minutes. The average application time of HEIST in the same study was 110 minutes, which was considerably longer than the other methods used in the study (SHERPA, HET, Human Error HAZOP.

Reliability and Validity

The reliability and validity of the HEIST technique is questionable. Whilst no data regarding the reliability and validity are offered by the authors of the method, (Marshall et al 2003) report that subjects using HEIST achieved a mean sensitivity index of 0.62 at time 1 and 0.58 at time 2 when using HEIST to predict design induced pilot error on the flight task 'Land aircraft X at New Orleans using the autoland system'. This represents only moderate validity and reliability ratings. In comparison to three other methods (SHERPA, HET and Human Error HAZOP) when used to predict design induced pilot error for the same flight task, participants using the HEIST technique achieved the poorest error prediction sensitivity ratings (Salmon et al 2003).

Tools Needed

To conduct a HEIST analysis, pen and paper is required. The analyst would also require functional diagrams of the system/interface under analysis and the eight HEIST tables containing the error identifier prompt questions.

The Human Error and Recovery Assessment Framework (HERA)

Background and Applications

The HERA framework is a prototype multiple method or 'toolkit' approach to human error identification that was developed by Kirwan (1998a, 1998b) in response to a review of HEI methods, which suggested that no single HEI/HRA technique possessed all of the relevant components required for efficient HRA/HEI analysis. In conclusion to a review of thirty-eight existing HRA/HEI techniques (Kirwan, 1998a), Kirwan (1998b) suggested that the best approach would be for practitioners to utilise a framework type approach to HEI, whereby a mixture of independent HRA/HEI tools would be used under one framework. Kirwan (1998b) suggested that one possible framework would be to use SHERPA, HAZOP, EOCA, Confusion matrix analyses, Fault symptom matrix analysis and the

SRK approach together. In response to this conclusion, Kirwan (1998b) proposed the Human Error and Recovery Assessment (HERA) system, which was developed for the UK nuclear power and reprocessing industry. Whilst the technique has yet to be applied to a concrete system, it is offered here as an example of an integrated framework or toolkit of HF methods.

Domain of Application

Nuclear power and chemical process industries.

Procedure and Advice

Step 1: Critical task identification
Before a HERA analysis is undertaken, the HERA team should determine how in-depth an analysis is required and also which tasks are to be analysed. Kirwan (1998b) suggests that the following factors should be taken into account: the nature of the plant being assessed and the cost of failure, the criticality of human operator roles in the plant, the novelty of the plant's design, the system life cycle, the extent to which the analysis is PSA driven and the resources available for the analysis. A new plant that is classed as highly hazardous, with critical operator roles would require an exhaustive HERA analysis, whilst an older plant that has no previous accident record and in which operators only take minor roles would require a scaled down, less exhaustive analysis. Once the depth of the analysis is determined, the HERA assessment team must then determine which operational stages are to be the focus of the analysis e.g. normal operation, abnormal operation and emergency operation.

Step 2: Task analysis
Once the scope of the analysis is determined and the scenarios under analysis are defined, the next stage of the HERA analysis is to describe the tasks or scenarios under analysis. It is recommended that task analysis is used for this purpose. According to Kirwan (1998b) two forms of task analysis are used during the HERA process. These are Initial Task Analysis (Kirwan, 1994) and HTA (Annett et al., 1971; Shepherd, 1989; Kirwan and Ainsworth, 1992). Initial task analysis involves describing the scenario under analysis, including the following key aspects:

- Scenario starting condition;
- The goal of the task;
- Number and type of tasks involved;
- Time available;
- Personnel available;
- Any adverse conditions;
- Availability of equipment;
- Availability of written procedures;
- Training; and
- Frequency and severity of the event.

Once the initial task analysis is completed, HTAs for the scenarios under analysis should be developed. A number of data collection techniques may be used in order to gather the information required for the HTAs, such as interviews with SMEs and observations of the scenario(s) under analysis.

Step 3: Error analysis
The error analysis part of the HERA framework comprises nine overlapping error identification modules. A brief description of these is presented below:

Mission analysis. The mission analysis part of the HERA analysis involves determining the scope for failure that exists for the task or scenario under analysis. The mission analysis module uses the following questions to identify the scope for failure.

- Could the task fail to be achieved in time?
- Could the task be omitted entirely?
- Could the wrong task be carried out?
- Could only part of the task be carried out unsuccessfully?
- Could the task be prevented or hampered by a latent or coincident failure?

For the HERA analysis to proceed further, one of the answers to the mission analysis questions must be yes.

Operations level analysis. The operations levels analysis involves the identification of the mode of failure for the task or scenario under analysis.

Goals analysis. Goals analysis involves focussing on the goals identified in the HTA and determining if any goal related errors can occur. To do this, the HERA team use twelve goal analysis questions designed to highlight any potential goal errors. An example of a goals analysis question used in HERA is, '*Could the operators have no goal, e.g. due to a flood of conflicting information; the sudden onset of an unanticipated situation; a rapidly evolving and worsening situation; or due to a disagreement or other decision-making failure to develop a goal?*' The goal error taxonomy used in the HERA analysis is presented below.

1. No goal.
2. Wrong goal.
3. Outside procedures.
4. Goal conflict.
5. Goal delayed.
6. Too many goals.
7. Goal inadequate.

Plans analysis. Plans analysis involves focusing on the plans identified in the HTA to determine whether any plan related errors could occur. The HERA team uses twelve plans analysis questions to identify any potential 'plan errors'. HERA plans analysis questions include, '*Could the operators fail to derive a plan, due to workload, or decision-making failure?*', or, '*Could the plan not be understood or communicated to all parties?*' The HERA plan error taxonomy is presented below.

1. No plan.
2. Wrong plan.
3. Incomplete plan.
4. Plan communication failure.
5. Plan co-ordination failure.
6. Plan initiation failure.

7. Plan execution failure.
8. Plan sequence error.
9. Inadequate plan.
10. Plan termination failure.

Error analysis. The HERA approach employs an EEM taxonomy derived from the SHERPA (Embrey, 1986) and THERP (Swain and Guttman, 1983) HEI approaches. This EEM taxonomy is used to identify potential errors that may occur during the task or scenario under analysis. This involves applying the EEMs to each bottom level task step in the HTA. Any credible errors are identified based upon the analyst(s)' subjective judgement. The HERA EEM taxonomy is listed below.

Omission	Action too little
Omits entire task step	Action in the wrong direction
Omits step in the task	Misalignment error
Timing	Other quality or precision error
Action too late	Selection error
Action too early	Right action on wrong object
Accidental timing with other event	Wrong action on right object
Action too short	Wrong action on wrong object
Action too long	Substitution error
Sequence	Information transmission error
Action in the wrong sequence	Information not communicated
Action repeated	Wrong information communicated
Latent error prevents execution	Rule violation
Quality	
Action too much	Other

PSF analysis. The HERA approach also considers the effect of PSFs on potential error. Explicit questions regarding environmental influences on performance are applied to each of the task steps in the HTA. This allows the HERA team to identify any errors that might be caused by situational or environmental factors. The HERA approach uses the following PSF categories: time, interface, training and experience, procedures, organisation, stress and complexity. Each PSF question has an EEM associated with it. Examples of HERA PSF questions from each category are provided below.

Time: Is there more than enough time available? (*Too Late*)

Interface: Is onset of the scenario clearly alarmed or cued, and is this alarm or cue compelling? (*Omission or detection failure*)

Training and experience: Have operators been trained to deal with this task in the past twelve months? (*Omission, too late, too early*)

Procedures: Are procedures required? *(Rule violation, wrong sequence, omission, quality error)*

Organisation: Are there sufficient personnel to carry out the task and to check for errors? (*Action too late, wrong sequence, omission, error of quality*)

Stress: Will the task be stressful, and are there significant consequences of task failure? (*omission, error of quality, rule violation*)
Complexity: Is the task complex or novel? (*omission, substitution error, other*)

PEM analysis. The PEM analysis part of the HERA approach is used to identify potential errors based upon the associated PEMs. The HERA approach uses fourteen PEM questions which are applied to each task step in the HTA. Each PEM question is linked to a set of associated EEMs.

HEIST analysis. The HEIST approach (see page 188 for description) is then used by the HERA team as a back-up check to ensure analysis comprehensiveness (i.e. that no potential errors have been missed). The HEIST approach is also used to provide error reduction guidelines.

Human Error HAZOP analysis. Finally, to ensure maximum comprehensiveness, a human error HAZOP (see page 174 for description) style analysis should be performed.

Advantages

1. The multi-method HERA framework ensures that it is highly exhaustive and comprehensive.
2. The HERA team are provided with maximum guidance when conducting the analysis. Each of the questions used during the approach prompt the analyst(s) for potential errors, and are also linked to the relevant EEMs.
3. The framework approach offers the analyst more than one chance to identify potential errors. This should ensure that no potential errors are missed.
4. The HERA framework allows analysis teams to see the scenario from a number of different perspectives.
5. HERA uses existing, proven HEI techniques, such as the human error HAZOP, THERP and SHERPA methods.

Disadvantages

1. A HERA analysis would require a huge amount of time and resources.
2. The technique could potentially become very repetitive, with many errors being identified over and over again by the different methods employed within the HERA framework.
3. Domain expertise would be required for a number of the modules.
4. Due to the many different methods employed within the HERA framework, the training time for such an approach would be extremely high.
5. A HERA team would have to be constructed. Such a team requires a mixed group made up of operators, human factors specialists, designers, engineers etc. Building such a team and making sure they can all be brought together at the same time would be a difficult thing to do.
6. Although the HERA technique is vast and contains a number of different modules, it is difficult to see how such an approach (using traditional EEM taxonomies) would perform better than far simpler and quicker approaches to HEI such as SHERPA and HET.
7. There is only limited evidence of the application of the HERA framework available in the literature.

Example

HERA has yet to be applied in a concrete analysis. The following examples are extracts of a hypothetical analysis described by Kirwan (1992b). As the output is so large, only a small extract is presented in Table 6.16. For a more comprehensive example, the reader is referred to Kirwan (1992b).

Table 6.16   Extract of Mission Analysis Output (Source: Kirwan, 1992b)

Identifier	Task step	Error identified	Consequence	Recovery	Comments
1. Fail to achieve in time	Goal 0: Restore power and cooling	Fail to achieve in time	Reactor core degradation	Grid re-connection	This is at the highest level of task-based failure description
2. Omit entire task	Goal 0: Restore power and cooling Goal A: Ensure reactor trip	Fail to restore power and cooling	Reactor core degradation Reactor core melt (ATWS)	Grid re-connection None	This is the anticipated transient without SCRAM (ATWS) scenario. It is not considered here but may be considered in another part of the risk assessment

Related Methods

The HERA framework employs a number of different methods, including initial task analysis, HTA, HEIST and Human Error HAZOP.

Approximate Training and Application Times

Although no training and application time is offered in the literature, it is apparent that the amount of time in both cases would be high. The training time would be considerable as analysts would have to be trained in the different methods employed within the HERA framework, such as initial task analysis, human error HAZOP, and HEIST. The application time would also be extremely high, due to the various different analyses that are conducted as part of a HERA analysis.

Reliability and Validity

No data regarding reliability and validity are offered by the authors. The technique was proposed as an example of the form that such an approach would take. At the present time, there are no reported applications of the HERA framework in the literature.

Tools Needed

The HERA technique comes in the form of a software package, although HERA analysis can be performed without using the software. This would require pen and paper and the goals, plans, PEM and PSF analysis questions. Functional diagrams for the system under analysis would also be required as a minimum.

System for Predictive Error Analysis and Reduction (SPEAR)

Background and Applications

The System for Predictive Error Analysis (SPEAR) was developed by the Centre for Chemical Process Safety for use in the American chemical processing industry's HRA programme. SPEAR is a systematic taxonomy-based approach to HEI that is very similar to the SHERPA method (Embrey, 1986). In addition to an external error mode taxonomy, the SPEAR method also uses a performance-shaping factors (PSF) taxonomy to aid the identification of environmental or situational factors that may enhance the possibility of error. The SPEAR method is typically applied to the bottom level tasks (or operations) of a HTA of the task under analysis. Using subjective judgement, the analyst uses the SPEAR human error taxonomy to classify each task step into one of the five following behaviour types:

1. Action.
2. Retrieval.
3. Check.
4. Selection.
5. Transmission.

Each behaviour has an associated set of EEMs, such as *action incomplete, action omitted and right action on wrong object*. The analyst then uses the taxonomy and domain expertise to determine any credible error modes for the task in question. For each credible error (i.e. those judged by the analyst to be possible) the analyst provides a description of the form that the error would take, such as, 'pilot dials in wrong airspeed'. Next, the analyst has to determine how the operator can recover the error and also any consequences associated with the error. Finally, error reduction measures are proposed, under the categories of procedures, training and equipment.

Domain of Application

The SPEAR method was developed for the chemical process industry. However, the method employs a generic external error mode taxonomy and can be applied in any domain.

Procedure and Advice

Step 1: Hierarchical task analysis (HTA)
The first step in a SPEAR analysis is to conduct a HTA of the task or scenario under analysis. The SPEAR method works by indicating which of the errors from the SPEAR EEM taxonomy are credible at each bottom level task step in a HTA of the task under analysis. A number of data collection techniques may be used in order to gather the information required for the HTA, such as interviews with SMEs and observations of the task under analysis.

Step 2: PSF analysis
The analyst should take the first/next bottom level task step from the HTA and consider each of the PSFs for that task step. This allows the analyst to determine whether any of the PSFs are relevant for the task step in question. The SPEAR method does provide the analyst with a specific PSF taxonomy, and in the past, the PSF taxonomy from the THERP method (Swain and Guttman 1983) has been used in conjunction with SPEAR.

Step 3: Task classification
Next, the analyst should classify the task step under analysis into one of the behaviour categories from the SPEAR behaviour taxonomy. The analyst should select appropriate behaviour and EEM taxonomies based upon the task under analysis. The analyst has to classify the task step into one of the behaviour categories; Action, Checking, Retrieval, Transmission, Selection and Plan.

Step 4: Error analysis
Taking the PSFs from step 2 into consideration, the analyst next considers each of the associated EEMs for the task step under analysis. The analyst uses subjective judgement to identify any credible errors associated with the task step in question. Each credible error should be recorded and a description of the error should be provided.

Step 5: Consequence analysis
For each credible error, the analyst should record the associated consequences.

Step 6: Error reduction analysis
For each credible error, the analyst should offer any potential error remedies. The SPEAR method uses three categories of error reduction guideline; Procedures, Training and Equipment. It is normally expected that a SPEAR analysis should provide at least one remedy for each of the three categories.

Advantages

1. SPEAR provides a structured approach to HEI.
2. The SPEAR method is simple to learn and use, requiring minimal training.
3. The taxonomy prompts the analyst for potential errors.
4. Unlike SHERPA, SPEAR also considers PSFs.
5. Quicker than most HEI techniques.
6. SPEAR is generic, allowing the method to be applied in any domain.

Disadvantages

1. For large, complex tasks, the method may become laborious and time consuming to apply.
2. The initial HTA adds additional time to the analysis.
3. Consistency of such techniques is questionable.
4. Appears to be an almost exact replica of SHERPA.
5. SPEAR does not consider the cognitive component of error.

Related Methods

The SPEAR method is a taxonomy-based approach to HEI. There are a number of similar HEI techniques available, such as SHERPA (Embrey, 1986) and HET (Marshall et al, 2003). A SPEAR analysis also requires an initial HTA to be performed for the task under analysis. The development of the HTA may involve the use of a number of data collection procedures, including interviews with SMEs and observational study of the task or scenario under analysis.

Table 6.17 Example SPEAR Output

Step	Error Type	Error Description	Recovery	Consequences	Error reduction recommendations		
					Procedures	Training	Equipment
2.3 Enter tanker target weight	Wrong information obtained (R2)	Wrong weight entered	On check	Alarm does not sound before tanker overfills.	Independent validation of target weight.	Ensure operator double checks entered date. Recording of values in checklist.	Automatic setting of weight alarms from unladen weight. Computerise logging system and build in checks on tanker reg. No. and unladen weight linked to warning system. Display differences.
3.2.2 Check tanker while filling	Check omitted (C1)	Tanker not monitored while filling	On initial weight alarm	Alarm will alert the operator if correctly set. Equipment fault e.g. leaks not detected early and remedial action delayed.	Provide secondary task involving other personnel. Supervisor periodically checks operation.	Stress importance of regular checks for safety.	Provide automatic log-in procedure.
3.2.3 Attend tanker during last 2-3 ton filling	Operation omitted (O8)	Operator fails to attend	On step 3.2.5	If alarm not detected within 10 minutes tanker will overfill.	Ensure work schedule allows operator to do this without pressure.	Illustrate consequences of not attending.	Repeat alarm in secondary area. Automatic interlock to terminate loading if alarm not acknowledged. Visual indication of alarm.
3.2.5 Cancel final weight alarm	Operation omitted (O8)	Final weight alarm taken as initial weight alarm	No recovery	Tanker overfills.	Note differences between the sound of the two alarms in checklist.	Alert operators during training about differences in sounds of alarms.	Use completely different tones for initial and final weight alarms.
4.1.3 Close tanker valve	Operation omitted (O8)	Tanker valve not closed	4.2.1	Failure to close tanker valve would result in pressure not being detected during the pressure check in 4.2.1.	Independent check on action. Use checklist.	Ensure operator is aware of consequences of failure.	Valve position indicator would reduce probability of error.
4.2.1 Vent and purge lines	Operation omitted (O8)	Lines not fully purged	4.2.4	Failure of operator to detect pressure in lines could lead to leak when tanker connections broken.	Procedure to indicate how to check if fully purged.	Ensure training covers symptoms of pressure in line.	Line pressure indicators at controls. Interlock device on line pressure.
4.4.2 Secure locking nuts	Operation omitted (O8)	Locking nuts left unsecured	None	Failure to secure locking nuts could result in leakage during transportation.	Use checklist.	Stress safety implications of training.	Locking nuts to give tactile feedback when secure.

Flowchart

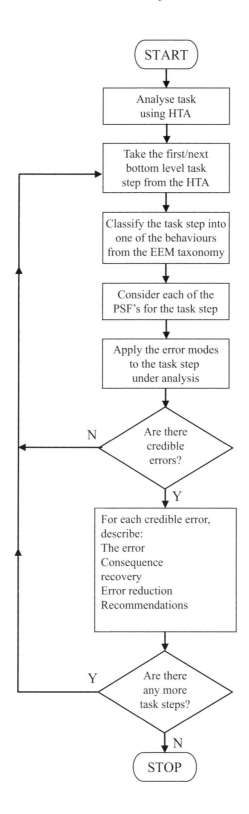

Approximate Training and Application Times

It is estimated that the training time associated with the SPEAR method is low. The SPEAR method is very similar to the SHERPA method, which typically takes around two to three hours to train to novice analysts. The application time is based on the size and complexity of the task under analysis. In general, the application time associated with the SPEAR method would be low. However, for large, complex scenarios the application time may increase considerably.

Reliability and Validity

No data regarding the reliability and validity of the SPEAR method are available in the literature. Since the method is very similar to the SHERPA method, it is estimated that the reliability and validity of the SPEAR method would be high.

Tools Needed

To conduct a SPEAR analysis, pen and paper is required. The analyst would also require functional diagrams of the system/interface under analysis and an appropriate EEM taxonomy, such as the SHERPA (Embrey, 1986) error mode taxonomy. A PSF taxonomy is also required, such as the one employed by the THERP method (Swain and Guttman, 1983).

Example

The example output presented in Table 6.17 is an extract from a SPEAR analysis of a chlorine tanker-filling problem (CCPS, 1994 cited in Karwowski and Marras, 1999).

Human Error Assessment and Reduction Technique (HEART)

Background and Applications

The Human Error Assessment and Reduction Technique (HEART; Williams, 1986) offers an approach for deriving numerical probabilities associated with error occurrence. HEART was designed as a quick, easy to use and understand HEI technique and is a highly structured approach that allows the analyst to quantify human error potential. One of the features of the HEART approach is that, in order to reduce resource usage, HEART only deals with those errors that will have a gross effect on the system in question (Kirwan, 1994). The method uses its own values of reliability and also 'factors of effect' for a number of error producing conditions (EPC). The HEART approach has been used in the UK for the Sizewell B risk assessment and also the risk assessments for UK Magnox and Advanced Gas-Cooled Reactor stations.

Domain of Application

HEART was developed for the nuclear power and chemical process industries.

Procedure and Advice

Step 1: Determine the task or scenario under analysis
The first step in a HEART analysis is to select an appropriate set of tasks for the system under analysis. In order to ensure that the analysis is exhaustive as possible, it is recommended that the analyst selects a set of tasks that are as representative of the system under analysis as possible.

Step 2: Conduct a HTA for the task or scenario under analysis
Once the tasks or scenarios under analysis are defined clearly, the next step involves describing the tasks or scenarios. It is recommended that HTA is used for this purpose. A number of data collection techniques may be used in order to gather the information required for the HTA, such as interviews with SMEs and observational study of the task under analysis.

Step 3: Conduct HEART screening process
The HEART technique uses a screening process, in the form of a set of guidelines that allow the analyst to identify the likely classes, sources and strengths of human error for the scenario under analysis (Kirwan, 1994).

Step 4: Task unreliability classification
Once the screening process has been conducted, the analyst must define the proposed nominal level of human unreliability associated with the task under analysis. To do this, the analyst uses the HEART generic categories to assign a human error probability to the task in question. For example, if the analysis was focused upon a non-routine, emergency situation in the control room, this would be classed as, *A) Totally unfamiliar, performed at speed with no real idea of likely consequences.* The probability associated with this would be 0.55. The HEART generic categories are presented in Table 6.18.

Step 5: Identification of error producing conditions
The next stage of a HEART analysis is the identification of error producing conditions (EPCs) associated with the task under analysis. To do this, the analyst uses the associated HEART EPCs to identify any EPCs that are applicable to the task under analysis. The HEART Error producing conditions are presented in Table 6.19.

Step 6: Assessed proportion of effect
Once the analyst has identified any EPCs associated with the task under analysis, the next step involves determining the assessed proportion of effect of each of the EPCs identified. This involves providing a rating between 0 and 1 (0 = Low, 1 = High) for each EPC. The ratings offered are based upon the subjective judgement of the analyst involved.

Step 7: Remedial measures
The next step involves identifying and proposing possible remedial measures for the errors identified. Although the HEART technique does provide some generic remedial measures, the analyst may also be required to provide more specific measures depending upon the nature of the error and the system under analysis. The remedial measures provided by the HEART methodology are generic and not system specific.

Step 8: Documentation stage
It is recommended that the HEART analysis is fully documented by the analyst. Throughout the analysis, every detail should be recorded by the analyst. Once the analysis is complete, the HEART analysis should be converted into a suitable presentation format.

Table 6.18   HEART Generic Categories

Generic Task	Proposed nominal human unreliability (5th – 95th percentile bounds)
Totally unfamiliar, performed at speed with no real idea of the likely consequences	0.55 (0.35 – 0.97)
Shift or restore system to a new or original state on a single attempt without supervision or procedures	0.26 (0.14 – 0.42)
Fairly simple task performed rapidly or given scant attention	0.16 (0.12 – 0.28)
Routine, highly practised, rapid task involving relatively low level of skill	0.09 (0.06 – 0.13)
Restore or shift a system to original or new state following procedures, with some checking	0.02 (0.007 – 0.045)
Completely familiar, well designed, highly practised, routine task occurring several times per hour, performed at the highest possible standards by highly motivated, highly trained and experienced person, totally aware of the implications of failure, with time to correct potential error, but without the benefit of significant job aids	0.003 (0.0008 – 0.0009)
Respond correctly to system command even when there is an augmented or automated supervisory system providing accurate interpretation of system stage	0.0004 (0.00008 – 0.009)
Respond correctly to system command even when there is an augmented or automated supervisory system providing accurate interpretation of system stage	0.00002 (0.000006 - 0.009)

Table 6.19   HEART EPCs (Source: Kirwan, 1994)

Error producing condition (EPC)	Maximum predicted Amount by which unreliability might change, going from good conditions to bad
Unfamiliarity with a situation which is potentially important but which only occurs infrequently, or which is novel	X17
A shortage of time available for error detection and correction	X11
A low signal to noise ratio	X10
A means of suppressing or overriding information or features which is too easily accessible	X9
No means of conveying spatial and functional information to operators in a form which they can readily assimilate	X8
A mismatch between an operator's model of the world and that imagined by a designer	X8
No obvious means of reversing an unintended action	X8
A channel capacity overload, particularly one caused by simultaneous presentation of non-redundant information	X6
A need to unlearn a technique and apply one which requires the application of an opposing philosophy	X6
The need to transfer specific knowledge from task to task without loss	X5.5
Ambiguity in the required performance standards	X5
A mismatch between perceived and real risk	X4
Poor, ambiguous or ill-matched system feedback	X4
No clear, direct and timely confirmation of an intended action from the portion of the system over which control is exerted	X4
Operator inexperience	X3
An impoverished quality of information conveyed procedures and person-person interaction	X3
Little or no independent checking or testing of output	X3
A conflict between immediate and long term objectives	X2.5

No diversity of information input for veracity checks	X2
A mismatch between the educational achievement level of an individual and the requirements of the task	X2
An incentive to use other more dangerous procedures	X2
Little opportunity to exercise mind and body outside the immediate confines of the job	X1.8
Unreliable instrumentation	X1.6
A need for absolute judgements which are beyond the capabilities or experience of an operator	X1.6
Unclear allocation of function and responsibility	X1.6
No obvious way to keep track or progress during an activity	X1.4

Example

An example of a HEART analysis output is presented in Table 6.20.

Table 6.20   HEART Output (Source: Kirwan, 1994)

Type of Task – F		Nominal Human Reliability – 0.003		
Error Producing conditions	Total HEART effect	Engineers POA	Assessed effect	
Inexperience	X3	0.4	$((3-1) \times 0.4) + 1 = 1.8$	
Opp Technique	X6	1.0	$((6-1) \times 1.0) + 1 = 6.0$	
Risk Misperception	X4	0.8	$((4-1) \times 0.8 + 1 = 3.4$	
Conflict of objectives	X2.5	0.8	$((2.5-1) \times 0.8) + 1 = 2.2$	
Low Morale	X1.2	0.6	$((1.2-1) \times 0.6 + 1 = 1.12$	

Assessed, nominal likelihood of failure = 0.27 (0.003 x 1.8 x 6 x 3.4 x 2.2 x 1.12)

For the example presented above, a nominal likelihood of failure of 0.27 was identified. According to Kirwan (1994) this represents a high predicted error probability and would warrant error reduction measures. In this instance, technique unlearning is the biggest contributory factor and so if error reduction measures were required, retraining or redesigning could be offered. Table 6.21 presents the remedial measures offered for each EPC in this example.

Table 6.21   Remedial Measures (Source: Kirwan, 1994)

Technique unlearning (x6)	The greatest possible care should be exercised when a number of new techniques are being considered that all set out to achieve the same outcome. They should not involve the adoption of opposing philosophies
Misperception of risk (x4)	It must not be assumed that the perceived level of risk, on the part of the user, is the same as the actual level. If necessary, a check should be made to ascertain where any mismatch might exist, and what its extent is
Objectives conflict (x2.5)	Objectives should be tested by management for mutual compatibility, and where potential conflicts are identified, these should either be resolved, so as to make them harmonious, or made prominent so that a comprehensive management-control programme can be created to reconcile such conflicts, as they arise, in a rational fashion
Inexperience (x3)	Personnel criteria should contain experience parameters specified in a way relevant to the task. Chances must not be taken for the sake of expediency
Low morale (x1.2)	Apart from the more obvious ways of attempting to secure high morale – by way of financial rewards, for example – other methods, involving participation, trust and mutual respect, often hold out at least as much promise. Building up morale is a painstaking process, which involves a little luck and great sensitivity

Advantages

1. The HEART approach is a simplistic one requiring only minimal training.
2. HEART is quick and simple to use.
3. Each error-producing condition has a remedial measure associated with it.
4. HEART gives the analyst a quantitative output.
5. HEART uses fewer resources than other methods such as SHERPA.
6. A number of validation studies have produced encouraging results for the HEART approach e.g. Kirwan (et al.) (1988, 1996, 1997), Waters (1989), Robinson (1981).

Disadvantages

1. Little guidance is offered to the analyst in a number of the key HEART stages, such as the assignment of EPCs. As a result, there are doubts over the reliability of the HEART approach.
2. Although HEART has been subject to a number of validation studies, the methodology still requires further validation.
3. Neither dependence nor EPC interaction is accounted for by HEART (Kirwan, 1994).
4. HEART is very subjective, reducing its reliability and consistency.
5. The HEART approach was developed specifically for the nuclear power domain, and would require considerable development to be applied in other domains.

Related Methods

Normally, a HEART analysis requires a description of the task or scenario under analysis. HTA is normally used for this purpose. The HEART approach is a HRA technique, of which there are many, such as THERP (Swain and Guttman, 1983) and JHEDI (Kirwan, 1994).

Approximate Training and Application Times

According to Kirwan (1994) the HEART technique is both quick to train and apply. The technique is certainly simple in its application and so the associated training and application times are estimated to be low.

Reliability and Validity

Kirwan (1997) describes a validation of nine HRA methods and reports that, of the nine methods, HEART, THERP, APJ and JHEDI performed moderately well. A moderate level of validity for HEART was reported. In a second validation study (Kirwan 1997), HEART, THERP and JHEDI were subject to a validation study. The highest precision rating associated with the HEART technique was 76.67%. Of 30 assessors using the HEART approach, 23 displayed a significant correlation between their error estimates and the real HEPs. According to Kirwan (1997) the results demonstrate a level of empirical validity of the three methods.

Tools Needed

The HEART approach can be applied using pen and paper. The associated HEART documentation is also required (HEART generic categories, HEART error producing conditions etc.).

Flowchart

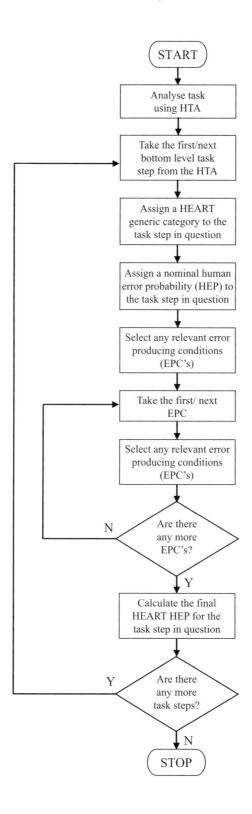

The Cognitive Reliability and Error Analysis Method (CREAM)

Background and Applications

The Cognitive Reliability and Error Analysis Method (CREAM; Hollnagel, 1998) is a recently developed HEI/HRA method that was developed in response to an analysis of existing HRA approaches. CREAM can be used both predictively, to predict potential human error, and retrospectively, to analyse and quantify error. According to Hollnagel (1998) CREAM enables the analyst to:

- Identify those parts of the work, tasks or actions that require or depend upon human cognition, and which therefore may be affected by variations in cognitive reliability;
- Determine the conditions under which the reliability of cognition may be reduced, and where therefore the actions may constitute a source of risk;
- Provide an appraisal of the consequences of human performance on system safety, which can be used in PRA/PSA; and
- Develop and specify modifications that improve these conditions, hence serve to increase the reliability of cognition and reduce the risk.

CREAM uses a model of cognition, the Contextual Control Model (COCOM), which focuses on how actions are chosen and assumes that the degree of control that an operator has over his actions is variable and determines the reliability of his performance. The COCOM describes four modes of control, *Scrambled control, Opportunistic control, Tactical control* and *Strategic control*. According to Hollnagel (1998) when the level of operator control rises, so does their performance reliability. The CREAM method uses a classification scheme consisting of a number of groups that describe the phenotypes (error modes) and genotypes (causes) of the erroneous actions. The CREAM classification scheme is used by the analyst to predict and describe how errors could potentially occur. The CREAM classification scheme allows the analyst to define the links between the causes and consequences of the error under analysis. Within the CREAM classification scheme there are three categories of causes (genotypes); *Individual, technological and organisational* causes. A brief description of each genotype category is provided below:

- *Individual related genotypes*. Specific cognitive functions, general person related functions (temporary) and general person related functions (permanent).
- *Technology related genotypes*. Equipment, procedures, interface (temporary) and interface (permanent).
- *Organisation related genotypes*. Communication, organisation, training, ambient conditions, working conditions.

The CREAM method uses a number of linked classification groups. The first classification group describes the CREAM error modes. The CREAM error modes are presented below.

1. *Timing* – too early, too late, omission.
2. *Duration* – too long, too short.
3. *Sequence* – reversal, repetition, commission, intrusion.
4. *Object* – wrong action, wrong object.
5. *Force* – too much, too little.
6. *Direction* – Wrong direction.
7. *Distance* – too short, too far.
8. *Speed* – too fast, too slow.

These eight different error mode classification groups are then divided further into the four sub-groups.

1. *Action at the wrong time* – includes the error mode's timing and duration.
2. *Action of the wrong type* – includes the error mode's force, distance, speed and direction.
3. *Action at the wrong object* – includes the error mode 'object'.
4. *Action in the wrong place* – includes the error mode 'sequence'.

The CREAM classification system is comprised of both phenotypes (error modes) and genotypes (causes of error). These phenotypes and genotypes are further divided into detailed classification groups, which are described in terms of general and specific consequents. The CREAM method also uses a set of common performance conditions (CPC) that are used by the analyst to describe the context in the scenario/task under analysis. These are similar to PSFs used by other HEI/HRA methods. The CREAM common performance conditions are presented in Table 6.22.

Domain of Application

Although the method was developed for the nuclear power industry, it is a generic approach and can be applied in any of domain involving the operation of complex, dynamic systems.

Table 6.22   Cream Common Performance Conditions

CPC Name	Level/Descriptors
Adequacy of organisation	The quality of the roles and responsibilities of team members, additional support, communication systems, safety management system, instructions and guidelines for externally orientated activities etc. Very efficient/Efficient/Inefficient/Deficient
Working Conditions	The nature of the physical working conditions such as ambient lighting, glare on screens, noise from alarms, task interruptions etc Advantageous/Compatible/Incompatible
Adequacy of MMI and operational support	The man machine interface in general, including the information available on control panels, computerised workstations, and operational support provided by specifically designed decision aids. Supportive/Adequate/Tolerable/Inappropriate
Availability of procedures/plans	Procedures and plans include operating and emergency procedures, familiar patterns of response heuristics, routines etc Appropriate/Acceptable/Inappropriate
Number of simultaneous goals	The number of tasks a person is required to pursue or attend to at the same time. Fewer than capacity/Matching current capacity/More than capacity
Available time	The time available to carry out the task Adequate/Temporarily inadequate/Continuously inadequate
Time of day (Circadian rhythm)	Time at which the task is carried out, in particular whether or not the person is adjusted to the current time. Day-time (adjusted)/Night time (unadjusted)
Adequacy of training and experience	Level and quality of training provided to operators as familiarisation to new technology, refreshing old skills etc. Also refers to operational experience. Adequate, high experience/Adequate, limited experience/Inadequate
Crew collaboration quality	The quality of collaboration between the crew members, including the overlap between the official and unofficial structure, level of trust, and the general social climate among crew members. Very efficient/Efficient/Inefficient/Deficient

Procedure and Advice (Prospective Analysis)

Step 1: Task analysis
The first step in a CREAM analysis involves describing the task or scenario under analysis. It is recommended that a HTA of the task or scenario under analysis is developed for this purpose. A number of data collection procedures may be used to collect the data required for the HTA, including interviews with SMEs and observational study of the task or scenario under analysis.

Step 2: Context description
Once the task or scenario under analysis is described, the analyst should begin by firstly describing the context in which the scenario under analysis takes place. This involves describing the context using the CREAM CPCs (Table 6.22). To do this, the analyst uses subjective judgement to rate each CPC regarding the task under analysis. For example, if the analyst assumes that the operator has little experience or training for the task under analysis, then the CPC '*Adequacy of training and experience*' should be rated '*limited experience/inadequate*'.

Step 3: Specification of the initiating events
The analyst then needs to specify the initiating events that will be subject to the error predictions. Hollnagel (1998) suggests that PSA event trees can be used for this step. However, since a task analysis has already been conducted in step 1 of the procedure, it is recommended that this be used. The analyst(s) should specify the tasks or task steps that are to be subject to further analysis.

Step 4: Error Prediction
Once the CPCs' analysis has been conducted and the initiating events are specified, the analyst should then determine and describe how an initiating event could potentially develop into an error occurrence. To predict errors, the analyst constructs a modified consequent/antecedent matrix. The rows on the matrix show the possible consequents whilst the columns show the possible antecedents. The analyst starts by finding the classification group in the column headings that correspond to the initiating event (e.g. for missing information it would be communication). The next step is to find all the rows that have been marked for this column. Each row should point to a possible consequent, which in turn may be found amongst the possible antecedents. Hollnagel (1998) suggests that in this way, the prediction can continue in a straightforward way until there are no further paths left (Hollnagel 1998). Each error should be recorded along with the associated causes (antecedents) and consequences (consequents).

Step 5: Selection of task steps for quantification
Depending upon the analysis requirements, a quantitative analysis may be required. If so, the analyst should select the error cases that require quantification. It is recommended that if quantification is required, then all of the errors identified should be selected for quantification.

Step 6: Quantitative performance prediction
CREAM has a basic and extended method for quantification purposes. Since this review is based upon the predictive use of CREAM, the error quantification procedure is not presented. For a description of the quantification procedure, the reader is referred to Hollnagel (1998).

Advantages

1. CREAM has the potential to be extremely exhaustive.
2. Context is considered when using CREAM.

3. CREAM is a clear, structured and systematic approach to error identification and quantification.
4. The CREAM method can be used both proactively to predict potential errors and retrospectively to analyse error occurrence.
5. The method is not domain specific and the potential for application in different domains is apparent.
6. CREAM's classification scheme is detailed and exhaustive, even taking into account system and environmental (sociotechnical) causes of error.

Disadvantages

1. To the novice analyst, the method appears complicated and daunting.
2. The exhaustiveness of the classification scheme serves to make the method larger and more resource intensive than other methods.
3. CREAM has not been used extensively.
4. It is apparent that the training and application time for the CREAM method would be considerable.
5. CREAM does not offer remedial measures i.e. ways to recover human erroneous actions are not provided or considered.
6. CREAM appears to be very complicated in its application.
7. CREAM would presumably require analysts with knowledge of human factors and cognitive ergonomics.
8. Application time would be high, even for very basic scenarios.

Related Methods

CREAM analyses are typically conducted on a HTA of the task or scenario under analysis. A number of data collection procedures may be used during the development of the HTA, including interviews with SMEs and observational study of the task or scenario in question. CREAM is a taxonomy-based approach to HEI. Other taxonomic approaches include SHERPA (Embrey, 1986), HET (Marshall et al, 2003) and TRACEr (Shorrock and Kirwan, 2000).

Approximate Training and Application Times

Although there is no data regarding training and application times presented in the literature, it is estimated that the associated times will be high in both cases.

Reliability and Validity

Validation data for the CREAM method is limited. Hollnagel, Kaarstad and Lee (1998) report a 68.6% match between errors predicted and actual error occurrences and outcomes when using the CREAM error taxonomy.

Tools Needed

At its simplest, CREAM can be applied using pen and paper only. A prototype software package has also been developed to aid analysts (Hollnagel 1998).

Flowchart – Prospective Analysis

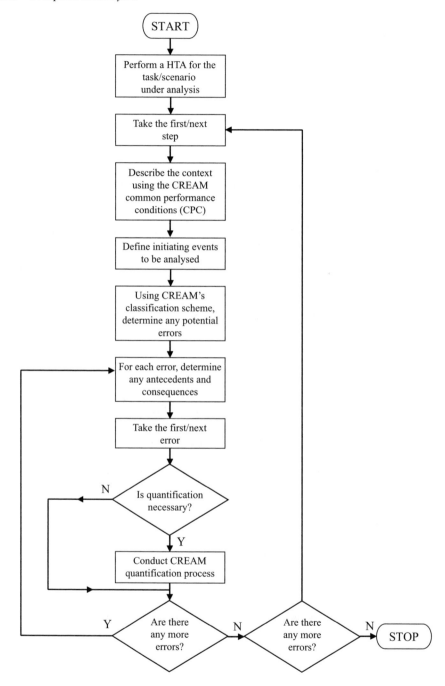

Chapter 7

Situation Awareness Assessment Methods

Over the past two decades, the idea of situation awareness (SA) has received considerable attention from the HF research community. According to Endsley (1995a) the construct was first identified during the First World War as an important aspect of military flight. However, the term only began to be used in research texts in the late 1980s (Stanton and Young, 2000). Despite its origin from within military aviation, SA has now evolved into an important research theme in a number of other work domains. SA research is currently widespread and ongoing within military research contexts (Stanton, Stewart, Harris, Houghton, Baber, McMaster, Salmon, Hoyle, Walker, Young, Linsell, Dymott and Green, 2005, Salmon, Stanton, Walker and Green, 2005), air traffic control, nuclear and petro-chemical plant operation, driving, and aviation to name a few.

There have been a number of attempts to define SA. In basic terms SA is as simple as it sounds, referring to the level of awareness that an actor has of the current situation that he or she is placed in. Despite various attempts, a universally accepted definition and model of SA is yet to emerge. The various models of SA proposed can be broadly classified into the following categories: individual approaches and distributed approaches. Individual approaches to SA consider the construct from an individual actor's perspective. Distributed approaches consider the SA from a systems perspective, arguing that SA resides not only within individual actors, but is also distributed across other actors and artefacts that comprise the total system.

There are currently two dominant 'individualistic' theories of SA. These are the three-level model of SA proposed by Endsley (1995a), and the perceptual cycle model of SA proposed by Smith and Hancock (1995). The construct of SA is most synonymous with the three-level model of SA proposed by Endsley (1995a), which is the most commonly used and widely cited theory of SA. Endsley (1995a) formally defines SA as:

> The perception of the elements in the environment within a volume of time and space, the comprehension of their meaning, and the projection of their status in the near future (Endsley, 1995a, p. 88).

The three level model is an information processing approach that describes SA as a state of knowledge or product that is separate to the processes used to achieve it. The three level model is presented in Figure 7.1. Endsley (1995a) suggests that SA is separate from decision-making and performance but highlights a link between SA and working memory, attention, workload and stress. The model depicts SA as an essential component of human decision-making activity. The achievement and maintenance of SA is influenced by actor and task related factors such as experience, training, workload and also interface design. The three level model of SA proposes that SA comprises the following hierarchical activity levels.

Level 1 SA The perception of the elements in the environment. The first level of SA involves the perception of task and situational related elements in the surrounding environment. Achieving level 1 SA involves perceiving the status, attributes and dynamics of the relevant elements in the environment (Endsley, 1995a). According to the model, attention is directed to the most pertinent environmental cues based upon actor goals and experience in the form of mental models.

Level 2 SA Comprehension of the elements and their meaning. Level 2 SA involves the comprehension of the meaning of the elements identified in the achievement in level 1 SA, in relation to task goals. In achieving level 2 SA, an actor develops a distinct understanding of the significance of the elements perceived in level 1 SA. The actor now possesses and understanding of what each element means in relation to his situation and task goals.

Level 3 SA Projection of future status. The highest level of SA involves forecasting the future states of the elements in the environment. Using the information from levels 1 and 2 SA and experience in the form of mental models, an actor predicts or forecasts future states in the situation. For example, an experienced driver may predict that the car in front will brake sharply, due to a build up of traffic up ahead. Actors can effectively project onto future states based upon previous experience and the preceding levels of SA. Endsley (1995a) suggests that experienced actors are more efficient at achieving level 3 SA, as they use mental models formed by experience of similar scenarios.

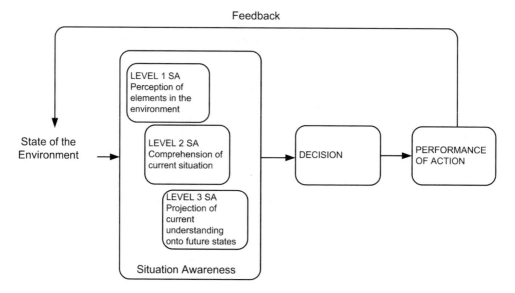

Figure 7.1   The Three Level Model of SA (Source: Endsley, 1995a)

The three level model of SA offers a simple and appealing model of SA. The description of three hierarchical levels of SA is neat and particularly useful for measuring the construct. The perceptual cycle model of SA proposed by Smith and Hancock (1995) offers an alternative model of SA. The model is based upon Niesser's (1976) perceptual cycle, which describes an individual's interaction with the world and the influential role of schemata. According to the perceptual cycle, actor interaction with the world (termed explorations) is directed by internally held schemata. The outcome of an actor's interaction then modifies the original schemata, which in turn directs further exploration. This process of directed interaction and modification continues in a cyclical manner.

Smith and Hancock (1995) use the perceptual cycle to explain the achievement and maintenance of SA. According to Smith and Hancock (1995) SA is neither resident in the world nor in the person, but that it resides through the interaction of the person with the world. Smith and Hancock (1995) describe SA as 'externally directed consciousness'. Unlike the three level model, which depicts SA as a product separate from the processes used to achieve it, SA is viewed as both process and product, offering an explanation for the cognitive activity involved in achieving SA. Just as Niesser (1976) describes an interaction whereby past experience directs an actor's anticipation and search for certain types of information within the current situation, which in turn directs behaviour, Smith and Hancock (1995) argue that the process of achieving and maintaining SA revolves around an actor's internally held models, which contain information regarding certain situations. These mental models facilitate the anticipation of situational events, directing the actor's attention to cues in the environment and directing their eventual course of action. The actor then carries out checks to confirm that the evolving situation conforms to their expectations. Any unexpected events prompt further search and exploration, and in turn modifies the individual's existing model. According to Smith and Hancock (1995), the perceptual cycle is continuously modifying an individual's mental models or schemata. The perceptual cycle model of SA is presented in Figure 7.2.

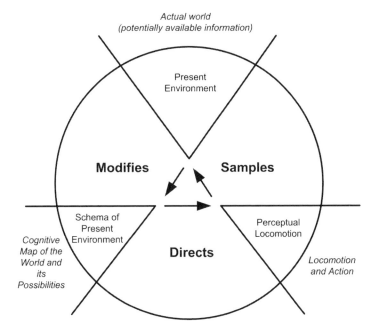

Figure 7.2   The Perceptual Cycle Model of SA (Smith and Hancock, 1995)

The perceptual cycle model offers a more comprehensive description of how SA is developed and maintained than the three level model. The model is complete in that it refers to both the process (the continuous sampling of the environment) and the product (the continually updated product of SA). The concept of internally held mental models or schemata based upon past events and experience is very similar to Endsley's description of the use of schemata to facilitate the achievement of SA. However, the perceptual cycle model of SA proposed by Smith and Hancock (1995) goes further to explain how it is that these models or schemata are continually developed and modified.

The main point of contention between theoretical perspectives lies in whether SA refers to the *processes* employed in achieving and maintaining it or the end *product* of SA, derived as a result of these processes. The three-level model proposed by Endsley (1995a) describes SA as a *product* comprised of the knowledge related outcomes of the three hierarchical levels, separate from the *processes* (labelled situation assessment) used to achieve it. The perceptual cycle model proposed by Smith and Hancock (1995) purports that SA resides through the interaction of the person with the world (Smith and Hancock, 1995) and describes SA both in terms of the cognitive *processes* used to engineer it and also the continuously updating *product* of SA.

The assessment of SA is used throughout the design lifecycle, either to determine the levels of SA provided by novel technology or designs or to assess SA in existing operational systems. According to Endsley (1995a) SA measures are necessary in order to evaluate the effect of new technologies and training interventions upon SA, to examine factors that affect SA, to evaluate the effectiveness of processes and strategies for acquiring SA and in investigating the nature of SA itself. There are a number of different SA assessment approaches available to the HF practitioner. In a review of SA measurement techniques, Endsley (1995b) describes a number of different approaches, including physiological measurement techniques (Eye tracker, P300), performance measures, external task measures, imbedded task measures, subjective rating techniques (self and observer rating), questionnaires (post-trial and on-line) and the freeze technique (e.g. SAGAT). The majority of SA measurement approaches focus on the measurement of SA from an individual actor perspective, and there has been only limited attention given to the assessment of team, or distributed SA. As a result of the methods review conducted as part of this effort, the following different categories of SA assessment technique were identified:

- SA requirements analysis techniques.
- Freeze probe techniques.
- Real-time probe techniques.
- Self-rating techniques.
- Observer-rating techniques.
- Distributed SA techniques.

The first step in a SA analysis in any environment is a SA requirements analysis. SA requirements analysis is used to determine exactly what it is that actually makes up operator SA in the task or environment under analysis. Endsley (1993) describes a generic procedure for conducting an SA requirements analysis that involves the use of unstructured interviews with SMEs, goal-directed task analysis and questionnaires in order to determine the SA requirements for a particular scenario. The output of an SA requirements analysis is typically used to inform the development of the SA assessment technique that will be used to assess SA for the scenario in question.

Freeze probe techniques involve the administration of SA related queries 'on-line' during 'freezes' in a simulation of the task under analysis (Salmon, Stanton, Walker and Green, in press). During these simulation freezes, displays and viewing windows are blanked, and a computer selects and administers appropriate SA queries for that portion of the task. Participants respond to the queries based upon their knowledge (SA) of the situation at the point of the freeze. Participant responses are taken as an indication of their SA at the point of the scenario when the freeze occurs. The main advantages associated with the freeze techniques are that they provide a direct measure or participant SA, they can be compared to the objective state of the world during the freeze (although the method cannot be properly regarded as 'objective' in itself), and they are relatively easy to use. The disadvantages are that significant work is required in developing the query content (e.g. SA requirements analysis), the simulation freezes are intrusive to primary task performance, and they typically require expensive simulations of the system and task under analysis in order to be used properly. A brief description of the freeze probe techniques reviewed is presented below.

The situation awareness global assessment technique (SAGAT; Endsley, 1995b) is an on-line freeze technique that was developed to assess pilot SA across the three levels proposed by Endsley (1995b). SAGAT uses a set of queries designed to assess participant SA, including level 1 SA (perception of the elements), level 2 SA (comprehension of their meaning) and level 3 SA (projection of future status). Although developed specifically for use in the military aviation domain, a number of different versions of SAGAT exist, including a specific air-to-air tactical aircraft version (Endsley, 1990), an advanced bomber aircraft version (Endsley, 1989) and an air traffic control version, SAGAT-TRACON (Endlsey and Kiris, 1995). SALSA (Hauss and Eyferth, 2003) is another on-line probe method that employs the freeze technique in its administration. Developed specifically for use in air traffic control, SALSA's SA queries are based upon fifteen aspects of aircraft flight, such as flight level, ground speed, heading, vertical tendency, conflict and type of conflict. The situation awareness control room inventory (SACRI; Hogg, Folleso, Strand-Volden and Torralba, 1995) is an adaptation of SAGAT (Endsley, 1995b) designed to assess control room operator SA. SACRI uses the freeze technique to administer control room based SA queries derived from a study conducted to investigate the application of SAGAT in process control rooms (Hogg et al, 1995).

Real-time probe techniques offer an alternative approach designed to remove the intrusive nature of freeze probe techniques. Real-time probe techniques involve the administration of SA related queries during the active scenario. The queries are typically developed on-line by appropriate SMEs. Probing participants for their SA in this way allows comparisons with the publicly observable state of the world, and removes the intrusion on primary task performance. Thus, it is argued that the advantages associated with 'real-time' probe techniques are reduced intrusiveness and that they offer a direct measure of participant SA. The disadvantages include a heavy burden placed upon the SME to develop SA related queries on-line, and despite claimed reductions, there remains some level of intrusiveness for primary task performance. The situation present assessment method (SPAM; Durso, Hackworth, Truitt, Crutchfield and Manning, 1998) was developed for use in the assessment of air traffic controller's SA. SPAM uses real-time on-line probes to assess operator SA. The analyst probes the operator for SA using task related SA queries based on pertinent information in the environment via telephone (e.g. which of the two aircraft A or B, has the highest altitude?). The query response time (for those responses that are correct) is taken as an indicator of the operator's SA. Additionally, the time taken to answer the telephone acts as a (very) crude indication of operator MWL. SASHA (Jeannot, Kelly and Thompson, 2003) was developed by Eurocontrol for the assessment of air traffic controller's SA in automated systems. The methodology consists of two techniques, SASHA_L (on-line probing technique) and SASHA_Q (post-trial questionnaire) and was developed as part of the solutions for human automation partnerships in European ATM (SHAPE) project, the purpose of which was to investigate the effects of an increasing use of automation in air traffic management (Jeannott, Kelly and Thompson, 2003). The SASHA_L technique is based upon the SPAM technique (Durso et al, 1998), and involves probing the participant on-line using real-time SA related queries. The response content and response time is taken as a measure of controller SA. When using SASHA_ L, participant response time is graded as 'too quick', 'OK' or 'too long', and the response content is graded as 'incorrect', 'OK' or 'correct'. Once the trial is completed, the participant completes the SASHA_Q questionnaire, which consists of ten questions designed to assess participant SA.

Self-rating techniques are used to elicit subjective estimates of SA from participants. Typically administered post-trial, self-rating techniques involve participants providing a subjective rating of their SA via an SA related rating scale. The primary advantage of such techniques is their low cost, ease of implementation and non-intrusive nature. However, self-rating techniques administered post-trial suffer from a number of disadvantages that are associated with reporting SA data 'after the fact'. These include the fact that participants are prone to forgetting periods of the trial when they had poor or low SA (Endsley, 1995b), or in other words they cannot be situationally aware of informational artefacts in the scenario that they are not aware of. The SA ratings elicited, therefore, may also be correlated with performance (Endsley, 1995b). Endsley (1995b) also points out that participants in these paradigms also suffer from primacy/recency type effects, so typically are poor at reporting detailed information about past events and that post-trial questionnaires only capture participant SA at the end of the task in question. However, one of the most popular self-rating approaches is the situation awareness rating technique (SART; Taylor 1990). SART offers a simplistic and quick approach for assessing SA and was originally developed for the assessment of pilot SA in military environments. SART uses the following ten dimensions to measure operator SA:

- Familiarity of the situation.
- Focusing of attention.
- Information quantity.
- Information quality.
- Instability of the situation.
- Concentration of attention.
- Complexity of the situation.
- Variability of the situation.
- Arousal.
- Spare mental capacity.

Participants provide a rating for each dimension on a seven point rating scale (1 = Low, 7 = High) in order to derive a subjective measure of SA. The ten SART dimensions can also be condensed into the 3 dimensional (3-D) SART, which involves participants rating attentional demand, attentional supply and understanding. The situation awareness rating scales technique (SARS; Waag and Houck, 1994) is a subjective rating SA measurement technique that was developed for the military aviation domain. When using the SARS technique, participants subjectively rate their performance on a six-point rating scale (from acceptable to outstanding) for 31 facets of fighter pilot SA. The SARS SA categories and associated behaviours were developed from interviews with experienced F-15 pilots. The 31 SARS behaviours are divided into seven categories representing phases of mission performance. The seven categories are:

- General traits (e.g. Decisiveness, spatial ability).
- Tactical game plan (e.g. Developing and executing plan).
- Communication (e.g. Quality).
- Information interpretation (e.g. Threat prioritisation).
- Tactical employment beyond visual range (e.g. Targeting decisions).
- Tactical employment visual (e.g. Threat evaluation).
- Tactical employment general (e.g. Lookout, defensive reaction).

According to Waag and Houck (1994) the 31 SARS behaviours represent those that are crucial to mission success. The Crew awareness rating scale (CARS; McGuiness and Foy, 2000) technique has been used to assess command and control 'commander's' SA and workload (McGuinness and Ebbage, 2000). The CARS comprises two separate sets of questions based upon Endsley's three level model of SA. CARS uses two subscales, the content subscale and the workload subscale. The content subscale consists of three statements designed to elicit ratings based upon ease of identification, understanding and projection of task SA elements (i.e. levels 1, 2 and 3 SA). The fourth statement is designed to assess how well the participant identifies relevant task related goals in the situation. The workload subscale also consists of four statements, which are designed to assess how difficult, in terms of mental effort, it is for the participant in question to identify, understand, and project the future states of the SA related elements in the situation. CARS is administered post-trial and involves participants rating each category on a scale of 1 (ideal) to 4 (worst) (McGuinness and Ebbage, 2000). The mission awareness rating scale (MARS) technique is a development of the CARS approach that was designed specifically for use in the assessment of SA in military exercises. The MARS technique was developed for use in real-world field settings, rather than in simulations of military exercises. The technique is normally administered post-trial, after the completion of the task or mission under analysis. The Cranfield situation awareness scale (C-SAS; Dennehy, 1997) is another self-rating scale that is used to assess student pilot SA during flight training exercises. C-SAS is administered either during task performance or post-trial and involves participants rating five SA related components on an appropriate rating scale. Each rating scale score is then summed in order to determine an overall SA score.

Observer-rating techniques are also used to assess SA. Observer-rating techniques typically involve appropriate subject matter experts (SMEs) observing participants performing the task under analysis and then providing an assessment or rating of each participant's SA. The SA ratings are based upon observable SA related behaviour exhibited by the participants during task performance. The primary advantages of observer-rating techniques are their low intrusiveness to the task under analysis and also the understanding of the SA requirements of the situation that the SMEs bring with them. However, such techniques can be criticised in terms of the construct validity that they possess. How far observers can accurately assess the internal construct of SA is questionable (Endsley, 1995b). Although external behaviours may offer an insight into SA, the degree to which they represent the participant's SA is certainly suspect. Access to the required SMEs may also prove very difficult. The situation awareness behavioural rating scale (SABARS) is an observer-rating technique that has been used to assess infantry personnel situation awareness in field training exercises (Matthews, Pleban, Endsley and Strater, 2000, Matthews and Beal 2002). SABARS involves domain experts observing participants during task performance and rating them on 28 observable SA related behaviours. A five point rating scale (1=Very poor, 5 =Very good) and an additional 'not applicable' category are used. The 28 behaviour rating items are designed specifically to assess platoon leader SA (Matthews, Pleban, Endsley and Strater, 2000).

As noted previously, the concept of distributed or team SA has previously only received limited attention, and consequently there are a lack of approaches designed for this. Recently, there has been interest in the use of network-based approaches for considering notions of situation awareness, particularly as it is distributed across team members. The idea that knowledge can be distributed across system components is at the heart of the work reported by Cooke and her colleagues (Gillan and Cooke, 2001; Cooke, 2004). In this work, the focus is on what might be termed global knowledge rather than on knowledge pertaining to specific situations. The approach enables Subject Matter Experts (SMEs) from the system to be explored with a small number of concepts. Cooke (2005) uses eleven concepts, and asks the SMEs to conduct pair-wise assessments of relatedness. The results then feed into the KNOT (knowledge network organizing tool) Pathfinder Network Analysis software in order to produce an indication of which concepts are grouped by specific roles within a system. The results indicate that different roles group the concepts in different ways. In this work, the structure of the network is derived post-hoc and is based on clustering a small number of concepts that are deemed relevant to the global mission of a system. Matheus et al. (2003) explore the possibility of constructing a core ontology for situation awareness. In their work, situation awareness is a function of a stream of measurements that can be fused with a set of theories about the state of the world. From this perspective, they create an ontology, using entity-relationship modelling, which relates the state of specific objects in the world to an overall 'SituationObject'. Stanton et al. (2005) describe the propositional network methodology, which has been used to measure and represent distributed SA in C4i environments.

Table 7.1   Summary of SA Methods

Method	Type of method	Domain	Training time	Application time	Related methods	Tools needed	Validation Studies	Advantages	Disadvantages
CARS	Self-rating technique	Military (infantry operations)	Low	Med	SART MARS SARS	Pen and paper	Yes	1) Developed for use in infantry environments. 2) Less intrusive than on-line techniques. 3) Quick, easy to use requiring little training.	1) Construct validity questionable. 2) Limited evidence of use and validation. 3) Possible correlation with performance.
MARS	Self-rating technique	Military (infantry operations)	Low	Med	SART CARS SARS	Pen and paper	Yes	1) Developed for use in infantry environments. 2) Less intrusive than on-line techniques. 3) Quick, easy to use requiring little training.	1) Construct validity questionable. 2) Limited evidence of use and validation. 3) Possible correlation with performance.
SABARS	Observer rating	Military (infantry operations)	High	Med	MARS	Pen and paper	Yes	1) SABARS behaviours generated from infantry SA requirements exercise. 2) Non-intrusive.	1) SMEs required. 2) The presence of observers may influence participant behaviour. 3) Access to field settings required.
SACRI	Freeze on-line probe technique	Nuclear Power	Low	Med	SAGAT	Simulator Computer	Yes	1) Removes problems associated with collecting SA data post-trial.	1) Requires expensive simulators. 2) Intrusive to primary task.
SAGAT	Freeze on-line probe technique	Aviation (military)	Low	Med	SACRI SALSA	Simulator Computer	Yes	1) Widely used in a number of domains. 2) Subject to numerous validation studies. 3) Removes problems associated with collecting SA data post-trial.	1) Requires expensive simulators. 2) Intrusive to primary task. 3) Substantial work is required to develop appropriate queries.
SALSA	Freeze on-line probe technique	ATC	Low	Med	SACRI SAGAT	Simulator Computer	Yes	1) Removes problems associated with collecting SA data post-trial e.g. correlation with performance, forgetting etc.	1) Requires expensive simulators. 2) Intrusive to primary task. 3) Limited use and validation.

Table 7.1 (continued)

	Type	Domain			Related techniques	Equipment	Freeze required	Advantages	Disadvantages
SASHA_L SASHA_Q	Real-time probe technique Post-trial quest	ATC	High	Med	SPAM	Simulator Computer Telephone Pen and paper	No	1) Offers two techniques for the assessment of SA.	1) Construct validity questionable. 2) Generation of appropriate SA queries places great burden upon analyst/SME. 3) Limited evidence of use or validation studies.
SARS	Self-rating technique	Aviation (military)	Low	Low	SART MARS CARS	Pen and paper	Yes	1) Quick and easy to use, requires little training 2) Non-intrusive to primary task.	1) Problems of gathering SA data post-trial e.g. correlation with performance, forgetting low SA. 2) Limited use and validation evidence.
SART	Self-rating technique	Aviation (military)	Low	Low	CARS MARS SARS	Pen and paper	Yes	1) Quick and easy to administer. Also low cost. 2) Generic – can be used in other domains. 3) Widely used in a number of domains.	1) Correlation between performance and reported SA. 2) Participants are not aware of their low SA. 3) Construct validity is questionable.
SA-SWORD	Paired comparison technique	Aviation	Low	Low	SWORD Pro - SWORD	Pen and paper	Yes	1) Easy to learn and use. Also low cost. 2) Generic – can be used in other domains. 3) Useful when comparing two designs.	1) Post-trial administration – correlation with performance, forgetting etc. 2) Limited use and validation evidence. 3) Does not provide a measure of SA.
SPAM	Real-time probe technique	ATC	High	Low	SASHA_L	Simulator Computer Telephone	Yes	1) No freeze required.	1) Low construct validity. 2) Limited use and validation. 3) Participants may be unable to verbalise spatial representations.
SA requirements analysis	N/A	Aviation Generic	High	High	Interview Task analysis Obs Quest	Pen and paper Recording equipment	No	1) Specifies the elements that comprise SA in the task environment under analysis. 2) Can be used to generate SA queries/probes. 3) Has been used extensively in a number of domains.	1) A huge amount of resources are required. 2) Analyst(s) may require training in a number of different HF techniques, such as interviews, task analysis and observations.
C-SAS	Self-rating technique	Aviation	Low	Low	SART CARS SARS	Pen and paper	No	1) Quick and very simple to use.	1) Unsophisticated measure of SA. 2) Not used in scientific analysis scenarios

Propositional networks use the CDM interview approach to identify the knowledge objects related to a particular task or scenario. Propositional networks consisting of the knowledge objects required during the scenario under analysis are then constructed for each phase identified by a CDM analysis. A summary of the SA measurement techniques reviewed is presented in Table 7.1.

SA Requirements Analysis

Background and Application

SA requirements analyses are conducted prior to an assessment of operator SA in order to identify what exactly comprises SA in the scenario or environment under analysis. This ensures the validity of the SA assessment technique used, in that it specifies what exactly SA in the environment under analysis is comprised of, and thus determines those elements of SA that the chosen assessment technique should measure. For example, when using an on-line probe technique such as SAGAT, the results of an SA requirements analysis form the content of the SA queries used. Similarly, the results of an SA requirements analysis are used to construct those behaviours that are rated in observer rating techniques such as SABARS. Whilst there are a plethora of techniques available to the HF practitioner for the assessment of SA, there is limited guidance available on how to conduct an SA requirements analysis in order to determine the features of SA that are measured. Endsley (1993) describes a procedure that can be used to determine the SA requirements within a particular operational environment. The procedure has been applied in order to determine the SA requirements in a number of different settings, including air-to-air flight combat (Endsley, 1993), advanced bomber missions (Endsley, 1989) and air traffic control (Endsley and Rogers, 1994). The SA requirements analysis procedure involves the use of unstructured interviews, goal-directed task analysis and structured questionnaires in order to determine the SA requirements for the task(s) or scenarios in question. The results of the SA requirements analysis are then used to inform the development of the SA queries that are used in the SAGAT analysis.

Domain of Application

Generic.

Procedure and Advice

Step 1: Define the task(s) under analysis
The first step in an SA requirements analysis is to clearly define the task or scenario under analysis. It is recommended that the task is described clearly, including the system used, the task goals and the environment within which the task is to take place. An SA requirements analysis requires that the task is defined explicitly in order to ensure that the appropriate SA requirements are comprehensively assessed.

Step 2: Select appropriate SMEs
The SA requirements analysis procedure is based upon eliciting SA related knowledge from domain experts or SMEs. Therefore, the analyst should begin by selecting a set of appropriate SMEs. The more experienced the SMEs are in the task environment under analysis the better, and the analyst should strive to use as many SMEs as possible to ensure comprehensiveness. In an SA requirements analysis of air-to-air combat fighters, Endsley (1993) used 10 SMEs (former military

pilots) with an average length of military service of 15.9 years during the interview process, and also 20 SMEs during the questionnaire process.

Step 3: Interview phase
Once the task under analysis is defined clearly, a series of unstructured interviews with the SMEs should be conducted. According to Endsley (1993), the SME should be first asked to describe in their own words what they feel comprises 'good' SA. They should then be asked what they would want to know in order to achieve perfect SA. Finally, the SME should be asked to describe what each of the SA elements identified are used for during the task under analysis e.g. decision making, planning, actions etc. Endsley (1993) also suggests that once the interviewer has exhausted the SME's knowledge, they should offer their own suggestions regarding SA requirements, and discuss their relevance. It is recommended that each interview is recorded either using either video or audio recording equipment.

Step 4: Conduct a goal-directed task analysis
Once the interview phase is complete, a goal-directed task analysis should be conducted for the task under analysis. It is recommended that a HTA is conducted for this purpose. Once the HTA is complete, the SA elements required for the completion of each bottom level task step in the HTA should be added. This step is intended to ensure that the list of SA requirements identified during the interview phase is comprehensive. In conducting the HTA of the task under analysis, observation and further interviews with SMEs may be required.

Step 5: Develop and administer SA requirements analysis questionnaire
The interview and task analysis phases should produce a comprehensive list of SA requirements for the task or scenario under analysis. These SA elements should then be integrated into a rating type questionnaire, along with any others that the analyst(s) feels are pertinent. Appropriate SMEs should then be asked to rate the criticality of each of the SA elements identified in relation to the task under analysis. Items should be rated as: *not important* (1), *somewhat important* (2) or *very important* (3). The ratings provided should then be averaged across subjects for item.

Step 6: Determine SA requirements
Once the questionnaires have been collected and scored, the analyst(s) should use them to determine the SA elements for the task or scenario under analysis. How this is done is dependent upon the analyst(s)' judgement. It may be that the elements specified in the questionnaire are presented as SA requirements, along with a classification in terms of importance (e.g. not important, somewhat important or very important).

Advantages

1. An SA requirements analysis output specifies the knowledge required for SA during the task or scenario under analysis.
2. The output can be used to develop queries designed to assess operator SA in the task or scenario under analysis.
3. If conducted properly, the technique has the potential to be very comprehensive.
4. Uses SMEs with high levels of relevant experience, ensuring comprehensiveness and validity.
5. The SA requirements analysis procedure has been used extensively in a number of different domains e.g. aviation (Endsley, 1989, 1993), air traffic control (Endsley and Rogers, 1994) and the military.

6. Provides guidance for the analyst in the development of SA measures for the task or scenario under analysis.
7. Can be applied in any domain.

Disadvantages

1. The SA requirements analysis procedure is a lengthy one, requiring interviews, observation, task analysis and the administration of questionnaires. A huge amount of resources are invested when conducting an SA requirements analysis.
2. Requires access to numerous SMEs for a lengthy period of time. This access may be difficult to obtain.
3. The identification of SA requirements is largely dependent upon the interview skills of the analysts involved and also the quality of the SMEs used.

Related Methods

The output of an SA requirements analysis is typically used to inform the development of SA related queries for the SAGAT SA measurement approach. In conducting an SA requirements analysis, a number of data collection procedures are employed, including interviews, observational study, task analysis and questionnaires.

Approximate Training and Application Times

Providing the analyst involved has experience in the use of interview, task analysis and questionnaire techniques, the training time for the SA requirements analysis technique would be low. However, for analysts with no experience in such techniques, it is estimated that the training time would be high. Such analysts would require training in the use of a number of HF techniques, such as interviews, observations, task analysis and questionnaires, which would incur a high training time. The application time for an SA requirements analysis would also be very high. The total application time would include interviews with SMEs, conducting an appropriate task analysis and developing, administering and scoring a number of questionnaires.

Reliability and Validity

There are no data regarding the reliability and validity of the SA requirements procedure available in the literature.

Tools Needed

At its most basic, the SA requirements analysis procedure can be conducted using pen and paper. However, in order to make the analysis as simple and as comprehensive as possible, it is recommended that video and audio recording equipment are used to record the interviews and that a computer with a word processing package (such as Microsoft Word) and SPSS are used during the design and analysis of the questionnaire. Microsoft Visio is also useful when producing the task analysis output.

Flowchart

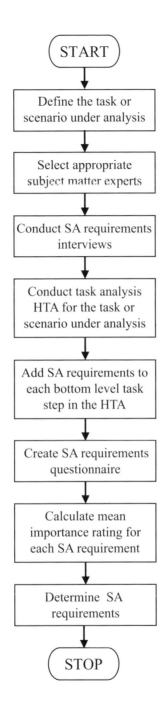

Situation Awareness Global Assessment Technique (SAGAT)

Background and Applications

The situation awareness (SA) global assessment technique (SAGAT) is an on-line probe technique that was developed to assess pilot SA across the three levels of SA proposed by Endsley (1995a) in her information processing based model. The SAGAT approach uses queries regarding the SA requirements for the task or environment under analysis, including level 1 SA (perception of the elements), level 2 SA (comprehension of their meaning) and level 3 SA (projection of future status). The technique itself is simulator based, and involves querying participants for their SA during random freezes in a simulation of the task or scenario under analysis. The freeze technique involves freezing the simulation at random points, blanking the simulation screen and administrating relevant SA queries for that point of the simulation. This technique allows SA data to be collected immediately and also removes the problems associated with collecting SA data post-trial (Endsley, 1995), such as a correlation between SA ratings and performance.

Endsley (1995b) describes a SAGAT approach used in the military aviation domain. The SAGAT queries used included level 1 SA questions regarding the aircraft heading, location, other aircraft heading, G level, Fuel level, Weapon quantity, Altitude, weapon selection and airspeed. Level 2 SA queries included questions regarding mission timing and status, impact of system degrades, time and distance available on fuel and the tactical status of threat aircraft. Finally, level 3 SA queries included questions regarding projected aircraft tactics and manoeuvres, firing position and timing (Endsley, 1995b). At the end of the trial the participant is given a SAGAT score. Alternatively, an error score (SAGAT query minus actual value) can be calculated (Endsley, 1995). Also, time elapsed between the stop in the simulation and the query answer is recorded and used as a measure.

The SAGAT approach is undoubtedly the most commonly used and well known of the various SA assessment techniques available. Consequently, a number of variations of the technique exist. The situation awareness probes (SAPS) technique (Jensen 1999) was developed by DERA to assess military helicopter pilot SA and is a modification of SAGAT that uses fewer probes to achieve minimal intrusiveness. SALSA (Hauss and Eyferth, 2002) is an adaptation of the SAGAT technique that has been used to assess air traffic controller SA. The SAVANT technique was developed by the FAA technical centre (Willems, 2000) and is a combination of the SAGAT and SPAM techniques.

Domain of Application

Military aviation, however, provided the SA requirements and associated probes are developed, the SAGAT procedure can be applied in any domain where a simulation of the task(s) under analysis is available.

Procedure and Advice

Step 1: Define task(s)
The first step in a SAGAT analysis (aside from the process of gaining access to the required systems and personnel) is to define the tasks that are to be subjected to analysis. The type of tasks analysed are dependent upon the focus of the analysis. For example, when assessing the effects on operator SA caused by a novel design or training programme, it is useful to analyse as representative a set of tasks as possible. To analyse a full set of tasks will often be too time consuming and labour intensive, and so it is pertinent to use a set of tasks that use all aspects of the system under analysis. Once the task(s) under analysis are defined clearly, a HTA should be conducted for each task. This allows the analyst(s) and participants to understand the task(s) fully.

Step 2: Development of SA queries
Next, the analyst(s) should conduct an SA requirements analysis in order to identify what comprises SA during the task or scenario under analysis. The results of the SA requirements analysis are then used to develop a set of SA queries for the task under analysis. The SA requirements analysis

procedure is described above. There are no rules regarding the number of queries per task. In a study of air traffic controller SA, Endsley et al (2000) used SAGAT queries regarding the following SA elements.

a. Level 1 SA – Perception of the traffic situation
Aircraft location.
Aircraft level of control.
Aircraft call sign.
Aircraft altitude.
Aircraft groundspeed.
Aircraft heading.
Aircraft flight path change.
Aircraft type.

b. Level 2 and 3 SA – comprehension and projection of traffic situation
Aircraft next sector.
Aircraft next separation.
Aircraft advisories.
Advisory reception.
Advisory conformance.
Aircraft hand-offs.
Aircraft communications.
Special airspace separation.
Weather impact.

Step 3: Selection of participants
Once the task(s) under analysis are defined, and the appropriate SAGAT queries have been developed, the next step involves selecting appropriate participants for the analysis. This may not always be necessary and it may suffice to simply select participants randomly on the day. However, if SA is being compared across rank or experience levels, then clearly effort is required to select the appropriate participants.

Step 4: Brief participants
Before the task(s) under analysis are performed, all of the participants involved should be briefed regarding the purpose of the study and the SAGAT technique. It may useful at this stage to take the participants through an example SAGAT analysis, so that they understand how the technique works and what is required of them as participants.

Step 5: Pilot run
Before the 'real' data collection process begins, it is recommended that the participants take part in a number of test scenarios or pilot runs of the SAGAT data collection procedure. A number of small test scenarios should be used to iron out any problems with the data collection procedure, and the participants should be encouraged to ask any questions. Once the participant is familiar with the procedure and is comfortable with his or her role, the 'real' data collection can begin.

Step 6: Task performance
Once the participants fully understand the SAGAT technique and the data collection procedure, they are free to undertake the task(s) under analysis as normal. The participant should begin task performance using an appropriate simulation of the task or scenario under analysis.

Step 7: Freeze the simulation
At any random point in time, the simulation is frozen or stopped and the displays and window screens are blanked. A computer is normally programmed to freeze the simulation at random points during the trial.

Step 8: SA query administration
Once the simulation is frozen at the appropriate point, the analyst should probe the participant's SA using the pre-defined SA queries. These queries are designed to allow the analyst to gain a measure of the participant's knowledge of the situation at that exact point in time. These questions are directly related to the participant's SA at that point in the simulation. A computer programmed with the SA queries is normally used to administer the queries. To stop any overloading of the participants, all SA queries are not administrated in any one stop. Only a randomly selected portion of the SA queries is administrated at any one time. Steps 7 and 8 are repeated throughout the simulation until enough data is obtained regarding the participant's SA. Jones and Kaber (2004) present the following guidelines for SAGAT query administration:

- The timing of SAGAT queries should be randomly determined;
- A SAGAT freeze should not occur within the first three to five minutes of the trial under analysis;
- SAGAT freezes should not occur within one minute of each other; and
- Multiple SAGAT stops can be used during the task under analysis.

Step 9: Query answer evaluation
Upon completion of the simulator trial, the participants query answers are compared to what was actually happening in the situation at the time of query administration. To achieve this, participant answers are compared to data from the simulation computers. Endsley (1995b) suggests that this comparison of the real and perceived situation provides an objective measure of the participants' SA.

Step 10: SAGAT score calculation
The final step of a SAGAT analysis involves the calculation of participant SA during the task or scenario under analysis. Typically, a SAGAT score is calculated for each participant. Additional measures or variations on the SAGAT score can be taken depending upon study requirements, such as time taken to answer queries.

Advantages

1. SAGAT directly measures participant SA.
2. SAGAT provides an objective assessment of participant SA.
3. SAGAT queries can be designed to encapsulate all operator SA requirements.
4. SAGAT has been extensively used in the past and has a wealth of associated validation evidence (Jones and Endsley, 2000, Durso et al, 1998, Garland and Endsley, 1995)
5. On-line probing aspect removes the problem of subjects biasing their attention towards certain aspects of the situation.
6. On-line probing also removes the various problems associated with participants reporting SA 'after the fact', such as a correlation between SA and performance and also participants forgetting parts of the trial where they had a low level of SA.
7. The use of random sampling provides unbiased SA scores that can be compared statistically across trials, subjects and systems (Endsley, 1995).
8. SAGAT possesses direct face validity (Endsley, 1995).
9. The method can be suitably tailored for use in any domain.

10. SAGAT is the most widely used and validated SA measurement technique available.

Disadvantages

1. Using the technique requires expensive high fidelity simulators and computers.
2. The SAGAT queries are intrusive to the primary task of system operation.
3. When using the SAGAT the simulation must be stopped or frozen a number of times in order to collect the data.
4. Due to the 'freeze technique' adopted by the SAGAT approach, its use in real-world or field settings is limited.
5. Based upon the very simplistic three level model of SA.
6. Significant development is required in order to use the technique in domains other than aviation.
7. The SAGAT approach is not suited to the assessment of team or distributed SA.
8. A SAGAT analysis requires extensive preparation. An appropriate SA requirements analysis is normally required, which requires considerable effort.

Example

Endsley et al (2000) describe a study that was conducted in order to evaluate the effects of an advanced display concept on air traffic controller SA, workload and performance. SAGAT, SART and an on-line probing technique similar to SPAM were used to assess controller SA. A SME rating of SA was also provided. The SAGAT data was collected during four random freezes in each of the trials. During the simulation freeze, the controller radar display was blanked and the simulation was frozen (Endsley et al 2000). A computer was used to administer the queries and also to record the participant's answers. The SAGAT queries used in the study are presented in Table 7.2.

Table 7.2   SAGAT Queries (Source: Endsley et al, 2000)

1. Enter the location of all aircraft (on the provided sector map).
Aircraft in track control.
Other aircraft in sector.
Aircraft will be in track control in the next two minutes.
2. Enter aircraft call sign (for aircraft highlighted of those entered in query 1).
3. Enter aircraft altitude (for aircraft highlighted of those entered in query 1).
4. Enter aircraft groundspeed (for aircraft highlighted of those entered in query 1).
5. Enter aircraft heading (for aircraft highlighted of those entered in query 1).
6. Enter aircraft's next sector (for aircraft highlighted of those entered in query 1).
7. Enter aircraft's current direction of change in each column (for aircraft highlighted of those entered in query 1) Altitude change/Turn/Climbing right turn/Descending left turn/ Level straight.
8. Enter aircraft type (for aircraft highlighted of those entered in query 1).
9. Which pairs of aircraft have lost or will lose separation if they stay on their current (intended) courses?
10. Which aircraft have been advisories for situations which have not been resolved?
11. Did the aircraft receive its advisory correctly? (for each of those entered in query 11)
12. Which aircraft are currently conforming to their advisories? (for each of those entered in query 11)
13. Which aircraft must be handed off to another sector/facility within the next two minutes?
14. Enter aircraft which are not in communication with you.
15. Enter the aircraft that will violate special airspace separation standards if they stay on their current (intended) paths.
16. Which aircraft are weather currently an impact on or will be an impact on in the next five minutes along their current course?

Endsley et al (2000) reported a significant difference between conditions in the participant knowledge of aircraft conformance to advisories. It was found that participants were three times more likely to understand correctly whether aircraft were conforming to their advisories when using the enhanced display. No other significant differences between trials or conditions were found.

Jones and Kaber (2004) present the following example of a SAGAT-TRACON analysis. The computerised presentation of the queries is presented in Figure 7.3 and Figure 7.4, and the associated queries are presented in Table 7.3.

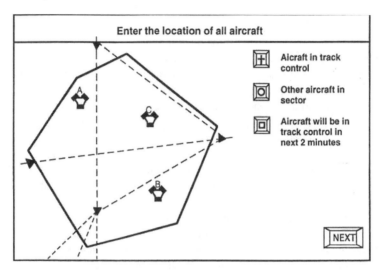

Figure 7.3   Query 1: Sector Map for TRACON Air Traffic Control (Jones and Kaber, 2004)

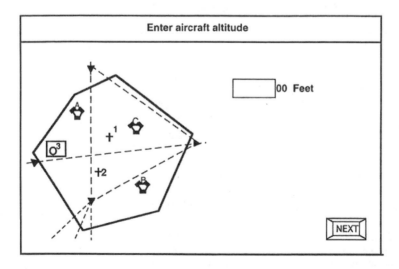

Figure 7.4   Additional Query on TRACON Simulation (Jones and Kaber, 2004)

Table 7.3   SAGAT Queries for Air Traffic Control (TRACON) (Endsley and Kiris, 1995)

Enter the location of all aircraft (on the provided sector map): aircraft in track control, other aircraft in sector, aircraft that will be in track control in next two minutes.
Enter aircraft callsign [for aircraft highlighted of those entered in Query 1].
Enter aircraft altitude [for aircraft highlighted of those entered in Query 1].
Enter aircraft groundspeed [for aircraft highlighted of those entered in Query 1].
Enter aircraft heading [for aircraft highlighted of those entered in Query 1].
Enter aircraft's next sector [for aircraft highlighted of those entered in Query 1].
Which pairs of aircraft have lost or will lose separation if they stay on their current (assigned) courses?
Which aircraft have been issued assignments (clearances) that have not been completed?
Did the aircraft receive its assignment correctly?
Which aircraft are currently conforming to their assignments?

Related Methods

SAGAT was the first SA measurement technique to utilise the 'freeze' technique of administration. A number of SA measurement techniques based on the SAGAT technique have since been developed, including SALSA (Hauss and Eyferth, 2003) and SAGAT-TRACON. SAGAT is also regularly used in conjunction with an SA subjective rating technique, such as SART (Selcon and Taylor, 1989). More recently, Matthews, Pleban, Endsley and Strater (2000) used SAGAT in conjunction with situation awareness behavioural rating scales (SABARS) and a participant situation awareness questionnaire (PSAQ) to measure SA in a military urban operations scenario.

Approximate Training and Application Times

It is estimated that the associated amount of training time would be minimal as the analyst would only have to familiarise themselves with the freeze technique and the administration of the SA queries. The application time associated with the SAGAT technique is dependent upon the duration of the task under analysis and the amount of SA data required. Endsley et al (2000) used SAGAT along with SART and SPAM to assess air traffic controller SA when using an advanced display concept. Ten scenarios were used (six test scenarios and four training scenarios), each of which lasted approximately 45 minutes each.

Reliability and Validity

Along with the SART technique, SAGAT is the most widely validated of all SA techniques. A wealth of validation evidence exists for the SAGAT approach to measuring SA. According to Jones and Kaber (2004) numerous studies have been performed to assess the validity of the SAGAT and the evidence suggests that the method is a valid metric of SA. Endsley (2000) reports that the SAGAT technique has been shown to have a high degree of validity and reliability for measuring SA. According to Endsley (2000) a study found SAGAT to have high reliability (test-retest scores of .98, .99, .99 and .92) of mean scores for four fighter pilots participating in two sets of simulation trials. Collier and Folleso (1995) also reported good reliability for SAGAT when measuring nuclear power plant operator SA. When used to measure SA in a driving task study (Gugerty, 1997) reported good reliability for the percentage of cars recalled, recall error and composite recall error. Fracker (1991) however reported low reliability for SAGAT when measuring participant knowledge of aircraft location. Regarding validity, Endsley et al (2000) reported a good level of sensitivity for SAGAT, but not for real-time probes (on-line queries with no freeze) and subjective SA measures. Endsley (1990) also report that SAGAT showed a degree of predictive validity when measuring pilot SA, with SAGAT scores indicative of pilot performance in a combat simulation. The study found that pilots who were able to report on enemy aircraft via SAGAT were three times more likely to later kill that target in the simulation. However, it is certainly questionable whether good performance is directly correlated with good or high SA. Presumably, within the three level model of SA, a pilot could theoretically have very high SA and still fail to kill the enemy target, thus achieving low performance. Basing validity on a correlation between measurement and performance is therefore not recommended.

Flowchart

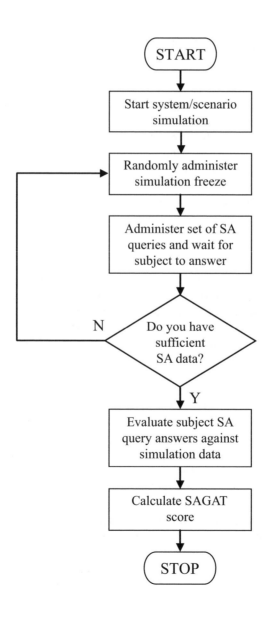

Tools Needed

In order to carry out a SAGAT type analysis, a high fidelity simulator of the system (e.g. aircraft) is required. The simulation should possess the ability to randomly blank all operator displays and 'window' displays, administer relevant SA queries and calculate participant SA scores.

Situation Awareness Rating Technique (SART)

Background and Applications

The situation awareness rating technique (SART; Taylor, 1990) is a quick and easy self–rating SA measurement technique that was developed by Taylor (1990) as part of a study conducted in order to develop methods for the subjective estimation of SA. The developed method was to contribute to the quantification and validation of design objectives for crew-systems integration (Taylor, 1990). The SART technique was developed from interviews with operational RAF aircrew aimed at eliciting relevant workload and SA knowledge. As a result of these interviews, 10 dimensions that could be used to measure pilot SA were derived. These 10 dimensions are used in conjunction with a likert scale, categories (low vs. high), or pairwise comparisons in order to rate pilot SA. When using these dimensions the technique becomes the 10D-SART. The 10 SART dimensions are presented in Table 7.4 below.

Table 7.4   SART Dimensions

Familiarity of the situation	Complexity of the situation
Focusing of attention	Variability of the situation
Information quantity	Arousal
Instability of the situation	Information quality
Concentration of attention	Spare capacity

A quicker version of the SART approach also exists, the 3D SART. The 3D SART uses the 10 dimensions described above grouped into the following three dimensions:

*   Demands on attentional resources: A combination of complexity, variability and instability of the situation.
*   Supply of attentional resources: A combination of arousal, focusing of attention, spare mental capacity and concentration of attention.
*   Understanding of the situation: A combination of information quantity, information quality and familiarity of the situation.

Participants are asked post-trial to rate each dimension on a likert scale of 1 to 7 (1=low, 7=high). Alternatively, specific categories (low vs. high) or pairwise comparisons can also be used. The SART rating sheet is presented in Figure 7.5.

Instability of Situation

> How changeable is the situation? Is the situation highly unstable
> and likely to change suddenly (high), or is it very stable and
> straightforward (low)?

Low ├───┤ High

> Complexity of Situation
> How complicated is the situation? Is it complex with
> many interrelated components (high) or is it simple and
> straightforward (low)?

Low ├───┤ High

> Variability of Situation
> How many variables are changing in the situation? Are there
> a large number of factors varying (high) or are there very few
> variables changing (low)?

Low ├───┤ High

> Arousal
> How aroused are you in the situation? Are you alert and ready
> for activity (high) or do you have a low degree of alertness
> (low)?

Low ├───┤ High

> Concentration of Attention
> How much are you concentrating on the situation? Are you
> bringing all your thoughts to bear (high) or is your attention
> elsewhere (low)?

Low ├───┤ High

> Division of Attention
> How much is your attention divided in the situation? Are you
> concentrating on many aspects of the situation (high) or focused
> on only one (low)?

Low ├───┤ High

> Spare Mental Capacity
> How much mental capacity do you have to spare in the
> situation? Do you have sufficient to attend to many variables
> (high) or nothing to spare at all (low)?

Low ├───┤ High

> Information Quantity
> How much information have you gained about the situation?
> Have you received and understood a great deal of knowledge
> (high) or very little (low)?

Low ├───┤ High

> Information Quality
> How good is the information you have gained about the
> situation? Is the knowledge communicated very useful (high) or
> is it a new situation (low)?

Low ├───┤ High

> Familiarity with situation
> How familiar are you with the situation? Do you have a great
> deal of relevant experience (high) or is it a new situation (low)?

Low ├───┤ High

Figure 7.5   SART 10D Rating Sheet

Domain of Application

The SART approach was originally developed for use in the military aviation domain. However, SART has since been applied in a number of different domains, and it is feasible that it could be used in any domain to assess operator SA.

Procedure and Advice

Step 1: Define task(s) under analysis
The first step in a SART analysis (aside from the process of gaining access to the required systems and personnel) is to define the tasks that are to be subjected to analysis. The type of tasks analysed are dependent upon the focus of the analysis. For example, when assessing the effects on operator SA caused by a novel design or training programme, it is useful to analyse as representative a set of tasks as possible. To analyse a full set of tasks will often be too time consuming and labour intensive, and so it is pertinent to use a set of tasks that use all aspects of the system under analysis. Once the task(s) under analysis are defined clearly, a HTA should be conducted for each task. This allows the analyst(s) and participants to understand the task(s) fully.

Step 2: Selection of participants
Once the task(s) under analysis are clearly defined, it may be useful to select the participants that are to be involved in the analysis. This may not always be necessary and it may suffice to simply select participants randomly on the day. However, if SA is being compared across rank or experience levels, then clearly effort is required to select the appropriate participants.

Step 3: Brief participants
Before the task(s) under analysis are performed, all of the participants involved should be briefed regarding the purpose of the study and the SART technique. It may be useful at this stage to take the participants through an example SART analysis, so that they understand how the technique works and what is required of them as participants.

Step 5: Pilot run
Before the 'real' data collection process begins, it is recommended that the participants take part in a number of test scenarios or pilot runs of the SART data collection procedure. A number of small test scenarios should be used to iron out any problems with the data collection procedure, and the participants should be encouraged to ask any questions. Once the participant is familiar with the procedure and is comfortable with his or her role, the 'real' data collection process can begin.

Step 6: Performance of task
The next stage of the SART analysis involves the performance of the task or scenario under analysis. For example, if the study is focusing on pilot SA in air-to-air tactical combat situations, the subject will perform a task in either a suitable simulator or in a real aircraft. If SA data is to be collected post-trial, then step 7 is conducted after the task performance is finished. However, if data is to be collected on-line, step 7 shall occur at any point during the trial as determined by the analyst.

Step 7: SA self-rating
Once the trial is stopped or completed, the participant is given the 10 SART SA dimensions and asked to rate his or her performance for each dimension on a likert scale of 1 (low) to 7 (high). The rating is based on the participant's subjective judgement and should be based upon

their performance during the task under analysis. The participant's ratings should not be influenced in any way by external sources. In order to reduce the correlation between SA ratings and performance, no performance feedback should be given until after the participant has completed the self-rating process.

Step 8: SART SA calculation
The final step in a SART analysis involves calculating the participant SA score. Once the participant has completed the SA rating process, SA is calculated using the following formula:

$$SA = U-(D-S)$$

Where: U = summed understanding
           D = summed demand
           S = summed supply

Advantages

1. SART is very quick and easy to apply, requiring minimal training.
2. SART provides a low-cost approach for assessing participant SA.
3. The SART dimensions were derived directly from interviews with RAF personnel, thus the technique was developed using specific aircrew knowledge.
4. SA dimensions are generic and so can be applied to other domains, such as command and control systems.
5. Non-intrusive to task performance when administered post-trial.
6. High ecological validity.
7. SART is a widely used method and has a number of associated validation studies.
8. Removes secondary task loading associated with other techniques such as SAGAT.

Disadvantages

1. Similar to other self-rating techniques SART suffers from problems with participants associating SA ratings with task performance. Typically, if a participant performs well during the trial, the SA rating elicited will be high, and if a participant performs poorly during the trial, the SA rating elicited will be low. This clearly is not always the case.
2. Endsley (1995b) points out that participants are often unaware of their own limited SA. It is difficult to see how participants can accurately rate low SA when they may not even be aware that they have low SA.
3. Data is usually obtained 'after the fact' which causes problems such as participants 'forgetting' periods when they had low SA and a correlation between SA ratings and performance.
4. The data obtained is subjective.
5. Administrating SART during performance/trials is intrusive upon primary task performance.
6. The SART dimensions only reflect a limited portion of SA.
7. SART consistently performs worse than SAGAT in various validation studies.
8. Testing of the technique often reveals a correlation between SA and performance, and also between SA and workload.

Flowchart

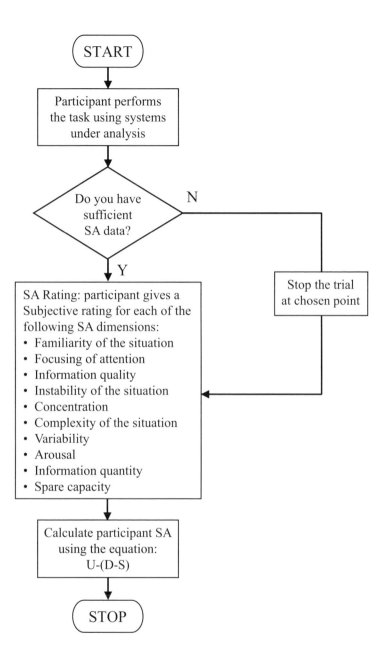

Related Methods

SART is used in conjunction with an appropriate rating technique, such as a Likert scale, category ratings (low vs. high) and pairwise comparisons. SART is also often used in conjunction with SAGAT or other on-line probe techniques. SART is one of a number of subjective SA assessment techniques available. Other subjective SA assessment techniques include SARS, CARS and SA-SWORD.

Approximate Training and Application Times

As the technique is a self-rating questionnaire, there is very little or no training involved. Thus the training time for the SART approach is low. Application time is also minimal. It is estimated that it would take no longer than 10 minutes for participants to complete the SART rating sheet.

Reliability and Validity

Along with SAGAT, SART is the most widely used and tested measure of SA (Endsley and Garland, 1995). According to Jones (2000) a study conducted by Vidulich, Crabtree and McCoy demonstrated that the SART technique appears to be sensitive to changes in SA. In a recent study designed to assess four techniques for their sensitivity and validity for assessing SA in air traffic control, the SART technique was found not to be sensitive to display manipulations. The construct validity of the SART technique is also questionable, and the degree to which the SART dimensions actually measure SA or workload has often been questioned (Uhlarik, 2002, Endsley 1995. Selcon et al, 1991). Further SART validation studies have been conducted (Taylor 1990, Taylor and Selcon, 1991, Selcon and Taylor, 1990). According to Jeannot, Kelly and Thompson (2003), the validation evidence associated with the technique is weak.

Tools Needed

SART is applied using pen and paper. The questionnaire is typically administered after the subject has completed the task or scenario under analysis. Obviously, the relevant tools for the task or scenario under analysis are also required, such as a simulator for the system in question.

Situation Awareness Subjective Workload Dominance (SA-SWORD)

Background and Applications

The Situation Awareness Subjective Workload Dominance technique (SA-SWORD; Vidulich and Hughes, 1991) is an adaptation of the SWORD workload assessment technique. The SA-SWORD technique is used to assess and compare the pilot SA when using two or more different cockpit displays or interfaces. The Subjective Workload Dominance Technique (SWORD) is a subjective workload assessment technique that has been used both retrospectively and predictively (Pro-SWORD; Vidulich, Ward and Schueren, 1991). SWORD uses subjective paired comparisons of tasks in order to provide a rating of workload for each individual task. When using SWORD, participants rate one task's dominance over another in terms of workload imposed. Vidulich and Hughes (1991) used a variation of the SWORD technique to assess pilot SA when using two different displays (FCR display and the HSF display). The SA-SWORD technique involves participants rating their SA across different combinations of factors such as displays, enemy threat and flight segment (Vidulich and Hughes, 1991). For example, when comparing two cockpit displays, participants are asked to rate with which display their SA was highest.

Domain of Application

Military aviation.

Procedure and Advice

Step 1: Define the task(s) under analysis
The first step in any SWORD analysis involves clearly defining the task(s) or artefact(s) under analysis. Once this is done a task or scenario description should be created. Each task should be described individually in order to allow the creation of the SWORD rating sheet. It is recommended that HTA is used for this purpose.

Step 2: Create SWORD rating sheet
Once a task description (e.g. HTA) is developed, the SWORD rating sheet can be created. When using SA-SWORD, the analyst should define a set of comparison conditions. For example, when using SA-SWORD to compare two F-16 cockpit displays, the comparison conditions used were FCR display Vs HSF display, flight segment (ingress and engagement) and threat level (low Vs high). To do this, the analyst should list all of the possible combinations of tasks or artefacts (e.g. AvB, AvC, BvC).

Step 3: SA and SA-SWORD briefing
Once the trial and comparison conditions are defined, the participants should be briefed on the construct of SA, the SA-SWORD technique and the purposes of the study. It is crucial that each participant has an identical, clear understanding of what SA actually is in order for the SA-SWORD technique to provide reliable, valid results. Therefore, it is recommended that the participants are given a group SA briefing, including an introduction to the construct, a clear definition of SA and an explanation of SA in terms of the operation of the system in question. It may also prove useful to define the SA requirements for the task under analysis. Once the participants clearly understand SA, an explanation of the SA-SWORD technique should be provided. It may be useful here to demonstrate the completion of an example SA-SWORD questionnaire. Finally, the participants should then be briefed on the purpose of the study.

Step 4: Conduct pilot run
Next, a pilot run of the data collection process should be conducted. Participants should perform a small task and then complete a SA-SWORD rating sheet. The participants should be taken step by step through the SA-SWORD rating sheet, and be encouraged to ask any questions regarding any aspects of the data collection procedure that they are not sure about.

Step 5: Task performance
SA-SWORD is administered post-trial. Therefore, the task under analysis should be performed first. The task(s) under analysis should be clearly defined during step 1 of the procedure. When assessing pilot SA, flight simulators are normally used. However, as the SA-SWORD technique is administered post-trial, task performance using the actual system(s) under analysis may be possible.

Step 6: Administer SA-SWORD rating sheet
Once task performance is complete, the SA-SWORD rating procedure can begin. This involves the administration of the SA-SWORD rating sheet. The participant should be presented with the SWORD rating sheet immediately after task performance has ended. The SWORD rating sheet lists all possible SA paired comparisons of the task conducted in the scenario under analysis e.g. display A versus display B, condition A versus condition B. A 17-point rating scale is typically used in the assessment of operator workload (SWORD). The 17 slots represent the possible ratings. The analyst has to rate the two variables (e.g. display A versus display B) in terms of the

level of SA that they provided during task performance. For example, if the participant feels that the two displays provided a similar level of SA, then they should mark the 'EQUAL' point on the rating sheet. However, if the participant feels that display A provided a slightly higher level of SA than display B did, they would move towards task A on the sheet and mark the 'weak' point on the rating sheet. If the participant felt that display A imposed a much greater level of SA than display B, then they would move towards display A on the sheet and mark the 'Absolute' point on the rating sheet. This allows the participant to provide a subjective rating of one display's SA dominance over the over. This procedure should continue until all of the possible combinations of SA variables in the scenario under analysis are exhausted and given a rating.

Step 7: Constructing the judgement matrix
Once all ratings have been elicited, the SWORD judgement matrix should be conducted. Each cell in the matrix should represent the comparison of the variables in the row with the variable in the associated column. The analyst should fill each cell with the participant's dominance rating. For example, if a participant rated displays A and B as equal, a '1' is entered into the appropriate cell. If display A is rated as dominant, then the analyst simply counts from the 'Equal' point to the marked point on the sheet, and enters the number in the appropriate cell. The rating for each variable (e.g. display) is calculated by determining the mean for each row of the matrix and then normalising the means (Vidulich, Ward and Schueren, 1991).

Step 8: Matrix consistency evaluation
Once the SWORD matrix is complete, the consistency of the matrix can be evaluated by ensuring that there are transitive trends amongst the related judgements in the matrix.

Advantages

1. SA-SWORD is quick and easy to use and requires only minimal training.
2. The SA-SWORD technique offers a low-cost approach to the assessment of SA.
3. The SA-SWORD technique can be used in any domain.
4. In a validation study pilots were interviewed in order to evaluate the validity and ease of use of the technique (Vidulich and Hughes, 1991). According to Vidulich and Hughes (1991) comments regarding the technique were either positive or neutral, indicating a promising level of face validity and user acceptance.
5. The SA-SWORD technique is very useful when comparing two different interface design concepts and their effect upon operator SA.
6. Intrusiveness is reduced, as SA-SWORD is administered post-trial.
7. Has the potential to be used as a back-up SA assessment technique.

Disadvantages

1. A very clear definition of SA would need to be developed in order for the technique to work. For example, each participant may have different ideas as to what SA actually is, and as a result, the data obtained would be incorrect. In a study testing the SA-SWORD technique, it was reported that the participants had very different views on what SA actually was (Vidulich and Hughes, 1991). Vidulich and Hughes (1991) recommend that the analysts provide a specific definition of SA and make sure that each participant understands it clearly.
2. The technique does not provide a direct measure of SA. The analyst is merely given an assessment of the conditions in which SA is highest.

3. The reporting of SA post-trial has a number of problems associated with it, such as a correlation between SA rating and task performance, and participants forgetting low SA periods during task performance.
4. There is limited evidence of the use of the SA-SWORD technique in the literature.
5. Limited validation evidence.
6. Unlike SAGAT, the SA-SWORD technique is not based upon any underpinning theory.

Example

Vidulich and Hughes (1991) used the SA-SWORD technique to compare two F-16 cockpit displays, the FCR display and the HSF display. The two displays are described below:

Fire control radar display (FCR display)
The FCR display provides information in a relatively raw format from the aircraft's own radar system.

The horizontal situation format display (HSF display)
The HSF display is a map-like display that combines data from external sources, such as an AWACS, with the aircraft's own data to provide a bird's-eye view of the area.

According to Vidulich and Hughes (1991), the HSF display contains more pertinent information than the FCR display does, such as threats approaching from behind. It was assumed that these differences between the two displays would cause a difference in the SA reported when using each display. The two displays were compared, using pilot SA-SWORD ratings, in an F-16 aircraft simulator. The trials conditions varied in terms of flight segment (ingress and engagement) and threat level (low and high).

A total of twelve pilots each performed eight flights, four with the FCR display and four with the HSF display. SA-SWORD ratings were collected post-trial. Participants rated their SA on each combination of display, flight segment and threat. It was found that pilots rated their SA as higher when using the HSF display, thus supporting the hypothesis that the HSF display provides the pilots with more pertinent information. However, no effect of flight segment or threat was found as was expected. Vidulich and Hughes (1991) suggest that the participants' different understanding of SA may explain these findings.

Related Methods

The SA-SWORD technique is an adaptation of the SWORD workload assessment technique. SA-SWORD appears to be unique in its use of paired comparisons to measure SA. SA-SWORD is a subjective rating SA technique, of which there are many, including SART, SARS and CARS.

Approximate Training and Application Times

The SA-SWORD technique appears to be an easy technique to learn and apply, and so it is estimated that the associated training time is low. The application time is associated with the SA-SWORD technique is also estimated to be minimal. However, it must be remembered that this is dependent upon the SA variables that are to be compared. For example, if two cockpit displays were under comparison, then the application time would be very low. However, if ten displays were under comparison across five different flight conditions, then the application time would increase significantly. The time taken for the task performance must also be considered.

Flowchart

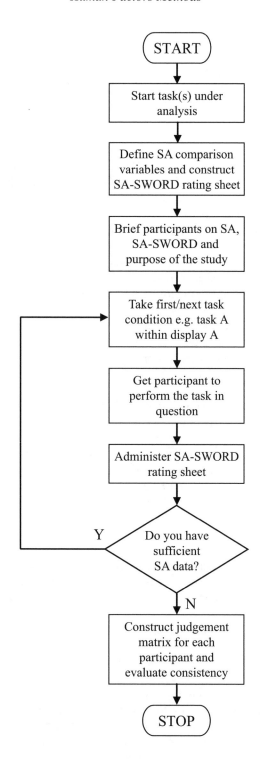

Reliability and Validity

It is apparent that the validity of the SA-SWORD technique is questionable. An analyst must be careful to ensure construct validity when using the SA-SWORD technique. Administered in its current form, the SA-SWORD technique suffers from a poor level of construct validity i.e. the extent to which it is actually measuring SA. Vidulich and Hughes (1991) encountered this problem and found that half of the participants understood SA to represent the amount of information that they were attempting to track, whilst the other half understood SA to represent the amount of information that they may be missing. This problem could potentially be eradicated by incorporating an SA briefing session or a clear definition of what constitutes SA on the SA-SWORD rating sheet. In a study comparing two different cockpit displays, the SA-SWORD technique demonstrated a strong sensitivity to display manipulation (Vidulich and Hughes, 1991). Vidulich and Hughes (1991) also calculated inter-rater reliability statistics for the SA-SWORD technique, reporting a grand inter-rater correlation of 0.705. According to Vidulich and Hughes, this suggests that participant SA-SWORD ratings were reliably related to the conditions apparent during the trials.

Tools Needed

The SA-SWORD technique can be administered using pen and paper. The system under analysis, or a simulation of the system under analysis is also required for the task performance part of the data collection procedure.

SALSA

Background and Applications

SALSA is an on-line probe SA measurement technique that was recently developed specifically for air traffic control (ATC) applications. In response to the recent overloading of ATC systems caused by an increase in air traffic, the 'Man-machine interaction in co-operative systems of ATC and flight guidance' (Hauss and Eyferth, 2003) research group set out to design and evaluate a future air traffic management (ATM) concept. The group based the ATM concept upon the guidelines and design principles presented in the ISO 1347 standard 'human centred design process for interactive systems'. A cognitive model of air traffic controllers' processes was developed (Eyferth, Niessen and Spath, 2003), which in turn facilitated the development of the SALSA technique. The SALSA technique itself is an on-line probe technique that is administered during simulation 'freezes', similar to the SAGAT approach proposed by Endsley (1995b). According to the authors, SALSA takes into account air traffic controllers' use of event based mental representations of the air traffic (Hauss and Eyferth, 2003) and considers the changing relevance of the elements in the environment. According to Hauss and Eyferth (2003) SALSA differs from SAGAT in three ways:

SALSA incorporates an expert rating system in order to determine the relevance of each item that the participant is queried on. The results of this are weighted with the results of the SA test. Thus, only the items judged to be relevant are considered. This measure is referred to as weighted reproduction performance (SAwrp) (Hauss and Eyferth, 2003). The reproduction test of SALSA is performed in a single stage. During each freeze, the complete set of SA queries is administered when using SALSA. This allows the collection of large amounts of data with only minimal intrusion. SALSA's SA queries are based upon 15 aspects of aircraft flight. Each parameter and its answer category are shown below in Table 7.5.

Table 7.5   SALSA Parameters (Source: Hauss and Eyferth, 2003)

Parameter	Category
Flight level	Numerical
Ground speed	Numerical
Heading	Numerical
Next sector	Free text
Destination	Free text
Vertical tendency	Level/descending/climbing
Type	Propeller/turboprop/jet
According to the flight plan	Yes/No
Aircraft was instructed	Yes/No
Instruction executed	Yes/No
Content of instruction	Free text
Conflict	No conflict/already solved/unsolved
Type of conflict	Crossing/same airway/vertical
Time to separation violation	Minutes/seconds
Call sign of conflicting a/c	Free text

When using SALSA, the simulation is frozen and a random aircraft is highlighted on the ATC display. Everything else on the display is blanked. The participant is then given the 15 parameters and has to complete each one regarding the highlighted aircraft. A NASA TLX is also administered after the end of the simulation in order to assess participant workload.

Domain of Application

Air traffic control.

Procedure and Advice

Step 1: Define the task(s) under analysis
The first step in the SALSA procedure is to clearly define the task or set of tasks under analysis. Once this is done a task or scenario description should be created. It is recommended that HTA is used in this case. A number of different data collection procedures may be used in the development of the HTA, including interviews with SMEs, observational study of the task or scenario under analysis and questionnaires.

Step 2: Brief participants
Once the task(s) under analysis are clearly defined and described, the participants should be briefed on the construct of SA, the SALSA technique and the purposes of the study. It is recommended that the participants are given a group SA briefing, including an introduction to the construct, a clear definition of SA and an explanation of SA in terms of the task(s) under analysis. It may prove useful to define the SA requirements for the task under analysis. Once the participants clearly understand SA, an explanation of the SALSA technique should be provided. It may also be useful here to demonstrate the freeze technique that is used during the administration of the SALSA questionnaire. Finally, the participants should then be briefed on the purpose of the study.

Step 3: Conduct pilot run
Next, a pilot run of the data collection procedure should be conducted. Participants should perform a small task incorporating a number of simulation freezes and SALSA administrations. The

participants should be encouraged to ask any questions regarding any aspects of the data collection procedure that they are not sure about. The pilot run is useful in identifying and eradicating any problems with the SALSA data collection procedure.

Step 4: Start simulation
Once the participants fully understand how the SALSA technique works, the data collection process can begin. The participant in question should now begin to perform the first task under analysis. In a study using SALSA, Hauss and Eyferth (2003) used a simulation of an ATC environment containing an MSP workstation, traffic simulation, pseudo pilot workstation and an area controller workstation.

Step 5: Freeze the simulation
At any random point during the trial, the simulation should be frozen. During this freeze, all information on the aircraft labels is hidden, the radar screen is frozen and a single aircraft is highlighted. A computer is normally used to randomly freeze the simulation and select the appropriate aircraft.

Step 6: Query administration
Whilst the simulation is still frozen, the participant should be given a sheet containing the 15 SALSA parameters. The participant should then complete each parameter for the highlighted aircraft. No assistance should be offered to the participant during step 6. Once the participant has completed each parameter for the highlighted aircraft, the simulation can be restarted. Steps 5 and 6 should be repeated throughout the trial until the required amount of data is obtained.

Step 7: Simulation replay
Once the trial is completed, the simulation should be replayed and observed by an appropriate SME. The SME is then required to rate the relevance of each of the SALSA parameters used at each freeze point.

Step 8: Weighting procedure and performance calculation
The results of the expert ratings should then be weighted with the results of the participant's SA trial. The weighted reproduction performance (Hauss and Eyferth, 2003) can then be calculated. This is defined by the following equation (Hauss and Eyferth, 2003).

$$SAwrp = \frac{\sum_{i=1}^{n} s\,(i) \cdot t\,(i)}{\sum_{i=1}^{n} t\,(i)}$$

Where;

$$\sigma\,(\chi) = \begin{cases} & 1 \text{ if the xth item is correctly reproduced, 0 otherwise} \end{cases}$$

$$\tau\,(\chi) = \begin{cases} & 1 \text{ if the xth item is rated as relevant, 0 otherwise} \end{cases}$$

Advantages

1. The expert rating procedure used in the SALSA technique allows the technique to consider only those factors that are relevant to the controller's SA at that specific point in time.
2. SALSA is a quick and easy to use technique.
3. On-line probing aspect removes the problem of subjects biasing their attention towards certain aspects of the situation.
4. On-line probing also removes the problem associated with subjects reporting SA 'after the fact'.
5. SALSA uses SA parameters from the widely used and validated SAGAT technique.

Disadvantages

1. Using the technique requires expensive high fidelity simulators and computers.
2. The SALSA queries are intrusive to primary task performance.
3. When using SALSA, the simulation must be stopped or frozen a number of times in order to collect the data.
4. Unlike the SAGAT approach, all of the SA queries are administered during simulation freezes. This may overload the participant.
5. The method cannot be used in real-world settings.
6. The SALSA technique is still in its infancy and validation evidence is scarce.
7. SALSA was developed specifically for ATC, and so its use in other domains, such as command and control, would be subject to redevelopment.
8. Very similar to SAGAT.

Example

Hauss and Eyferth (2003) applied SALSA to a future operational concept for air traffic management. The concept involved used a multi-sector-planner to optimise air traffic flow. The aim of the study was to determine whether SALSA was a feasible and suitable approach to determine SA in ATC. The working conditions of a conventional radar controller were compared to that of a multi-sector-planner. Eleven air traffic controllers took part in the study. Each subject controlled traffic in each of the two conditions for 45 minutes. Each simulation was frozen 13 times. At each freeze point, the screen was frozen and a single aircraft was highlighted. Participants then had to complete 15 SA parameter queries for the highlighted aircraft. The results of the study demonstrated that the mean weighted reproduction performance increased significantly from 84.2 (without MSP) to a mean score of 88.9.

Related Methods

The NASA TLX workload assessment tool is normally administered after the SALSA trial has finished. SALSA is also very closely related to the situation awareness global assessment tool (SAGAT) and SAGAT-TRACON, which are both on-line probe SA measurement techniques. The SALSA technique uses SAGAT TRACON's SA parameters.

Flowchart

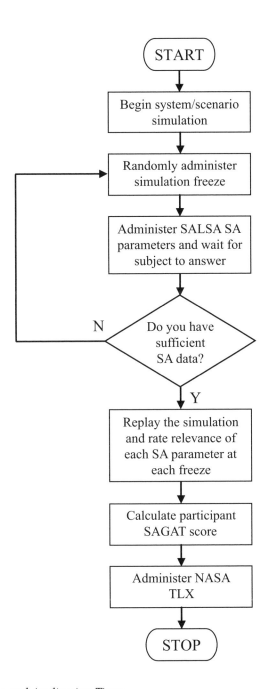

Approximate Training and Application Times

The estimated training time for SALSA is very low, as the analyst is only required to freeze the simulation and then administer a query sheet. The application of SALSA is dependent upon the length of the simulation and the amount of SA data required. In Hauss and Eyferth's (2003) study, each trial lasted 45 minutes each. The additional use of a NASA TLX would also add further time to the SALSA application time.

Reliability and Validity

No data regarding the reliability and validity of the SALSA technique are offered by the authors.

Situation Awareness Control Room Inventory (SACRI)

Background and Applications

The Situation Awareness Control Room Inventory (SACRI; Hogg, Folleso, Strand-Volden and Torralba, 1995) is a SA measurement tool that was developed as part of the OECD Halden Reactor project. According to Hogg et al (1995) the main aim of the research project was to develop a measure of situation awareness that would be:

1. Applicable to pressurised water reactors;
2. Objective;
3. Able to assess the dynamic nature of SA;
4. Able to assess operator awareness of plant state situation; and
5. Generic across process state situations.

The technique is an adaptation of the situation awareness global assessment technique (Endsley, 1995b) and was developed as a result of a study investigating the use of SAGAT in process control rooms (Hogg et al, 1995). The study focused upon the following areas; query content, requirements for operator competence, scenario design, response scoring and comparing alternative system design. In developing the SACRI query content, the authors collaborated with domain experts and also carried out a review of the Halden Man-Machine Laboratory (HAMMLAB) documentation. Examples of the SACRI query inventory are shown below. For the full list of SACRI queries, the reader is referred to Hogg et al (1995).

Questions comparing the current situation with that of the recent past

1. In comparison with the recent past, how have the temperatures in the hot legs of the primary circuit developed?
2. In comparison with the recent past, how have the temperatures in the cold legs of the primary circuit developed?
3. In comparison with the recent past, how has the average reactor temperature developed?

SACRI also uses queries that ask the operator to compare the current situation with normal operations and also queries that require the operator to predict future situation developments. Examples of these two categories of queries are given below.

Questions comparing the current situation with normal operations
In comparison with the normal status, how would you describe the temperature at the steam line manifold?

Questions about predicting future situation developments
In comparison with now, predict how the temperature at the steam line manifold will develop over the next few minutes.

Participants are required to answer the queries using one of the following four separate answer categories.

1. Increase/same;
2. Decrease/same;
3. Increase/same/decrease;
4. Increase in more than one/Increase in one/Same/Decrease in one/Decrease in more than one/Drift in both directions.

Hogg et al (1995) recommend that 12 of the SACRI queries are randomly administered during any one trial. A computer is used to randomly select and administer the query, document the participant's answer and also to calculate the overall SA score. Overall participant SA scores are based upon a comparison with the actual plant state at the time each query was administered. Hogg et al (1995) describe two separate ways of calculating participant SA scores. The first method of calculating an overall score involves simply calculating the percentage of correct query responses. The second method proposed is to use the signal detection theory. When using signal detection theory to calculate participant SA scores, participant responses are categorised as one of the following (Hogg et al, 1995):

HIT = A parameter drift that is detected by the participant;
MISS = A parameter drift that is not detected by the participant;
CORRECT ACCEPTANCE = No parameter drift, not reported by the participant;
FALSE ALARM = No parameter drift, but one is reported by the subject.

This classification is then used to derive a psychophysical measure of 'sensitivity', the higher the measure the greater the accord between the operator's SA and the true state of events.

Procedure and Advice

Step 1: Define the task(s) under analysis
The first step in the SACRI procedure is to clearly define the task or set of tasks under analysis. Once this is done a task or scenario description should be created. It is recommended that a HTA be developed for this purpose.

Step 2: Brief participants
Once the task(s) under analysis are clearly defined and described, the participants should be briefed on the construct of SA, the SACRI technique and the purposes of the study. It is recommended that the participants are given a group SA briefing, including an introduction to the construct, a clear definition of SA and an explanation of SA in terms of control room operation. It may also prove useful to define the SA requirements for the task(s) under analysis. Once the participants clearly understand SA, an explanation of the SACRI technique should be provided. It may be useful here to demonstrate an example SACRI analysis. Finally, the participants should then be briefed on the purpose of the study.

Step 3: Conduct pilot run
Next, a pilot run of the data collection procedure should be conducted. Participants should perform a small task incorporating the SACRI questionnaire. The participants should be taken step by step through the SACRI data collection procedure and be encouraged to ask any questions regarding any aspects of the data collection procedure that they are not sure or unclear about. The pilot run is useful in identifying and eradicating any problems with the SACRI data collection procedure.

Step 4: Begin simulation/trial
Next, the SACRI data collection process can begin. The first stage of data collection phase is to begin the simulation of the process control scenario under analysis. Hogg et al (1995) tested the SACRI technique using 33 minute scenarios per participant. The participant should be instructed to perform the task or scenario under analysis as they normally would in day to day operation of the system.

Step 5: Randomly freeze the simulation
A computer should be used to randomly freeze the scenario simulation. During each freeze, all information displays are hidden from the participant.

Step 6: Administer SACRI query
A computer should be used to randomly select and administer the appropriate SACRI queries for the frozen point in the task. Hogg et al (1995) recommend that twelve queries should be administered per trial. A computer should also be used to administer the query and the participant should submit their answer using the computer. Steps 5 and 6 should be repeated throughout the trial until the required amount of SA is obtained.

Step 7: Calculate participant SA score
Once the trial is finished, the participant's overall SA score should be calculated. Hogg et al (1995) describe two separate ways of calculating participant SA scores. The first method of calculating an overall score involves simply calculating the percentage of correct query responses. The second method proposed is to use the signal detection theory. When using signal detection theory to calculate participant SA scores, participant responses are categorised as one of the following (Hogg et al, 1995):

HIT
MISS
CORRECT
ACCEPTANCE
FALSE ALARM

This classification is then used to derive a measure of operator SA. This is achieved via calculating A'. The formula for this is presented below:

$$A' = 0.5 + (H-F)(1-H-F)/[4H(1-F)].$$

Where:
H= Hit
F= False alarm

Flowchart

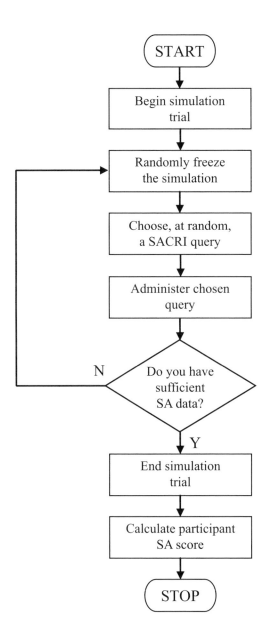

Example

The following example of a SACRI analysis is taken from Hogg et al (1995). Six research staff with experience of the HAMMLAB simulator were presented with two scenarios containing several disturbances in different process areas (Hogg et al, 1995). Scenario one lasted 60 minutes and included eight SACRI queries. Scenario two lasted 90 minutes and included 13 SACRI queries. The timeline presented in Table 7.6 shows scenario A. Two groups were also used in the study. One of the groups was subjected to an updated alarm list and the other group was not. An extract of the results obtained are presented in Table 7.7.

Table 7.6   SACRI Study Timeline (Source: Hogg et al, 1995)

0 Min	Start of simulator in normal mode
5 Min	Introduction of disturbance 1: Failure in pressuriser controller and small leak in primary circuit
10 Min	1st administration of SACRI
13 Min	Pressuriser level alarms
15 Min	2nd administration of SACRI
21 Min	3rd administration of SACRI
25 Min	Introduction of disturbance 2: Pump trip in sea-water supply system for condenser
27 Min	4th administration of SACRI
30 Min	Turbine and reactor power reductions
33 Min	5th administration of SACRI
35 Min	Condenser alarms
39 Min	6th administration of SACRI
44 Min	7th administration of SACRI
51 Min	Turbine trip on 10 train
52 Min	8th administration of SACRI
57 Min	9th administration of SACRI
62 Min	10th administration of SACRI
66 Min	Introduction of disturbance 3: Steam generator leakage outside containment
72 Min	11th administration of SACRI
78 Min	12th administration of SACRI
80 Min	Feedwater pump trip in 2nd train
84 Min	13th administration of SACRI
85 Min	Reactor trip

Table 7.7   Results from SACRI Study (Source: Hogg et al, 1995)

Subject, ranked as prediction of competence before the study	Number of observations	Rank of A' score	Mean A'	SD of A' scores
1	21	1	.79	0.13
2	21	2	.71	.21
3	16	3	.68	.21
4	21	6	.56	.32
5	21	4	.58	.32
6	21	4	.58	.33

Advantages

1. SACRI directly measures participant SA.
2. SACRI queries can be modified to encapsulate all operator SA requirements.
3. SACRI is a development of SAGAT, which has been extensively used in the past and has a wealth of associated validation evidence (Jones and Endsley, 2000; Durso et al, 1998; Garland and Endsley, 1995).
4. On-line probing aspect removes the problem of subjects biasing their attention towards certain aspects of the situation.
5. On-line probing also removes the various problems associated with subjects reporting SA 'after the fact', such as a correlation between reported SA and performance.
6. Simple to learn and use.

Disadvantages

1. Freezing the simulation and administering queries regarding participant SA is an intrusive method of obtaining data regarding participant SA.
2. The SACRI technique is limited to use in the process industries.
3. Using the technique requires expensive high fidelity simulators and computers.
4. When using the SACRI the simulation must be stopped or frozen a number of times in order to collect the data.
5. The method cannot be used in real-world settings.
6. Based upon SAGAT, which in turn is based upon the very simplistic three level model of SA.
7. Evidence of validation studies using SACRI is scarce.
8. The validity and reliability of SACRI requires further scrutiny.

Related Methods

SACRI is a development of the Situation Awareness Global Assessment Technique (Endsley 1995b). There are a number of on-line probe techniques, such as SAGAT (Endsley, 1995b) and SALSA (Hauss and Eyferth, 2003).

Approximate Training and Application Times

It is estimated that the training time associated with the SACRI technique is minimal, due to the technique's simplistic nature. The application time would depend upon the scenario and how much SA data was required. In one study (Hogg et al, 1995) subjects performed two scenarios. Scenario A lasted 60 minutes and scenario 2 lasted 90 minutes. This represents a minimal application time.

Reliability and Validity

Hogg et al (1995) conducted four separate studies using SACRI. It was reported that SACRI was sensitive to differences in test subjects' competence and also that SACRI could potentially be sensitive to the effects of alarm system interfaces on operator SA. In terms of content validity, a crew of operators evaluated SACRI, with the findings indicating that SACRI displayed good content validity. However, the reliability of SACRI remains untested as such. It is clear that the validity and reliability of the technique needs testing further.

Tools Needed

In order to carry out a SACRI analysis, a high fidelity simulator of the system (e.g. process control room) is required. The simulation should possess the ability to randomly freeze the simulation, blank all operator displays, randomly select and administer the queries, and record participant responses.

Situation Awareness Rating Scales (SARS)

Background and Applications

The situation awareness rating scales technique (SARS; Waag and Houck, 1994) is a subjective rating SA measurement technique that was developed for the military aviation domain. According to Jones (2000) the SARS technique was developed in order to define the SA construct, to determine how well pilots can assess other pilots' SA and also to examine the relationship between pilot judgements of SA and actual performance. When using the SARS technique, participants subjectively rate their performance, post-trial, on a six-point rating scale (from acceptable to outstanding) for 31 facets of fighter pilot SA. The SARS SA categories and associated behaviours were developed from interviews with experienced F-15 pilots. The 31 SARS behaviours are divided into eight categories representing phases of mission performance. The eight categories are: general traits, tactical game plan, communication, information interpretation, tactical employment beyond visual range, tactical employment visual and tactical employment general. According to Waag and Houck (1994) the 31 SARS behaviours are representative of those behaviours that are crucial to mission success. The SARS behaviours are presented in Table 7.8.

Table 7.8   SARS SA Categories (Source: Waag and Houck, 1994)

General traits	Information interpretation
Discipline	Interpreting vertical situation display
Decisiveness	Interpreting threat warning system
Tactical knowledge	Ability to use controller information
Time-sharing ability	Integrating overall information
Spatial ability	Radar sorting
Reasoning ability	Analysing engagement geometry
Flight management	Threat prioritisation
Tactical game plan	Tactical employment – BVR
Developing plan	Targeting decisions
Executing plan	Fire-point selection
Adjusting plan on-the-fly	Tactical employment – Visual
System operation	Maintain track of bogeys/friendlies
Radar	Threat evaluation
Tactical electronic warfare system	Weapons employment
Overall weapons system proficiency	Tactical employment – General
Communication	Assessing offensiveness/defensiveness
Quality (brevity, accuracy, timeliness)	Lookout
Ability to effectively use information	Defensive reaction
	Mutual support

Procedure and Advice

Step 1: Define task(s)
The first step in a SARS analysis (aside from the process of gaining access to the required systems and personnel) is to define the tasks that are to be subjected to analysis. The type of tasks analysed are dependent upon the focus of the analysis. For example, when assessing the effects on operator SA caused by a novel design or training programme, it is useful to analyse as representative a set of tasks as possible. To analyse a full set of tasks will often be too time consuming and labour intensive, and so it is pertinent to use a set of tasks that use all aspects of the system under analysis. Once the task(s) under analysis are defined clearly, a HTA should be conducted for each task. This allows the analyst(s) and participants to understand the task(s) fully.

Step 2: Selection of participants
Once the task(s) under analysis are defined, it may be useful to select the participants that are to be involved in the analysis. This may not always be necessary and it may suffice to simply select participants randomly on the day. However, if SA is being compared across rank or experience levels, then clearly effort is required to select the appropriate participants.

Step 3: Brief participants
Before the task(s) under analysis are performed, all of the participants involved should be briefed regarding the purpose of the study, the construct of SA and the SARS technique. It is recommended that an introduction to the construct of SA be given, along with a clear definition of SA in aviation. It may be useful at this stage to take the participants through an example SARS analysis, so that they understand how the technique works and what is required of them as participants.

Step 4: Pilot run
Before the data collection procedure begins, it is recommended that the participants take part in a number of test scenarios or pilot runs of the SARS data collection procedure. A number of small test scenarios incorporating the completion of SARS rating sheets should be used to iron out any problems with the data collection procedure, and the participants should be encouraged to ask any questions. Once the participant is familiar with the procedure and is comfortable with his or her role during the trial, the data collection procedure can begin.

Step 5: Performance of task
The next step in a SARS analysis involves the performance of the task or scenario under analysis. For example, if the study is focusing on pilot SA in air-to-air tactical combat situations, the subject will perform a task in either a suitable simulator or in a real aircraft. SARS is normally administered post-trial, and so step 6 begins once the task or scenario is complete.

Step 6: Administer SARS scales
Once the trial is stopped or completed, the participant is given the SARS scales and asked to rate his or her SA for each behaviour on a likert scale of 1 (acceptable) to 6 (outstanding). The ratings provided are based on the participant's subjective judgement and should reflect the participant's perceived SA performance. The participant's SA rating should not be influenced in any way by external sources. In order to remove potential correlation between SA ratings and task performance, no performance feedback should be given to the participant until after the self-rating stage is complete.

Step 7: Calculate participant SA score
Once the participant has completed the SARS rating procedure, an SA score must be calculated In a SARS validation study, self-report SARS scores were calculated by calculating an average score for each category (i.e. general trait score = sum of general trait ratings/7) and also a total SARS score (sum of all ratings). Therefore, the analyst should produce nine scores in total for each participant. A hypothetical example SARS scale is presented in Table 7.9 and Table 7.10 to demonstrate the scoring system.

Table 7. 9   Example SARS Rating Scale

General traits	Rating	Information interpretation	Rating
Discipline	6	Interpreting vertical situation display	5
Decisiveness	5	Interpreting threat warning system	5
Tactical knowledge	5	Ability to use controller information	6
Time-sharing ability	6	Integrating overall information	6

Spatial ability	6	Radar sorting	6
Reasoning ability	6	Analysing engagement geometry	6
Flight management	6	Threat prioritisation	2
Tactical game plan		Tactical employment-BVR	
Developing plan	3	Targeting decisions	2
Executing plan	5	Fire-point selection	2
Adjusting plan on-the-fly	3	Tactical employment-Visual	
System operation		Maintain track of bogeys/friendlies	1
Radar	6	Threat evaluation	2
Tactical electronic warfare system	6	Weapons employment	5
Overall weapons system proficiency	6	Tactical employment – General	
Communication		Assessing offensiveness/defensiveness	3
Quality (brevity, accuracy, timeliness)	4	Lookout	2
Ability to effectively use information		Defensive reaction	5
		Mutual support	6

Table 7.10   Example SARS Scoring Sheet

Category	SARS score
General traits	5.7
Tactical game plan	3.6
System operation	6
Communication	4
Information interpretation	5.1
Tactical employment-BVR	2
Tactical employment-Visual	2.6
Tactical employment-General	4
Total	141/186

Advantages

1. The 31 dimensions appear to offer an exhaustive account of fighter pilot SA.
2. The technique goes further than other SA techniques such as SAGAT in that it assesses other facets of SA, such as decision making, communication and plan development.
3. Encouraging validation data (Jones, 2000; Waag and Houck, 1994).
4. A very simple and quick to use technique requiring little training.
5. Less intrusive than freeze techniques.
6. The technique can be used in real-world settings, as well as simulated ones.
7. The technique does not restrict itself to the three levels of SA proposed by Endsley (1995).

Disadvantages

1. As the SARS behaviours represent SA requirements when flying F-15s in combat type scenarios, the use of the technique in other domains is very doubtful. Significant re-development would have to take place for the technique to be used in other domains.
2. The technique has been subjected to only limited use and requires further validation.
3. The technique is administered post-trial, which carries a number of associated problems. Typically, post-trial subjective ratings of SA correlate with task performance (i.e. I performed well, so I must have had good SA). Also, participants may forget the periods of the task when they possessed a poor level of SA.
4. The SA data is subjective.

Related Methods

The SARS technique is a subjective self-rating SA measurement technique of which a number exist. Techniques such as SART and CARS require participants to subjectively rate facets of their SA during or after task performance. It is also recommended that a HTA of the task or scenario under analysis is conducted, in order to familiarise analysts with the relevant tasks.

Approximate Training and Application Times

The SARS technique requires very little training and also takes very little time to apply. It is estimated that it would take under 30 minutes to train the technique. Application time represents the time taken by the participant to rate their performance on 31 aspects of SA, and also the time taken for task performance. It is estimated that the SARS application time would be very low.

Reliability and Validity

Jones (2000) describes a validation study conducted by Waag and Houck (1994). Participants were asked to rate their own performance using the SARS rating technique. Furthermore, participants were also asked to rate the other participants' performance using the SARS technique and also to rate the other participants' general ability and SA ability, and to rank order them based upon SA ability. Finally, squadron leaders were also asked to complete SARS ratings for each participant. The analysis of the SARS scores demonstrated that the SARS scale possessed a high level of consistency and inter-rater reliability (Jones, 2000) and that the technique possessed a consistent level of construct validity. Furthermore, Jones (2000) reports that further analysis of the data revealed a significant correlation between ratings of SA and mission performance. Bell and Waag (1995) found that the SARS ratings obtained from a pilot squadron correlated moderately with SARS ratings provided by expert pilots who observed the pilot performances.

Tools Needed

The SARS technique can be conducted using pen and paper only. However, tools required for the performance of the task under analysis may vary widely. For example, in some cases, a simulator based upon the system and task under analysis may suffice. Alternatively, the system under analysis may be required if no simulation exists.

Flowchart

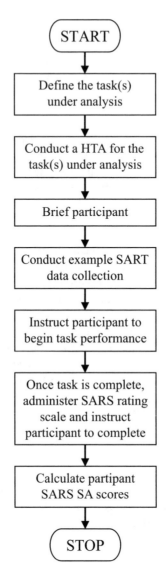

Situation Present Assessment Method (SPAM)

Background and Applications

The use of real-time probes to measure participant SA (without simulation freezes) has also been investigated. The situation present assessment method (SPAM; Durso, Hackworth, Truitt, Crutchfield and Manning, 1998) is one such technique developed by the University of Oklahoma for use in the assessment of air traffic controller SA. The SPAM technique focuses upon operator ability to locate information in the environment as an indicator of SA, rather than the recall of specific information regarding the current situation. The technique involves the use of on-line probes to evaluate operator SA. The analyst probes the operator for SA using task related SA queries based on pertinent information in the environment (e.g. which of the two aircraft A or B, has the highest altitude?) via telephone landline. The query response time (for those responses that are correct) is taken as an indicator of the operator's SA. Additionally, the time taken to answer the telephone is recorded and acts as an indicator of workload. A number of variations of the SPAM technique also exist, including the SAVANT technique and the SASHA technique, which has been developed by Eurocontrol to assess air traffic controller SA as a result of a review of existing SA assessment techniques (Jeannott, Kelly and Thompson, 2003). Endsley et al (2000) used a technique very similar to SPAM in a study of air traffic controllers. Examples of the probes used by Endsley et al (2000) are presented in Table 7.11.

Table 7.11   Example Probes (Source: Endsley et al, 2000)

Level 1 SA probes
1. What is the current heading for aircraft X?
2. What is the current flight level for aircraft X?
3. Climbing, descending or level: which is correct for aircraft X?
4. Turning right, turning left, or on course: which is correct for aircraft X?
Level 2 & 3 SA probes
1. Which aircraft have lost or will lose separation within the next five minutes unless an action is taken to avoid it?
2. Which aircraft will be affected by weather within the next five minutes unless an action is taken to avoid it?
3. Which aircraft must be handed off within the next three minutes?
4. What is the next sector for aircraft X?

Domain of Application

Air traffic control, however, the principles behind the approach (assessing participant SA using real-time probes) could be applied in any domain.

Procedure and Advice

Step 1: Define task(s)
The first step in a SPAM analysis (aside from the process of gaining access to the required systems and personnel) is to define the tasks that are to be subjected to analysis. The type of tasks analysed are dependent upon the focus of the analysis. For example, when assessing the effects on operator SA caused by a novel design or training programme, it is useful to analyse as representative a set of tasks as possible. To analyse a full set of tasks will often be too time consuming and labour intensive, and so it is pertinent to use a set of tasks that use all aspects of the system under analysis. Once the task(s) under analysis are defined clearly, a HTA should be conducted for each task. This allows the analyst(s) and participants to understand the task(s) fully.

Step 2: Development of SA queries
Next, the analyst(s) should use the task analysis description developed during step 1 to develop a set of SA queries for the task under analysis. There are no rules regarding the number of queries per task. Rather than concentrate on information regarding single aircraft (like the SAGAT technique) SPAM queries normally ask for 'gist type' information (Jeannott, Kelly and Thompson 2003).

Step 3: Selection of participants
Once the task(s) under analysis are defined, it may be useful to select the participants that are to be involved in the analysis. This may not always be necessary and it may suffice to simply select participants randomly on the day. However, if SA is being compared across rank or experience levels, then clearly effort is required to select the appropriate participants.

Step 4: Brief participants
Before the task(s) under analysis are performed, all of the participants involved should be briefed regarding the purpose of the study and the SPAM technique. It may be useful at this stage to take the participants through an example SPAM analysis, so that they understand how the technique works and what is required of them as participants.

Step 5: Conduct pilot run
It is useful to conduct a pilot run of the data collection process in order to ensure that any potential problems are removed prior to the real data collection process. The participants should perform a small task incorporating a set of SPAM queries. Participants should be encouraged to ask questions regarding the data collection process at this stage.

Step 6: Task performance
Once the participants fully understand the SPAM technique and the data collection procedure, they are free to undertake the task(s) under analysis as normal. The task is normally performed using a simulation of the system and task under analysis. Participants should be instructed to begin task performance as normal.

Step 7: Administer SPAM query
The analyst should administer SPAM queries at random points during the task. This involves calling the participant via landline and verbally asking them a question regarding the situation. Once the analyst has asked the question, a stopwatch should be started in order to measure participant response time. The query answer, query response time and time to answer the landline should be recorded for each query administered. Step 7 should be repeated until the required amount of data is collected.

Step 8: Calculate participant SA/workload scores
Once the task is complete, the analyst(s) should calculate participant SA based upon the query response times recorded (only correct responses are taken into account). A measure of workload can also be derived from the landline response times recorded.

Advantages

1. Quick and easy to use, requiring minimal training.
2. There is no need for a freeze in the simulation.
3. Objective measure of SA.
4. On-line administration removes the various problems associated with collecting SA data post-trial.

Disadvantages

1. Using response time as an indicator of SA is a questionable way of assessing SA.
2. The technique does not provide a measure of participant's SA. At best, only an indication of SA is given.

3. The SPAM queries are intrusive to primary task performance. One could argue that on-line real-time probes are more intrusive to primary task performance, as the task is not frozen and therefore the participant is still performing the task whilst answering the SA query.
4. Little evidence of the technique's use in an experimental setting.
5. Limited published validation evidence.
6. Poor construct validity. It is questionable whether the technique is actually measuring operator SA or not.
7. Often it is required that the SA queries are developed on-line during task performance. This places a great burden on the analyst involved.

Example

Jones and Endsley (2000) describe a study that was conducted in order to assess the validity of the use of real-time probes (like those used by the SPAM technique). A simulator was used to construct two scenarios, one 60 minute low to moderate workload (peace) scenario and one 60 minute moderate to high workload (war) scenario. Five teams, each consisting of one system surveillance technician, one identification technician, one weapons director and one weapons director technician, performed each scenario. The following measures were taken in order to assess both SA and workload.

Real time probes: 16 real time probes were administered randomly throughout each scenario.
SAGAT queries: SAGAT queries were administered during six random simulation freezes.
Secondary task performance measures: 12 secondary task performance measures were taken at random points in each trial.
SART: Upon completion of the task, participants completed the SART SA rating questionnaire.
NASA-TLX: In order to assess workload, participants completed a NASA-TLX upon completion of the task.

The sensitivity and validity of real-time probes was assessed. Participant response time and response accuracy to each probe were recorded and analysed. The real-time probes demonstrated a significant sensitivity to the differences between the two scenarios. The validity of the real-time probes was assessed in two ways. Firstly, accuracy and response time data were compared to the SAGAT data, and secondly, response time data were compared to the secondary task response time data. A weak but significant correlation was found between the real-time probe data and the SAGAT data. According to Jones and Endsley (2000), this demonstrated that the real-time probes were in effect measuring participant SA. Jones and Endsley (2000) concluded that the real-time probes were measuring participant SA, and recommended that an increased number of probes should be used in future in order to enhance the technique's sensitivity.

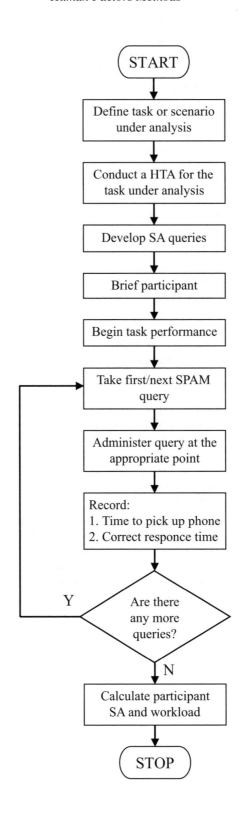

Related Methods

Jones and Endsley (2000) report the use of real-time probes in the assessment of operator SA. The SASHA technique (Jeannott, Kelly and Thompson, 2003) is also a development of the SPAM technique, and uses real-time probes generated on-line to assess participant SA. The SAVANT technique is also a combination of the SPAM and SAGAT techniques and uses real-time probes to assess participant SA.

Training and Application Times

It is estimated that the training time required for the SPAM technique is considerable, as the analyst requires training in the development of SA queries on-line. The application time is estimated to be low, as the technique is applied during task performance. Therefore, the application time for the SPAM technique is associated with the length of the task or scenario under analysis.

Reliability and Validity

There is only limited data regarding the reliability and validity of the SPAM technique available in the open literature. Jones and Endsley (2000) conducted a study to assess the validity of real-time probes as a measure of SA (See example). In conclusion, it was reported that the real-time probe measure demonstrated a level of sensitivity to SA in two different scenarios and also that the technique was measuring participant SA, and not simply measuring participant response time.

Tools Needed

Correct administration of the SPAM technique requires a landline telephone located in close proximity to the participant's workstation. A simulation of the task and system under analysis is also required.

SASHA_L and SASHA_Q

Background and Applications

SASHA is a methodology developed by Eurocontrol for the assessment of air traffic controllers' SA in automated systems. The methodology consists of two techniques, SASHA_L (on-line probing technique) and SASHA_Q (post-trial questionnaire) and was developed as part of the solutions for human automation partnerships in European ATM (SHAPE) project, the purpose of which was to investigate the effects of an increasing use of automation in ATM (Jeannott, Kelly and Thompson, 2003). The SASHA methodology was developed as a result of a review of existing SA assessment techniques (Jeannott, Kelly and Thompson, 2003) in order to assess air traffic controllers' SA when using computer or automation assistance. The SASHA_L technique is based upon the SPAM technique (Durso et al 1998), and involves probing the participant using real-time SA related queries. The response content and response time are recorded. When using SASHA_L, participant response time is graded as 'too quick', 'OK' or 'too long', and the response content is graded as 'incorrect', 'OK' or 'correct'. Once the trial is complete, the participant completes the SASHA_Q questionnaire, which consists of ten questions designed to assess participant SA during task performance. Examples of queries used in the SASHA_L technique are presented in Table 7.12. The SASHA_Q questionnaire is presented in Figure 7.6.

Domain of Application

Air traffic control.

Procedure and Advice

Step 1: Define task(s)
The first step in a SASHA analysis (aside from the process of gaining access to the required systems and personnel) is to define the tasks that are to be subjected to analysis. The type of tasks analysed are dependent upon the focus of the analysis. For example, when assessing the effects on operator SA caused by a novel design or training programme, it is useful to analyse as representative a set of tasks as possible. To analyse a full set of tasks will often be too time consuming and labour intensive, and so it is pertinent to use a set of tasks that use all aspects of the system under analysis.

Step 2: Conduct a HTA for the task(s) under analysis
Once the task(s) under analysis are defined clearly, a HTA should be conducted for each task. This allows the analyst(s) and participants to understand the task(s) fully. Unlike the SPAM technique, where the queries are generated beforehand, the SASHA technique requires the analyst to generate queries on-line or during task performance. In order to do this adequately, it is recommended that the analyst has a complete understanding of the task(s) under analysis. The development of a HTA for the task(s) under analysis is therefore crucial. The analyst should be involved during the development of the HTA and should be encouraged to examine the task(s) thoroughly. A number of data collection procedures could be employed to aid the development of the HTA, including interviews with SMEs, observational study of the task or scenario under analysis, and questionnaires.

Step 3: Selection of participants
Once the task(s) under analysis are clearly defined and described, it may be useful to select the participants that are to be involved in the analysis. This may not always be necessary and it may suffice to simply select participants randomly on the day. However, if SA is being compared across rank or experience levels, then clearly effort is required to select the appropriate participants.

Step 4: Brief participants
Before the task(s) under analysis are performed, all of the participants involved should be briefed regarding the purpose of the study, SA and the SASHA technique. It may be useful at this stage to take the participants through an example SASHA analysis, so that they understand how the technique works and what is required of them as participants.

Step 5: Conduct pilot run
It is useful to conduct a pilot run of the data collection procedure. Participants should perform a small task incorporating a set of SASHA_L queries. Once the task is complete, the participant should complete a SASHA_Q questionnaire. The pilot run is essential in identifying any potential problems with the data collection procedure. It also allows the participants to get a feel for the procedure and to fully understand how the SASHA technique works.

Step 6: Task performance
Once the participants fully understand the SASHA techniques and the data collection procedure, and the analyst is satisfied with the pilot run, the task performance can begin. Participants should be instructed to begin performing the task(s) under analysis as normal.

Step 7: Generate and administer SA query
When using the SASHA_L technique, the SA queries are generated and administered on-line during the task performance. Jeannott, Kelly and Thompson (2003) recommend that the analyst should ensure that the queries used test the participants' SA from an operational point of view, that they are administered at the appropriate time (approximately one every five minutes), and that the query is worded clearly and concisely. It is also recommended that approximately one third of the queries used are based upon the information provided to the participant by the relevant automation tools, one third are based upon the evolution or future of the situation and one third are based upon the operator's knowledge of the current situation (Jeannott, Kelly and Thompson, 2003). Each query administered should be recorded on a Query pro-forma, along with the participant's reply. The analyst should also rate the participant's answer in terms of content and response time as it is received. Step 7 should be repeated until either the task is complete or sufficient SA data is collected.

Step 7: Administer SASHA_Q questionnaire
Once the task is complete or sufficient SA data is collected, the participant should be given a SASHA_Q questionnaire and asked to complete it.

Step 8: Double check query answer ratings
Whilst the participant is completing the SASHA_Q questionnaire, the analyst should return to the query answers and double check them to ensure that the ratings provided are correct. An example SASHA_L pro-forma is presented in Figure 7.7.

Step 9: Calculate participant SA score
The final step in the SASHA procedure is to calculate the participant SA scores.

Advantages

1. The SASHA methodology offers two separate assessments of operator SA.
2. The use of real-time probes removes the need for a freeze in the simulation.

Disadvantages

1. The generation of appropriate SA queries on-line requires great skill and places a heavy burden on the SME used.
2. The appropriateness of response time as a measure of SA is questionable.
3. Low construct validity.
4. The on-line queries are intrusive to primary task performance. One could argue that on-line real-time probes are more intrusive to primary task performance, as the task is not frozen and therefore the participant is still performing the task whilst answering the SA query.
5. No validation data available.
6. There is no evidence of the technique's usage available in the literature.
7. Access to a simulation of the task/system under analysis is required.
8. SMEs are required to generate the SA queries during the trial.

Example

There is no evidence of the technique's use available in the literature. Therefore, the following example SASHA documentation is provided as an example, reflecting what is required in a SASHA analysis. The following SASHA literature was taken from Jeannott, Kelly and Thompson (2003). Example SASHA_L queries are presented in Table 7.12. The SASHA_Q questionnaire is presented in Figure 7.6. The SASHA_L query pro-forma is presented in Figure 7. 7.

Table 7.12   Example SASHA_L Queries (Source: Jeannott, Kelly and Thompson, 2003)

1. Will US Air 1650 and Continental 707 be in conflict if no further action is taken?
2. Which sector, shown in the communication *tool* window, has requested a change of FL at handover?
3. Are there any speed conflicts on the J74 airway?
4. What is the time of the situation displayed in the *tool* window?
5. Are you expecting any significant increase in workload in the next 15 minutes?
6. Which aircraft needs to be transferred next?
7. Which aircraft has the fastest ground speed? US Air 992 or Air France 2249?
8. Which of the two conflicts shown in *tool* is more critical?
9. Which aircraft would benefit from a direct route? BA1814 or AF5210?
10. Which aircraft is going to reach its requested flight level first – AA369 or US Air 551?
11. With which sector do you need to co-ordinate AF222 exit level?
12. Which of the two conflicts shown in *tool* is more critical?

Related Methods

The SASHA_L on-line probing technique is an adaptation of the SPAM (Durso et al, 1998) SA assessment technique, the only real difference being that the SA queries are developed beforehand when using SPAM, and not during the task performance as when using SASHA_L. The SASHA_Q is an SA related questionnaire. A HTA of the task or scenario under analysis should also be conducted prior to a SASHA_L analysis.

Training and Application Times

Whilst the SASHA technique seems to be a simple one, it is estimated that the associated training time would be high. This reflects the time taken for the analyst (who should be an appropriate SME) to become proficient at generating relevant SA queries during the task. This would be a difficult thing to do, and requires considerable skill on the behalf of the analyst. The application time is dependent upon the duration of the task under analysis. However, it is estimated that it would be low, as the SASHA_Q contains ten short questions and it is felt that the tasks under analysis would probably not exceed one hour in duration.

Reliability and Validity

There is no evidence of reliability and validity data for the SASHA technique available in the open literature.

Tools Needed

A simulation of the system and task(s) under analysis is required. Otherwise, the technique can be applied using pen and paper. Copies of the query pro-forma and SASHA_Q questionnaire are also required.

Q1 – Did you have the feeling that you were ahead of the traffic, able to predict the evolution of the traffic?

Never ☐ ☐ ☐ ☐ ☐ Always

Q2 – Did you have the feeling that you were ahead to plan and organise your work as you wanted?

Never ☐ ☐ ☐ ☐ ☐ Always

Q3 – Have you been surprised by an a/c call that you were not expecting?

Never ☐ ☐ ☐ ☐ ☐ Always

Q4 – Did you have the feeling of starting to focus too much on a single problem and/or area of the sector?

Never ☐ ☐ ☐ ☐ ☐ Always

Q5 – Did you forget to transfer any aircraft?

Never ☐ ☐ ☐ ☐ ☐ Always

Q6 – Did you have any difficulties finding an item of (static) information?

Never ☐ ☐ ☐ ☐ ☐ Always

Q7 – Do you think the (name of tool) provided you with useful information?

Never ☐ ☐ ☐ ☐ ☐ Always

Q8 – Were you paying too much attention to the functioning of the (name of tool)?

Never ☐ ☐ ☐ ☐ ☐ Always

Q9 – Did the (name of tool) help you to have a better understanding of the situation?

Never ☐ ☐ ☐ ☐ ☐ Always

Q10 – Finally, how would you rate your SA during this exercise?

Poor ☐ Quite poor ☐ ☐ ☐ Quite good ☐ Very good

Okay

Figure 7.6   SASHA_Q Questionnaire (Source: Jeannott, Kelly and Thompson, 2003)

SASHA On-Line Query No:

Query: Will US Air 1650 and Continental 707 be in conflict if no further action is taken?

Query's operational importance   – [ ][ ][ ][ ][ ][ ][ ] +

Answers operational accuracy   Incorrect [ ]   OK [ ]   Correct [ ]

Time to answer   Too short [ ]   OK [ ]   Too long [ ]

Figure 7.7   SASHA_L Query Pro-forma (Source: Jeannott, Kelly and Thompson, 2003)

Flowchart

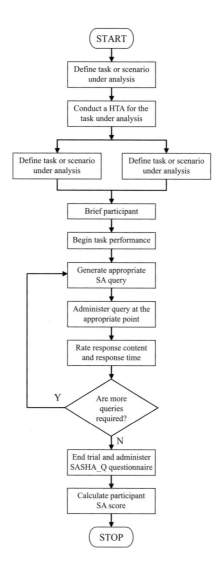

Mission Awareness Rating Scale (MARS)

Background and Applications

The mission awareness rating scale (MARS; Matthews and Beal, 2002) technique is a situation awareness assessment technique designed specifically for use in the assessment of SA in military exercises. MARS is a development of the crew awareness rating scale (CARS; McGuiness and Foy, 2000) technique that has been used to assess operator SA in a number of domains. The MARS technique comprises two separate sets of questions based upon the three level model of SA (Endsley, 1988). MARS also comprises two subscales, the content subscale and the workload subscale. The content subscale consists of three statements designed to elicit ratings based upon ease of identification, understanding and projection of mission critical cues (i.e. levels 1, 2 and 3 SA). The fourth statement is designed to assess how aware the participant felt they were during the mission. The workload subscale also consists of four statements, which are designed to assess how difficult, in terms of mental effort, it is for the participant in question to identify, understand, and project the future states of the mission critical cues in the situation. The fourth statement in the workload subscale is designed to assess how difficult it was mentally for the participant to achieve the appropriate mission goals. The MARS technique was developed for use in 'real-world' field settings, rather than in simulations of military exercises. The technique is normally administered post-trial or on completion of the task or mission under analysis. The MARS questionnaire is presented in Figure 7.8. To score the ratings, a rating scale of 1 (*Very Easy*) to 4 (*Very Difficult*) is used.

Content subscales

Please rate your ability to identify mission-critical cues in this mission.

- Very easy- able to identify all cues
- Fairly easy – could identify most cues
- Somewhat difficult – many cues hard to identify
- Very difficult – had substantial problems identifying most cues

How well did you understand what was going on during the mission?

- Very well – fully understood the situation as it unfolded
- Fairly well – understood most aspects of the situation
- Somewhat poorly – had difficulty understanding much of the situation
- Very poorly – the situation did not make sense to me

How well could you predict what was about to occur next in the mission?

- Very well – could predict with accuracy what was about to occur
- Fairly well – could make accurate predictions most of the time
- Somewhat poor – misunderstood the situation much of the time
- Very poor – unable to predict what was about to occur

How aware were you of how to best achieve your goals during this mission?

- Very aware – knew how to achieve goals at all times
- Fairly aware – knew most of the time how to achieve mission goals
- Somewhat unaware – was not aware of how to achieve some goals
- Very unaware – generally unaware of how to achieve goals

Workload subscales

How difficult, in terms of mental effort required, was it for you to identify or detect mission critical cues during the mission?

☐ Very easy – could identify relevant cues with little effort
☐ Fairly easy – could identify relevant cues, but some effort required
☐ Somewhat difficult – some effort was required to identify most cues
☐ Very difficult – substantial effort required to identify relevant cues

How difficult, in terms of mental effort, was it to understand what was going on during the mission?

☐ Very easy – understood what was going on with little effort
☐ Fairly easy – understood events with only moderate effort
☐ Somewhat difficult – hard to comprehend some aspects of the situation
☐ Very difficult – hard to understand most or all aspects of the situation

How difficult, in terms of mental effort, was it to predict what was about to happen during the mission?

☐ Very easy – little or no effort required
☐ Fairly easy – moderate effort required
☐ Somewhat difficult – many projections required substantial effort
☐ Very difficult – substantial effort required on most or all projections

How difficult, in terms of mental effort, was it to decide on how to best achieve mission goals during this mission?

☐ Very easy – little or no effort required
☐ Fairly easy – moderate effort required
☐ Somewhat difficult – substantial effort needed on some decisions
☐ Very difficult – most or all decisions required substantial effort

Figure 7.8   MARS Questionnaire (Source: Matthews and Beal, 2002)

Domain of Application

Military (infantry operations).

Procedure and Advice

Step 1: Define task(s) under analysis
The first step in a MARS analysis (aside from the process of gaining access to the required systems and personnel) is to define the tasks that are to be subjected to analysis. The type of tasks analysed are dependent upon the focus of the analysis. For example, when assessing the effects on operator SA caused by a novel design or training programme, it is useful to analyse as representative a set of tasks as possible. To analyse a full set of tasks will often be too time consuming and labour intensive, and so it is pertinent to use a set of tasks that use all aspects of the system under analysis. Once the task(s) under analysis are defined clearly, a HTA should be conducted for each task. This allows the analyst(s) and participants to understand the task(s) fully.

Step 2: Selection of participants
Once the task(s) under analysis are clearly defined and described, it may be useful to select the participants that are to be involved in the analysis. This may not always be necessary and it may suffice to simply select participants randomly on the day. However, if SA is being compared across rank or experience levels, then clearly effort is required to select the appropriate participants. For example, Matthews and Beal (2002) report a study comparing the SA of platoon leaders and less experienced squad leaders in an infantry field training exercise.

Step 3: Brief participants
Before the task(s) under analysis are performed, all of the participants involved should be briefed regarding the purpose of the study, the construct of SA, and the MARS technique. It may be useful at this stage to take the participants through an example MARS analysis, so that they understand how the technique works and what is required of them as participants.

Step 4: Conduct pilot run
Before the data collection process begins, it is recommended that a pilot run of the procedure is conducted, in order to highlight any potential problems with the experimental procedure and to ensure that the participants fully understand the process. Participants should perform a small task and then complete the MARS questionnaire. Participants should be encouraged to ask any questions regarding the procedure during the pilot run.

Step 5: Task performance
Once the participants fully understand the MARS technique and the data collection procedure, they are free to undertake the task(s) under analysis as normal. To reduce intrusiveness, the MARS questionnaire is administered post-trial. Other 'on-line' techniques can be used in conjunction with the MARS technique. Analysts may want to observe the task being performed and record any behaviours or errors relating to the participants' SA. Matthews and Beal (2002) report the use of the SABARS technique in conjunction with MARS, whereby domain experts observe and rate SA related behaviours exhibited by participants during the trial.

Step 6: Administer MARS questionnaire
Once the technique is completed, the MARS questionnaire should be given to the participants involved in the study. The technique consists of two A4 pro-formas and is completed using a pen or pencil. Ideally, participants should complete the questionnaire in isolation. However, if they require assistance they should be permitted to ask the analysts for help.

Step 7: Calculate participant SA/workload scores
Once the MARS questionnaires are completed, the analyst(s) should calculate and record the SA and workload ratings for each participant. These can then be analysed using various statistical tests.

Advantages

1. The MARS technique was developed specifically for infantry exercises and has been applied in that setting.
2. The method is less intrusive than on-line probe techniques such as the SAGAT technique.
3. MARS is based upon the CARS technique, which has been applied extensively in other domains.

4. The techniques generic make-up allows the MARS technique to be used across domains with minimal modification.
5. Quick and easy to use, requiring minimal training.
6. The MARS technique could potentially be used in conjunction with on-line probe techniques to ensure comprehensiveness.

Disadvantages

1. The construct validity of the technique is questionable. It could be argued that rather than measuring SA itself, MARS is actually rating the difficulty in acquiring and maintaining SA.
2. The technique has only limited validation evidence associated with it. The technique requires further validation in military or infantry settings.
3. As the MARS questionnaire is administered and completed post-trial, it is subject to the various problems associated with post-trial data collection, such as correlation with performance and poor recall of events. It is also apparent that participants are limited in the accurate recall of mental operations. For lengthy scenarios, participants may not be able to recall events whereby they were finding it difficult or easy to perceive mission critical cues.
4. Only an overall rating is acquired, rather than a rating at different points in the task. It may be that the output of the technique is of limited use. For example, a design concept may only acquire an overall rating associated with SA, rather than numerous SA ratings throughout the task, some of which would potentially pinpoint specific problems with the new design.

Related Methods

MARS is a development of the CARS (McGuinness and Foy, 2000) subjective SA assessment technique. The technique elicits self-ratings of SA post-trial from participants. There are a number of other SA self-rating techniques that use this procedure, such as SART and SARS. It may also be pertinent to use MARS in conjunction with other SA assessment techniques to ensure comprehensiveness. Matthews and Beal (2002) report the use of MARS in conjunction with SABARS (behavioural rating SA technique) and PSAQ (SA related questionnaire).

Flowchart

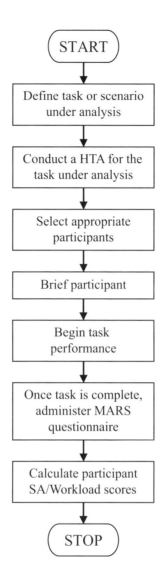

Example

The MARS questionnaire is presented in Figure 7.8. Matthews and Beal (2002) describe a study carried out by the U.S Army Research Institute for the Behavioural and Social Sciences Institute. The study involved the use of MARS to compare the SA of platoon leaders to that of less experienced squadron leaders. Eight platoon leaders and eight squadron leaders were assessed using the MARS, SABARS and PSAQ techniques for their SA during a field training exercise. It was hypothesised that the more experienced platoon leaders would have a more complete picture of the situation than the less experienced squadron leaders, and so would possess a greater level of SA. Participants took part in a military operation in urbanised terrain (MOUT) field training exercise. Each platoon was firstly required to attack and secure a heavily armed command and control structure, and then to enter and secure the MOUT village (Matthews and Beal, 2002). The scenario was highly difficult and required extensive planning before an attack was carried out (between four to six hours).

Once the mission was completed, MARS and SABARS data were collected from the platoon and squad leaders involved in the task. The MARS data indicated that for the content subscale, the squad leaders rated all four items (identification, comprehension, projection and decision) as more difficult to achieve than the platoon leaders did. The squad leaders also rated the identification of critical mission cues as the most difficult task, whilst platoon leaders rated deciding upon action as the most difficult. For the workload subscale, both groups of participants rated the identification of critical cues as the same in terms of mental effort imposed. The squad leaders rated the other three items (comprehension, projection and decision) as more difficult in terms of mental effort imposed than the platoon leaders did. It was concluded that the MARS technique was able to differentiate between different levels of SA achieved between the squad and platoon leaders.

Training and Application Times

It is estimated that the training and application times associated with the MARS technique would be very low. Matthews and Beal (2002) report that the MARS questionnaire takes on average five minutes to complete. However, if the task under analysis's duration is included in the overall applications time, then the application time for a typical MARS analysis could be very high. For example, the task used in the study described by Matthews and Beal (2002) took around seven hours to complete, and the task was conducted on eight separate occasions.

Reliability and Validity

The MARS technique has been tested in field training exercises (See example). However, there is limited validation evidence associated with the technique. Further testing regarding the reliability and validity of the technique as a measure of SA is required.

Tools Needed

MARS can be applied using pen and paper.

Situation Awareness Behavioural Rating Scale (SABARS)

Background and Applications

The situation awareness behavioural rating scale (SABARS; Matthews and Beal, 2002) is an objective SA rating technique that has been used to assess infantry personnel situation awareness in field training exercises (Matthews, Pleban, Endsley and Strater, 2000; Matthews and Beal, 2002). The technique involves domain experts observing participants during task performance and rating them on 28 observable SA related behaviours. A five point rating scale (1=Very poor, 5 =Very good) and an additional 'not applicable' category are used. The 28 behaviour items were gathered during an SA requirements analysis of military operations in urbanised terrain (MOUT) and are designed specifically to assess platoon leader SA (Matthews et al, 2000). The SABARS scale is presented in Table 7.13.

Table 7.13   Situation Awareness Behavioural Rating Scale (Source: Matthews and Beal, 2002)

Behaviour	Rating					
	1	2	3	4	5	N/A
1. Sets appropriate levels of alert						
2. Solicits information from subordinates						
3. Solicits information from civilians						
4. Solicits information from commanders						
5. Effects co-ordination with other platoon/squad leaders						
6. Communicates key information to commander						
7. Communicates key information to subordinates						
8. Communicates key information to other platoon/squad leaders						
9. Monitors company net						
10. Assesses information received						
11. Asks for pertinent intelligence information						
12. Employs squads/fire teams tactically to gather needed information						
13. Employs graphic or other control measures for squad execution						
14. Communicates to squads/fire teams, situation and commanders intent						
15. Utilises a standard reporting procedure						
16. Identifies critical mission tasks to squad/fire team leaders						
17. Ensures avenues of approach are covered						
18. Locates self at vantage point to observe main effort						
19. Deploys troops to maintain platoon/squad communications						
20. Uses assets to effectively assess information						
21. Performs a leader's recon to assess terrain and situation						
22. Identifies observation points, avenues of approach, key terrain, obstacles, cover and concealment						
23. Assesses key finds and unusual events						
24. Discerns key/critical information from maps, records, and supporting site information						
25. Discerns key/critical information from reports received						
26. Projects future possibilities and creates contingency plans						
27. Gathers follow up information when needed						
28. Overall situation awareness rating						

Procedure and Advice

Step 1: Define task(s) to be analysed
The first step in a SABARS analysis is to define clearly the task or set of tasks that are to be analysed. This allows the analyst(s) to gain a clear understanding of the task content, and also allows for the modification of the behavioural rating scale, whereby any behaviours missing from the scale that may be evident during the task are added. It is recommended that a HTA is conducted for the task(s) under analysis.

Step 2: Select participants to be observed
Once the analyst(s) have gained a full understanding of the task(s) under analysis, the participants that are to be observed can be selected. This may be dependent upon the purpose of the analysis. For example Matthews and Beal (2002) conducted a comparison of platoon and squad leader SA, and so eight platoon and eight squad leaders were selected for assessment. If a general assessment

of SA in system personnel is required, then participants can be selected randomly. Typically, SA is compared across differing levels of expertise. If this is the case, participants with varying levels of expertise, ranging from novice to expert may be selected.

Step 3: Select appropriate observers
The SABARS technique requires SMEs to observe the participants during task performance. It is therefore necessary to select a group of appropriate observers before any analysis can begin. It is crucial that SMEs are used as observers when applying the SABARS technique. Matthews and Beal (2002) used a total of ten infantry officers, including two majors, four captains (with between eight and 22 years of active experience), three sergeants and one staff sergeant (with between four and 13 years of active experience). It is recommended that, in the selection of the observers, those with the most appropriate experience in terms of duration and similarity are selected. Regarding the number of observers used, it may be most pertinent to use more than one observer for each participant under observation. If numerous observers can be acquired, it may be useful to use two observers for each participant, so that reliability can be measured for the SABARS technique. However, more often than not it is difficult to acquire sufficient observers, and so it is recommended that the analyst(s) use as many observers as is possible. In the study reported by Matthews and Beal (2002) six of the participants were observed by two observers each, and the remaining participants were observed by one observer.

Step 4: Brief participants
In most cases, it is appropriate to brief the participants involved regarding the purpose of the study and the techniques used. However, in the case of the SABARS technique, it may be that revealing too much about the behaviours under analysis may cause a degree of bias in the participant behaviour exhibited. It is therefore recommended then that participants are not informed of the exact nature of the 28 behaviours under analysis. During this step it is also appropriate for the observers to be notified regarding the subjects that they are to observe during the trial.

Step 5: Begin task performance
The SABARS data collection process begins when the task under analysis starts. The observers should use the SABARS rating sheet and a separate notepad to make any relevant notes during task performance.

Step 6: Complete SABARS rating sheet
Once the task under analysis is complete, the observers should complete the SABARS rating sheet. The ratings are intended to act as overall ratings for the course of the task, and so the observers should consult the notes taken during the task.

Step 7: Calculate SABARS rating(s)
Once the SABARS rating sheets are completed for each participant, the analyst should calculate overall SA scores for each participant. This involves summing the rating score for each of the 28 SABARS behaviours. The scale scoring system used is shown in Table 7.14.

Table 7.14   SABARS Scoring System

Rating	Score
Very poor	1
Poor	2
Borderline	3
Good	4
Very Good	5
N/A	0

Example

Matthews and Beal (2002) describe a study comparing the SA of platoon and squad leaders during a field training exercise. SABARS was used in conjunction with the MARS and PSAQ SA assessment techniques. Eight platoon leaders and eight squad leaders were assessed for their SA during a field training exercise. A total of ten observers were used, including two majors, four captains, three sergeants and one staff sergeant. The two majors and four captains had between eight and 22 years of active experience, whilst the sergeants and staff sergeant had between four and 13 years of active experience. The incident required the platoons to attack and secure a heavily armed and defended command and control installation, and then to enter and secure a nearby village. The village site was also inhabited by actors assuming the role of civilians who actively interacted with the infantry soldiers. Upon completion of the exercise, observers completed SABARS evaluations for the appropriate platoon and squad leaders. MARS and PSAQ data were also collected. According to Matthews and Beal (2002), the SABARS ratings for platoon and squad leaders were compared. It was found that the platoon and squad groups did not differ significantly on any of the SABARS comparisons. This differed to the findings of the MARS analysis, which indicated that there were significant differences between the achievement and level of SA possessed by the two groups of participants. According to Matthews and Beal (2002) the results obtained by the SABARS technique in this case were quite disappointing. An evaluation of the user acceptance of the SABARS technique was also conducted. Each observer was asked to rate the technique on a five point rating scale (1= strongly disagree, 5 = strongly agree) for the following statements (Source: Matthews and Beal, 2002).

1. SABARS included questions important in assessing situation awareness for small infantry teams;
2. SABARS was easy to use;
3. My ratings on SABARS could be used to give useful feedback to the leader on his or her mission performance;
4. Providing a way for observers to give trainees feedback on SA is an important goal for improving training.

The results indicated that the observers regarded the SABARS technique in a positive light (Matthews and Beal, 2002). The mean responses were 4.06 (agree) for statement 1, 3.94 (agree) for statement 2, 4.12 (agree) for statement 3 and 4.25 (agree) for statement 4.

Advantages

1. The behaviour items used in the SABARS scale were generated from an infantry SA requirements exercise (Strater et al 2001).
2. The technique is quick and easy to use.
3. Requires minimal training.
4. Has been used in a military context.
5. It appears that SABARS shows promise as a back-up measure of SA. It seems that the technique would be suited for use alongside a direct measure of SA, such as SAGAT. This would allow a comparison of the SA measured and the SA related behaviours exhibited.

Disadvantages

1. As SABARS is an observer-rating tool, the extent to which it measures SA is questionable. SABARS only offers expert opinion on observable, SA related behaviours. Therefore it should be remembered that the technique does not offer a direct assessment of SA.
2. The extent to which an observer can rate the internal construct of SA is questionable.
3. To use the technique correctly, a number of domain experts are required.
4. Access to the tasks under analysis is required. This may be difficult to obtain, particularly in military settings.
5. To use the technique elsewhere, a new set of domain specific behaviours would be required. This requires significant effort in terms of time and manpower.
6. Limited validation evidence.
7. The technique could be prone to participant bias.
8. The technique has been subjected to only limited use.
9. Matthews and Beal (2002) report disappointing results for the SABARS technique.
10. According to Endsley (1995) using observation as an assessment of participant SA is limited.

Related Methods

Observer ratings have been used on a number of occasions to assess operator SA. However, the SABARS technique is unique in terms of the 28 military specific behaviours used to assess SA. In terms of usage, SABARS has been used in conjunction with the MARS and PSAQ measures of SA.

Approximate Training and Application Times

The training required for the SABARS technique is minimal, as domain experts are used, who are familiar with the construct of SA and the types of behaviours that require rating. In terms of completing the rating sheet, the application time is very low. According to Matthews and Beal (2002) the SABARS rating sheet takes, on average, five minutes to complete. This represents a very low application time. However one might also take into account the length of the observation associated with the technique. This is dependent upon the type of task under analysis. The task used in the study conducted by Matthews and Beal (2002) took between four and seven hours to complete, and was conducted eight times (once a day for eight days). This would represent a high application time for the technique. As the SA ratings are based upon the observations made, high application time has to be estimated for the SABARS technique in this case.

Reliability and Validity

There is limited reliability and validity data concerning the SABARS technique. Reports regarding the use of the technique in the open literature are limited and it seems that much further validation is required. The study reported by Matthews and Beal (2002) returned poor results for the SABARS technique. Furthermore, the construct validity of the technique is highly questionable. The degree to which an observer rating technique assesses SA is subject to debate. Endsley (1995b) suggests that observers would have limited knowledge of what the operator's concept of the situation is, and that operators may store information regarding the situation internally. Observers have no real way of knowing what the participants are and are not aware of during task performance and so the validity of the SA rating provided comes under great scrutiny.

Tools Needed

SABARS can be applied using a pen and paper.

Flowchart

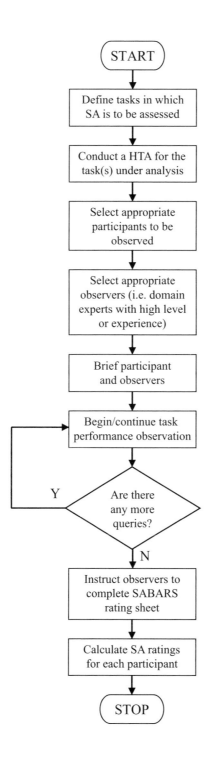

Crew Awareness Rating Scale (CARS)

Background and Applications

The Crew awareness rating scale (CARS; McGuiness and Foy, 2000) is a situation awareness assessment technique that has been used to assess command and control 'commander's' SA and workload (McGuinness and Ebbage, 2000). The CARS technique comprises two subscales based upon the three level model of SA (Endsley, 1995a), the content subscale and the workload subscale. The content subscale consists of three statements designed to elicit ratings based upon ease of identification, understanding and projection of task SA elements (i.e. levels 1, 2 and 3 SA). The fourth statement is designed to assess how well the participant identifies relevant task related goals in the situation. The workload subscale also consists of four statements, which are designed to assess how difficult, in terms of mental effort, it is for the participant in question to identify, understand, project the future states of the SA related elements in the situation. The fourth statement in the workload subscale is designed to assess how difficult it was mentally for the participant to achieve the appropriate task goals. The technique is normally administered post-trial, upon completion of the task under analysis. The CARS categories are presented below (Source: McGuiness and Ebbage, 2000).

1. *Perception.* Perception of task relevant environmental information
2. *Comprehension.* Understanding what the information perceived means in relation to task and task goals
3. *Projection.* Anticipation of future events and states in the environment
4. *Integration.* The combination of the above information with the individual's course of action

Each category identified above is rated by participants on a scale of 1 (*Ideal*) to 4 (*Worst*) for the following (McGuiness and Ebbage, 2000):

1. The content (SA). Is it reliable and accurate?
2. The processing (workload). Is it easy to maintain?

Domain of Application

Military.

Procedure and Advice

Step 1: Define task(s)
The first step in a CARS analysis (aside from the process of gaining access to the required systems and personnel) is to define the tasks that are to be subjected to analysis. The type of tasks analysed are dependent upon the focus of the analysis. For example, when assessing the effects on operator SA caused by a novel design or training programme, it is useful to analyse as representative a set of tasks as possible for the device or programme in question. To analyse a full set of tasks will often be too time consuming and labour intensive, and so it is often pertinent to use a set of tasks that use all aspects of the system under analysis. Once the task(s) under analysis are defined clearly, a HTA should be conducted for each task. This allows the analyst(s) and participants to understand the task(s) fully.

Step 2: Selection of participants

Once the task(s) under analysis are defined, it may be useful to select the participants that are to be involved in the analysis. This may not always be necessary and it may suffice to simply select participants randomly on the day. However, if SA is being compared across rank or experience levels, then clearly effort is required to select the appropriate participants. For example, Matthews and Beal (2002) report a study comparing the SA of platoon leaders and less experienced squad leaders in an infantry field training exercise.

Step 3: Brief participants

Before the task(s) under analysis are performed, all of the participants involved should be briefed regarding the purpose of the study, SA and the CARS technique. It may useful at this stage to take the participants through an example CARS analysis, so that they understand how the technique works and what is required of them as participants.

Step 4: Conduct pilot run

It is recommended that a pilot run of the experimental procedure be conducted prior to the data collection phase. Participants should perform a small task and then complete the CARS questionnaire. Participants should be encouraged to ask any questions regarding the procedure during the pilot run.

Step 5: Task performance

Once the participants fully understand the CARS technique and the data collection procedure, they are free to undertake the task(s) under analysis as normal. To reduce intrusiveness, the CARS questionnaire is administered post-trial. Other 'on-line' techniques can be used in conjunction with the CARS technique. Analysts may want to observe the task being performed and record any behaviours or errors relating to the participants' SA. Matthews and Beal (2002) report the use of the SABARS technique in conjunction with MARS (SA measurement technique similar to CARS), which involved domain experts observing and rating SA related behaviours exhibited by participants during task performance.

Step 6: Administer MARS questionnaire

Once the task under analysis is complete, the CARS questionnaire should be given to the participants involved in the study. The questionnaire consists of two A4 pro-formas and is completed using a pen or pencil. Ideally, participants should complete the questionnaire in isolation. However, if they require assistance they should be permitted to ask the analysts for help.

Step 7: Calculate participant SA/workload scores

Once the CARS questionnaires are completed, the analyst(s) should calculate and record the SA and workload ratings for each participant. These can then be analysed using various statistical tests.

Advantages

1. The CARS technique was developed specifically for infantry exercises and has been applied in that setting.
2. The method is less intrusive than on-line probe techniques such as the SAGAT technique.
3. CARS is a generic technique and requires minimal modification to be used in other domains e.g. the MARS technique.
4. Quick and easy to use, requiring minimal training.

5. The CARS technique could potentially be used in conjunction with on-line probe techniques to ensure comprehensiveness.
6. CARS offers a very low cost means of assessing SA and workload.

Disadvantages

1. Questions may be asked regarding the construct validity of the technique. It could be argued that rather than measuring SA itself, CARS is actually rating the difficulty in acquiring and maintaining SA.
2. There is only limited validation evidence associated with the technique.
3. Subjective rating of SA post-trial is beset by a number of problems, including a correlation between perceived SA and performance, poor recall and participants forgetting periods of low SA during the task.
4. Only an overall rating is acquired, rather than a rating at different points in the task. This could inhibit the usefulness of the output. For example, a design concept may only acquire an overall rating associated with SA, rather than different SA ratings throughout the task, some of which would potentially pinpoint specific problems with the new design.
5. Limited validation evidence.

Tools Needed

CARS can be applied using pen and paper.

Example

The CARS technique was used to measure the effect of the use of digitised command and control technology on commanders' workload and SA simulated battlefield scenarios (McGuinness and Ebbage, 2000). Participants took part in two exercises, one using standard communications (voice radio net) and one using digital technology, such as data link, text messaging and automatic location reporting (McGuinness and Ebbage, 2000). Performance measures (timing, expert observer ratings), SA measures (CARS, mini situation reports) and workload measures (ISA, NASA –TLX) were used to assess the effects of the use of digital technology. The CARS processing ratings showed no significant differences between the two conditions. The CARS content ratings (confidence in awareness) were higher in the condition using digital technology by both team members (McGuinness and Ebbage, 2000).

Related Methods

MARS is a development of the CARS subjective SA assessment technique. The technique requires subjective ratings of SA from participants. There are a number of other SA self-rating techniques that use this procedure, such as SART and SARS. It may also be pertinent to use CARS in conjunction with other SA assessment techniques to ensure comprehensiveness. Matthews and Beal (2002) report the use of MARS in conjunction with SABARS (behavioural rating SA technique) and PSAQ (SA questionnaire).

Flowchart

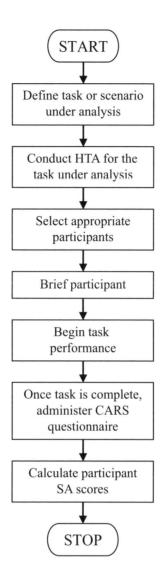

Training and Application Times

It is estimated that the training time associated with the CARS technique would be very low. Matthews and Beal (2002) report that the MARS questionnaire takes on average five minutes to complete. The time associated with the application time of the CARS technique would be dependent upon the duration of the task under analysis. For example, the task used in the study cited (Matthews and Beal, 2002) in the example took around seven hours to complete, and was conducted on eight separate occasions. This would represent a relatively high application time for an SA assessment technique.

Reliability and Validity

There is limited validation evidence associated with the technique. Further testing regarding the reliability and validity of the technique as a measure of SA is required.

Cranfield Situation Awareness Scale (C-SAS)

Background and Application

The Cranfield situation awareness scale (C-SAS; Dennehy, 1997) is a simplistic, quick and easy SA rating scale that can be applied either during or post-trial performance. Originally developed for the assessment of student pilot SA during training procedures, C-SAS can also be applied either subjectively (completed by the participant) or objectively (completed by an observer). Ratings are provided for five SA related sub-scales using an appropriate rating scale e.g. 1 (*Very poor*) to 5 (*Very good*). An overall SA rating is then derived by summing the sub-scale ratings. The C-SAS sub-scales are:

1. Pilot knowledge.
2. Understanding and anticipation of future events.
3. Management of stress, effort and commitment.
4. Capacity to perceive, assimilate and assess information.
5. Overall SA.

Domain of Application

Aviation.

Procedure and Advice (Subjective Use)

Step 1: Define task(s) under analysis
The first step in a C-SAS analysis is to define clearly the task or set of tasks that are to be analysed. This allows the analyst(s) to gain a clear understanding of the task content. It is recommended that a HTA is conducted for the task(s) under analysis.

Step 2: Brief participants
When using the technique as a subjective rating tool, the participants should be briefed regarding the nature and purpose of the analysis. It is recommended that the subjects are not exposed to the C-SAS technique until after the task is completed.

Step 3: Begin task performance
The task performance can now begin. Although the C-SAS technique can be applied during the task performance, it is recommended that when using the technique as a subjective rating tool, it is completed post-trial to reduce intrusion on primary task performance. The participant should complete the task under analysis as normal. This may be in an operational or simulated setting, depending upon the nature of the analysis.

Step 4: Administer C-SAS
Immediately after the task is completed, the participant should be given the C-SAS rating sheet. The C-SAS rating sheet should contain comprehensive instructions regarding the use of the technique, including definitions of and examples of each sub-scale. Participants should be instructed to complete the C-SAS rating sheet based upon their performance during the task under analysis.

Step 5: Calculate participant SA score
Once the participant has completed the C-SAS rating sheet, their SA score can be calculated and recorded. The score for each sub-scale and an overall SA score should be recorded. The overall score is calculated by simply summing the five sub-scale scores.

Procedure and Advice (Objective Use)

Step 1: Define task(s) under analysis
The first step in a C-SAS analysis is to define clearly the task or set of tasks that are to be analysed. This allows the analyst(s) to gain a clear understanding of the task content. It is recommended that a HTA is conducted for the task(s) under analysis.

Step 2: Select appropriate observers
When using the C-SAS technique objectively as an observer-rating tool, domain experts are required to observe the participants under analysis. It is therefore necessary to select a group of appropriate observers before any analysis can begin. It is crucial that domain experts are used as observers when applying the technique. It is recommended that, in the selection of the observers, those with the most appropriate experience in terms of duration and similarity are selected. Normally, one observer is used per participant.

Step 3: Train observer(s)
A short training session should be given to the selected observer(s). The training session should include an introduction to SA, and an explanation of the C-SAS technique, including an explanation of each sub-scale used. The observers should also be taken through an example C-SAS analysis. It may also be useful to conduct a small pilot run, whereby the observers observe a task and complete the C-SAS scale for selected participants. This procedure allows the observers to fully understand how the technique works and also to highlight any potential problems in the experimental process. The observers should be encouraged to ask questions regarding the C-SAS technique and its application.

Step 4: Brief participant
Next, the participant under analysis should be briefed regarding the nature of the analysis.

Step 5: Begin task performance
Task performance can now begin. Participants should complete the task under analysis as normal. This may be in an operational or simulated setting, depending upon the nature of the analysis. The observers should observe the whole task performance, and it is recommended that they take notes regarding the five C-SAS subscales throughout the task.

Step 6: Complete C-SAS rating procedure
Once the task under analysis is complete, the observers should complete the C-SAS rating sheet based upon their observations.

Step 7: Calculate participant SA score
Once the observer has completed the C-SAS rating sheet, the participant's SA score is calculated
and recorded. The score for each sub-scale and an overall SA score should be recorded. Overall SA
is derived by simply summing the five sub-scale scores.

Flowchart (Subjective Rating Technique)

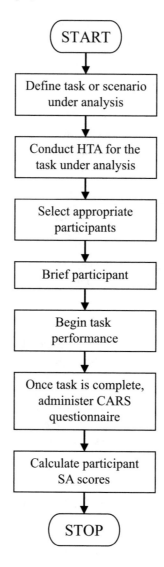

Flowchart (Observer Rating Tool)

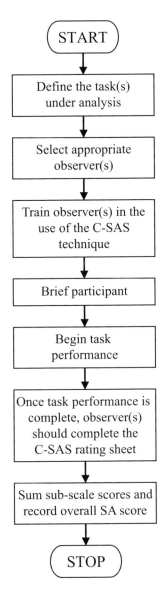

Advantages

1. The technique is very quick and easy to use, requiring almost no training.
2. Offers a low cost means of assessing participant SA.
3. Although developed for use in aviation, the C-SAS sub-scales are generic and could potentially be used in any domain.
4. C-SAS shows promise as a back-up measure of SA. It seems that the technique would be suited for use alongside a direct measure of SA, such as SAGAT. This would allow a comparison of the SA measured and the SA related behaviours exhibited.

Disadvantages

1. When used as an observer-rating tool, the extent to which it measures SA is questionable. As C-SAS can only offer an expert's view on observable, SA related behaviours, it should be remembered that the technique does not offer a direct assessment of SA.
2. The extent to which an observer can rate the internal construct of SA is questionable.
3. To use the technique appropriately, domain experts are required.
4. There are no data regarding the reliability and validity of the technique available in the literature.
5. The technique has been subjected to only limited use.
6. According to Endsley (1995) the rating of SA by observers is limited.
7. When used as a self-rating tool, the extent to which the sub-scales provide an assessment of SA is questionable.
8. Participants are rating SA 'after the fact'.
9. A host of problems are associated with collecting SA data post-trial, such as forgetting, and a correlation between SA ratings and performance.

Related Methods

The C-SAS can be used as a self-rating technique or an observer-rating technique. There are a number of self-rating SA assessment techniques, such as SART, SARS and CARS. The use of observer ratings to assess SA is less frequent, although techniques for this do exist, such as SABARS. It may be that the C-SAS technique is most suitably applied in conjunction with an on-line probe technique such as SAGAT.

Approximate Training and Application Times

Both the training and application times associated with the C-SAS technique are estimated to be very low.

Reliability and Validity

There are no data regarding the reliability and validity of the technique available in the literature. The construct validity of the technique is questionable, that is, the extent to which the C-SAS sub-scales are actually measuring SA. Also, the degree to which an observer rating technique assesses SA is subject to debate. Endsley (1995) suggests that observers would have limited knowledge of what the operators' concept of the situation is, and that operators may store information regarding the situation internally. Observers have no real way of knowing what the participants are and are not aware of in the situation and so the validity of the SA rating provided comes under great scrutiny.

Tools Needed

C-SAS can be applied using a pen and the appropriate rating sheet.

Propositional Networks

Background and Applications

Propositional networks are used to identify the knowledge objects related to a particular task or scenario, and also the links between each of the knowledge objects identified. According to Baber and Stanton (2004) the concept of representing 'knowledge' in the form of a network has been subjected to major discussion within cognitive psychology since the 1970s. Propositional networks consist of a set of nodes that represent knowledge, sources of information, agents, and artefacts that are linked through specific causal paths. Thus the propositional network offers a way of presenting the 'ideal' collection of knowledge required during the scenario in question. Networks are constructed from an initial critical decision method analysis of the scenario in question. A simple content analysis is used to identify the knowledge objects for each scenario phase as identified by the CDM analysis. A propositional network is then constructed for each phase identified by the CDM analysis, comprised of the knowledge objects and the links between them. Propositional networks have been used to represent knowledge and distributed situation awareness as part of the EAST methodology (Baber and Stanton, 2004), which is described in Chapter 13.

Domain of Application

Generic.

Procedure and Advice

Step 1: Define scenario
The first step in a propositional network analysis is to define the scenario under analysis. The scenario in question should be defined clearly. This allows the analyst(s) to determine the data collection procedure that follows and also the appropriate SMEs required for the CDM phase of the analysis.

Step 2: Conduct a HTA for the scenario
Once the scenario has been clearly defined, the next step involves describing the scenario using HTA. A number of data collection techniques may be used in order to gather the information required for the HTA, such as interviews with SMEs and observations of the task under analysis.

Step 3: Conduct a CDM analysis
The propositional networks are based upon a CDM analysis of the scenario in question. The CDM analysis should be conducted using appropriate SMEs (see Chapter 4 for a full description of the CDM procedure). The CDM involves dividing the scenario under analysis into a number of key phases and then probing the SME using pre-defined 'cognitive' probes, designed to determine pertinent features associated with decision making during each scenario phase.

Step 4: Conduct content analysis
Once the CDM data is collected, a simple content analysis should be conducted for each phase identified during the CDM analysis. In order to convert the CDM tables into propositions, a content analysis is performed. In the first stage, this simply means separating all content words from any function words. For example, the entry in table one 'Respiratory problems caused by unknown, airborne material' would be reduced to the following propositions 'respiratory problems', 'airborne'

and 'material'. Working through the table leads to a set of propositions. These are checked to ensure that duplication is minimised and then used to construct the propositional network.

In order to specify the knowledge objects for each phase, the analyst simply takes the CDM output for each phase and using a simple content analysis, identifies the required knowledge objects. Knowledge objects include any knowledge, information, agents and artefacts identified by the CDM analysis. A simple list of knowledge objects should be made for each scenario phase.

Step 5: Define links between knowledge objects

Once the knowledge objects for each scenario phase have been identified, the next step involves defining the links between the knowledge objects in each phase. The following knowledge objects links taxonomy is used:

Has
Is
Causes
Knows
Requires
Prevents

For those knowledge objects that are linked during the scenario, the type of link should be defined using the links taxonomy above.

Step 6: Construct propositional networks

The final step is to construct the propositional network diagrams for each scenario phase. A propositional network diagram should be constructed for the overall scenario (i.e. including all knowledge objects) and then separate propositional network diagrams should be constructed for each phase, with the knowledge objects required highlighted in red. Further coding of the knowledge objects may also be used e.g. shared knowledge objects can be striped in colour, and inactive knowledge objects that have been used in previous scenario phases are typically shaded.

Advantages

1. The output represents the ideal collection of knowledge required for performance during the scenario under analysis.
2. The knowledge objects are defined for each phase of the scenario under analysis, and the links between the knowledge objects are also specified.
3. The technique is easy to learn and use.
4. The technique is also quick in its application.
5. Propositional networks are ideal for analysing teamwork and representing shared situation awareness during a particular scenario.

Disadvantages

1. The initial HTA and CDM analysis add considerable time to the associated application time.
2. Inter- and intra-analyst reliability of the technique is questionable.
3. A propositional network analysis is reliant upon acceptable CDM data.
4. It may be difficult to gather appropriate SMEs for the CDM part of the analysis.

Flowchart

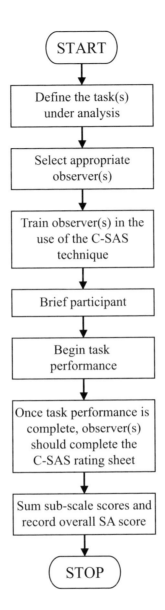

Example

The following example is taken from an analysis of a switching scenario drawn from the civil energy distribution domain (Salmon et al 2004). The propositional networks presented in Figure 7.9 through Figure 7.13 present the knowledge objects (shaded in red) identified from the corresponding CDM output for that phase. The CDM outputs are presented in Table 7.15 through to Table 7.18. The propositional network consists of a set of nodes that represent sources of information, agents, and objects etc. that are linked through specific causal paths. From this network, it is possible to identify required information and possible options relevant to this incident. The concept behind using a propositional network in this manner is that it represents the 'ideal' collection of knowledge for the scenario. As the incident unfolds, so participants will have access to more of this knowledge (either through communication with other agents or through recognising changes in the incident status). Consequently, within this propositional network, Situation Awareness can be represented as the change in weighting of links. Propositional networks were developed for the overall scenario and also the incident phases identified during the CDM analysis. The propositional networks indicate which of the knowledge objects are active (i.e. agents are using them) during each incident phase. The white nodes in the propositional networks represent unactivated knowledge objects (i.e. knowledge is available but is not required nor is it being used). The dark nodes represent active (or currently being used) knowledge objects.

Table 7.15   CDM Phase 1: First Issue of Instructions

Goal Specification	Establish what isolation the SAP at Barking is looking for. Depends on gear?
Cue identification	Don't Believe It (DBI) alarm is unusual – faulty contact (not open or closed) questionable data from site checking rating of earth switches (may be not fully rated for circuit current – so additional earths may be required). Check that SAP is happy with instructions as not normal.
Expectancy	Decision expected by DBI is not common.
Conceptual Model	Recognised instruction but not stated in WE1000 – as there are not too many front and rear shutters metal clad switch gear.
Uncertainty	Confirm from field about planned instruction – make sure that SAP is happy with the instruction.
Information	Reference to front and rear busbars.
Situation Awareness	WE1000 procedure Metal clad switchgear Barking SGT1A/1B substation screen SAP at Barking
Situation Assessment	Ask colleagues if needed to
Options	No alternatives
Stress	N/A
Choice	WE1000 – need to remove what does not apply Could add front and rear busbar procedures
Analogy	Best practice guide for metal clad EMS switching

Table 7.16   CDM Phase 2: Deal with Switching Requests

Goal Specification	Obtain confirmation from NOC that planned isolation is still required.
Cue identification	Approaching time for planned isolation. Switching phone rings throughout building. Airblast circuit breakers (accompanied by sirens) can be heard to operate remotely (more so in Barking 275 than Barking C 132).
Expectancy	Yes – routine planned work according to fixed procedures.
Conceptual Model	Wokingham have performed remote isolations already. Circuit configured ready for local isolation.
Uncertainty	Physical verification of apparatus always required (DBI – don't believe it).
Information	Proceduralised information from NOC – circuit, location, time, actions required etc. Switching log.
Situation Awareness	Switching log. Physical status of apparatus. Planning documentation. Visual or verbal information from substation personnel.
Situation Assessment	Planning documentation used only occasionally.

Options	Refusal of switching request.
	Additional conditions to switching request.
Stress	Some time pressure.
Choice	Yes – highly proceduralised anyway.
Analogy	Yes – routine activity.

Table 7.17   CDM Phase 3: Perform Isolation

Goal Specification	Ensure it is safe to perform local isolation.
	Confirm circuits/equipment to be operated.
Cue identification	Telecontrol displays/circuit loadings.
	Equipment labels.
	Equipment displays.
	Other temporary notices.
Expectancy	Equipment configured according to planned circuit switching.
	Equipment will function correctly.
Conceptual Model	Layout/type/characteristics of circuit.
	Circuit loadings/balance.
	Function of equipment.
Uncertainty	Will equipment physically work as expected (will something jam etc.?).
	Other work being carried out by other parties (e.g. EDF).
Information	Switching log.
	Visual and verbal information from those undertaking the work.
Situation Awareness	Physical information from apparatus and telecontrol displays.
Situation Assessment	All information used
Options	Inform NOC that isolation cannot be performed/other aspects of switching instructions cannot be carried out.
Stress	Some time pressure.
	Possibly some difficulties in operating or physically handling the equipment.
Choice	Yes – proceduralised within equipment types. Occasional non-routine activities required to cope with unusual/unfamiliar equipment, or equipment not owned by NGT.
Analogy	Yes – often. Except in cases with unfamiliar equipment.

Table 7.18   CDM Phase 4: Report Back to NOC

Goal Specification	Inform NOC of isolation status.
Cue identification	Switching telephone.
	NOC operator answers.
Expectancy	NOC accepts.
Conceptual Model	Manner in which circuit is now isolated.
	Form of procedures.
Uncertainty	No – possibly further instructions, possibly mismatches local situation and remote displays in NOC.
Information	Switching log.
Situation Awareness	Verbal information from NOC.
	Switching log.
Situation Assessment	Yes – all information used.
Options	No (raise or add on further requests etc. to the same call?)
Stress	No
Choice	Yes – highly proceduralised
Analogy	Yes – frequently performed activity

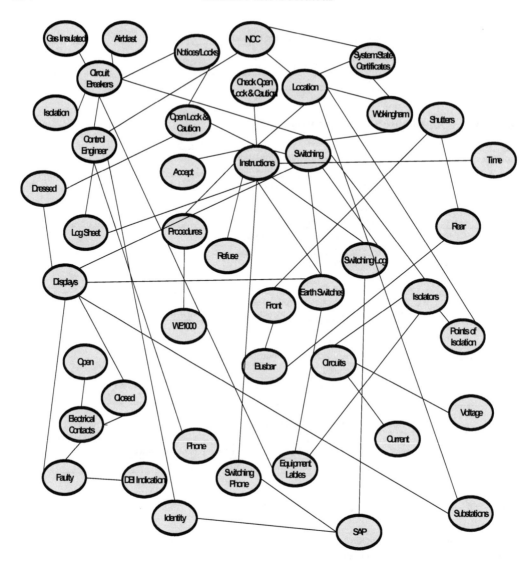

Figure 7.9   Propositional Network for Objects Referred to in CDM Tables

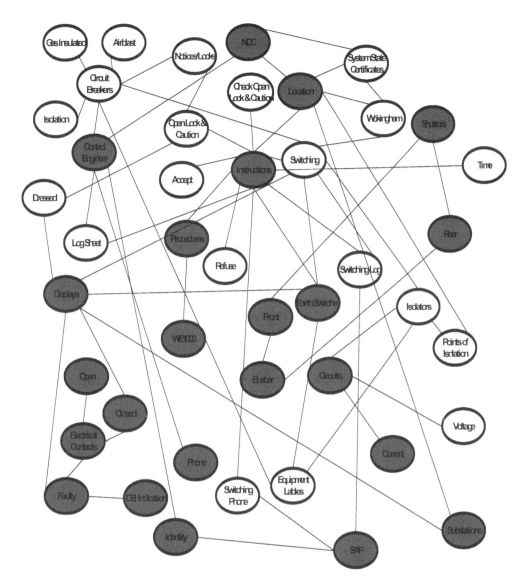

Figure 7.10   Propositional Network for CDM Phase One

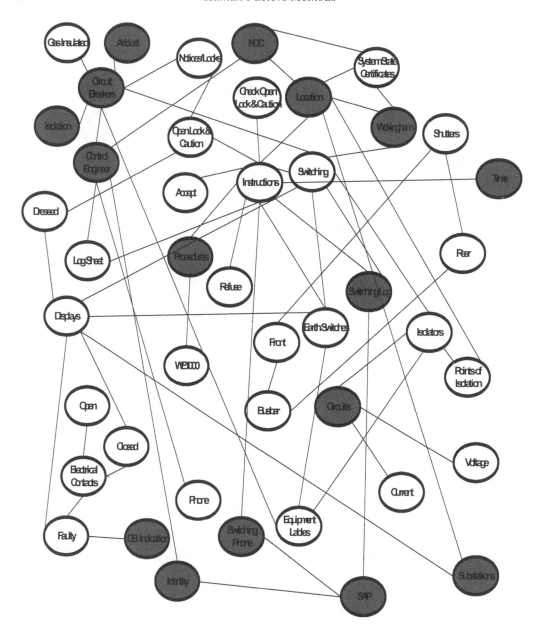

Figure 7.11   Propositional Network for CDM Phase Two

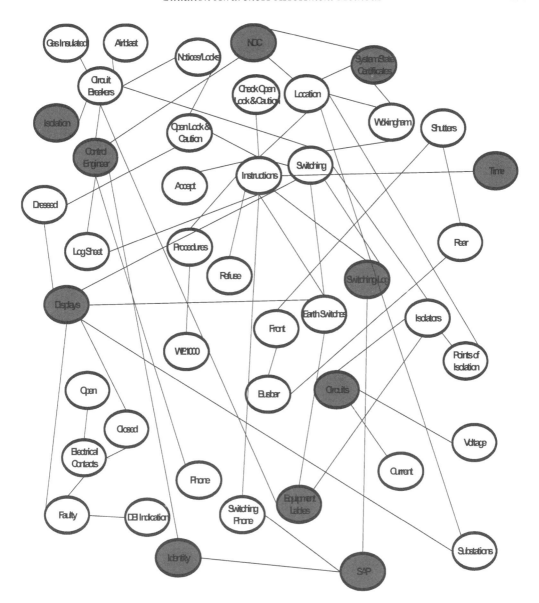

Figure 7.12   Propositional Network for CDM Phase Three

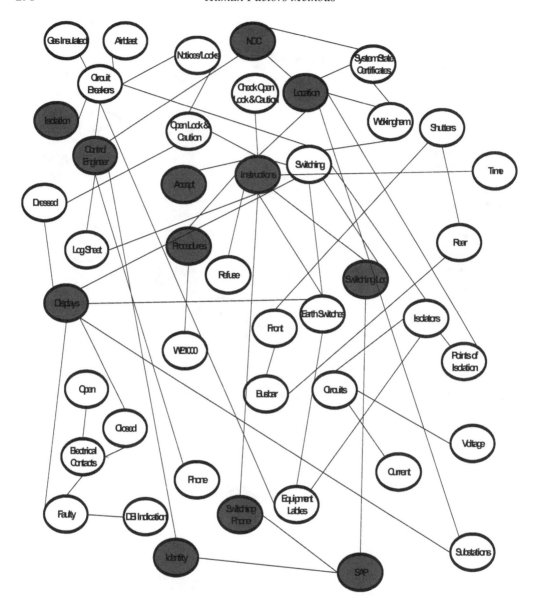

Figure 7.13   Propositional Network for CDM Phase Four

Related Methods

Propositional networks require an initial CDM analysis as an input. A HTA is also typically conducted prior to the propositional network analysis. The technique has also been used in conjunction with a number of other techniques (HTA, observation, co-ordination demands analysis, comms usage diagram, social network analysis) in the form of the event analysis of systemic teamwork (EAST) methodology (Baber et al, 2004), which has been used to analyse C4i activity in a number of domains.

Approximate Training and Application Times

The propositional network methodology requires only minimal training. In a recent HF methods training session, the training time for the propositional network technique was approximately one hour. However, the analyst should be competent in the HTA and CDM procedure in order to conduct the analysis properly. The application time for propositional networks alone is high, as it involves a content analysis (on CDM outputs) and also the construction of the propositional networks.

Reliability and Validity

No data regarding the reliability and validity of the technique are available. From previous experience, it is evident that the reliability of the technique may be questionable. Certainly, different analysts may identify different knowledge objects for the same scenario (intra-analyst reliability). Also, the same analyst may identify different knowledge objects for the same scenario on different occasions (inter-analyst reliability).

Tools Needed

A propositional network analysis can be conducted using pen and paper. However, it is recommended that during the CDM procedure, an audio recording device is used. When constructing the propositional network diagrams it is recommended that Microsoft Visio is used.

Chapter 8

Mental Workload Assessment Methods

The assessment of mental workload (MWL) is of crucial importance during the design and evaluation of complex systems. The increased role of technology and the use of complex procedures have led to a greater level of demand being imposed on operators. Individual operators possess a malleable but ultimately finite attentional capacity, and these attentional resources are allocated to the relevant tasks. MWL represents the proportion of resources demanded by a task or set of tasks. An excessive demand on resources imposed by the task(s) attended to typically results in performance degradation. There has been much debate as to the nature of MWL, with countless attempts at providing a definition. Rather than reviewing these (often competing) definitions, we opt for the approach proposed by Megaw (2005), which is to consider MWL in terms of a framework of interacting stressors on an individual (see Figure 8.1). The arrows indicate the direction of effects within this framework and imply that when we measure MWL we are examining the impact of a whole host of factors on both performance and response. Clearly this means that we are facing a multidimensional problem that is not likely to be amenable to single measures.

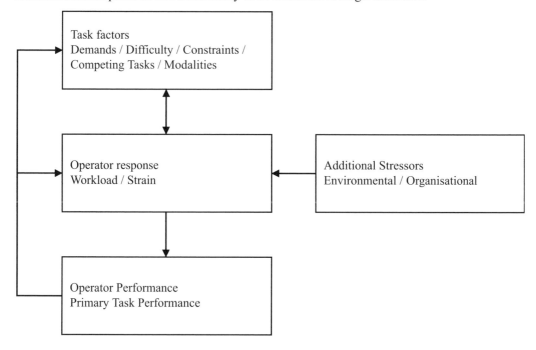

Figure 8.1   Framework of Interacting Stressors Affecting MWL (adapted from Megaw, 2005)

The construct of MWL has been investigated in a wide variety of domains, including aviation, air traffic control, military operations, driving and control room operation to name only a few. The assessment or measurement of MWL is used throughout the design life cycle, to inform system and task design and to provide an evaluation of MWL imposed by existing operational systems and procedures. MWL assessment is also used to evaluate the workload imposed during the operation of existing systems. There are a number of different MWL assessment procedures available to the HF practitioner. Traditionally, using a single approach to measure operator MWL has proved inadequate, and as a result a combination of the methods available is typically used. The assessment of operator MWL typically requires the use of a battery of MWL assessment techniques, including primary task performance measures, secondary task performance measures (reaction times, embedded tasks), physiological measures (HRV, HR), and subjective rating techniques (SWAT, NASA TLX). The methods review identified the following categories of MWL assessment techniques:

1. Primary and secondary task performance measures;
2. Physiological measures; and
3. Subjective-rating techniques.

A brief description of each category and also of each MWL assessment technique considered is given below.

Primary task performance measures of operator MWL involve the measurement of the operator's ability to perform the primary task under analysis. It is expected that operator performance of the task under analysis will diminish as MWL increases. Specific aspects of the primary task are assessed in order to measure performance. For example, in a study of driving with automation, Young and Stanton (2004) measured speed, lateral position and headway as indicators of performance on a driving task. According to Wierwille and Eggemeier (1993), primary tasks measures should be included in any assessment of operator MWL. The main advantages associated with the use of primary task measures for the assessment of operator MWL are their reported sensitivity to variations in workload (Wierwille and Eggemeier, 1993) and their ease of use, since performance of the primary task is normally measured anyway. There are a number of disadvantages associated with this method of MWL assessment, including the ability of operators to perform efficiently under high levels of workload, due to factors such as experience and skill. Similarly, performance may suffer during low workload parts of the task. It is recommended that great care is taken when interpreting the results obtained through primary task performance assessment of MWL.

Secondary task performance measures of MWL involve the measurement of the operator's ability to perform an additional secondary task in addition to the primary task. Typical secondary task measures include memory recall tasks, mental arithmetic tasks, reaction time measurement and tracking tasks. The use of secondary task performance measures is based upon the assumption that as operator workload increases, the ability to perform the secondary task will diminish due to a reduction in spare capacity, and so secondary task performance will suffer. The main disadvantages associated with secondary task performance assessment techniques are a reported lack of sensitivity to minor workload variations (Young and Stanton, 2004) and their intrusion on primary task performance. One way around this is the use of embedded secondary task measures, whereby the operator is required to perform a secondary task with the system under analysis. Since the secondary task is no longer external to that of operating the system, the level of intrusion is reduced. According to Young and Stanton (2004) researchers adopting a secondary task measurement approach to the assessment of MWL are advised to adopt discrete stimuli, which occupy the same attentional resource pools as the primary task. For example, if the primary task is a driving one, then the secondary task should be a visio-spatial one involving manual response

(Young and Stanton, 2004). This ensures that the technique really is measuring spare capacity and not an alternative resource pool.

Physiological measures of MWL involve the measurement of those physiological aspects that may be affected by increased or decreased levels of workload. Heart rate, heart rate variability, eye movement and brain activity have all been used to provide a measure of operator workload. The main advantage associated with the use of physiological measures of MWL is that they do not intrude upon primary task performance and also that they can be applied in the field, as opposed to simulated settings. There are a number of disadvantages associated with the use of physiological techniques, including the high cost, physical obtrusiveness and reliability of the technology used and the doubts regarding the construct validity and sensitivity of the techniques.

Subjective-rating MWL assessment techniques are administered either during or post-task performance and involve participants providing ratings regarding their perceived MWL during task performance. Subjective-rating techniques can be categorised as either uni-dimensional or multi-dimensional, depending upon the workload dimensions that they assess. Young and Stanton (2004) suggest that the data obtained when using uni-dimensional techniques is far simpler to analyse than the data obtained when using multi-dimensional techniques. However, multi-dimensional techniques possess a greater level of diagnosticity than uni-dimensional techniques. Subjective-rating assessment techniques are attractive due to their ease and speed of application, and also the low cost involved. Subjective-rating techniques are also un-intrusive to primary task performance and can be used in the field in 'real-world' settings, rather than in simulated environments. That said, subjective MWL assessment techniques are mainly only used when there is an operational system available and therefore it is difficult to employ them during the design process, as the system under analysis may not actually exist, and simulation can be extremely costly. There are also a host of problems associated with collecting subjective data post-trial. Often, MWL ratings correlate with performance on the task under analysis. Participants are also prone to forgetting certain parts of the task where variations in their workload may have occurred. A brief description of the subjective MWL assessment techniques reviewed is given below.

The NASA Task Load Index (TLX; Hart and Staveland, 1988) is a multi-dimensional subjective rating tool that is used to derive a MWL rating based upon a weighted average of six workload sub-scale ratings. The six sub-scales are mental demand, physical demand, temporal demand, effort, performance and frustration level. The TLX is the most commonly used subjective MWL assessment technique and there have been a number of validation studies associated with the technique. The subjective workload assessment technique (SWAT; Reid and Nygren, 1988) is a multi-dimensional tool that measures three dimensions of operator workload, time load, mental effort load and stress load. After an initial weighting procedure, participants are asked to rate each dimension and an overall workload rating is calculated. Along with the NASA TLX technique of subjective workload, SWAT is probably the most commonly used of the subjective workload assessment techniques.

The DRA workload scale (DRAWS) uses four different workload dimensions to elicit a rating of operator workload. The dimensions used are input demand, central demand, output demand and time pressure. The technique is typically administered on-line, and involves verbally querying the participant for a subjective rating between 0 and 100 for each dimension during task performance. The workload profile (Tsang and Velazquez, 1996) technique is based upon multiple resource theory (Wickens, Gordon and Lui, 1998) and involves participants rating the demand imposed by the task under analysis for each dimension proposed by multiple resource theory. The workload dimensions used are perceptual/central processing, response selection and execution, spatial processing, verbal processing, visual processing, auditory processing manual output and speech output. Participant ratings for each dimension are summed in order to determine an overall workload rating for the task(s) under analysis.

The Modified Cooper Harper Scale (MCH; Wierwille and Casali, 1986) is a uni-dimensional measure that uses a decision tree to elicit a rating of operator mental workload. MCH is a modified version of the Cooper Harper scale (Cooper and Harper, 1969) that was originally developed as an aircraft handling measurement tool. The scales were used to attain subjective pilot ratings of the controllability of aircraft. The output of the scale is based upon the controllability of the aircraft and also the level of input required by the pilot to maintain suitable control. The Subjective Workload Dominance Technique (SWORD; Vidulich and Hughes, 1991) uses paired comparison of tasks in order to provide a rating of workload for each individual task. Administered post-trial, participants are required to rate one task's dominance over another in terms of workload imposed. The Malvern capacity estimate (MACE) technique uses a rating scale to determine air traffic controllers' remaining capacity. MACE is a very simple technique, involving querying air traffic controllers for subjective estimations of their remaining mental capacity during a simulated task. The Bedford scale (Roscoe and Ellis, 1990) uses a hierarchical decision tree to assess spare capacity whilst performing a task. Participants simply follow the decision tree to gain a workload rating for the task under analysis. The Instantaneous self-assessment (ISA) of workload technique involves participants self-rating their workload during a task (normally every two minutes) on a scale of 1 (low) to 5 (high).

A more recent theme in the area of MWL assessment is the use of assessment techniques to predict operator MWL. Analytical techniques are those MWL techniques that are used to predict the level of MWL that an operator may experience during the performance of a particular task. Analytical techniques are typically used during system design, when an operational version of the system under analysis is not yet available. Although literature regarding the use of predictive MWL is limited, a number of these techniques do exist. In the past, models have been used to predict operator workload, such as the timeline model or Wicken's multiple resource model. Subjective MWL assessment techniques such as Pro-SWORD have also been tested for their use in predicting operator MWL (Vidulich, Ward and Schueren, 1991). Although the use of MWL assessment techniques in a predictive fashion is limited, Salvendy (1997) reports that SME projective ratings tend to correlate well with operator subjective ratings. It is apparent that analytical mental or predictive workload techniques are particularly important in the early stages of system design and development. A brief description of the analytical techniques reviewed is given below.

Cognitive task load analysis (CTLA; Neerincx, 2003) is used to assess or predict the cognitive load of a task or set of tasks imposed upon an operator. CTLA is based upon a model of cognitive task load (Neerincx, 2003) that describes the effects of task characteristics upon operator MWL. According to the model, cognitive (or mental) task load is comprised of percentage time occupied, level of information processing and the number of task set switches exhibited during the task in question. Pro-SWAT is a variation of the SWAT (Reid and Nygren, 1988) technique that has been used to predict operator MWL. SWAT is a multi-dimensional tool that uses three dimensions of operator workload; time load, mental effort load and stress load. The Subjective Workload Dominance Technique (SWORD) is a subjective workload assessment technique that has been used both retrospectively and predictively (Pro-SWORD; Vidulich, Ward and Schueren 1991). SWORD uses paired comparison of tasks in order to provide a rating of workload for each individual task. Participants are required to rate one task's dominance over another in terms of workload imposed. When used predictively, tasks are rated for their dominance before the trial begins, and then rated post-test to check for the sensitivity of the predictions. Vidulich, Ward and Schueren (1991) report the use of the SWORD technique for predicting the workload imposed upon F-16 pilots by a new HUD attitude display system.

Typical MWL assessments use a selection of techniques from each of the three categories described above. The multi-method approach to the assessment of MWL is designed to ensure comprehensiveness. The suitability of MWL assessment techniques can be evaluated on a number of dimensions. Wierwille and Eggemeier (1993) suggest that for a MWL assessment technique to be recommended for use in a test and evaluation procedure, it should possess the following properties:

- *Sensitivity*. Represents the degree to which the technique can discriminate between differences in the levels of MWL imposed on a participant.
- *Limited intrusiveness*. The degree to which the assessment technique intrudes upon primary task performance.
- *Diagnosticity*. Represents the degree to which the technique can determine the type or cause of the workload imposed on a participant.
- *Global sensitivity*. Represents the ability to discriminate between variations in the different types of resource expenditure or factors affecting workload.
- *Transferability*. Represents the degree to which the technique can be applied in different environments than what it was designed for.
- *Ease of implementation*. Represents the level of resources required to use the technique, such as technology and training requirements.

Wierwille and Eggemeier (1993) suggest that non-intrusive workload techniques that possess a sufficient level of global sensitivity are of the most importance in terms of test and evaluation applications. According to Wierwille and Eggemeier (1993) the most frequently used and therefore most appropriate for use test and evaluation scenarios are the modified cooper harper scale (MCH) technique, the subjective workload assessment technique (SWAT) and the NASA-TLX technique. A summary of the MWL assessment techniques reviewed is presented in Table 8.1.

Primary and Secondary Task Performance Measures

Background and Applications

MWL assessment typically involves the use of a combination or battery of MWL assessment techniques. Primary task performance measures, secondary task performance measures and physiological measures are typically used in conjunction with post-trial subjective rating techniques. Primary task performance measures of MWL involve assessing suitable aspects of participant performance during the task(s) under analysis, assuming that an increase in MWL will facilitate a performance decrement of some sort. Secondary task performance measures typically involve participants performing an additional task in addition to that of primary task performance. Participants are required to maintain primary task performance and also perform the secondary task as and when the primary task allows them to. The secondary task is designed to compete for the same resources as the primary task. Any differences in workload between primary tasks are then reflected in the performance of the secondary task. Examples of secondary task used in the past include tracking tasks, memory tasks, rotated figures tasks and mental arithmetic tasks.

Domain of Application

Generic.

Table 8.1   Summary of Mental Workload Assessment Techniques

Method	Type of method	Domain	Training time	App time	Related methods	Tools needed	Validation studies	Advantages	Disadvantages
Primary task performance measures	Performance measure	Generic	Low	Low	Physiological measures Subjective assessment techniques	Simulator Laptop	Yes	1) Primary task performance measures offer a direct index of performance. 2) Primary task performance measures are particularly effective when measuring workload in tasks that are lengthy in duration (Young and Stanton In Press). 3) Can be easily used in conjunction with secondary task performance, physiological and subjective measures	1) Primary task performance measures may not always distinguish between levels of workload. 2) Not a reliable measure when used in isolation.
Secondary task performance measures	Performance measure	Generic	Low	Low	Physiological measures Subjective assessment techniques	Simulator Laptop	Yes	1) Sensitive to workload variations when performance measures are not. 2) Easy to use. 3) Little extra work is required to set up a secondary task measure.	1) Secondary task measures have been found to be sensitive only to gross changes in workload. 2) Intrusive to primary task performance. 3) Great care is required when designing the secondary task, in order to ensure that it uses the same resource pool as the primary task.
Physiological measures	Physiological measure	Generic	High	Low	Primary and secondary task performance measures Subjective assessment techniques	Heart rate monitor Eye tracker EEG	Yes	1) Various physiological measures have demonstrated sensitivity to variations in task demand. 2) Data is recorded continuously throughout the trial. 3) Can be used in real-world settings.	1) Data is often confounded by extraneous interference. 2) Measurement equipment is temperamental and difficult to use. 3) Measurement equipment is physically obtrusive.
NASA-Task Load Index	Multi-dimensional subjective rating tool	Generic	Low	Low	Primary and secondary task performance measures Physiological measures	Pen and paper	Yes	1) Quick and easy to use, requiring little training or cost. 2) Consistently performs better than SWAT. 3) TLX scales are generic, allowing the technique to be applied in any domain.	1) More complex to analyse than uni-dimensional tools. 2) TLX weighting procedure is laborious. 3) Caters for individual workload only.

Table 8.1(continued)

MCH – Modified Cooper Harper Scales	Uni-dimensional subjective rating tool	Generic	Low	Low	Primary and secondary task measures Physiological measures	Pen and paper	Yes	1) Quick and easy to use, requiring little training or cost. 2) Widely used in a number of domains. 3) Data obtained is easier to analyse than multi-dimensional data.	1) Unsophisticated measure of workload. 2) Limited to manual control tasks. 3) Not as sensitive as the TLX or SWAT.
SWAT – Subjective Workload Assessment Technique	Multi-dimensional subjective rating tool	Generic (Aviation)	Low	Low	Primary and secondary task performance measures Physiological measures	Pen and paper	Yes	1) Quick and easy to use, requiring little training or cost. 2) Multi-dimensional. 3) SWAT sub-scales are generic, allowing the technique to be applied in any domain.	1) More complex to analyse than uni-dimensional tools. 2) A number of studies suggest that the NASA-TLX is more sensitive to workload variations. 3) MWL ratings may correlate with task performance.
SWORD – Subjective Workload Dominance	Subjective paired comparison technique	Generic (Aviation)	Low	Low	Primary and secondary task performance measures Physiological measures	Pen and paper	Yes	1) Quick and easy to use, requiring little training or cost. 2) Very effective when comparing the MWL imposed by two or more interfaces	1) More complex to analyse than uni-dimensional tools. 2) Data is collected post-trial. There are a number of problems with this, such as a correlation with performance.
DRAWS – Defence Research Agency Workload Scales	Multi-dimensional subjective rating tool	Generic (Aviation)	Low	Low	Primary and secondary task performance measures Physiological measures	Pen and paper	No	1) Quick and easy to use, requiring little training or cost.	1) More complex to analyse than uni-dimensional tools. 2) Data is collected post-trial. There are a number of problems with this, such as a correlation with performance. 2) Limited use and validation.

Table 8.1(continued)

MACE – Malvern Capacity Estimate	Uni-dimensional subjective rating tool	ATC	Low	Low	Primary and secondary task performance measures Physiological measures	Pen and paper	No	1) Quick and easy to use, requiring little training or cost.	1) Data is collected post-trial. There are a number of problems with this, such as a correlation with performance. 2) Limited evidence of use or reliability and validity.
Workload Profile Technique	Multi-dimensional subjective rating tool	Generic	Med	Low	Primary and secondary task performance measures Physiological measures	Pen and paper	Yes	1) Quick and easy to use, requiring little training cost. 2) Based upon sound theoretical underpinning (Multiple resource theory).	1) More complex to analyse than uni-dimensional tools. 2) Data is collected post-trial. There are a number of problems with this, such as a correlation with performance. 3) More complex than other MWL techniques.
Bedford Scale	Multi-dimensional subjective rating tool	Generic	Low	Low	Primary and secondary task performance measures Physiological measures	Pen and paper	Yes	1) Quick and easy to use, requiring little training or cost.	1) More complex to analyse than uni-dimensional tools. 2) Data is collected post-trial. There are a number of problems with this, such as a correlation with performance.

Procedure and Advice

Step 1: Define primary task under analysis
The first step in an assessment of operator workload is to clearly define the task(s) under analysis. It is recommended that for this purpose, a HTA is conducted for the task(s) under analysis. When assessing the MWL associated with the use of a novel or existing system or interface, it is recommended that the task(s) assessed are as representative of the system or interface under analysis as possible i.e. the task is made up of tasks using as much of the system or interface under analysis as possible.

Step 2: Define primary task performance measures
Once the task(s) under analysis is clearly defined and described, the analyst should next define those aspects of the task that can be used to measure participant performance. For example, in a driving task Young and Stanton (2004) used speed, lateral position and headway as measures of primary task performance. The measures used may be dependent upon the equipment that is used during the analysis. The provision of a simulator that is able to record various aspects of participant performance is especially useful. The primary task performance measures used are dependent upon the task and system under analysis.

Step 3: Design secondary task and associated performance measures
Once the primary task performance measures are clearly defined, an appropriate secondary task measure should be selected. Stanton and Young (2004) recommend that great care is taken to ensure that the secondary task competes for the same attentional resources as the primary task. For example, Young and Stanton (2004) used a visual-spatial task that required a manual response as their secondary task when analysing driver workload. The task was designed to use the same attentional resource pool as the primary task of driving the car. As with the primary task, the secondary task used is dependent upon the system and task under analysis.

Step 4: Test primary and secondary tasks
Once the primary and secondary task performance measures are defined, they should be thoroughly tested in order to ensure that they are sensitive to variations in task demand. The analyst should define a set of tests that are designed to ensure the validity of the primary and secondary task measures chosen.

Step 5: Brief participants
Once the measurement procedure has been subjected to sufficient testing, the appropriate participants should be selected and then briefed regarding the purpose of the analysis and the data collection procedure employed. It may be useful to select the participants that are to be involved in the analysis prior to the data collection date. This may not always be necessary and it may suffice to simply select participants randomly on the day of analysis. However, if workload is being compared across rank or experience levels, then clearly effort is required to select the appropriate participants. Before the task(s) under analysis are performed, all of the participants involved should be briefed regarding the purpose of the study, MWL, MWL assessment and the techniques that are being employed. Before data collection begins, participants should have a clear understanding of MWL theory, and of the measurement techniques being used. It may be useful at this stage to take the participants through an example workload assessment analysis, so that they understand how primary and secondary task performance measurement works and what is required of them as participants. If a subjective workload assessment technique is also being used, participants should be briefed regarding the chosen technique.

Step 6: Conduct pilot run
Once the participant(s) understand the data collection procedure, a small pilot run should be conducted to ensure that the process runs smoothly and efficiently. Participants should be instructed to perform a small task (separate from the task under analysis), and an associated secondary task. Upon completion of the task, the participant(s) should be instructed to complete the appropriate subjective workload assessment technique. This acts as a pilot run of the data collection procedure and serves to highlight any potential problems. The participant(s) should be instructed to ask any questions regarding their role in the data collection procedure.

Step 7: Begin primary task performance
Once a pilot run of the data collection procedure has been successfully completed, and the participants are comfortable with their role during the trial, the 'real' data collection procedure can begin. The participant should be instructed to begin the task under analysis, and to attend to the secondary task when they feel that they can. The task should run for a set amount of time, and the secondary task should run concurrently.

Step 8: Administer subjective workload assessment technique
Typically, subjective workload assessment techniques, such as the NASA-TLX (Hart and Staveland, 1988) are used in conjunction with primary and secondary task performance measures to assess participant workload. The chosen technique should be administered immediately once the task under analysis is completed, and participants should be instructed to rate the appropriate workload dimensions based upon the primary task that they have just completed.

Step 9: Analyse data
Once the data collection procedure is completed, the data should be analysed appropriately. Young and Stanton (2004) used the frequency of correct responses on a secondary task to indicate the amount of spare capacity the participant had i.e. the greater the correct responses on the primary task, the greater the participant's spare capacity was assumed to be.

Advantages

1. When using a battery of MWL assessment techniques to assessment MWL, the data obtained can be crosschecked for reliability purposes.
2. Primary task performance measures offer a direct index of performance.
3. Primary task performance measures are particularly effective when measuring workload in tasks that are lengthy in duration (Young and Stanton, 2004).
4. Primary task measures are also useful when measuring operator overload.
5. Requires no further effort on behalf of the analyst to set up and record, as primary task performance is normally measured anyway.
6. Secondary task performance measures are effective at discriminating between tasks when no difference was observed assessing performance alone.
7. Primary and secondary task performance measures are easy to use, as a computer typically records the required data.

Disadvantages

1. Primary task performance measures alone may not distinguish between different levels of workload, particularly minimal ones. Different operators may still achieve the same performance levels under completely different workload conditions.
2. Young and Stanton (2004) suggest that primary task performance is not a reliable measure when used in isolation.
3. Secondary task performance measures have been found to be only sensitive to gross changes in MWL.
4. Secondary task performance measures are intrusive to primary task performance.
5. Great care is required during the design and selection of the secondary task to be used. The analyst must ensure that the secondary task competes for the same resources as the primary task. According to Young and Stanton (2004) the secondary task must be carefully designed in order to be a true measure of spare attentional capacity.
6. Extra work and resources are required in developing the secondary task performance measure.
7. The techniques need to be used together to be effective.
8. Using primary and secondary task performance measures may prove expensive, as simulators and computers are required.

Example

Young and Stanton (2004) describe the measurement of MWL in a driving simulator environment (Figure 8.2). Primary task performance measurement included recording data regarding speed, lateral position and headway (distance from the vehicle in front). A secondary task was used to assess spare attentional capacity. The secondary task used was designed to compete for the same attentional resources as the primary task of driving the car. The secondary task was comprised of a rotated figures task (Baber, 1991) whereby participants were randomly presented with a pair of stick figures (one upright; the other rotated through 0°, 90°, 180° or 270°) holding one or two flags. The flags were made up of either squares or diamonds. Participants were required to make a judgement, via a button, as to whether the figures were the same or different, based upon the flags that they were holding. The participants were instructed to attend to the secondary task only when they felt that they had time to do so. Participant correct responses were measured, and it was assumed that the higher the frequency of correct responses was, the greater participant spare capacity was assumed to be.

Related Methods

Primary and secondary task performance measures are typically used in conjunction with physiological measures and subjective workload techniques in order to measure operator MWL. A number of secondary task performance measurement techniques exist, including task reaction times, tracking tasks, memory recall tasks and mental arithmetic tasks. Physiological measures of workload include measuring participant heart rate, heart rate variability, blink rate and brain activity. Subjective workload assessment techniques are completed post-trial by participants and involve participants rating specific dimensions of workload. There are a number of subjective workload assessment techniques, including the NASA-TLX (Hart and Staveland, 1988), the subjective workload assessment technique (SWAT; Reid and Nygren, 1988) and the Workload Profile technique (Tsang and Velazquez, 1996).

Training and Application Times

The training and application times associated with both primary and secondary task performance measures of MWL are typically estimated to be low. However, substantial time is typically required for the development of an appropriate secondary task measure.

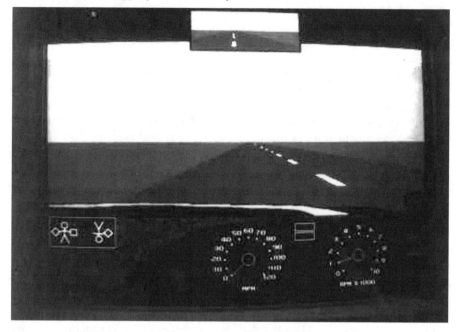

Figure 8.2   Screenshot of the Driving Simulator (Source: Young and Stanton, 2004)

Reliability and Validity

According to Young and Stanton (2004), it is not possible to comment on the reliability and validity of primary and secondary performance measures of MWL, as they are developed specifically for the task and application under analysis. The reliability and validity of the techniques used can be checked to an extent by using a battery of techniques (primary task performance measures, secondary task performance measures, physiological measures and subjective assessment techniques). The validity of the secondary task measure can be assured by making sure that the secondary task competes for the same attentional resources as the primary task.

Tools Needed

The tools needed are dependent upon the nature of the analysis. For example, in the example described above a driving simulator and a PC were used. The secondary task is normally presented separately from the primary task via a desktop or laptop computer. The simulator or a PC is normally used to record participant performance on the primary and secondary tasks.

Flowchart

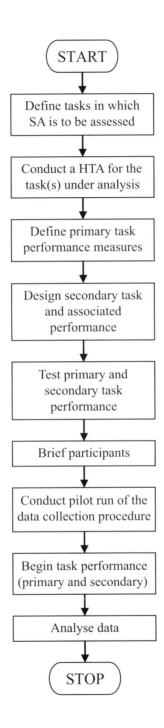

Physiological Measures

Background and Applications

Physiological or psychophysiological measures have also been used in the assessment of participant SA. Physiological measurement techniques are used to measure variations in participant physiological responses to the task under analysis. The use of physiological measures as indicators of MWL is based upon the assumption that as task demand increases, marked changes in various participant physiological systems are apparent. There are a number of different physiological measurement techniques available to the HF practitioner. In the past, heart rate, heart rate variability, endogenous blink rate, brain activity, electrodermal response, eye movements, papillary responses and event-related potentials have all been used to assess operator MWL. Measuring heart rate is one of the most common physiological measures of workload. It is assumed that an increase in workload causes an increase in operator heart rate. Heart rate variability has also been used as an indicator of operator MWL. According to Salvendy (1997) laboratory studies have reported a decrease in heart rate variability (heart rhythm) under increase workload conditions. Endogenous eye blink rate has also been used in the assessment of operator workload. Increased visual demands have been shown to cause a decreased endogenous eye blink rate (Salvendy, 1997). According to Wierwille and Eggemeier (1993) a relationship between blink rate and visual workload has been demonstrated in the flight environment. It is assumed that a higher visual demand causes the operator to reduce his or her blink rate in order to achieve greater visual input. Measures of brain activity involve using EEG recordings to assess operator MWL. According to Wierwille and Eggemeier (1993) measures of evoked potentials have demonstrated a capability of discriminating between levels of task demand.

Domain of Application

Generic.

Procedure and Advice

The following procedure offers advice on the measurement of heart rate as a physiological indicator of workload. When using other physiological techniques, it is assumed that the procedure is the same, only with different equipment being used.

Step 1: Define primary task under analysis
The first step in an assessment of operator workload is to clearly define the task(s) under analysis. It is recommended that a HTA is conducted for the task(s) under analysis. When assessing the MWL associated with the use of a novel or existing system or interface, it is recommended that the task(s) assessed are as representative of the system or interface under analysis as possible i.e. the task is made up of tasks using as much of the system or interface under analysis as possible.

Step 2: Select the appropriate measuring equipment
Once the task(s) under analysis is clearly defined and described, the analyst should select the appropriate measurement equipment. For example, when measuring MWL in a driving task Young and Stanton (2004) measured heart rate using a Polar Vantage NV Heart Rate Monitor. The polar heart rate monitors are relatively cheap to purchase and comprise a chest belt and a watch. The type of measures used may be dependent upon the environment in which the analysis is taking place. For example, in infantry operations, it may be difficult to measure blink rate or brain activity.

Step 3: Conduct initial testing of the data collection procedure

It is recommended that a pilot run of the data collection procedure is conduced in-house, in order to test the measuring equipment used and the appropriateness of the data collected. Physiological measurement equipment is typically temperamental and difficult to use. Consequently, it may take some time for the analyst(s) to become proficient in its use. It is recommended that the analyst(s) involved practise using the equipment until they become proficient in its use.

Step 4: Brief participants

Once the measurement procedure has been subjected to sufficient testing, the appropriate participants should be selected and briefed regarding the purpose of the study and the data collection procedure employed. It may be useful to select the participants that are to be involved in the analysis prior to the data collection date. This may not always be necessary and it may suffice to simply select participants randomly on the day of analysis. However, if workload is being compared across rank or experience levels, then clearly effort is required to select the appropriate participants. Before the task(s) under analysis are performed, all of the participants involved should be briefed regarding the purpose of the study, MWL, MWL assessment and the physiological techniques employed. Before data collection begins, participants should have a clear understanding of MWL theory, and of the measurement techniques being used. It may be useful at this stage to take the participants through an example workload assessment analysis, so that they understand how the physiological measures in question work and what is required of them as participants. If a subjective workload assessment technique is also being used, participants should also be briefed regarding the chosen technique.

Step 5: Fit measuring equipment

Next, the participant(s) should be fitted with the appropriate physiological measuring equipment. The heart rate monitor consists of a chest strap, which is placed around the participant's chest, and a watch, which the participant can wear on their wrist or the analyst can hold. The watch collects the data and is then connected to a computer post-trial in order to download the data collected.

Step 6: Conduct pilot run

Once the participant(s) understand the data collection procedure, a small pilot run should be conducted to ensure that the process runs smoothly and efficiently. Participants should be instructed to perform a small task (separate from the task under analysis), and an associated secondary task whilst wearing the physiological measurement equipment. Upon completion of the task, the participant(s) should be instructed to complete the appropriate subjective workload assessment technique. This acts as a pilot run of the data collection procedure and serves to highlight any potential problems. The participant(s) should be instructed to ask any questions regarding their role in the data collection procedure.

Step 7: Begin primary task performance

Once a pilot run of the data collection procedure has been successfully completed, and the participants fully understand their role during the trial, the data collection procedure can begin. The participant should be instructed to begin the task under analysis, and to attend to the secondary task when they feel that they can. The task should run for a set amount of time, and the secondary task should run concurrently. The heart rate monitor continuously collects participant heart rate data throughout the task. Upon completion of the task, the heart rate monitor should be turned off and removed from the participant's chest.

Step 8: Administer subjective workload assessment technique
Typically, subjective workload assessment techniques, such as the NASA-TLX (Hart and Staveland, 1988) are used in conjunction with primary, secondary task performance measures and physiological measures to assess participant workload. The chosen technique should be administered immediately once the task under analysis is completed, and participants should be instructed to rate the appropriate workload dimensions based upon the primary task that they have just completed.

Step 9: Download collected data
The heart rate monitor data collection tool (typically a watch) can now be connected to a laptop computer in order to download the data collected.

Step 10: Analyse data
Once the data collection procedure is completed, the data should be analysed appropriately. It is typically assumed that an increase in workload causes an increase in operator heart rate. Heart rate variability has also been used as an indicator of operator MWL. According to Salvendy (1997), laboratory studies have reported a decrease in heart rate variability (heart rhythm) under increased workload conditions

Advantages

1. Various physiological techniques have demonstrated a sensitivity to task demand variations.
2. When using physiological techniques, data is recorded continuously throughout task performance.
3. Physiological measurements can often be taken in a real-world setting, removing the need for a simulation of the task.
4. Advances in technology have resulted in an increased accuracy and sensitivity of the various physiological measurement tools.
5. Physiological measurement does not interfere with primary task performance.

Disadvantages

1. The data is easily confounded by extraneous interference (Young and Stanton, 2004).
2. The equipment used to measure physiological responses is typically physically obtrusive.
3. The equipment is also typically expensive to acquire, temperamental and difficult to operate.
4. Physiological data is very difficult to obtain and analyse.
5. In order to use physiological techniques effectively, the analyst(s) requires a thorough understanding of physiological responses to workload.
6. It may be difficult to use certain equipment in the field e.g. brain and eye measurement equipment.

Example

Hilburn (1997) describes a study that was conducted in order to validate a battery of objective physiological measurement techniques when used to assess operator workload. The techniques were to be used to assess the demands imposed upon ATC controllers under free flight conditions. Participants completed an ATC task based upon the Maastricht-Brussels sector, during which heart rate variability, pupil diameter and eye scan patterns were measured. Participant heart rate variability was measured using the Vitaport® system. Respiration was measured using inductive strain gauge transducers and an Observer® eye-tracking system was used to measure participant eye scan patterns. It was concluded that all three measures (pupil diameter in particular) were sensitive to varied levels of traffic load (Hilburn, 1997).

Related Methods

A number of different physiological measures have been used to assess operator workload, including heart rate, heart rate variability, and brain and eye activity. Physiological measures are typically used in conjunction with other MWL assessment techniques, such as primary and secondary task measures and subjective workload assessment techniques. Primary task performance measures involve measuring certain aspects of participant performance on the task(s) under analysis. Secondary task performance measures involve measuring participant performance on an additional task, separate to the primary task under analysis. Subjective workload assessment techniques are completed post-trial by participants and involve participants rating specific dimensions of workload. There are a number of subjective workload assessment techniques, including the NASA-TLX (Hart and Staveland, 1988), the subjective workload assessment technique (SWAT; Reid and Nygren, 1988) and the Workload Profile technique (Tsang and Velazquez, 1996).

Training and Application Times

The training time associated with physiological measurement techniques is estimated to be high. The equipment is often difficult to operate, and the data may also be difficult to analyse and interpret. The application time for physiological measurement techniques is dependent upon the duration of the task under analysis. For lengthy, complex tasks, the application time for a physiological assessment of workload may be high. However, it is estimated that the typical application time for a physiological measurement of workload is low.

Reliability and Validity

According to Young and Stanton (2004) physiological measures of MWL are supported by a considerable amount of research, which suggests that heart rate variability (HRV) is probably the most promising approach. Whilst a number of studies have reported the sensitivity of a number of physiological techniques to variations in task demand, a number of studies have also demonstrated a lack of sensitivity to demand variations using the techniques.

Tools Needed

When using physiological measurements techniques, expensive equipment is often required. Monitoring equipment such as heart rate monitors, eye trackers, EEG measurement equipment and electro-oculographic measurement tools is needed, depending upon the chosen measurement approach. A laptop computer is also typically used to transfer data from the measuring equipment.

Flowchart

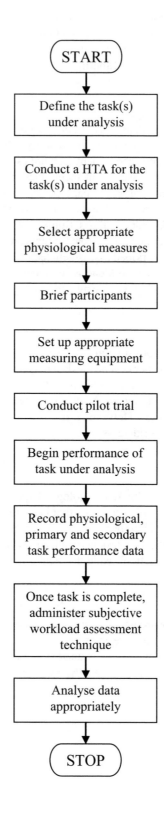

NASA Task Load Index (NASA TLX)

Background and Applications

The NASA Task Load Index (NASA TLX; Hart and Staveland, 1988) is a subjective MWL assessment tool that is used to measure participant MWL during task performance. The NASA TLX is a multi-dimensional rating tool that is used to derive an overall workload rating based upon a weighted average of six workload sub-scale ratings. The TLX uses the following six sub-scales: mental demand, physical demand, temporal demand, effort, performance and frustration level. A brief description of each sub-scale is provided below.

1. *Mental demand.* How much mental demand and perceptual activity was required (e.g. thinking, deciding, calculating, remembering, looking, searching etc)? Was the task easy or demanding, simple or complex, exacting or forgiving?

2. *Physical demand.* How much physical activity was required e.g. pushing, pulling, turning, controlling, activating etc.? Was the task easy or demanding, slow or brisk, slack or strenuous, restful or laborious?

3. *Temporal demand.* How much time pressure did you feel due to the rate or pace at which the tasks or task elements occurred? Was the pace slow and leisurely or rapid and frantic?

4. *Effort.* How hard did you have to work (mentally and physically) to accomplish your level of performance?

5. *Performance.* How successful do you think you were in accomplishing the goals of the task set by the analyst (or yourself)? How satisfied were you with your performance in accomplishing these goals?

6. *Frustration level.* How insecure, discouraged, irritated, stressed and annoyed versus secure, gratified, content, relaxed and complacent did you feel during the task?

Each sub-scale is presented to the participants either during or after the experimental trial and they are asked to rate their score on an interval scale ranging from low (1) to high (20). The TLX also employs a paired comparisons procedure. This involves presenting 15 pairwise combinations to the participants and asking them to select the scale from each pair that has the most effect on the workload during the task under analysis. This procedure accounts for two potential sources of between-rater variability; differences in workload definition between the raters and also differences in the sources of workload between the tasks. The NASA-TLX is the most commonly used subjective MWL assessment technique, and has been applied in numerous domains including civil and military aviation, driving, nuclear power plant control room operation and air traffic control. Extensions of the NASA TLX technique have also been developed for different domains, for example, the RNASA TLX (Cha and Park, 1997), which is designed to assess driver workload when using in-car navigation systems.

Domain of Application

Generic.

Procedure and Advice (Computerised Version)

Step 1: Define task(s)
The first step in a NASA-TLX analysis (aside from the process of gaining access to the required systems and personnel) is to define the tasks that are to be subjected to analysis. The type of tasks analysed are dependent upon the focus of the analysis. For example, when assessing the effects on operator workload caused by a novel design or a new process, it is useful to analyse a set of tasks that are as representative of the device's operations as possible. To analyse a full set of tasks will often be too time consuming and labour intensive, and so it is pertinent to use a set of tasks that use all aspects of the system under analysis.

Step 2: Conduct a HTA for the task(s) under analysis
Once the task(s) under analysis are defined clearly, a HTA should be conducted for each task. This allows the analyst(s) and participants to understand the task(s) fully.

Step 3: Selection of participants
Once the task(s) under analysis are clearly defined and described, it may be useful to select the participants that are to be involved in the analysis. This may not always be necessary and it may suffice to simply select participants randomly on the day. However, if workload is being compared across rank or experience levels, then clearly effort is required to select the appropriate participants.

Step 4: Brief participants
Before the task(s) under analysis are performed, all of the participants involved should be briefed regarding the purpose of the study and the NASA-TLX technique. It is recommended that participants are given a workshop on MWL and MWL assessment. It may also be useful at this stage to take the participants through an example NASA-TLX application, so that they understand how the technique works and what is required of them as participants. It may even be pertinent to get the participants to perform a small task, and then get them to complete a workload profile questionnaire. This would act as a 'pilot run' of the procedure and would highlight any potential problems.

Step 5: Performance of task under analysis
Next, the participant(s) should perform the task under analysis. The NASA TLX can be administered either during or post-trial. However, it is recommended that the TLX is administered post-trial as on-line administration is intrusive to primary task performance. If on-line administration is required, then the TLX should be administered and responded to verbally.

Step 6: Weighting procedure
When the task under analysis is complete, the weighting procedure can begin. The WEIGHT software presents 15 pair-wise comparisons of the six sub-scales (mental demand, physical demand, temporal demand, effort, performance and frustration level) to the participant. The participants should be instructed to select, from each of the fifteen pairs, the sub-scale from each pair that contributed the most to the workload of the task. The WEIGHT software then calculates the total number of times each sub-scale was selected by the participant. Each scale is then rated by the software based upon the number of times it is selected by the participant. This is done using a scale of 0 (not relevant) to 5 (more important than any other factor).

Step 7: NASA-TLX rating procedure
Participants should be presented with the interval scale for each of the TLX sub-scales (this is done via the RATING software). Participants are asked to give a rating for each sub-scale, between 1 (Low) and 20 (High), in response to the associated sub-scale questions. The ratings provided are based entirely on the participants' subjective judgement.

Step 8: TLX score calculation
The TLX software is then used to compute an overall workload score. This is calculated by multiplying each rating by the weight given to that sub-scale by the participant. The sum of the weighted ratings for each task is then divided by 15 (sum of weights). A workload score of between 0 and 100 is then derived for the task under analysis.

Advantages

1. The NASA TLX provides a quick and simple technique for estimating operator workload.
2. The NASA TLX sub-scales are generic, so the technique can be applied to any domain. In the past, the TLX has been used in a number of different domains, such as aviation, air traffic control, command and control, nuclear reprocessing and petro-chemical and automotive domains.
3. The NASA TLX has been tested thoroughly in the past and has also been the subject of a number of validation studies e.g. Hart and Staveland (1988).
4. The provision of the TLX software package removes most of the work for the analyst, resulting in a very quick and simple procedure.
5. For those without computers, the TLX is also available in a pen and paper format (Vidulich and Tsang, 1986a).
6. Probably the most widely used technique for estimating operator workload.
7. The NASA TLX is a multi-dimensional approach to workload assessment.
8. A number of studies have shown its superiority over the SWAT technique (Hart and Staveland, 1988; Hill et al, 1992; Nygren, 1991).
9. When administered post-trial the approach is non-intrusive to primary task performance.
10. According to Wierwille and Eggemeier (1993) the TLX technique has demonstrated sensitivity to demand manipulations in numerous flight experiments.

Disadvantages

1. When administered on-line, the TLX can be intrusive to primary task performance.
2. When administered after the fact, participants may have forgotten high workload aspects of the task.
3. Workload ratings may be correlated with task performance e.g. subjects who performed poorly on the primary task may rate their workload as very high and vice versa.
4. The sub-scale weighting procedure is laborious and adds more time to the procedure.

Flowchart

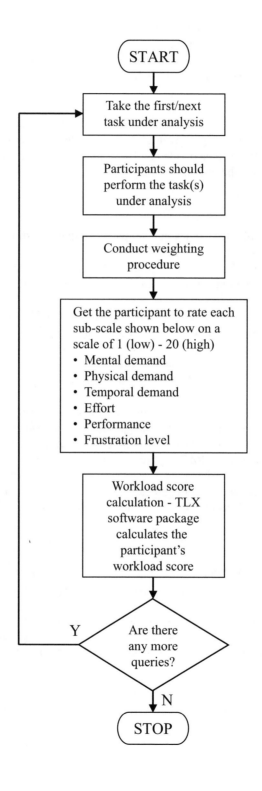

Example

An example NASA-TLX pro-forma is presented in Figure 8.3.

NASA Task Load Index

Mental Demand

How much mental and perceptual activity was required (e.g., thinking, deciding, calculating, remembering, looking, searching, etc.)? Was the task easy or demanding, simple or complex, exacting or forgiving?

Low ⊢————————————————————————⊣ High

Physical Demand

How much physical activity was required (e.g., pushing, pulling, turning, controlling, activating, etc.)? Was the task easy or demanding, slow or brisk, slack or strenuous, restful or laborious?

Low ⊢————————————————————————⊣ High

Temporal Demand

How much time pressure did you feel due to the rate or pace at which the tasks or task elements occurred? Was the pace slow and leisurely, or rapid and frantic?

Low ⊢————————————————————————⊣ High

Performance

How successful do you think you were in accomplishing the goals of the task set by the experimenter (or yourself)? How satisfied were you with your performance in accomplishing these goals?

Low ⊢————————————————————————⊣ High

Effort

How hard did you have to work (mentally and physically) to accomplish your level of performance?

Low ⊢————————————————————————⊣ High

Frustration Level

How insecure, discouraged, irritated, stressed and annoyed versus secure, gratified, content, relaxed and complacent did you feel during the task?

Low ⊢————————————————————————⊣ High

Figure 8.3   NASA TLX Pro-forma

Related Methods

The NASA-TLX technique is one of a number of multi-dimensional subjective workload assessment techniques. Other multi-dimensional techniques include the subjective workload assessment technique (SWAT), Bedford scales, DRAWS, and the Malvern capacity estimate (MACE) technique. Along with SWAT, the NASA-TLX is probably the most commonly used subjective workload assessment technique. When conducting a NASA-TLX analysis, a task analysis (such as HTA) of the task or scenario is often conducted. Also, subjective workload assessment techniques are typically used in conjunction with other workload assessment techniques, such as primary and secondary task performance measures. In order to weight the sub-scales, the TLX uses a pair-wise comparison weighting procedure.

Approximate Training and Application Times

The NASA TLX technique is simple to use and quick to apply. The training times and application times are typically low. Rubio et al (2004) reports that in a study comparing the NASA-TLX, SWAT and workload profile techniques the NASA-TLX took 60 minutes to apply.

Reliability and Validity

A number of validation studies concerning the NASA TLX method have been conducted (e.g. Hart and Staveland, 1988; Vidulich and Tsang, 1985, 1986). Vidulich and Tsang (1985, 1986b) reported that NASA TLX produced more consistent workload estimates for participants performing the same task than the SWAT (Reid and Nygren, 1988) technique did. Hart and Staveland (1988) reported that the NASA TLX workload scores suffer from substantially less between-rater variability than one-dimensional workload ratings did. Luximon and Goonetilleke (2001) also reported that a number of studies have shown that the NASA TLX is superior to SWAT in terms of sensitivity, particularly for low mental workloads (Hart and Staveland, 1988; Hill et al, 1992; Nygren, 1991). In a comparative study of the NASA TLX, the RNASA TLX, SWAT and MCH techniques, Cha (2001) reported that the RNASA TLX is the most sensitive and acceptable when used to assess driver mental workload during in-car navigation based tasks.

Tools Needed

A NASA TLX analysis can either be conducted using either pen and paper or the software method. Both the pen and paper method and the software method can be purchased from NASA Ames Research Center, USA.

Modified Cooper Harper Scales (MCH)

Background and Applications

The modified Cooper Harper scale is a uni-dimensional measure that uses a decision tree flowchart to elicit subjective ratings of MWL. The Cooper Harper Scales (Cooper and Harper, 1969) is a decision tree rating scale that was originally developed to measure aircraft handling capability. In their original form, the scales were used to elicit subjective pilot ratings of the controllability of aircraft. The output of the scale was based upon the controllability of the aircraft and also the level of input required by the pilot to maintain suitable control. The modified Cooper Harper Scale (Wierwille and Casali,

1986) works on the assumption that there is a direct relationship between the level of difficulty of aircraft controllability and pilot workload. The MCH scale is presented in Figure 8.4.

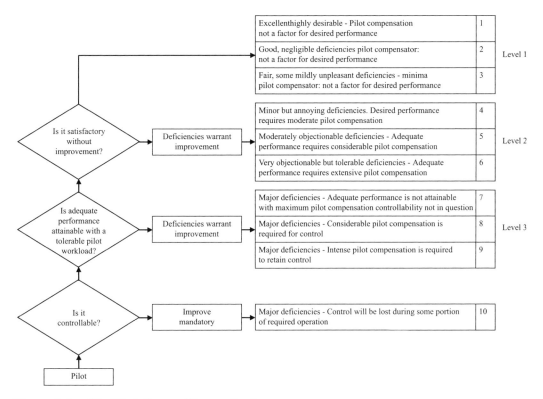

Figure 8.4   Modified Cooper Harper Scale

The MCH is administered post-trial, and participants simply follow the decision tree, answering questions regarding the task and system under analysis, in order to provide an appropriate MWL rating.

Domain of Application

Aviation.

Procedure and Advice

Step 1: Define task(s)
The first step in a MCH analysis (aside from the process of gaining access to the required systems and personnel) is to define the tasks that are to be subjected to analysis. The type of tasks analysed are dependent upon the focus of the analysis. For example, when assessing the effects on operator workload caused by a novel design or a new process, it is useful to analyse a set of tasks that are as representative of the full functionality of the interface, device or procedure as possible. To analyse a full set of tasks will often be too time consuming and labour intensive, and so it is pertinent to use a set of tasks that use all aspects of the system under analysis.

Step 2: Conduct a HTA for the task(s) under analysis
Once the task(s) under analysis are defined clearly, a HTA should be conducted for each task. This allows the analyst(s) and participants to understand the task(s) fully.

Step 3: Selection of participants
Once the task(s) under analysis are clearly defined and described, it may be useful to select the participants that are to be involved in the analysis. This may not always be necessary and it may suffice to simply select participants randomly on the day. However, if workload is being compared across rank or experience levels, then clearly effort is required to select the appropriate participants.

Step 4: Brief participants
Before the task(s) under analysis are performed, all of the participants involved should be briefed regarding the purpose of the study and the MCH technique. It is recommended that participants are also given a workshop on MWL and MWL assessment. It may also be useful at this stage to take the participants through an example MCH application, so that they understand how the technique works and what is required of them as participants. It may even be pertinent to get the participants to perform a small task, and then get them to complete a workload profile questionnaire. This would act as a 'pilot run' of the procedure and would highlight any potential problems.

Step 5: Performance of the task under analysis
Next, the subject should perform the task under analysis. The MCH is normally administered post-trial.

Step 6: Completion of the Cooper Harper scale
Once the participant has completed the task in question, they should complete the MCH scale. To do this, the participant simply works through the decision tree to arrive at a MWL rating for the task under analysis. If there are further task(s), then the participant should repeat steps 5 and 6 until all tasks have been assigned a workload rating.

Advantages

1. Very easy and quick to use, requiring only minimal training.
2. Non-intrusive measure of workload.
3. A number of validation studies have been conducted using the Cooper Harper scales. Wierwinke (1974) reported a high co-efficient between subjective difficulty rating and objective workload level.
4. The MCH scales have been widely used to measure workload in a variety of domains.
5. According to Casali and Wierwille (1986) the Cooper Harper scales are inexpensive, unobtrusive, easily administered and easily transferable.
6. High face validity.
7. According to Wierwille and Eggemeier (1993) the MCH technique has been successfully applied to workload assessment in numerous flight simulation experiments incorporating demand manipulations.
8. The data obtained when using uni-dimensional tools is easier to analyse than when using multi-dimensional tools.

Disadvantages

1. Dated.
2. Developed originally to rate controllability of aircraft.
3. Limited to manual control tasks.
4. Data is collected post-trial. This is subject to a number of problems, such as a correlation with performance. Participants are also poor at reporting past mental events.
5. Uni-dimensional.

Flowchart

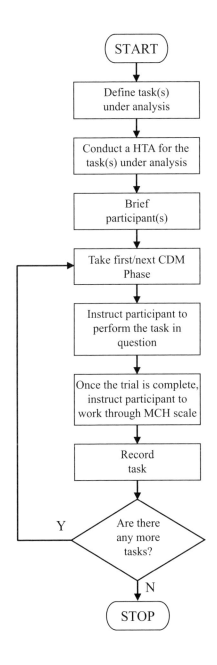

Related Methods

There are a number of other subjective MWL assessment techniques, including the NASA TLX, SWAT, workload profile, DRAWS, MACE and Bedford scales. MCH is a uni-dimensional, decision tree based workload assessment technique, which is similar to the Bedford scale workload assessment technique. It is also recommended that a task analysis (such as HTA) of the task or scenario under analysis is conducted before the MCH data collection procedure begins.

Approximate Training and Application Times

The MCH scale is a very quick and easy procedure, so training and application times are both estimated to be very low. The application time is also dependent upon the length of the task(s) under analysis.

Reliability and Validity

Wierwinke (1974) reported an extremely high co-efficient between subjective task difficulty rating and objective workload level.

Subjective Workload Assessment Technique (SWAT)

Background and Applications

The subjective workload assessment technique (SWAT; Reid and Nygren, 1988) is a MWL assessment technique that was developed by the US Air force Armstrong Aerospace Medical Research laboratory at the Wright Patterson Air force Base, USA. SWAT was originally developed to assess pilot workload in cockpit environments but has also been used in a pro-active manner (Pro-SWAT) in order to predict operator workload (Kuperman, 1985). Along with the NASA TLX technique of subjective workload, SWAT is probably the most commonly used of the subjective workload assessment techniques available. SWAT is a multi-dimensional tool that measures three dimensions of operator MWL: time load, mental effort load and stress load. A brief description of each dimension is given below:

- *Time load.* Refers to the time limit within which the task under analysis is performed, and also the extent to which multiple tasks must be performed concurrently.
- *Mental load.* Refers to the attentional or mental demands associated with the task under analysis, and
- *Stress load.* Refers to the level of stress imposed on the participant during the task under analysis, and includes fatigue, confusion, risk, frustration and anxiety.

After an initial weighting procedure, participants are asked to rate each dimension (time load, mental effort load and stress load) on a scale of 1 to 3. A workload rating is then calculated for each dimension and an overall workload score between 1 and 100 is derived. The SWAT scales are presented in Table 8.2.

Domain of Application

The SWAT scales were originally developed for the aviation domain. However they are generic and could potentially be applied in any domain.

Table 8.2   SWAT Rating Scales

Time Load	Mental Effort Load	Stress Load
1. Often have spare time: interruptions or overlap among other activities occur infrequently or not at all	1. Very little conscious mental effort or concentration required: activity is almost automatic, requiring little or no attention	1. Little confusion, risk, frustration, or anxiety exists and can be easily accommodated
2. Occasionally have spare time: interruptions or overlap among activities occur frequently	2. Moderate conscious mental effort or concentration required: complexity of activity is moderately high due to uncertainty, unpredictability, or unfamiliarity; considerable attention is required	2. Moderate stress due to confusion, frustration, or anxiety noticeably adds to workload: significant compensation is required to maintain adequate performance
3. Almost never have spare time: interruptions or overlap among activities are very frequent, or occur all of the time	3. Extensive mental effort and concentration are necessary: very complex activity requiring total attention	3. High to very intense stress due to confusion, frustration, or anxiety: high to extreme determination and self-control required

Procedure and Advice

Step 1: Define task(s)
The first step in a SWAT analysis (aside from the process of gaining access to the required systems and personnel) is to define the tasks that are to be subjected to analysis. The type of tasks analysed are dependent upon the focus of the analysis. For example, when assessing the effects on operator workload caused by a novel design or a new process, it is useful to analyse a set of tasks that are as representative of the full functionality of the interface, device or procedure as possible. To analyse a full set of tasks will often be too time consuming and labour intensive, and so it is pertinent to use a set of tasks that use all aspects of the system under analysis.

Step 2: Conduct a HTA for the task(s) under analysis
Once the task(s) under analysis are defined clearly, a HTA should be conducted for each task. This allows the analyst(s) and participants to understand the task(s) fully.

Step 3: Selection of participants
Once the task(s) under analysis are clearly defined and described, it may be useful to select the participants that are to be involved in the analysis. This may not always be necessary and it may suffice to simply select participants randomly on the day. However, if workload is being compared across rank or experience levels, then clearly effort is required to select the appropriate participants.

Step 4: Brief participants
Before the task(s) under analysis are performed, all of the participants involved should be briefed regarding the purpose of the study and the SWAT technique. It is recommended that participants are also given a workshop on MWL and MWL assessment. It may also be useful at this stage to take the participants through an example SWAT application, so that they understand how the technique works and what is required of them as participants. It may also be pertinent to get the participants to perform a small task, and then get them to complete a workload profile questionnaire. This would act as a 'pilot run' of the procedure and would highlight any potential problems.

Step 5: Scale development
Once the participants understand how the SWAT technique works, the SWAT scale development process can take place. This involves participants placing in rank order all possible 27 combinations of the three workload dimensions, time load, mental effort load and stress load, according to their effect on workload. This 'conjoint' measurement is used to develop an interval scale of workload rating, from 1 to 100.

Step 6: Performance of task under analysis
Once the initial SWAT ranking has been completed, the participant(s) should perform the task under analysis. SWAT can be administered during the trial or after the trial. It is recommended that the SWAT is administered after the trial, as on-line administration is intrusive to primary task performance. If on-line administration is required, then the SWAT should be administered and completed verbally.

Step 7: SWAT scoring
The participants are required to provide a subjective rating of workload for the task by assigning a value of 1 to 3 to each of the three SWAT workload dimensions. It may be useful to get participants to rate MWL for different portions of the task and also for the complete task.

Step 8: SWAT score calculation
For the workload score, the analyst should take the scale value associated with the combination given by the participant. The scores are then translated into individual workload scores for each SWAT dimension. Finally, an overall workload score should be calculated.

Advantages

1. The SWAT technique offers a quick, simple and low-cost procedure for estimating participant MWL.
2. The SWAT workload dimensions are generic, so the technique can be applied to any domain. In the past, the SWAT technique has been used in a number of different domains, such as aviation, air traffic control, command and control, nuclear reprocessing and petro-chemical, and automotive domains.
3. The SWAT technique is one of the most widely used and well known subjective workload assessment techniques available, and has been subjected to a number of validation studies (Hart and Staveland, 1988; Vidulich and Tsang, 1985, 1986b).
4. The Pro-SWAT variation allows the technique to be used to predict operator workload.
5. SWAT is a multi-dimensional approach to workload assessment.
6. Non-intrusive when administered post-trial.
7. According to Wierwille and Eggemeier (1993) the SWAT technique has demonstrated a sensitivity to demand manipulations in flight environments.

Disadvantages

1. SWAT can be intrusive if administered on-line.
2. In a number of validation studies it has been reported that the NASA TLX is superior to SWAT in terms of sensitivity, particularly for low mental workloads (Hart and Staveland, 1988; Hill et al, 1992; Nygren, 1991).
3. SWAT has been constantly criticised for having a low sensitivity to mental workloads (Luximon and Goonetilleke, 2001).

4. The initial SWAT combination ranking procedure is time consuming and laborious.
5. The post-trial collection of MWL data has a number of associated disadvantages including a potential correlation between MWL ratings and task performance, and participants 'forgetting' different portions of the task when workload was especially low.

Flowchart

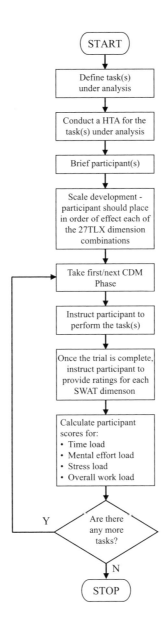

Related Methods

There are a number of other multi-dimensional subjective MWL assessment techniques, such as the NASA TLX, workload profile and DRAWS technique. There is also a predictive version of SWAT (Pro-SWAT), which can be used to predict operator MWL.

Approximate Training and Application Times

The training time for SWAT is estimated to be low. The application time is estimated to be low to medium, due to the initial SWAT ranking procedure. The completion and scoring phase of the SWAT technique is simple and quick, incurring only minimal time cost. In a study comparing the NASA-TLX, workload profile and SWAT techniques (Rubio et al, 2004), SWAT took approximately 70 minutes to apply, which represented the longest application time for the three techniques involved in the study.

Reliability and Validity

A number of validation studies concerning the SWAT technique have been conducted (Hart and Staveland, 1988; Vidulich and Tsang, 1985, 1986b). Vidulich and Tsang (1985, 1986b) reported that NASA TLX produced more consistent workload estimates for participants performing the same task than the SWAT approach did (Reid and Nygren, 1988). Luximon and Goonetilleke (2001) also reported that a number of studies have shown that the NASA TLX is superior to SWAT in terms of sensitivity, particularly for low mental workloads (Hart and Staveland, 1988; Hill et al, 1992; Nygren, 1991).

Tools Needed

SWAT is normally applied using pen and paper, however, a software version of the technique also exists.

Subjective Workload Dominance Technique (SWORD)

Background and Applications

The Subjective Workload Dominance Technique (SWORD; Vidulich, 1989) is a subjective MWL assessment technique that has been used both retrospectively and predictively (Pro-SWORD; Vidulich, Ward and Schueren, 1991). SWORD uses paired comparison of tasks in order to elicit ratings of MWL for individual tasks. The SWORD technique is administered post-trial and requires participants to rate one task's dominance over another in terms of the MWL imposed.

Domain of Application

Generic.

Procedure and Advice

Step 1: Define task(s) under analysis
The first step in a SWORD analysis (aside from the process of gaining access to the required systems and personnel) is to define the tasks that are to be subjected to analysis. The type of tasks analysed are dependent upon the focus of the analysis. For example, when assessing the effects on operator workload caused by a novel design or a new process, it is useful to analyse a set of tasks that are as representative of the full functionality of the interface, device or procedure as possible. To analyse a full set of tasks will often be too time consuming and labour intensive, and so it is pertinent to use a set of tasks that use all aspects of the system under analysis.

Step 2: Conduct a HTA for the task(s) under analysis
Once the task(s) under analysis are defined clearly, a HTA should be conducted for each task. This allows the analyst(s) and participants to understand the task(s) fully.

Step 3: Create SWORD rating sheet
Once a task description (e.g. HTA) is developed, the SWORD rating sheet can be created. The analyst should list all of the possible combinations of tasks involved in the scenario under analysis (e.g. task A v B, A v C, B v C etc.) and also the dominance rating scale. An example of a SWORD rating sheet is presented in Figure 8.5.

Step 4: Selection of participants
Once the task(s) under analysis are defined, it may be useful to select the participants that are to be involved in the analysis. This may not always be necessary and it may suffice to simply select participants randomly on the day. However, if workload is being compared across rank or experience levels, then clearly effort is required to select the appropriate participants.

Step 5: Brief participants
Before the task(s) under analysis are performed, all of the participants involved should be briefed regarding the purpose of the study and the SWORD technique. It is recommended that participants are also given a workshop on MWL and MWL assessment. It may also be useful at this stage to take the participants through an example SWORD application, so that they understand how the technique works and what is required of them as participants. It may also be pertinent to get the participants to perform a small task, and then get them to complete a workload profile questionnaire. This would act as a 'pilot run' of the procedure and would highlight any potential problems.

Step 6: Performance of task(s) under analysis
Once the participants understand the purpose of the study and also what is required of them as participants, they should be instructed to perform the tasks under analysis as normal.

Step 7: Administration of SWORD questionnaire
Once the task under analysis is complete, the SWORD data collection process begins. This involves the administration of the SWORD rating sheet (Figure 8.5). The participant should be presented with the SWORD rating sheet immediately after task performance has ended. The SWORD rating sheet lists all possible paired comparisons of the tasks conducted in the scenario under analysis. A 17-point rating scale is used.

The 17 slots represent the possible ratings. The analyst has to rate the two tasks (e.g. task A vs. B) in terms of their level of workload imposed, against each other. For example, if the participant feels that the two tasks imposed a similar level of workload, then they should mark the 'EQUAL' point on the rating sheet. However, if the participant feels that task A imposed a slightly higher level of workload than task B did, they would move towards task A on the sheet and mark the 'Weak' point on the rating sheet. If the participant felt that task A imposed a much greater level of workload than task B, then they would move towards task A on the sheet and mark the 'Absolute' point on the rating sheet. This allows the participant to provide a subjective rating of one task's MWL dominance over the other. This procedure should continue until all of the possible combinations of tasks in the scenario under analysis are assigned SWORD ratings.

Task	Absolute	Very Strong	Strong	Weak	EQUAL	Weak	Strong	Very Strong	Absolute	Task
A										B
A										C
A										D
A										E
B										C
B										D
B										E
C										D
C										E
D										E

Figure 8.5   Example SWORD Rating Sheet

Step 8: Constructing the judgement matrix
Once all ratings have been elicited, the SWORD judgement matrix should be conducted. Each cell in the matrix should represent the comparison of the task in the row with the task in the associated column. The analyst should fill each cell with the participant's dominance rating. For example, if a participant rated tasks A and B as equal, a '1' is entered into the appropriate cell. If task A is rated as dominant, then the analyst simply counts from the 'Equal' point to the marked point on the SWORD dominance rating sheet, and enters the number in the appropriate cell. The rating for each task is calculated by determining the mean for each row of the matrix and then normalising the means (Vidulich, Ward and Schueren 1991).

Step 9: Matrix consistency evaluation
Once the SWORD matrix is complete, the consistency of the matrix can be evaluated by ensuring that there are transitive trends amongst the related judgements in the matrix. For example, if task A is rated twice as hard as task B, and task B is rated 3 times as hard as task C, then task A should be rated as 6 times as hard as task C (Vidulich, Ward and Schueren, 1991). The final step in the analysis involves checking the consistency of participant MWL dominance ratings. To do this, the analyst uses the completed SWORD matrix to check the consistency of participant ratings.

Advantages

1. The SWORD approach offers a quick, simple to use, low-cost approach for assessing participant MWL.
2. SWORD is especially useful when comparing the MWL imposed by different tasks or devices. One potential evaluation would be for the evaluation of the MWL imposed by different design concepts.
3. SWORD is administered post-trial and so is non-intrusive to task performance.
4. High face validity.
5. SWORD has been demonstrated to have a sensitivity to workload variations (Reid and Nygren, 1988).

Disadvantages

1. The post-trial collection of MWL data has a number of associated disadvantages including a potential correlation between MWL ratings and task performance, and participants 'forgetting' different portions of the task when workload was especially low.
2. Only limited validation evidence is available in the literature.
3. The SWORD technique has not been as widely used as other MWL assessment techniques, such as SWAT and the NASA TLX.
4. The SWORD output does not offer a rating of participant MWL as such, only a rating of which tasks or devices imposed greater MWL than others.

Related Methods

SWORD is one of a number of subjective MWL techniques, including the NASA-TLX, SWAT, MCH and DRAWS. However, the SWORD approach is unique in its use of paired comparisons to rate the dominance of one task or device over another in terms of the level of MWL imposed. The SWORD approach has also been used to predict participant MWL in the form of the Pro-SWORD approach. Other MWL assessment techniques have also been used in this way, for example the SWAT technique has been used in the form of Pro-SWAT.

Approximate Training and Application Times

Although no data is offered in the literature regarding the training and application times for the SWORD technique, it is apparent that the training time for such a simple technique would be minimal. The application time associated with the SWORD technique would be based upon the scenario under analysis. For large, complex scenarios involving a great number of tasks, the application time would be high as an initial HTA would have to be performed, then the scenario would have to performed, and then the SWORD technique administered. The actual application time associated with only the administration of the SWORD technique is very low.

Reliability and Validity

Vidulich, Ward and Schueren (1991) tested the SWORD technique for its accuracy in predicting the workload imposed upon F-16 pilots by a new HUD attitude display system. Participants included F-16 pilots and college students and were divided into two groups. The first group (F-16 pilots experienced with the new HUD display) retrospectively rated the tasks using the traditional SWORD technique, whilst the second group (F-16 pilots who had no experience of the new HUD display) used the Pro-SWORD variation to predict the workload associated with the HUD tasks. A third group (college students with no experience of the HUD) also used the Pro-SWORD technique to predict the associated workload. In conclusion, it was reported that the pilot Pro-SWORD ratings correlated highly with the pilot SWORD (retrospective) ratings (Vidulich, Ward and Schueren, 1991). Furthermore, the Pro-SWORD ratings correctly anticipated the recommendations made in an evaluation of the HUD system. Vidulich and Tsang (1986) also reported that the SWORD technique was more reliable and sensitive than the NASA TLX technique.

Tools Needed
The SWORD technique can be applied using pen and paper. The system or device under analysis is also required.

DRA Workload Scales (DRAWS)

Background and Applications

The DRA workload scales (DRAWS) is a subjective MWL assessment technique that was developed during a three-year experimental programme at DRA Farnborough, of which the aim was to investigate the construct of workload and its underlying dimensions, and to develop and test a workload assessment technique (Jordan, Farmer and Belyavin, 1995). The DRAWS technique offers a multi-dimensional measure of participant MWL and involves querying participants for subjective ratings of four different workload dimensions: input demand, central demand, output demand and time pressure. The technique is typically administered on-line (though it can also be administered post-trial), and involves verbally querying the participant for a subjective rating between 0 and 100 for each dimension during task performance. A brief description of each DRAWS workload dimension is given below.

- Input demand: Refers to the demand associated with the acquisition of information from any external sources;
- Central demand: Refers to the demand associated with the operator's cognitive processes involved in the task;
- Output demand: Refers to the demand associated with any required responses involved in the task; and
- Time pressure: Refers to the demand associated with any time constraints imposed upon the operator.

Domain of Application

Aviation.

Procedure and Advice

Step 1: Define task(s) under analysis
The first step in a DRAWS analysis (aside from the process of gaining access to the required systems and personnel) is to define the tasks that are to be subjected to analysis. The type of tasks analysed are dependent upon the focus of the analysis. For example, when assessing the effects on operator workload caused by a novel design or a new process, it is useful to analyse a set of tasks that are as representative of the full functionality of the interface, device or procedure as possible. To analyse a full set of tasks will often be too time consuming and labour intensive, and so it is pertinent to use a set of tasks that use all aspects of the system under analysis.

Step 2: Conduct a HTA for the task(s) under analysis
Once the task(s) under analysis are defined clearly, a HTA should be conducted for each task. This allows the analyst(s) and participants to understand the task(s) fully.

Step 3: Define DRAWS administration points
Before the task performance begins, the analyst should determine when the administration of the DRAWS workload dimensions will occur during the task. This depends upon the scope and focus of the analysis. However, it is recommended that the DRAWS are administered at points where task complexity is low, medium and high, allowing the sensitivity of the technique to be tested. Alternatively, it may be useful to gather the ratings at regular intervals e.g. ten-minute intervals.

Step 4: Selection of participants
Once the task(s) under analysis are defined, it may be useful to select the participants that are to be involved in the analysis. This may not always be necessary and it may suffice to simply select participants randomly on the day. However, if workload is being compared across rank or experience levels, then clearly effort is required to select the appropriate participants.

Step 5: Brief participant(s)
Next, the participant(s) should be briefed regarding the purpose of the analysis and the functionality of the DRAWS technique. In a workload assessment study (Jordan, Farmer and Belyavin, 1995) participants were given a half-hour introductory session. It is recommended that the participants be briefed regarding the DRAWS technique, including what it measures and how it works. It may be useful to demonstrate a DRAWS data collection exercise for a task similar to the one under analysis. This allows the participants to understand how the technique works and also what is required of them as participants. It is also crucial at this stage that the participants have a clear understanding of the DRAWS workload scale being used. In order for the results to be valid, the participants should have the same understanding of each component of the DRAWS workload scale. It is recommended that the participants are taken through the scale and examples of workload scenarios are provided for each level on the scale. Once the participants fully understand the DRAWS workload scale being used, the analysis can proceed to the next step.

Step 6: Pilot run
Once the participant has a clear understanding of how the DRAWS technique works and what is being measured, it is useful to perform a pilot run of the experimental procedure. Whilst performing a small task, participants should be subjected to a DRAWS MWL data collection exercise. This allows participants to experience the technique in a task performance setting. Participants should be encouraged to ask questions during the pilot run in order to fully understand the technique and the experimental procedure adopted.

Step 7: Performance of task under analysis
Once the participant clearly understands how the DRAWS technique works and what is required of them as participants, performance of the task under analysis should begin. The DRAWS are typically administered during task performance but can also be administered after the post-trial upon completion of the task.

Step 8: Administer workload dimensions
Once the task performance has begun, the analyst should ask the participant to subjectively rate each workload dimension on a scale of 1 100 (1=low, 100=high). The point at which the participant is required to rate their workload is normally defined before the trial. The analyst should verbally ask the participant to subjectively rate each dimension at that point in the task. Participants should then call out a subjective rating for each DRAWS dimension for that point of the task under analysis. The frequency which participants are asked to rate the four DRAWS dimensions is determined by the analyst. Step 7 should continue until sufficient data regarding the participant MWL is collected.

Step 9: Calculate participant workload score
Once the task performance is completed and sufficient data is collected, the participant's MWL score should be calculated. Typically, a mean value for each of the DRAWS workload dimensions is calculated for the task under analysis. Since the four dimensions are separate facets of workload, a total workload score is not normally calculated.

Advantages

1. DRAWS offers a simple, quick and low-cost approach for assessing participant MWL.
2. Data is obtained on-line during task performance and so the problems of collecting post-trial MWL data are removed.
3. High face validity.
4. Sensitivity to workload variation has been demonstrated (Jordan, Farmer and Belyavin, 1995).
5. The workload dimensions used in the DRAWS technique were validated in a number of studies during the development of the technique.
6. Although developed for application in the aviation domain, the workload dimensions are generic, allowing the technique to be applied in any domain.

Disadvantages

1. Intrusive to primary task performance.
2. Limited applications reported in the literature.
3. The workload ratings may correlate highly with task performance at the point of administration.
4. Limited validation evidence is available in the literature. The technique requires further validation.

Example

There is no evidence relating to the use of the DRAWS MWL assessment technique available in the literature.

Related Methods

The DRAWS technique is one of a number of subjective workload assessment techniques, such as NASA TLX, SWAT and the MCH technique. Such techniques are normally used in conjunction with primary task measures, secondary task measures and physiological measures in order to assess operator workload. The DRAWS technique was developed through an analysis of the validity of existing workload dimensions employed by other workload assessment techniques, such as the NASA TLX and Prediction of Operator Performance technique (POP; Farmer et al. 1995).

Training and Application Times

The DRAWS technique requires very little training (approximately half and hour) and is quick in its application, using only four workload dimensions. The total application time is ultimately dependent upon the amount of workload ratings that are required by the analysis and the length of time associated with performing the task under analysis.

Flowchart

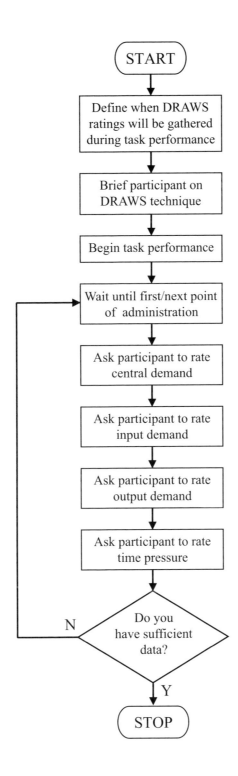

Reliability and Validity

During the development of the technique, nine workload dimensions were evaluated for their suitability for use in assessing operator workload. It was found that the four dimensions, input demand, central demand, output demand and time pressure were capable of discriminating between the demands imposed by different tasks (Jordan, Farmer and Belyavin, 1995). Furthermore, Jordan, Farmer and Belyavin (1995) report that scores for the DRAWS dimensions were found to be consistent with performance across tasks with differing demands, demonstrating a sensitivity to workload variation. It is apparent that the DRAWS technique requires further testing in relation to its reliability and validity.

Tools Needed

The DRAWS technique can be applied using pen and paper. If task performance is simulated, then the appropriate simulator is also required.

Malvern Capacity Estimate (MACE)

Background and Applications

The Malvern capacity estimate (MACE) technique was developed by DERA in order to measure air traffic controllers' mental workload capacity. MACE is a very simple technique, involving querying air traffic controllers for subjective estimations of their remaining mental capacity during a simulated task. As such, the MACE technique assumes that controllers can accurately estimate how much remaining capacity they possess during a task or scenario. The MACE technique uses a rating scale designed to elicit ratings of spare capacity.

Domain of Application

Air traffic control.

Procedure and Advice

Step 1: Define task(s) under analysis
The first step in a MACE analysis (aside from the process of gaining access to the required systems and personnel) is to define the tasks that are to be subjected to analysis. The type of tasks analysed are dependent upon the focus of the analysis. For example, when assessing the effects on operator workload caused by a novel design or a new process, it is useful to analyse a set of tasks that are as representative of the full functionality of the interface, device or procedure as possible. To analyse a full set of tasks will often be too time consuming and labour intensive, and so it is pertinent to use a set of tasks that use all aspects of the system under analysis.

Step 2: Conduct a HTA for the task(s) under analysis
Once the task(s) under analysis are defined clearly, a HTA should be conducted for each task. This allows the analyst(s) and participants to understand the task(s) fully.

Step 3: Selection of participants
Once the task(s) under analysis are defined, it may be useful to select the participants that are to be involved in the analysis. This may not always be necessary and it may suffice to simply select participants randomly on the day. However, if workload is being compared across rank or experience levels, then clearly effort is required to select the appropriate participants.

Step 4: Brief participant(s)
The participants should be briefed regarding the MACE technique, including what it measures and how it works. It may be useful to demonstrate a MACE data collection exercise for a task similar to the one under analysis. This allows the participants to understand how the technique works and also what is required of them. It is also crucial at this stage that the participants have a clear understanding of the MACE rating scale. In order for the results to be valid, the participants should have the same understanding of each level of the workload scale i.e. what level of perceived workload constitutes a rating of 50% on the MACE workload scale and what level constitutes a rating of –100%. It is recommended that the participants are taken through the scale and examples of workload scenarios are provided for each level on the scale. Once the participants fully understand the MACE rating scale, the analysis can proceed to the next step.

Step 5: Conduct pilot run
Once the participant has a clear understanding of how the MACE technique works and what is being measured, it is useful to perform a pilot run. Whilst performing a small task, participants should be subjected to the MACE data collection procedure. This allows participants to experience the technique in a task performance setting. Participants should be encouraged to ask questions during the pilot run in order to understand the technique and the experimental procedure fully.

Step 6: Begin task performance
The participant can now begin performance of the task or scenario under analysis. The MACE technique is typically applied on-line during task performance in a simulated system.

Step 7: Administer MACE rating scale
The analyst should administer the MACE rating scale and ask the participant for an estimation of their remaining capacity. The timing of the administration of the MACE rating scale is dependent upon the analysis requirements. It is recommended that this is defined prior to the onset of the trial. Participants can be queried for their spare capacity any number of times during task performance. It is recommended that capacity ratings are elicited during low and high complexity portions of the task, and also during routine portions of the task.

Step 8: Calculate capacity
Once the trial is complete and sufficient data is collected, participant spare capacity should be calculated for each MACE administration.

Example

According to (Goillau and Kelly, 1996) the MACE technique has been used to assess ATC controller workload and the workload estimates provided showed a high degree of consistency. According to Goillau and Kelly (1996) the MACE approach has been tested and validated in a number of unpublished ATC studies. However, there are no outputs of the MACE analyses available in the literature.

Flowchart

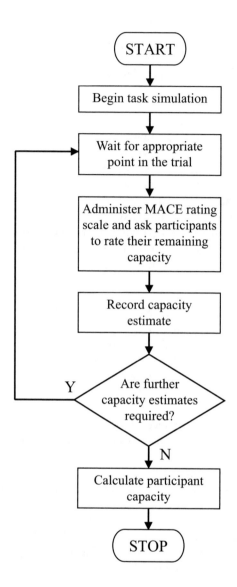

Advantages

1. The MACE technique offers a quick, simple and low-cost approach for assessing participant spare capacity.
2. The output is potentially very useful, indicating when operators are experiencing mental overload and mental underload.
3. Provides a direct measure of operator capacity.
4. On-line administration removes the problems associated with the collection of MWL post-trial (e.g. correlation with performance, forgetting certain portions of the task etc).

Disadvantages

1. The technique is totally dependent upon the participant's ability to estimate their remaining capacity.
2. The technique remains largely unvalidated.
3. The reliability and accuracy of such a technique is questionable.
4. The MACE technique has only been used in simulators. It would be a very intrusive technique if applied on-line during task performance in the 'real-world'.

Related Methods

The MACE technique is one of a number of subjective workload assessment techniques, including the NASA TLX, SWAT and Bedford scales. However, the MACE technique is unique in that it is used to elicit ratings of remaining operator capacity rather than a direct measure of perceived workload.

Approximate Training and Application Times

The MACE technique is a very simple and quick technique to apply. As a result, it is estimated that the training and application times associated with the MACE technique are very low. Application time is dependent upon the duration of the task under analysis.

Reliability and Validity

There is limited reliability and validity data associated with the MACE technique, and the authors stress that the technique requires further validation and testing (Goillau and Kelly, 1996). During initial testing of the technique Goillau and Kelly (1996) report that estimates of controllers' absolute capacity appeared to show a high degree of consistency and that peak MACE estimates were consistently higher than sustained MACE capacity estimates. However, Goillau and Kelly also reported that individual differences in MACE scores were found between controllers for the same task, indicating a potential problem with the reliability of the technique. The techniques reliance upon operators to subjectively rate their own spare capacity is certainly questionable.

Workload Profile Technique

Background and Applications

The workload profile (Tsang and Velazquez, 1996) technique is a recently developed multi-dimensional subjective mental workload assessment technique that is based upon the multiple resources model of attentional resources proposed by Wickens (1987). The workload profile technique is used to elicit ratings of demand imposed by the task under analysis for the following eight MWL dimensions:

1. Perceptual/Central processing.
2. Response selection and execution.
3. Spatial processing.
4. Verbal processing.
5. Visual processing.
6. Auditory processing.

7. Manual output.
8. Speech output.

Once the task(s) under analysis is completed, participants provide a rating between 0 (no demand) and 1 (maximum demand) for each of the MWL dimensions. The ratings for each task are then summed in order to determine an overall MWL rating for the task(s) under analysis. An example of the workload profile pro-forma is shown in Table 8.3.

Table 8.3   Workload Profile Pro-forma

Workload Dimensions								
	Stage of processing		Code of processing		Input		Output	
Task	Perceptual/ Central	Response	Spatial	Verbal	Visual	Auditory	Manual	Speech
1.1								
1.2								
1.3								
1.4								
1.5								
1.6								
1.7								

Domain of Application

Generic.

Procedure and Advice

Step 1: Define task(s) under analysis
The first step in a workload profile analysis (aside from the process of gaining access to the required systems and personnel) is to define the tasks that are to be subjected to analysis. The type of tasks analysed are dependent upon the focus of the analysis. For example, when assessing the effects on operator workload caused by a novel design or a new process, it is useful to analyse a set of tasks that are as representative of the full functionality of the interface, device or procedure as possible. To analyse a full set of tasks will often be too time consuming and labour intensive, and so it is pertinent to use a set of tasks that use all aspects of the system under analysis.

Step 2: Conduct a HTA for the task(s) under analysis
Once the task(s) under analysis are defined clearly, a HTA should be conducted for each task. This allows the analyst(s) and participants to understand the task(s) fully.

Step 3: Create workload profile pro-forma
Once it is clear which tasks are to be analysed and which of those tasks are separate from one another, the workload profile pro-forma should be created. An example of a workload profile pro-forma is shown in Table 8.3. The left hand column contains those tasks that are to be assessed. The workload dimensions, as defined by Wickens multiple resource theory are listed across the page.

Step 4: Selection of participants
Once the task(s) under analysis are defined, it may be useful to select the participants that are to be involved in the analysis. This may not always be necessary and it may suffice to simply select participants randomly on the day. However, if workload is being compared across rank or experience levels, then clearly effort is required to select the appropriate participants.

Step 5: Brief participants
Before the task(s) under analysis are performed, all of the participants involved should be briefed regarding the purpose of the study, MWL, multiple resource theory and the workload profile technique. It is recommended that participants are given a workshop on MWL, MWL assessment and also multiple resource theory. The participants used should have a clear understanding of multiple resource theory, and of each dimension used in the workload profile technique. It may also be useful at this stage to take the participants through an example workload profile analysis, so that they understand how the technique works and what is required of them as participants.

Step 6: Conduct pilot run
Once the participant has a clear understanding of how the workload profile technique works and what is being measured, it is useful to perform a pilot run. The participant should perform a small task and then be instructed to complete a workload profile pro-forma. This allows participants to experience the technique in a task performance setting. Participants should be encouraged to ask questions during the pilot run in order to understand the technique and the experimental procedure fully.

Step 7: Task performance
Once the participants fully understand the workload profile techniques and the data collection procedure, they are free to undertake the task(s) under analysis as normal.

Step 8: Completion of workload profile pro-forma
Once the participant has completed the relevant task, they should provide ratings for the level of demand imposed by the task for each dimension. Participants should assign a rating between 0 (no demand) and 1(maximum demand) for each MWL dimension. If there are any tasks requiring analysis left, the participant should then move onto the next task.

Step 9: Calculate workload ratings for each task
Once the participant has completed and rated all of the relevant tasks, the analyst(s) should calculate MWL ratings for each of the tasks under analysis. In order to do this, the individual workload dimension ratings for each task are summed in order to gain an overall workload rating for each task (Rubio et al, 2004).

Advantages

1. The technique is based upon sound underpinning theory (Multiple Resource Theory; Wickens, 1987).
2. Quick and easy to use, requiring minimal analyst training.
3. As well as offering an overall task workload rating, the output also provides a workload rating for each of the eight workload dimensions.
4. Multi-dimensional MWL assessment technique.
5. As the technique is applied post-trial, it can be applied in real-world settings.

Disadvantages

1. It may be difficult for participants to rate workload on a scale of 0 to 1. A more sophisticated scale may be required in order to gain a more appropriate measure of workload.
2. The post-trial collection of MWL data has a number of associated disadvantages including a potential correlation between MWL ratings and task performance, and participants 'forgetting' different portions of the task when workload was especially low.
3. There is little evidence of the actual usage of the technique.
4. Limited validation evidence associated with the technique.
5. Participants require an understanding of MWL and multiple resource theory.
6. The dimensions used by the technique may not be fully understood by participants with limited experience of psychology and human factors. In a study comparing the NASA-TLX, SWAT and workload profile techniques, Rubio et al (2004) report that there were problems with some of the participants understanding the different dimensions used in the workload profile technique.

Example

A comparative study was conducted in order to test the workload profile, Bedford scale (Roscoe and Ellis, 1990) and psychophysical techniques for the following criteria (Tsang and Velazquez, 1996):

*   Sensitivity to manipulation in task demand.
*   Concurrent validity with task performance.
*   Test-retest reliability.

Sixteen subjects completed a continuous tracking task and a Sternberg memory task. The tasks were performed either independently from one another or concurrently. Subjective workload ratings were collected from participants' post-trial. Tsang and Velazquez (1996) report that the workload profile technique achieved a similar level of concurrent validity and test-retest reliability to the other workload assessment techniques tested. Furthermore, the workload profile technique also demonstrated a level of sensitivity to different task demands.

Related Methods

The workload profile is one of a number of multi-dimensional subjective MWL assessment techniques. Other multi-dimensional MWL assessment techniques include the NASA-TLX (Hart and Staveland, 1988), the subjective workload assessment technique (SWAT; Reid and Nygren, 1988), and the DERA workload scales (DRAWS). When conducting a workload profile analysis, a task analysis (such as HTA) of the task or scenario is normally required. Also, subjective MWL assessment techniques are normally used in conjunction with other MWL measures, such as primary and secondary task measures.

Training and Application Times

The training time for the workload profile technique is estimated to be low, as it is a very simple technique to understand and apply. The application time associated with the technique is based upon the number and duration of the task(s) under analysis. The application time is also lengthened somewhat by the requirement of a multiple resource theory workshop to be provided for the participants. In a study using the workload profile technique (Rubio et al, 2004), it was reported that the administration time was 60 minutes.

Flowchart

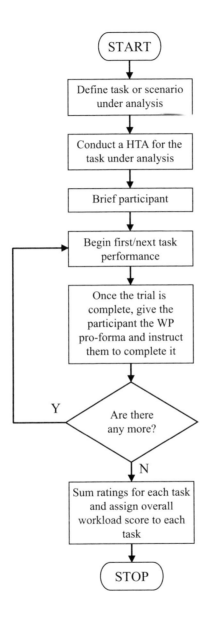

Reliability and Validity

Rubio et al (2004) conducted a study in order to compare the NASA-TLX, SWAT and workload profile techniques in terms of intrusiveness, diagnosticity, sensitivity, validity (convergent and concurrent) and acceptability. It was found that the workload profile technique possessed a higher sensitivity than the NASA-TLX and SWAT techniques. The workload profile technique also possessed a high level of convergent validity and diagnosticity. In terms of concurrent validity, the workload profile was found to have a lower correlation with performance than the NASA-TLX technique.

Tools Needed

The workload profile is applied using pen and paper.

Bedford Scales

Background and Applications

The Bedford scale (Roscoe and Ellis, 1990) is a uni-dimensional MWL assessment technique that was developed by DERA to assess pilot workload. The technique is a very simple one, involving the use of a hierarchical decision tree to assess participant workload via an assessment of spare capacity whilst performing a task. Participants simply follow the decision tree to derive a workload rating for the task under analysis. A scale of 1 (low MWL) to 10 (high MWL) is used. The Bedford scale is presented in Figure 8.6. The scale is normally completed post-trial but it can also be administered during task performance.

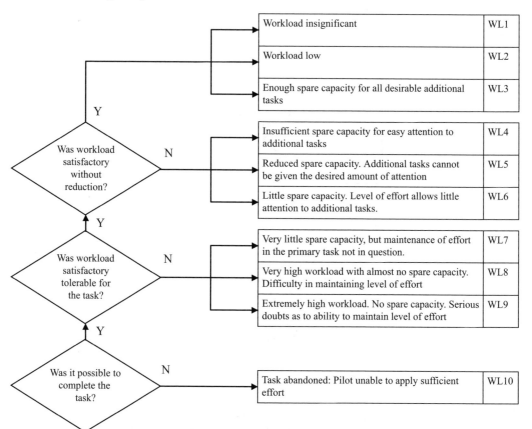

Figure 8.6   **Bedford Scale** (Roscoe and Ellis, 1990)

Domain of Application

Aviation.

Procedure and Advice

Step 1: Define task(s)
The first step in a Bedford scale analysis (aside from the process of gaining access to the required systems and personnel) is to define the tasks that are to be subjected to analysis. The type of tasks analysed are dependent upon the focus of the analysis. For example, when assessing the effects on operator MWL caused by a novel design or a new process, it is useful to analyse a set of tasks that are as representative of the full functionality of the interface, device or procedure as possible. To analyse a full set of tasks will often be too time consuming and labour intensive, and so it is pertinent to use a set of tasks that use all aspects of the system under analysis.

Step 2: Conduct a HTA for the task(s) under analysis
Once the task(s) under analysis are defined clearly, a HTA should be conducted for each task. This allows the analyst(s) and participants to understand the task(s) fully.

Step 3: Selection of participants
Once the task(s) under analysis are defined, it may be useful to select the participants that are to be involved in the analysis. This may not always be necessary and it may suffice to simply select participants randomly on the day. However, if workload is being compared across rank or experience levels, then clearly effort is required to select the appropriate participants.

Step 4: Brief participants
Before the task(s) under analysis are performed, all of the participants involved should be briefed regarding the purpose of the study and the Bedford scale technique. It is recommended that participants are given a workshop on MWL and MWL assessment. It may also be useful at this stage to take the participants through an example Bedford scale analysis, so that they understand how the technique works and what is required of them as participants. It may even be pertinent to get the participants to perform a small task, and then get them to complete a Bedford scale questionnaire. This acts as a 'pilot run' of the procedure highlighting any potential problems.

Step 6: Task performance
Once the participants fully understand the Bedford scale technique and the data collection procedure, they are free to undertake the task(s) under analysis as normal.

Step 7: Completion of bedford scale
Once the participant has completed the relevant task, they should be given the Bedford scale and instructed to work through it, based upon the task that they have just completed. Once they have finished working through the scale, a rating of participant MWL is derived. If there are any tasks requiring analysis left, the participant should then move onto the next task and repeat the procedure.

Advantages

1. Very quick and easy to use, requiring minimal analyst training.
2. The scale is generic and so the technique can easily be applied in different domains.

3. May be useful when used in conjunction with other techniques of MWL assessment.
4. Low intrusiveness.

Disadvantages

1. There is little evidence of actual use of the technique.
2. Limited validation evidence associated with the technique.
3. Limited output.
4. Participants are not efficient at reporting mental events 'after the fact'.

Flowchart

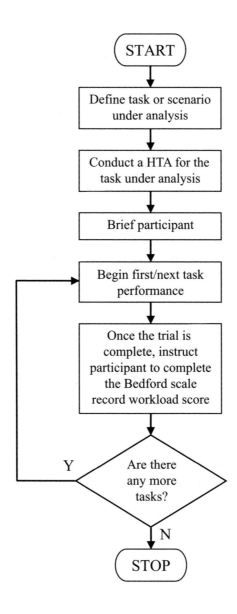

Related Methods

The Bedford scale technique is one of a number of subjective MWL assessment techniques. Other subjective MWL techniques include the MCH, the NASA-TLX, the subjective MWL assessment technique (SWAT), DRAWS, and the Malvern capacity estimate (MACE). It is especially similar to the MCH technique, as it uses a hierarchical decision tree in order to derive a measure of participant MWL. When conducting a Bedford scale analysis, a task analysis (such as HTA) of the task or scenario is normally required. Also, subjective MWL assessment techniques are normally used in conjunction with other MWL assessment techniques, such as primary and secondary task measures.

Training and Application Times

The training and application times for the Bedford scale are estimated to be very low.

Reliability and Validity

There are no data regarding the reliability and validity of the technique available in the literature.

Tools Needed

The Bedford scale technique is applied using pen and paper.

Instantaneous Self-Assessment (ISA)

Background and Applications

The ISA workload technique is another very simple subjective MWL assessment technique that was developed by NATS for use in the assessment of air traffic controller MWL during the design of future ATM systems (Kirwan, Evans, Donohoe, Kilner, Lamoureux, Atkinson, and MacKendrick, 1997). ISA involves participants self-rating their workload during a task (normally every two minutes) on a scale of 1 (low) to 5 (high). Kirwan et al (1997) used the following ISA scale to assess air traffic controllers (ATC) workload (Table 8.4).

Table 8.4   Example ISA Workload Scale (Source: Kirwan et al, 1997)

Level	Workload Heading	Spare Capacity	Description
5	Excessive	None	Behind on tasks; losing track of the full picture
4	High	Very Little	Non-essential tasks suffering. Could not work at this level very long.
3	Comfortable Busy Pace	Some	All tasks well in hand. Busy but stimulating pace. Could keep going continuously at this level.
2	Relaxed	Ample	More than enough time for all tasks. Active on ATC task less than 50% of the time.
1	Under-Utilised	Very Much	Nothing to do. Rather boring.

Typically, the ISA scale is presented to the participants in the form of a colour-coded keypad. The keypad flashes when a workload rating is required, and the participant simply pushes the button that corresponds to their perceived workload rating. Alternatively, the workload ratings can be requested and acquired verbally. The ISA technique allows a profile of operator workload throughout the task to be constructed, and allows the analyst to ascertain excessively high or low workload parts of the task under analysis. The appeal of the ISA technique lies in its low resource usage and its low intrusiveness.

Domain of Application

Generic. ISA has mainly been used in ATC.

Procedure and Advice

Step 1: Construct a task description
The first step in any workload analysis is to develop a task description for the task or scenario under analysis. It is recommended that hierarchical task analysis is used for this purpose.

Step 2: Brief participant(s)
The participants should be briefed regarding the ISA technique, including what it measures and how it works. It may be useful to demonstrate an ISA data collection exercise for a task similar to the one under analysis. This allows the participants to understand how the technique works and also what is required of them. It is also crucial at this stage that the participants have a clear understanding of the ISA workload scale being used. In order for the results to be valid, the participants should have the same understanding of each level of the workload scale i.e. what level of perceived workload constitutes a rating of 5 on the ISA workload scale and what level constitutes a rating of 1. It is recommended that the participants are taken through the scale and examples of workload scenarios are provided for each level on the scale. Once the participants fully understand the ISA workload scale being used, the analysis can proceed to the next step.

Step 3: Pilot run
Once the participant has a clear understanding of how the ISA technique works and what is being measured, it is useful to perform a pilot run. Whilst performing a small task, participants should be subjected to the ISA technique. This allows participants to experience the technique in a task performance setting. Participants should be encouraged to ask questions during the pilot run in order to understand the technique and the experimental procedure fully.

Step 4: Begin task performance
Next, the participant should begin the task under analysis. Normally, a simulation of the system under analysis is used, however this is dependent upon the domain of application. ISA can also be used during task performance in a real-world setting, although it has mainly been applied in simulator settings. Simulators are also useful as they can be programmed to record the workload ratings throughout the trial.

Step 5: Request and record workload rating
The analyst should request a workload rating either verbally, or through the use of flashing lights on the workload scale display. The frequency and timing of the workload ratings should be determined beforehand by the analyst. Typically, a workload rating is requested every two minutes. It is crucial that the provision of a workload rating is as un-intrusive to the participant's

primary task performance as possible. Step 4 should continue at regular intervals until the task is completed. The analyst should make a record of each workload rating given.

Step 6: Construct task workload profile
Once the task is complete and the workload ratings are collected, the analyst should construct a workload profile for the task under analysis. Typically a graph is constructed, highlighting the high and low workload points of the task under analysis. An average workload rating for the task under analysis can also be calculated.

Advantages

1. ISA is a very simple technique to learn and use.
2. The output allows a workload profile for the task under analysis to be constructed.
3. ISA is very quick in its application as data collection occurs during the trial.
4. Has been used extensively in numerous domains.
5. Requires very little in the way of resources.
6. Whilst the technique is obtrusive to the primary task, it is probably the least intrusive of the on-line workload assessment techniques.
7. Low cost.

Disadvantages

1. ISA is intrusive to primary task performance.
2. Limited validation evidence associated with the technique.
3. ISA is a very simplistic technique, offering only a limited assessment of operator workload.
4. Participants are not very efficient at reporting mental events.

Related Methods

ISA is a subjective workload assessment technique of which there are many, such as NASA TLX, MACE, MCH, DRAWS and the Bedford scales. To ensure comprehensiveness, ISA is often used in conjunction with other subjective techniques, such as the NASA TLX.

Training and Application Times

It is estimated that the training and application times associated with the ISA technique are very low. Application time is dependent upon the duration of the task under analysis.

Reliability and Validity

No data regarding the reliability and validity of the technique is available in the literature.

Tools Needed

ISA can be applied using pen and paper.

Flowchart

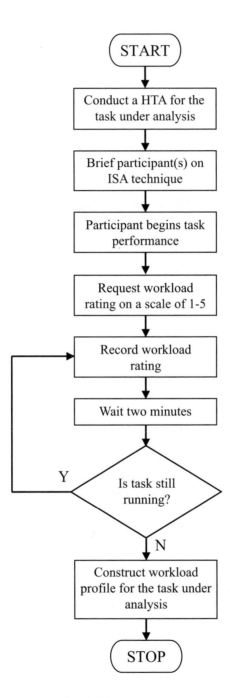

Cognitive Task Load Analysis (CTLA)

Background and Applications

Cognitive task load analysis (CTLA) is a technique used to assess or predict the cognitive load of a task or set of tasks imposed upon an operator. CTLA is typically used early in the design process to aid the provision of an optimal cognitive load for the system design in question. The technique has been used in its present format in a naval domain (Neerincx, 2003). The CTLA is based upon a model of cognitive task load (Neerincx, 2003) that describes the effects of task characteristics upon operator mental workload. According to the model, cognitive (or mental) task load is comprised of percentage time occupied, level of information processing and the number of task set switches exhibited during the task. According to Neerincx (2003), the operator should not be occupied by one task for more than 70-80% of the total time. The level of information processing is defined using the SRK framework (Rasmussen 1986). Finally, task set switches are defined by changes of applicable task knowledge on the operating and environmental level exhibited by the operators under analysis (Neerincx, 2003). The three variables: time occupied, level of information processing and task set switches are combined to determine the level of cognitive load imposed by the task. High ratings for the three variables equal a high cognitive load imposed on the operator by the task.

Domain of Application

Maritime.

Procedure and Advice

The following procedure is adapted from Neerincx (2003).

Step 1: Define task(s) or scenario under analysis
The first step in analysing operator cognitive load is to define the task(s) or scenario(s) under analysis.

Step 2: Data collection
Once the task or scenario under analysis is clearly defined, specific data should be collected regarding the task. Observation, interviews, questionnaires and surveys are typically used.

Step 3: Task decomposition
The next step in the CTLA involves defining the overall operator goals and objectives associated with each task under analysis. Task structure should also be described fully.

Step 4: Create event list
Next, a hierarchical event list for the task under analysis should be created. According to Neerincx (2003), the event list should describe the event classes that trigger task classes, providing an overview of any situation driven elements.

Step 5: Describe scenario(s)
Once the event classes are described fully, the analyst should begin to describe the scenarios involved in the task under analysis. This description should include sequences of events and their consequences. Neerincx (2003) recommends that this information is displayed on a timeline.

Step 6: Describe basic action sequences (BAS)
BAS describe the relationship between event and task classes. These action sequences should be depicted in action sequence diagrams.

Step 7: Describe compound action sequences (CAS)
CAS describe the relationship between event and task instances for situations and the associated interface support. The percentage time occupied, level of information processing and number of task set switches are elicited from the CAS diagram.

Step 8: Determine percentage time occupied, level of information processing and number of task set switches
Once the CAS are described, the analyst(s) should determine the operators' percentage time occupied, level of information processing and number of task set switches exhibited during the task or scenario under analysis.

Step 9: Determine cognitive task load
Once percentage time occupied, level of information processing and number of task set switches are defined, the analyst(s) should determine the operator(s)' cognitive task load. The three variables should be mapped onto the model of cognitive task load.

Advantages

1. The technique is based upon sound theoretical underpinning.
2. Can be used during the design of systems and processes to highlight tasks or scenarios that impose especially high cognitive task demands.
3. Seems to be suited to analysing control room type tasks or scenarios.

Disadvantages

1. The technique appears to be quite complex.
2. Such a technique would be very time consuming in its application.
3. A high level of training would be required.
4. There is no guidance on the rating of cognitive task load. It would be difficult to give task load a numerical rating based upon the underlying model.
5. Initial data collection would be very time consuming.
6. The CTLA technique requires validation.
7. Evidence of the use of the technique is limited.

Related Methods

The CTLA technique uses action sequence diagrams, which are very similar to operator sequence diagrams. In the data collection phase, techniques such as observation, interviews and questionnaires are used.

Approximate Training and Application Times

It is estimated that the training and application times associated with the CTLA technique would both be very high.

Reliability and Validity

No data regarding the reliability and validity of the technique are offered in the literature.

Tools Needed

Once the initial data collection phase is complete, CTLA can be conducted using pen and paper. The data collection phase would require video and audio recording equipment and a PC.

Subjective Workload Assessment Technique (SWAT)

Background and Applications

The subjective workload assessment technique (SWAT; Reid and Nygren, 1988) is a MWL assessment technique that was developed by the US Air force Armstrong Aerospace Medical Research laboratory at the Wright Patterson Air force Base, USA. SWAT was originally developed to assess pilot MWL in cockpit environments but more recently has been used predictively (Pro-SWAT) (Salvendy, 1997). Along with the NASA TLX technique of subjective MWL, SWAT is probably one the most commonly used of the subjective techniques to measure operator MWL. Like the NASA TLX, SWAT is a multi-dimensional tool that uses three dimensions of operator MWL; *time load, mental effort load* and *stress load*. Time load refers to the extent to which a task is performed within a time limit and the extent to which multiple tasks must be performed concurrently. Mental effort load refers to the associated attentional demands of a task, such as attending to multiple sources of information and performing calculation. Finally, stress load includes operator variables such as fatigue, level of training and emotional state. After an initial weighting procedure, participants are asked to rate each dimension (time load, mental effort load and stress load), on a scale of 1 to 3. A MWL score is then calculated for each dimension and an overall workload score of between 1 and 100 is derived. The SWAT rating scale is presented in Table 8.5.

Table 8.5   SWAT Three Point Rating Scale

Time Load	Mental Effort Load	Stress Load
1. Often have spare time: interruptions or overlap among other activities occur infrequently or not at all	1. Very little conscious mental effort or concentration required: activity is almost automatic, requiring little or no attention	1. Little confusion, risk, frustration, or anxiety exists and can be easily accommodated
2. Occasionally have spare time: interruptions or overlap among activities occur frequently	2. Moderate conscious mental effort or concentration required: complexity of activity is moderately high due to uncertainty, unpredictability, or unfamiliarity; considerable attention is required	2. Moderate stress due to confusion, frustration, or anxiety noticeably adds to workload: significant compensation is required to maintain adequate performance
3. Almost never have spare time: interruptions or overlap among activities are very frequent, or occur all of the time	3. Extensive mental effort and concentration are necessary: very complex activity requiring total attention	3. High to very intense stress due to confusion, frustration, or anxiety: high to extreme determination and self-control required

A MWL score is derived for each of the three SWAT dimensions, time load, mental effort load and stress load. An overall MWL score between 1 and 100 is also calculated.

Domain of Application

Aviation.

Procedure and Advice

Step 1: Scale development
Firstly, participants are required to place in rank order all possible 27 combinations of the three workload dimensions, time load, mental effort load and stress load, according to their effect on workload. This 'conjoint' measurement is used to develop an interval scale of workload rating, from 1 to 100.

Step 2: Task demo/walkthrough
The SMEs should be given a walkthrough or demonstration of the task that they are to predict the workload for. Normally a verbal walkthrough will suffice.

Step 3: Workload prediction
The SMEs should now be instructed to predict the workload imposed by the task under analysis. They should assign a value of 1 to 3 to each of the three SWAT workload dimensions.

Step 4: Performance of task under analysis
Once the initial SWAT ranking has been completed, the subject should perform the task under analysis. SWAT can be administered during the trial or after the trial. It is recommended that the SWAT is administered after the trial, as on-line administration is intrusive to the primary task. If on-line administration is required, then the SWAT should be administered and completed verbally.

Step 5: SWAT scoring
The participants are required to provide a subjective rating of workload by assigning a value of 1 to 3 to each of the three SWAT workload dimensions.

Step 6: SWAT score calculation
Next, the analyst should calculate the workload scores from the SME predictions and also the participant workload ratings. For the workload scores, the analyst should take the scale value associated with the combination given by the participant. The scores are then translated into individual workload scores for each SWAT dimension. Finally, an overall workload score should be calculated.

Step 7: Compare workload scores
The final step is to compare the predicted workload scores to the workload scores provided by the participants who undertook the task under analysis.

Advantages

1. The SWAT technique provides a quick and simple technique for estimating operator workload.
2. The SWAT workload dimensions are generic, so the technique can be applied to any domain. In the past, the SWAT technique has been used in a number of different domains, such as aviation, air traffic control, command and control, nuclear reprocessing and petro-chemical, and automotive domains.

3. The SWAT technique is one of the most widely used and well known subjective workload assessment techniques available, and has been subjected to a number of validation studies (Hart and Staveland, 1988; Vidulich and Tsang 1985, 1986b)
4. The Pro-SWAT variation allows the technique to be used predictively.
5. SWAT is a multi-dimensional approach to workload assessment.
6. Unobtrusive.

Disadvantages

1. SWAT can be intrusive if administered on-line.
2. Pro-SWAT has yet to be validated thoroughly.
3. In a number of validation studies it has been reported that the NASA TLX is superior to SWAT in terms of sensitivity, particularly for low mental workloads (Hart and Staveland, 1988; Hill et al, 1992; Nygren, 1991).
4. SWAT has been constantly criticised for having a low sensitivity for mental workloads (Luximon and Goonetilleke, 2001).
5. The initial SWAT combination ranking procedure is very time consuming (Luximon and Goonetilleke, 2001).
6. Workload ratings may be correlated with task performance e.g. subjects who performed poorly on the primary task may rate their workload as very high and vice versa. This is not always the case.
7. When administered after the fact, participants may have forgotten high or low workload aspects of the task.
8. Unsophisticated measure of workload. NASA TLX appears to be more sensitive.
9. The Pro-SWAT technique is still in its infancy.

Related Methods

The SWAT technique is similar to a number of subjective workload assessment techniques, such as the NASA TLX, Cooper Harper Scales and Bedford Scales. For predictive use, the Pro-SWORD technique is similar.

Approximate Training and Application Times

Whilst the scoring phase of the SWAT technique is very simple to use and quick to apply, the initial ranking phase is time consuming and laborious. Thus, the training times and application times are estimated to be quite high.

Reliability and Validity

A number of validation studies concerning the SWAT technique have been conducted Hart and Staveland, 1988; Vidulich and Tsang, 1985, 1986). Vidulich and Tsang (1985, 1986a and b) reported that NASA TLX produced more consistent workload estimates for participants performing the same task than the SWAT (Reid and Nygren, 1988) technique did. Luximon and Goonetilleke (2001) also reported that a number of studies have shown that the NASA TLX is superior to SWAT in terms of sensitivity, particularly for low mental workloads (Hart and Staveland, 1988; Hill et al, 1992; Nygren, 1991).

Tools Needed

A SWAT analysis can either be conducted using pen and paper. A software version also exists. Both the pen and paper method and the software method can be purchased from various sources.

Flowchart

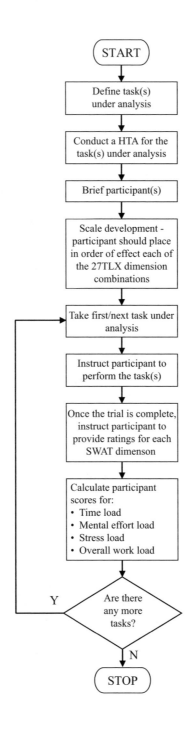

Pro-SWORD – Subjective Workload Dominance Technique

Background and Applications

The Subjective Workload Dominance Technique (SWORD) is a subjective MWL assessment technique that has been used both retrospectively and predictively (Pro-SWORD) (Vidulich, Ward and Schueren, 1991). Originally designed as a retrospective MWL assessment technique, SWORD uses paired comparison of tasks in order to provide a rating of MWL for each individual task. Administered post-trial, participants are required to rate one task's dominance over another in terms of workload imposed. When used predictively, tasks are rated for their dominance before the trial begins, and then rated post-test to check for the sensitivity of the predictions.

Domain of Application

Generic.

Procedure and Advice – Workload Assessment

The procedure outlined below is the procedure recommended for an assessment of operator MWL. In order to predict operator MWL, it is recommended that SMEs are employed to predict MWL for the task under analysis before step 3 in the procedure below. The task should then be performed and operator workload ratings obtained using the SWORD technique. The predicted MWL ratings should then be compared to the subjective ratings in order to calculate the sensitivity of the MWL predictions made.

Step 1: Task description
The first step in any SWORD analysis is to create a task or scenario description of the scenario under analysis. Each task should be described individually in order to allow the creation of the SWORD rating sheet. Any task description can be used for this step, such as HTA or tabular task analysis.

Step 2: Create SWORD rating sheet
Once a task description (e.g. HTA) is developed, the SWORD rating sheet can be created. The analyst should list all of the possible combinations of tasks (e.g. AvB, AvC, BvC) and the dominance rating scale. An example of a SWORD dominance rating sheet is shown in Table 8.6.

Step 3: Conduct walkthrough of the task
A walkthrough of the task under analysis should be given to the SMEs.

Step 4: Administration of SWORD questionnaire
Once the SMEs have been given an appropriate walkthrough or demonstration of the task under analysis, the SWORD data collection process begins. This involves the administration of the SWORD rating sheet. The participant should be presented with the SWORD rating sheet and asked to predict the MWL dominance of the interface under analysis. The SWORD rating sheet lists all possible paired comparisons of the tasks conducted in the scenario under analysis. A 17-point rating scale is used.

Step 5: Performance of task
SWORD is normally applied post-trial. Therefore, the task under analysis should be performed first. As SWORD is applied after the task performance, intrusiveness is reduced and the task under analysis can be performed in its real-world setting.

Step 6: Administration of SWORD questionnaire
Once the task under analysis is complete, the SWORD data collection process begins. This involves the administration of the SWORD rating sheet. The participant should be presented with the SWORD rating sheet (Table 8.6) immediately after task performance has ended. The SWORD rating sheet lists all possible paired comparisons of the tasks conducted in the scenario under analysis. A 17-point rating scale is used.

Table 8.6   Example SWORD Rating Sheet

Task	Absolute	Very Strong	Strong	Weak	EQUAL	Weak	Strong	Very Strong	Absolute	Task
A										B
A										C
A										D
A										E
B										C
B										D
B										E
C										D
C										E
D										E

The 17 slots represent the possible ratings. The analyst has to rate the two tasks (e.g. task AvB) in terms of their level of MWL imposed, against each other. For example, if the participant feels that the two tasks imposed a similar level of MWL, then they should mark the 'EQUAL' point on the rating sheet. However, if the participant feels that task A imposed a slightly higher level of MWL than task B did, they would move towards task A on the sheet and mark the 'Weak' point on the rating sheet. If the participant felt that task A imposed a much greater level of workload than task B, then they would move towards task A on the sheet and mark the 'Absolute' point on the rating sheet. This allows the participant to provide a subjective rating of one task's MWL dominance over the other. This procedure should continue until all of the possible combinations of tasks in the scenario under analysis are exhausted and given a rating.

Step 7: Constructing the judgement matrix
Once all ratings have been elicited, the SWORD judgement matrix should be conducted. Each cell in the matrix should represent the comparison of the task in the row with the task in the associated column. The analyst should fill each cell with the participant's dominance rating. For example, if a participant rated tasks A and B as equal, a '1' is entered into the appropriate cell. If task A is rated as dominant, then the analyst simply counts from the 'Equal' point to the marked point on the sheet, and enters the number in the appropriate cell. An example SWORD judgement matrix is shown in Table 8.7. The rating for each task is calculated by determining the mean for each row of the matrix and then normalising the means (Vidulich, Ward and Schueren, 1991).

Table 8.7   Example SWORD Matrix

	A	B	C	D	E
A	1	2	6	1	1
B	-	1	3	2	2
C	-	-	1	6	6
D	-	-	-	1	1
E	-	-	-	-	1

Step 8: Matrix consistency evaluation
Once the SWORD matrix is complete, the consistency of the matrix can be evaluated by ensuring that there are transitive trends amongst the related judgements in the matrix. For example, if task A is rated twice as hard as task B, and task B is rated 3 times as hard as task C, then task A should be rated as 6 times as hard as task C (Vidulich, Ward and Schueren, 1991). Therefore the analyst should use the completed SWORD matrix to check the consistency of the participant's ratings.

Step 9: Compare predicted ratings to retrospective ratings
The analyst should now compare the predicted MWL ratings against the ratings offered by the participants post-trial.

Advantages

1. Easy to learn and use.
2. Non-intrusive.
3. High face validity.
4. SWORD has been demonstrated to have a sensitivity to workload variations (Reid and Nygren, 1988).
5. Very quick in its application.

Disadvantages

1. Data is collected post-task.
2. SWORD is a dated approach to workload assessment.
3. Workload projections are more accurate when domain experts are used.
4. Further validation is required.
5. The SWORD technique has not been as widely used as other workload assessment techniques, such as SWAT, MCH and the NASA TLX.

Example

Vidulich, Ward and Schueren (1991) tested the SWORD technique for its accuracy in predicting the MWL imposed upon F-16 pilots by a new HUD attitude display system. Participants included F-16 pilots and college students and were divided into two groups. The first group (F-16 pilots experienced with the new HUD display) retrospectively rated the tasks using the traditional SWORD technique, whilst the second group (F-16 pilots who had no experience of the new HUD display) used the Pro-SWORD variation to predict the MWL associated with the HUD tasks. A third group (college students with no experience of the HUD) also used the Pro-SWORD technique to predict the associated MWL. In conclusion, it was reported that the pilot Pro-SWORD ratings correlated highly with the pilot SWORD (retrospective) ratings (Vidulich, Ward and Schueren, 1991). Furthermore, the Pro-SWORD ratings correctly anticipated the recommendations made in an evaluation of the HUD system. Vidulich and Tsang (1987) also report that the SWORD technique was more reliable and sensitive than the NASA TLX technique.

Related Methods

SWORD is one of a number of MWL assessment techniques, including the NASA-TLX, SWAT, MCH and DRAWS. A number of the techniques have also been used predictively, such as Pro-SWAT and MCH. A SWORD analysis requires a task description of some sort, such as HTA or a tabular task analysis.

Approximate Training and Application Times

Although no data is offered regarding the training and application times for the SWORD technique, it is apparent that the training time for such a simple technique would minimal. The application time associated with the SWORD technique would be based upon the scenario under analysis. For large, complex scenario's involving a great number of tasks, the application time would be high as an initial HTA would have to be performed, then the scenario would have to performed, and then the SWORD technique. The actual application time associated purely the administration of the SWORD technique is very low.

Reliability and Validity

Vidulich, Ward and Schueren (1991) tested the SWORD technique for its accuracy in predicting the MWL imposed upon F-16 pilots by a new HUD attitude display system. In conclusion, it was reported that the pilot Pro-SWORD ratings correlated highly with the pilot SWORD (retrospective) ratings (Vidulich, Ward and Schueren, 1991). Furthermore, the Pro-SWORD ratings correctly anticipated the recommendations made in an evaluation of the HUD system. Vidulich and Tsang (1987) also reported that the SWORD technique was more reliable and sensitive than the NASA TLX technique.

Tools Needed

The SWORD technique can be applied using pen and paper. Of course, the system or device under analysis is also required.

Chapter 9

Team Assessment Methods

An increased use of teams of actors within complex systems has led to the emergence of various approaches for the assessment of different features associated with team performance. According to Savoie (1998; cited by Salas, 2004) the use of teams has risen dramatically with reports of 'team presence' from workers rising from 5% in 1980 to 50% in the mid 1990s. Over the last two decades, the performance of teams in complex systems has received considerable attention from the HF community, and a number of methods have been developed in order to assess and evaluate team performance. Research into team performance is currently being undertaken in a number of areas, including the aviation domain, the military, air traffic control, and the emergency services domain amongst others.

A team can be defined in simple terms as a group of actors working collaboratively within a system. According to Salas (2004) a team consists of two or more people dealing with multiple information sources who are working to accomplish a shared goal of some sort. With regards to the roles that teams take within complex systems, Cooke (2004) suggests that teams are required to detect and interpret cues, remember, reason, plan, solve problems, acquire knowledge and make decisions as an integrated and co-ordinated unit. Team-based activity in complex systems comprises two components: teamwork and taskwork. Teamwork refers to those instances where actors within a team or network co-ordinate their behaviour in order to achieve tasks related to the team's goals. Taskwork refers to those tasks that are conducted by team members individually or in isolation from one another.

The complex nature of team-based activity ensures that sophisticated assessment methods are required for team performance assessment. Team-based activity involves multiple actors with multiple goals performing both teamwork and taskwork activity. The activity is typically complex (hence the requirement for a team) and may be dispersed across a number of different geographical locations. Consequently there are a number of different team performance methods available to the HF practitioner, each designed to assess certain aspects of team performance in complex systems. The team performance methods considered in this review can be broadly classified into the following categories:

1. Team task analysis (TTA) methods.
2. Team cognitive task analysis methods.
3. Team communication assessment methods.
4. Team behavioural assessment methods.
5. Team MWL assessment methods.

A brief description of each team method's category is given below, along with a brief outline of the methods considered in the review.

Team Task Analysis (TTA) techniques are used to describe team performance in terms of requirements (knowledge, skills and attitudes) and the tasks that require either teamwork or individual (taskwork) performance (Burke, 2005). According to Baker, Salas and Bowers (1998) TTA refers to the analysis of team tasks and also the assessment of a team's teamwork requirements (knowledge, skills and abilities). TTA outputs are typically used in the development of team training interventions, such as crew resource management training programmes, for the evaluation of team performance, and also to identify operational and teamwork skills required within teams (Burke, 2005). According to Salas (2004) optimising team performance and effectiveness involves understanding a number of components surrounding the use of teams, such as communication and task requirements, team environments and team objectives. The team task analysis techniques reviewed in this document attempt to analyse such components. Groupware Task Analysis (Welie and Van Der Veer, 2003) is a team task analysis method that is used to study and evaluate group or team activities in order to inform the design and analysis of similar team systems. Team Task Analysis (Burke, 2005) is a task analysis method that provides a description of tasks distributed across a team and the requirements associated with the tasks in terms of operator knowledge, skills, and abilities. HTA (T) (Annett, 2004) is a recent adaptation of HTA that caters for team performance in complex systems.

Team cognitive task analysis (CTA) techniques are used to elicit and describe the cognitive processes associated with team decision making and performance (Klein, 2000) a team CTA provides a description of the cognitive skills required for a team to perform a task. Team CTA techniques are used to assess team performance and then to inform the development of strategies designed to improve it. The output of team CTA techniques is typically used to aid the design of team-based technology, the development of team-training procedures, task allocation within teams and also the organisation of teams. Team CTA (Klein, 2000) is a method that is used to describe the cognitive skills that a team or group of individuals are required to undertake in order to perform a particular task or set of tasks. The decision requirements exercise is a method very similar to team CTA that is used to specify the requirements or components (difficulties, cues and strategies used, errors made) associated with decision making in team scenarios.

Communication between team members is crucial to successful performance. Team communication assessment techniques are used to assess the content, frequency, efficiency, technology used and nature of communication between the actors within a particular team. The output of team communication assessment techniques can be used to determine procedures for effective communication, to specify appropriate technology to use in communications, to aid the design of team training procedures, to aid the design of team processes and to assess existing communication procedures. The Comms Usage Diagram (CUD; Watts and Monk, 2000) approach is used to analyse and represent communications between actors dispersed across different geographical locations. The output of a CUD analysis describes how, why and when communications between team members occur, which technology is involved in the communication, and the advantages and disadvantages associated with the technology used. Social Network Analysis (SNA; Driskell and Mullen, 2004; Wasserman and Faust, 1994) is used to analyse and represent the relationships between actors within a social network which can be considered analogous to the concept of a team. SNA uses mathematical methods from graph theory to analyse these relationships, and can be used to identify key agents and other aspects of a particular social network that might enhance or constrain team performance.

Team behavioural assessment techniques are used to assess performance or behaviours exhibited by teams during a particular task or scenario. Behavioural assessment techniques have typically been used in the past to evaluate the effectiveness of team training interventions such as crew resource management programmes. Behavioural observation scales (BOS; Baker, 2005) are a general class of observer-rating approaches that are used to assess different aspects of team performance. Co-ordination demands analysis (CDA; Burke, 2005) is used to rate the level of co-ordination between team members during task performance. The TTRAM method (Swezey, Ownes, Burgondy and Salas, 2000) uses a number of techniques to identify team-based task training requirements and also to evaluate any associated training technologies that could potentially be used in the delivery of team training. Questionnaires for Distributed Assessment of Team Mutual Awareness (Macmillan, Paley, Entin and Entin, 2005) comprise a series of self-rating questionnaires designed to assess team member mutual awareness (individual awareness and team awareness).

The assessment of team MWL has previously received only minimal attention. Team MWL assessment techniques are used to assess the MWL imposed on both the actors within a team and also on the team as a whole during task performance. The team workload method is an approach to the assessment of team workload described by Bowers and Jentsch (2004) that involves the use of a modified NASA-TLX (Hart and Staveland, 1988). As we saw in Chapter 7, there is also some interest in studying Shared Situation Awareness, although this is still in the early stages of development. A summary of the team performance analysis techniques considered in this review is presented in Table 9.1.

Behavioural Observation Scales (BOS)

Background and Applications

Behavioural observation scales (BOS; Baker, 2004) are a general class of observer-rating techniques used to assess different aspects of team performance in complex systems. Observer-rating approaches work on the notion that appropriate SMEs can accurately rate participants on externally exhibited behaviours based upon an observation of the task or scenario under analysis. Observer-rating techniques have been used to measure a number of different constructs, including situation awareness (e.g. SABARS; Endsley, 2000, Matthews and Beal, 2002) and Crew Resource Management skills (e.g. NOTECHS; Flin, Goeters, Hormann and Martin, 1998). BOS techniques involve appropriate SMEs observing team-based activity and then providing ratings of various aspects of team performance using an appropriate rating scale. According to Baker (2004) BOS techniques are typically used to provide performance feedback during team training exercises. However, it is apparent that BOS techniques can be used for a number of different purposes, including analysing team performance, situation awareness, error, CRM related skills and C4i activity.

Domain of Application

Generic. Providing an appropriate rating scale is used, BOS techniques can be applied in any domain.

Procedure and Advice

The following procedure describes the process of conducting an analysis using a pre-defined BOS. For an in depth description of the procedure involved in the development of a BOS, the reader is referred to Baker (2004).

Step 1: Define task(s) under analysis
Firstly, the task(s) and team(s) under analysis should be defined clearly. Once the task(s) under analysis are clearly defined, it is recommended that a HTA be conducted for the task(s) under analysis. This allows the analyst(s) to gain a complete understanding of the task(s) and also an understanding of the types of the behaviours that are likely to be exhibited during the task. A number of different data collection procedures may be adopted during the development of the HTA, including observational study, interviews and questionnaires.

Table 9.1   Summary of Team Performance Analysis Techniques

Method	Type of method	Domain	Training time	App time	Related methods	Tools needed	Validation studies	Advantages	Disadvantages
BOS – Behavioural Observation Scales	Team performance analysis	Generic (Military)	Med-High	High	Behavioural rating scale Observation	Pen and paper	No	1) Can be used to assess multiple aspects of team performance. 2) Seems suited to use in analysis of C4i analysis. 3) Easy to use.	1) There is a limit to what can be accurately assessed through observing participant performance. 2) A new BOS scale may need to be developed. 3) Reliability is questionable.
Comms Usage Diagram	Comms analysis	Generic (Medical)	Low	Med	OSD HTA Observation	Pen and paper Video & Audio recording equipment	No	1) Output provides a comprehensive description of task activity. 2) The technology uses are analysed and recommendations are offered. 3) Seems suited to use in the analysis of C4i activity.	1) Limited reliability and validity evidence. 2) Time nor error occurrence are catered for. 3) Could be time consuming and difficult to construct for large, complex tasks.
Co-ordination Demands Analysis	Co-ordination analysis	Generic	Low	Med	HTA Observation	Pen and paper	No	1) Very useful output, providing an assessment of team co-ordination. 2) Seems suited to use in the analysis of C4i activity.	1) Requires SMEs. 2) Rating procedure is time consuming and laborious.
Decision Requirements Exercise	Decision-making assessment	Generic (Military)	Med	Med-High	Critical Decision Method Observation	Pen and paper Video & Audio recording equipment	No	1) Output is very useful, offering an analysis of team decision making in a task or scenario. 2) Based upon actual incidents, removing the need for simulation. 3) Seems suited to use in the analysis of C4i activity.	1) Data is based upon past events, which may be subject to memory degradation. 2) Reliability is questionable. 3) May be time consuming.

Table 9.1 (continued)

Method	Type of method	Domain	Training time	App time	Related methods	Tools needed	Validation studies	Advantages	Disadvantages
Groupware Task Analysis	Design	Generic	Med	High	N/A	Pen and paper	No	1) The output specifies information requirements and the potential technology to support task performance.	1) Limited use. 2) Resource intensive. 3) A number of analyst(s) are required.
HTA (T)	Team performance analysis	Generic	Med	Med	HEI Task analysis	Pen and paper	Yes	1) Team HTA based upon extensively used HTA technique. 2) Caters for team-based tasks.	1) Limited use.
Questionnaires for Distributed Assessment of Team Mutual Awareness	Team awareness Workload assessment	Generic	Low	Med	Questionnaires NASA-TLX	Pen and paper	No	1) Provides an assessment of team awareness and team workload. 2) Low cost, easy to use requiring little training.	1) Data is collected post-trial. 2) Limited use.
Social Network Analysis	Team analysis	Generic	High	High	Observation	Pen and paper	No	1) Highlights the most important relationships and roles within a team. 2) Seems suited to use in the analysis of C4i activity.	1) Difficult to use for complex tasks involving multiple actors. 2) Data collection could be time consuming.
Team Cognitive Task Analysis	Team cognitive task analysis	Generic (military)	High	High	Observation Interviews Critical decision method	Pen and paper Video and audio recording equipment	Yes	1) Can be used to elicit specific information regarding team decision making in complex environments. 2) Seems suited to use in the analysis of C4i activity. 3) Output can be used to develop effective team decision-making strategies.	1) Reliability is questionable. 2) Resource intensive. 3) High level of training and expertise is required in order to use the method properly.

Table 9.1 (continued)

Method	Type of method	Domain	Training time	App time	Related methods	Tools needed	Validation studies	Advantages	Disadvantages
Team Communications Analysis	Comms Analysis	Generic	Med	Med	Observation Checklists Frequency counts	Pen and paper Observer PC	No	1) Provides an assessment of communications taking place within a team. 2) Suited to use in the analysis of C4i activity. 3) Can be used effectively during training.	1) Coding of data is time consuming and laborious. 2) Initial data collection may be time consuming.
Team Task Analysis	Team task analysis	Generic	Med	Med	Co-ordination demand analysis Observation	Pen and paper	No	1) Output specifies the knowledge, skills and abilities required during task performance. 2) Useful for team training procedures. 3) Specifies which of the tasks are team based and which are individual based.	1) Time consuming in application. 2) SMEs are required throughout the procedure. 3) Great skill is required on behalf of the analyst(s).
Team Workload Assessment	Workload assessment	Generic	Low	Low	NASA-TLX	Pen and paper	No	1) Output provides an assessment of both individual and team workload. 2) Quick, and easy to use requiring little training or cost. 3) Based upon the widely used and validated NASA-TLX measure.	1) Extent to which team members can provide an accurate assessment of overall team workload and other team member workload is questionable. 2) Requires much further testing. 3) Data is collected post-trial.
TTRAM – Task and Training Requirements Methodology	Training analysis	Generic	High	High	Observation Interview Questionnaire	Pen and paper	No	1) Useful output, highlighting those tasks that are prone to skill decay. 2) Offers training solutions.	1) Time consuming in application. 2) SMEs required throughout. 3) Requires a high level of training.

Step 2: Select or develop appropriate BOS

Once the task(s) and team(s) under analysis are clearly defined and described, an appropriate BOS scale should be selected. If an appropriate scale does not already exist, then one should be developed. It may be that an appropriate BOS already exists, and if this is the case, the scale can be used without modification. Typically, an appropriate BOS is developed from scratch to suit the analysis requirements. According to Baker (2004) the development of a BOS scale involves the following key steps:

1. Conduct Critical Incident analysis.
2. Develop behavioural statements.
3. Identify teamwork dimensions.
4. Classify behavioural statements into teamwork categories.
5. Select appropriate metric e.g. five point rating scale (1 = almost never, 5 = almost always), checklist etc.
6. Pilot test BOS.

Step 3: Select appropriate SME raters

Once the BOS is developed and tested appropriately, the SME raters who will use the method to assess team performance during the task(s) under analysis should be selected. It is recommended that SMEs for the task and system under analysis are used. The appropriate SMEs should possess an in-depth knowledge of the task(s) under analysis and also of the various different types of behaviours exhibited during performance of the task under analysis. The number of raters used is dependent upon the type, complexity of the task and also the scope of the analysis effort.

Step 4: Train raters

Once an appropriate set of SME raters are selected, they should be given adequate training in the BOS method. Baker (2004) recommends that a combination of behavioural observation training (BOT; Thornton and Zorich, 1980) and frame of reference training (FOR; Bernardin and Buckley, REF) be used for this purpose. BOT involves teaching raters how to accurately detect, perceive, recall, and recognize specific behavioural events during the task performance (Baker, 2004). FOR training involves teaching raters a set of standards for evaluating team performance. The raters should be encouraged to ask any questions during the training process. It may also be useful for the analyst to take the raters through an example BOS rating exercise.

Step 5: Assign participants to raters

Once the SME raters fully understand the BOS method, they should be informed which of the participants they are to observe and rate. It may be that the raters are observing the team as a whole, or that they are rating individual participants.

Step 6: Begin task performance

Once the raters fully understand how the BOS works and what is required of them, the data collection phase can begin. Prior to task performance, the participants should be briefed regarding the nature and purpose of the analysis. Performance of the task(s) under analysis should then begin, and the raters should observe their assigned team members. It is recommended that the raters make additional notes regarding the task performance, in order to assist the rating process. It may also be useful to record the task using a video recorder. This allows the raters to consult footage of the task if they are unsure of a particular behaviour or rating.

Step 7: Rate observable behaviours
Ratings can be made either during task performance or post-trial. If a checklist approach is being used, then they simply check those behaviours observed during the task performance.

Step 8: Calculate BOS scores
Once task performance is complete and all ratings and checklists are compiled, appropriate BOS scores should be calculated. The scores calculated depend upon the focus of the analysis. Typically, scores for each behaviour dimension (e.g. communication, information exchange) and an overall score are calculated. Baker (2004) recommends that BOS scores are calculated by summing all behavioural statements within a BOS. Each team's overall BOS score can then be calculated by summing each of the individual team member scores.

Advantages

1. BOS techniques offer a simple approach to the assessment of team performance.
2. BOS techniques are low cost and easy to use.
3. BOS can be used to provide an assessment of observable team behaviours exhibited during task performance, including communication, information exchange, leadership, teamwork and taskwork performance.
4. BOS seems to be suited for use in the assessment of team performance in C4i environments.
5. The output can be used to inform the development of team training exercises and procedures.
6. BOS can be used to assess both teamwork and taskwork.
7. BOS is a generic procedure and can be used to assess multiple features of performance in a number of different domains.

Disadvantages

1. Existing scales may require modification for use in different environments. Scale development requires considerable effort on behalf of the analyst(s) involved.
2. Observer-rating techniques are limited in what they can accurately assess. For example, the BOS can only be used to provide an assessment of observable behaviour exhibited during task performance. Other pertinent facets of team performance, such as SA, MWL, and decision making cannot be accurately assessed using a BOS.
3. A typical BOS analysis is time consuming to conduct, requiring the development of the scale, training of the raters, observation of the task under analysis and rating of the required behaviours. Even for a small-scale analysis, considerable time may be required.
4. The reliability and validity of such techniques remains a concern.

Approximate Training and Application Times

It is estimated that the total application time for a BOS analysis would be high. A typical BOS analysis involves training the raters in the use of the method, observing the task performance and then completing the BOS sheet. According to Baker (2004), rater training could take up to four hours and the application time may require up to three hours per team.

Flowchart

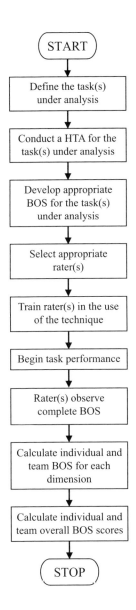

Example

Baker (2004) presents the following example (Table 9.2) of a behavioural checklist.

Related Methods

Observer-rating techniques are used in the assessment of a number of different HF constructs. For example, the SABARS (Endsley, 2000) approach is used to assess situation awareness in military environments, and the NOTECHS (Flin et al, 1998) observer-rating method is used to assess pilot non-technical skills in the aviation domain.

Table 9.2   Communication Checklist

Title: Communication
Definition: Communication involves sending and receiving signals that describe team goals, team resources and constraints, and individual team member tasks. The purpose of communication is to clarify expectations, so that each team member understands what is expected of him or her. Communication is practised by all team members.
Example Behaviours ___ Team leader establishes a positive work environment by soliciting team members' input ___ Team leader listens non-evaluatively ___ Team leader identifies bottom-line safety conditions ___ Team leader establishes contingency plans (in case bottom line is exceeded) ___ Team members verbally indicate their understanding of the bottom-line conditions ___ Team members verbally indicate their understanding of the contingency plans ___ Team members provide consistent verbal and non-verbal signals ___ Team members respond to queries in a timely manner

Reliability and Validity

There is limited reliability and validity data available regarding BOS techniques. According to Barker (2004) research suggests that with the appropriate training given to raters, BOS techniques can achieve an acceptable level of reliability and validity.

Tools Needed

BOS can be applied using pen and paper.

Comms Usage Diagram (CUD)

Background and Applications

Comms Usage Diagram (CUD; Watts and Monk 2000) is used to describe collaborative activity between teams of actors dispersed across different geographical locations. A CUD output describes how and why communications between actors occur, which technology is involved in the communication, and the advantages and disadvantages associated with the technology used. The CUD method was originally developed and applied in the area of medical telecommunications and was used to analyse telemedical consultation scenarios (Watts and Monk, 2000). The method has more recently been modified and used in the analysis of C4i activity in a number of domains, including energy distribution, naval warfare, fire services, air traffic control, military, rail and aviation domains. A CUD analysis is typically based upon observational data of the task or scenario under analysis, although talk-through analysis and interview data can also be used (Watts and Monk, 2000).

Domain of Application

Generic. Although the method was originally developed for use in the medical domain, it is generic and can be applied in any domain that involves distributed activity.

Procedure and Advice

Step 1: Define the task or scenario under analysis
The first step in a CUD analysis is to clearly define the task or scenario under analysis. It may be useful to conduct a HTA of the task under analysis for this purpose. A clear definition of the task under analysis allows the analyst(s) to prepare for the data collection phase.

Step 2: Data collection
Next, the analyst(s) should collect specific data regarding the task or scenario under analysis. A number of data collection procedures may be used for this purpose, including observational study, interviews and questionnaires. It is recommended that specific data regarding the activity conducted, the actors and individual task steps involved, the communication between actors, the technology used and the different geographical locations should be collected.

Step 3: Create task or scenario transcript
Once sufficient data regarding the task under analysis has been collected, a transcript of the task or scenario should be created using the data collected as its input. The transcript should contain all of the data required for the construction of the CUD i.e. the communications between different actors and the technology used.

Step 4: Construct CUD
The scenario transcript created during step 3 of the procedure is then used as the input into the construction of the CUD. The CUD contains a description of the activity conducted at each geographical location, the communication between the actors involved, the technology used for the communications and the advantages and disadvantages associated with that technology medium and also a recommended technology if there is one. Arrows are used to represent the communication and direction of communication between personnel at each of the different locations. For example, if person A at site A communicates with person B at site B, the two should be linked with a two-way arrow. Column three of the CUD output table specifies the technology used in the communication and column four lists any advantages and disadvantages associated with the particular technology used during the communication. In column five, recommended technology mediums for similar communications are provided. The advantages, disadvantages and technology recommendations are based upon analyst subjective judgement.

Advantages

1. The CUD method is simple to use and requires only minimal training.
2. The CUD output is particularly useful, offering a description of the task under analysis, and also a description of the communications between actors during the task, including the order of activity, the personnel involved, the technology used and the associated advantages and disadvantages.
3. The output of a CUD analysis is particularly useful for highlighting communication flaws in a particular network.
4. The CUD method is particularly useful for the analysis of teamwork, distributed collaboration and C4i activity.
5. The CUD method is also flexible, and could potentially be modified to make it comprehensive. Factors such as time, error and workload could potentially be incorporated, ensuring that a much more exhaustive analysis is produced.

6. Although the CUD method was developed and originally used in the medical domain, it
    is a generic method and could potentially be applied in any domain involving distributed
    collaboration or activity.

Disadvantages

1. For large, complex tasks involving multiple actors, conducting a CUD analysis may become
    time consuming and laborious.
2. The initial data collection phase of the CUD method is also time consuming and labour
    intensive, potentially including interviews, observational analysis and talk-through analysis.
    As the activity is dispersed across different geographical locations, a team of analysts is
    also required for the data collection phase.
3. No validity or reliability data are available for the method.
4. Application of the CUD method appears to be limited.
5. Limited guidance is offered to analysts using the method. For example, the advantages and
    disadvantages of the technology used and the recommended technology sections are based
    entirely upon the analyst's subjective judgement.

Example

The CUD method has recently been used as part of the Event Analysis of Systemic Teamwork
(EAST, Baber and Stanton, 2004) method in the analysis of C4i activity in the fire service, naval
warfare, aviation, energy distribution (Salmon, Stanton, Walker, McMaster and Green, 2005),
air traffic control and rail (Walker, Gibson, Stanton, Baber, Salmon and Green, 2004) domains.
The following example is a CUD analysis of an energy distribution task. The task involved the
return from isolation of a high voltage circuit. The data collection phase involved an observational
study of the scenario using two observers. The first observer was situated at the (NGT) National
Operations Centre (NOC) and observed the activity of the NOC control room operator (CRO). The
second observer was situated at the substation and observed the activity of the senior authorised
person (SAP) and authorised person (AP) who completed work required to return the circuit from
isolation. From the observational data obtained, a HTA of the scenario was developed. The HTA
acted as the main input for the CUD. The CUD analysis for the energy distribution task is presented
in Figure 9.1.

Related Methods

The CUD data collection phase may involve the use of a number of different procedures, including
observational study, interviews, questionnaires and walk-through analysis. It is also useful to
conduct a HTA of the task under analysis prior to performing the CUD analysis. The CUD method
has also recently been integrated with a number of other methods (HTA, observation, co-ordination
demands analysis, social network analysis, operator sequence diagrams and propositional networks)
to form the event analysis of systemic teamwork (EAST; Baber and Stanton, 2004) methodology,
which has been used for the analysis of C4i activity.

Approximate Training and Application Times

The training time for the CUD method is minimal, normally no longer than one to two hours,
assuming that the practitioner involved is already proficient in data collection methods such as

interviews and observational study. The application time for the method is also minimal, providing the analyst has access to an appropriate drawing package such as Microsoft Visio. For the C4i scenario presented in the example section, the associated CUD application time was approximately two hours.

Flowchart

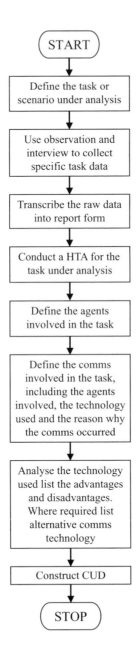

Reliability and Validity

No data regarding the reliability and validity of the method are available in the literature.

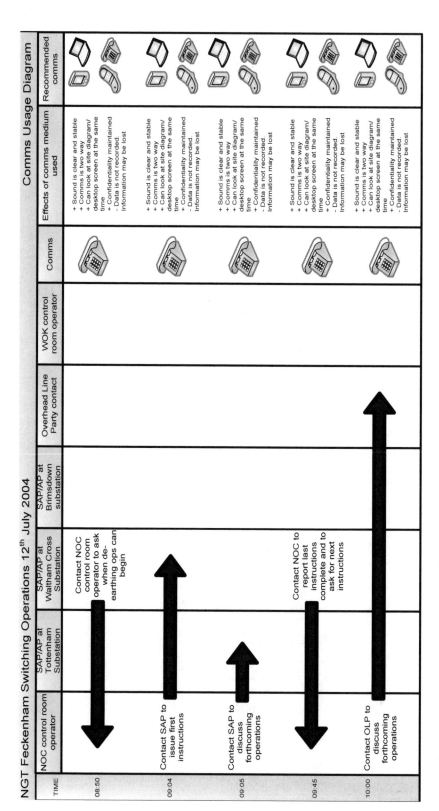

Figure 9.1   Comms Usage Diagram for Energy Distribution Task (Salmon et al, 2004)

Tools Needed

A CUD analysis requires the various tools associated with the data collection methods adopted. For example, an observation of the task under analysis would require video and/or audio recording equipment. An appropriate drawing software package is also required for the construction of the CUD, such as Microsoft Visio. Alternatively, the CUD can be constructed in Microsoft Word.

Co-ordination Demands Analysis (CDA)

Background and Application

Co-ordination demands analysis (CDA) is used to rate the co-ordination between actors involved in teamwork or collaborative activity. CDA uses the taxonomy of teamwork related behaviours presented in Table 9.3. The CDA procedure involves identifying the teamwork-based activity involved in the task or scenario under analysis and then providing ratings, on a scale of 1 (Low) to 3 (High), for each behaviour from the teamwork taxonomy for each of the teamwork task steps involved. From the individual ratings a total co-ordination figure for each teamwork task step and a total co-ordination figure for the overall task is derived.

Table 9.3   A Teamwork Taxonomy (Source: Burke, 2005)

Co-ordination Dimension	Definition
Communication	Includes sending, receiving, and acknowledging information among crew members.
Situational Awareness (SA)	Refers to identifying the source and nature of problems, maintaining an accurate perception of the aircraft's location relative to the external environment, and detecting situations that require action.
Decision Making (DM)	Includes identifying possible solutions to problems, evaluating the consequences of each alternative, selecting the best alternative, and gathering information needed prior to arriving at a decision.
Mission analysis (MA)	Includes monitoring, allocating, and co-ordinating the resources of the crew and aircraft; prioritizing tasks; setting goals and developing plans to accomplish the goals; creating contingency plans.
Leadership	Refers to directing activities of others, monitoring and assessing the performance of crew members, motivating members, and communicating mission requirements.
Adaptability	Refers to the ability to alter one's course of action as necessary, maintain constructive behaviour under pressure, and adapt to internal or external changes.
Assertiveness	Refers to the willingness to make decisions, demonstrating initiative, and maintaining one's position until convinced otherwise by facts.
Total Co-ordination	Refers to the overall need for interaction and co-ordination among crew members.

Domain of Application

The CDA method is generic and can be applied to any task that involves teamwork or collaboration.

Procedure and Advice

Step 1: Define task(s) under analysis
The first step in a CDA is to define the task or scenario that will be analysed. This is dependent upon the focus of the analysis. It is recommended that if team co-ordination in a particular type of system (e.g. command and control) is under investigation, then a set of scenarios that are representative of all aspects of team performance in the system under analysis should be used. If time and financial constraints do not allow this, then a task that is as representative as possible of team performance in the system under analysis should be used.

Step 2: Select appropriate teamwork taxonomy
Once the task(s) under analysis are defined, an appropriate teamwork taxonomy should be selected. Again, this may depend upon the purpose of the analysis. However, it is recommended that the taxonomy used covers all aspects of teamwork in the task under analysis. A generic CDA teamwork taxonomy is presented in Table 9.3.

Step 3: Data collection phase
The next step involves collecting the data that will be used to inform the CDA. Typically, observational study of the task or scenario under analysis is used as the primary data source for a CDA. It is recommended that specific data regarding the task under analysis should be collected during this process, including information regarding each task step, each team member's roles, and all communications made. It is also recommended that particular attention is given to the teamwork activity involved in the task under analysis. Further, it is recommended that video and audio recording equipment are used to record any observations or interviews conducted during this process.

Step 4: Conduct a HTA for the task under analysis
Once sufficient data regarding the task under analysis has been collected, a HTA should be conducted.

Step 5: Construct CDA rating sheet
Once a HTA for the task under analysis is completed, a CDA rating sheet should be created. The rating sheet should include a column containing each bottom level task step as identified by the HTA. The teamwork behaviours from the taxonomy should run across the top if the table. An extract of a CDA rating sheet is presented in Table 9.4.

Step 6: Taskwork/teamwork classification
Only those task steps that involve teamwork are rated for the level of co-ordination between the actors involved. The next step of the CDA procedure involves the identification of teamwork and taskwork task steps involved in the scenario under analysis. Those task steps that are conducted by individual actors involving no collaboration are classified as taskwork, whilst those task steps that are conducted collaboratively, involving more than one actor are classified as teamwork.

Step 7: SME rating phase
Appropriate SMEs should then rate the extent to which each teamwork behaviour is required during the completion of each teamwork task step. This involves presenting the task step in question and discussing the role of each of the teamwork behaviours from the taxonomy in the completion of the task step. An appropriate rating scale should be used e.g. low (1), medium (2) and high (3).

Step 8: Calculate summary statistics
Once all of the teamwork task steps have been rated according to the teamwork taxonomy, the final step is to calculate appropriate summary statistics. In its present usage, a total co-ordination value and mean co-ordination value for each teamwork task step are calculated. The mean co-ordination is simply an average of the ratings for the teamwork behaviours for the task step in question. A mean overall co-ordination value for the entire scenario is also calculated.

Example

The CDA method has recently been used as part of the Event Analysis of Systemic Teamwork (EAST, Baber and Stanton, 2004) framework for the analysis of C4i activity in the fire service, naval warfare, aviation, energy distribution (Salmon, Stanton, Walker, McMaster and Green, 2005), air traffic control and rail (Walker, Gibson, Stanton, Baber, Salmon and Green, 2004) domains. The following example is an extract of a CDA analysis of an energy distribution task. The task involved the switching out of three circuits at a high voltage electricity substation. Observational data from the substation and the remote control centre was used to derive a HTA of the switching scenario. Each bottom level task in the HTA was then defined by the analyst(s) as either taskwork or teamwork. Each teamwork task was then rated using the CDA taxonomy on a scale of 1 (low) to 3 (high). An extract of the HTA for the task is presented in Figure 9.2. An extract of the CDA is presented in Table 9.4. The overall CDA results are presented in Table 9.5.

NGC Switching operations HTA

0. Co-ordinate and carry out switching operations on circuits SGT5. SGT1A and 1B at Bark s/s (*Plan 0. Do 1 then 2 then 3, EXIT*)
1. Prepare for switching operations (*Plan 1. Do 1.1, then 1.2, then 1.3, then 1.4, then 1.5, then 1.6, then 1.7, then 1.8, then 1.9,then 1.10 EXIT*)
    1.1. Agree SSC (Plan 1.1. Do 1.1.1, then 1.1.2, then 1.1.3, then 1.1.4, then 1.1.5, EXIT)
        1.1.1. (WOK) Use phone to Contact NOC
        1.1.2. (WOK + NOC) Exchange identities
        1.1.3. (WOK + NOC) Agree SSC documentation
        1.1.4. (WOK+NOC) Agree SSC and time (Plan 1.1.4. Do 1.1.4.1, then 1.1.4.2, EXIT)
            1.1.4.1. (NOC) Agree SSC with WOK
            1.1.4.2. (NOC) Agree time with WOK
        1.1.5. (NOC) Record and enter details (Plan 1.1.5. Do 1.1.5.1, then 1.1.5.2, EXIT)
            1.1.5.1. Record details on log sheet
            1.1.5.2. Enter details into worksafe
    1.2. (NOC) Request remote isolation (Plan 1.2. Do 1.2.1, then 1.2.2, then 1.2.3, then 1.2.4,   EXIT)
        1.2.1. (NOC) Ask WOK for isolators to be opened remotely
        1.2.2. (WOK) Perform remote isolation
        1.2.3. (NOC) Check Barking s/s screen
        1.2.4. (WOK + NOC) End communications
    1.3. Gather information on outage at transformer 5 at Bark s/s
    (Plan 1.3. Do 1.3.1, then 1.3.2, then 1.3.3, then 1.3.4, EXIT)
        1.3.1. (NOC) Use phone to contact SAP at Bark
        1.3.2. (NOC + SAP) Exchange identities

Figure 9.2   Extract of HTA for NGT Switching Scenario

Table 9.4 Extract of a CDA Rating Sheet (Source: Salmon et al, 2005)

Task Step	Agent	Step No.	Task Work	Team Work	Comm	SA	DM	MA	Lead	Ad	Ass	TOT CO-ORD Mode	TOT CO-ORD Mean
1.1.1	WOK control room operator	Use phone to contact NOC	1										
1.1.2	WOK control room operator	Exchange identities		1	3	3	1	1	1	1	1	1.00	1.57
	NOC control room operator												
1.1.3	WOK control room operator	Agree SSC documentation		1	3	3	3	1	1	1	1	1.00	1.86
	NOC control room operator												
1.1.4.1	NOC control room operator	Agree SSC with WOK		1	3	3	3	1	1	1	1	1.00	1.86
1.1.4.2	NOC control room operator	Agree time with WOK		1	3	3	3	1	1	1	1	1.00	1.86
1.1.5.1	NOC control room operator	Record details onto log sheet	1										
1.1.5.2	NOC control room operator	Enter details into WorkSafe	1										
1.2.1	NOC control room operator	Ask for isolators to be opened remotely		1	3	3	1	2	2	1	1	1.00	1.86
1.2.2	WOK control room operator	Perform remote isolation	1										
1.2.3	NOC control room operator	Check Barking s/s screen	1										
1.2.4	WOK control room operator	End communications		1	3	1	1	1	1	1	1	1.00	1.29
	NOC control room operator												
1.3.1	NOC control room operator	Use phone to contact SAP at Barking	1										
1.3.2	NOC control room operator	Exchange identities		1	3	3	1	1	1	1	1	1.00	1.57
	SAP at Barking												

Table 9.5 **CDA Results** (Source: Salmon et al, 2005)

Category	Result
Total task steps	314
Total taskwork	114 (36%)
Total teamwork	200 (64%)
Mean Total Co-ordination	1.57
Modal Total Co-ordination	1.00
Minimum Co-ordination	1.00
Maximum Co-ordination	2.14

The CDA indicated that of the 314 individual task steps involved in the switching scenario, 64% were classified as teamwork related and 36% were conducted individually. A mean total co-ordination figure of 1.57 (out of 3) was calculated for the teamwork task steps involved in the switching scenario. This represents a medium level of co-ordination between the actors involved.

Advantages

1. The output of a CDA is very useful, offering an insight into the use of teamwork behaviours and also a rating of co-ordination between actors in a particular network or team.
2. Co-ordination can be compared across scenarios, different teams and also different domains.
3. CDA is particularly useful for the analysis of C4i activity.
4. The teamwork taxonomy presented by Burke (2005) covers all aspects of team performance and co-ordination. The taxonomy is also generic, allowing the method to be used in any domain without modification.
5. Providing the appropriate SMEs are available, the CDA procedure is simple to apply and requires only minimal training.
6. The taskwork/teamwork classification of the task steps involved is also useful.
7. CDA provides a breakdown of team performance in terms of task steps and the level of co-ordination required.
8. The method is generic and can be applied to teamwork scenarios in any domain.

Disadvantages

1. The CDA rating procedure is time consuming and laborious. The initial data collection phase and the creation of a HTA for the task under analysis also add further time to the analysis.
2. For the method to be used properly, the appropriate SMEs are required. It may be difficult to gain sufficient access to SMEs for the required period of time.
3. Intra-analyst and inter-analyst reliability is questionable. Different SMEs may offer different teamwork ratings for the same task (intra-analyst reliability), whilst SMEs may provide different ratings on different occasions.

Flowchart

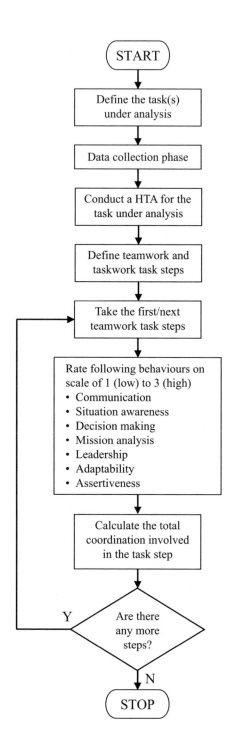

Related Methods

In conducting a CDA analysis, a number of other HF methods are used. Data regarding the task under analysis are typically collected using observational study and interviews. A HTA for the task under analysis is normally conducted, the output of which feeds into the CDA. A likert style rating scale is also normally used during the team behaviour rating procedure. Burke (2005) also suggests that a CDA should be conducted as part of an overall team task analysis procedure. The CDA method has also recently been integrated with a number of other methods (HTA, observation, comms usage diagram, social network analysis, operator sequence diagrams and propositional networks) to form the event analysis of systemic teamwork (EAST; Baber and Stanton, 2004) methodology, which has been used to analyse C4i activity in a number of domains.

Approximate Training and Application Times

The training time for the CDA method is minimal, requiring only that the SMEs used understand each of the behaviours specified in the teamwork taxonomy and also the rating procedure. The application time is high, involving observation of the task under analysis, conducting an appropriate HTA and the lengthy ratings procedure. In the CDA provided in the analysis, the ratings procedure alone took approximately four hours. This represents a low application time in itself, however, when coupled with the data collection phase and completion of a HTA, the application time is high. For the example presented, the overall analysis, including data collection, development of the HTA, identification of teamwork and taskwork task steps, and the rating procedure, took approximately two weeks to complete.

Reliability and Validity

There are no data regarding the reliability and validity of the method available in the literature. Certainly both the intra-analyst and inter-analyst reliability of the method may be questionable, and this may be dependent upon the type of rating scale used e.g. it is estimated that the reliability may be low when using a scale of 1-10, whilst it may be improved using a scale of one to three (low to high).

Tools Needed

During the data collection phase, video (e.g. camcorder) and audio (e.g. recordable mini-disc player) recording equipment are required in order to make a recording of the task or scenario under analysis. Once the data collection phase is complete, the CDA method can be conducted using pen and paper.

Decision Requirements Exercise (DRX)

Background and Applications

The team decision requirements exercise (DRX; (Klinger and Hahn, 2004) is an adaptation of the critical decision method (Klein and Armstrong, 2004) that is used to highlight critical decisions made by a team during task performance, and also to analyse the factors surrounding decisions e.g. why the decision was made, how it was made, what factors affected the decision etc. The DRX method was originally used during the training of nuclear power control room crews, as a debriefing tool (Klinger and Hahn, 2004). Typically, a decision requirements table is constructed, and a number of critical decisions are analysed within a group-interview type scenario. According to Klinger and Hahn (2004) the DRX should be used for the following purposes:

- To calibrate a team's understanding of its own objectives.
- To calibrate understanding of roles, functions and the requirements of each team member.
- To highlight any potential barriers to information flow.
- To facilitate the sharing of knowledge and expertise across team members.

Domain of Application

The DRX method was originally developed for use in nuclear power control room training procedures. However, the method is generic and can be used in any domain.

Procedure and Advice

Step 1: Define task under analysis
The first step in a DRX analysis involves clearly defining the type of task(s) under analysis. This allows the analyst to develop a clear understanding of the task(s) under analysis and also the types of decisions that are likely to be made. It is recommended that a HTA is conducted for the task(s) under analysis. A number of data collection procedures may be used for this purpose, including observational study, interviews and questionnaires.

Step 2: Select appropriate decision probes
It may be useful to select the types of factors surrounding the decisions that are to be analysed before the analysis begins. This is often dependent upon the scope and nature of the analysis. For example, Klinger and Hahn (2004) suggest that difficulty, errors, cues used, factors used in making the decision, information sources used and strategies are all common aspects of decisions that are typically analysed. The chosen factors should be given a column in the decision requirements table and a set of appropriate probes should be created. These probes are used during the DRX analysis in order to elicit the appropriate information regarding the decision under analysis. An example set of probes are presented in step 7 of this procedure.

Step 3: Describe task and brief participants
Once the task(s) are clearly defined and understood, the analyst(s) should gather appropriate information regarding the performance of the task. If a real-world task is being used, then typically observational data is collected (It is recommended that video/audio recording equipment is used to record any observations made). If a training scenario is being used, then a task description of the scenario will suffice. Once the task under analysis has been performed and/or adequately described, the team members involved should be briefed regarding the DRX method and what is required of them as participants in the study. It may be useful to take the participants through an example DRX analysis, or even perform a pilot run for a small task. Participants should be encouraged to ask questions regarding the use of the method and their role in the data collection process. Only when all participants fully understand the method can the analysis proceed to the next step.

Step 4: Construct decision requirements table
The analyst(s) should next gather all of the team members at one location. Using a whiteboard, the analyst should then construct the decision requirements table (Klinger and Hahn, 2004).

Step 5: Determine critical decisions
Next, the analyst(s) should 'walk' the team members through the task, asking for any critical decisions that they made. Each critical decision elicited should be recorded. No further discussion regarding the decisions identified should take place at this stage, and this step should only be used to identify the critical decisions made during the task.

Step 6: Select appropriate decisions
Typically, numerous decisions are made during the performance of a team-based task. The analyst(s) should use this step to determine which of the decisions gathered during step 5 are the most critical. According to Klinger and Hahn (2004) four or five decisions are normally selected for further analysis, although the number selected is dependent upon the time constraints imposed on the analysis. Each decision selected should be entered into the decision requirements table.

Step 7: Analyse selected decisions
The analyst(s) should take the first decision and begin to analyse the features of the decision using the probes selected during step 2 of the procedure. Participant responses should be recorded in the decision requirements table. A selection of typical DRX probes are presented below (Source: Klinger and Hahn, 2004).

Why was the decision difficult?
What is difficult about making this decision?
What can get in the way when you make this decision?
What might a less experienced person have trouble with when making this decision?

Common errors
What errors have you seen people make when addressing this decision?
What mistakes do less experienced people tend to make in this situation?
What could have gone wrong (or did go wrong) when making this decision?

Cues and factors
What cues did you consider when you made this decision?
What were you thinking about when you made the decision?
What information did you use to make the decision?
What made you realise that this decision had to be made?

Strategies
Is there a strategy you used when you made this decision?
What are the different strategies that can be used for this kind of decision?
How did you use various pieces of information when you made this decision?

Information sources
Where did you get the information that helped you make this decision?
Where did you look to get the information to help you here?
What about sources, such as other team members, individuals outside the team, technologies and mechanical indicators, and even tools like maps or diagrams?

Suggested changes
How could you do this better next time?

What would need to be changed with the process or the roles of team members to make this decision easier next time?

What will you pay attention to next time to help you with this decision?

Example

The following example was developed as part of the analysis of C4i activity in the fire service. Observational study of fire service training scenarios was used to collect required data. A hazardous chemical incident was described as part of a fire service-training seminar. Students on a Hazardous Materials course at the Fire Service Training College participated in the exercise, which consisted of a combination of focus group discussion with paired activity to define appropriate courses of action to deal with a specific incident. The incident involved the report of possible hazardous materials on a remote farm. Additional information was added to the incident as the session progressed e.g., reports of casualties, problems with labelling on hazardous materials etc. The exercise was designed to encourage experienced fire-fighters to consider risks arising from hazardous materials and the appropriate courses of action they would need to take, e.g., in terms of protective equipment, incident management, information seeking activity etc. In order to investigate the potential application of the DRX method in the analysis of C4i activity, a team DRX was conducted for the hazardous chemical incident, based upon the observational data obtained. An extract of the DRX is presented in Table 9.6.

Advantages

1. Specific decisions are analysed and recommendations made regarding the achievement of effective decision making in future similar scenarios.
2. The output seems to be very useful for team training purposes.
3. The analyst can control the analysis, selecting the decisions that are analysed and also the factors surrounding the decisions that are focused upon.
4. The DRX can be used to elicit specific information regarding team decision making in complex systems.
5. The incidents which the method considers have already occurred, removing the need for costly, time consuming to construct observations or event simulations.
6. Real life incidents are analysed using the DRX, ensuring a more comprehensive, realistic analysis than simulation methods.

Disadvantages

1. The reliability of such a method is questionable. Klein and Armstrong (2004) suggest that methods that analyse retrospective incidents are associated with concerns of data reliability, due to evidence of memory degradation.
2. DRX may struggle to create an exact description of an incident.
3. The DRX is a resource intensive method, typically incurring a high application time.
4. A high level of expertise and training is required in order to use the DRX method to its maximum effect (Klein and Armstrong, 2004).
5. The DRX method relies upon interviewee verbal reports in order to reconstruct incidents. How far a verbal report accurately represents the cognitive processes of the decision maker is questionable. Facts could be easily misrepresented by the participants and glorification of events can potentially occur.
6. It may be difficult to gain sole access to team members for the required period of time.

7. After the fact data collection has a number of concerns associated with it, including memory degradation, and a correlation with task performance.

Table 9.6   Extract of Decision Requirements Exercise for Hazardous Chemical Incident

Decision	What did you find difficult when making this decision?	What cues did you consider when making this decision?	Which information sources did you use when making this decision?	Were any errors made whilst making this decision?	How could you make a decision more efficiently next time?
Level of protection required when conducting search activity.	The level of protection required is dependent upon the nature of the chemical hazard within farmhouse. This was unknown at the time. There was also significant pressure from the hospital for positive ID of the substance.	Urgency of diagnosis required by hospital. Symptoms exhibited by child in hospital. Time required to get into full protection suits.	Correspondence with hospital personnel. Police Officer. Fire control.	Initial insistence upon full suit protection before identification of chemical type.	Diagnose chemical type prior to arrival, through comms with farmhouse owner. Consider urgency of chemical diagnosis as critical.
Determine type of chemical substance found and relay information to hospital	The chemical label identified substance as a liquid, but the substance was in powder form.	Chemical drum labels. Chemical form e.g. powder, liquid. Chemdata information Chemsafe data.	Chemical drum. Chemdata database. Fire control (chemsafe database).	Initial chemical diagnosis made prior to confirmation with chemdata and chemsafe databases.	Use chemdata and chemsafe resources prior to diagnosis. Contact farmhouse owner en route to farmhouse.

Flowchart

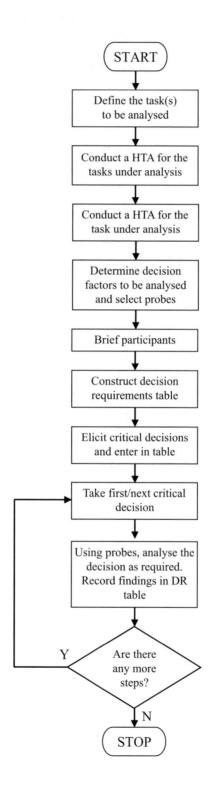

Related Methods

The DRX is an adaptation of the CDM method (Klein and Armstrong, 2004) for use in the analysis of team performance. The DRX uses a group interview or focus group type approach to analyse critical decisions made during task performance. Task analysis methods (such as HTA) may also be used in the initial process of task definition.

Training and Application Times

According to Klinger and Hahn (2004) the DRX method requires between one and two hours per scenario. However, it is apparent that significant work may be required prior to the analysis phase, including observation, task definition, task analysis and determining which aspects of the decisions are to be analysed. The training time associated with the method is estimated to take around one day. It is worthwhile pointing out, however, that the data elicited is highly dependent upon the interview skills of the analyst(s). Therefore, it is recommended that the analysts used possess considerable experience and skill in interview type methods.

Reliability and Validity

No data regarding the reliability and validity of the method are available in the literature.

Tools Needed

The team decision requirements exercise can be conducted using pen and paper. Klinger and Hahn (2004) recommend that a whiteboard is used to display the decision requirements table.

Groupware Task Analysis (GTA)

Background and Applications

Groupware Task Analysis (GTA; Welie and Van Der Veer, 2003) is a team task analysis method that is used to analyse team activity in order to inform the design and analysis team systems. GTA comprises a conceptual framework focusing upon the relevant aspects that require consideration when designing systems or processes for teams or organisation. The method involves describing the following two task models.

Task model 1
Task model 1 offers a description of the situation at the current time in the system that is being designed. This is developed in order to enhance the design team's understanding of the current work situation. For example, in the design of C4i systems, Task Model 1 would include a description of the current operational command and control system.

Task model 2
Task model 2 involves redesigning the current system or situation outlined in task model 1. This should include technological solutions to problems highlighted in task model 1 and also technological answers to requirements specified (Van Welie and Van Der Veer, 2003). Task model 2 should represent a model of the future task world when the new design is implemented.

According to (Van Welie and Van Der Veer, 2003), task models should comprise description of the following features of the system under analysis:

- *Agents*. Refers to the personnel who perform the activity within the system under analysis, including teams and individuals. Agents should be described in terms of their goals, roles (which tasks the agent is allocated), organisation (relationship between agents and roles) and characteristics (agent experience, skills etc);
- *Work*. The task or tasks under analysis should also be described, including unit and basic task specification (Card, Moran and Newell 1983). It is recommended that a HTA is used for this aspect of task model 1. Events (triggering conditions for tasks) should also be described.
- *Situation*. The situation description should include a description of the environment and any objects in the environment.

The methods used when conducting a GTA are determined by the available resources. For guidelines on which methods to employ the reader is referred to Van Welie and Van Der Veer (2003). Once the two task models are completed, the design of the new system can begin, including specification of functionality and also the way in which the system is presented to the user (Van Welie and Van Der Veer, 2003). According to the authors, the task model can be used to answer the following design questions (Van Welie and Van Der Veer, 2003).

1. What are the critical tasks?
2. How frequently are those tasks performed?
3. Are they always performed by the same user?
4. Which types of user are there?
5. Which roles do they have?
6. Which tasks belong to which roles?
7. Which tasks should be possible to undo?
8. Which tasks have effects that cannot be undone?
9. Which errors can be expected?
10. What are the error consequences for users?
11. How can prevention be effective?

Domain of Application

Generic.

Procedure and Advice

Step 1: Define system under analysis
The first step in a GTA is to define the system(s) under analysis. For example, in the design of C4i systems, existing command and control systems would be analysed, including railway, air traffic control, security and gas network command and control systems.

Step 2: Data collection phase
Before task model 1 can be constructed, specific data regarding the existing systems under analysis should be collected. Traditional methods should be used during this process, including observational analysis, interviews and questionnaires. The data collected should be as comprehensive as possible,

including information regarding the task (specific task steps, procedures, interfaces used etc.), the personnel (roles, experience, skills etc.) and the environment.

Step 3: Construct task model 1
Once sufficient data regarding the system or type of system under analysis has been collected, task model 1 should be constructed. Task model 1 should completely describe the situation as it currently stands, including the agents, work and situation categories outlined above.

Step 4: Construct task model 2
The next stage of the GTA is to construct task model 2. Task model 2 involves redesigning the current system or situation outlined in task model 1. The procedure used for constructing task model 2 is determined by the design teams, but may include focus groups, scenarios and brainstorming sessions.

Step 5: Redesign the system
Once task model 2 has been constructed, the system redesign should begin. Obviously, this procedure is dependent upon the system under analysis and the design team involved. The reader is referred to Van Welie and Van Der Veer (2003) for guidelines.

Advantages

1. GTA output provides a detailed description of the system requirements and highlights specific issues that need to be addressed in the new design.
2. Task model 2 can potentially highlight the technologies required and their availability.
3. GTA provides the design team with a detailed understanding of the current situation and problems.
4. GTA seems to be suited to the analysis of existing command and control systems.

Disadvantages

1. GTA appears to be extremely resource intensive and time consuming in its application.
2. Limited evidence of use in the literature.
3. The method provides limited guidance for its application.
4. A large team of analysts would be required in order to conduct a GTA analysis.

Flowchart

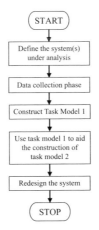

Related Methods

GTA analysis is a team task analysis method and so is related to CUD, SNA and team task analysis. The data collection phase may involve the use of a number of approaches, including observational study interviews, surveys, questionnaires and HTA.

Approximate Training and Application Times

It estimated that the training and application times for the GTA method would be very high.

Reliability and Validity

There are no data regarding the reliability and validity of the GTA method available in the literature.

Tools Needed

Once the initial data collection phase is complete, GTA can be conducted using pen and paper. The data collection phase would require video and audio recording devices and a PC.

Hierarchical Task Analysis for Teams: HTA(T)

*Professor John Annett, Department of Psychology,
University of Warwick, Coventry, UK*

Background and Applications

Traditionally, task analysts have used HTA to describe the goals of individual workers, but Annett and others have argued that HTA can provide sub-goal hierarchies at many levels within a system. The analyst can choose to focus on the human agents, machine agents or the entire system. Annett (2004) shows how an adaptation of HTA can produce an analysis of team-based activity. HTA (T). The enduring popularity of HTA can be put down to two key points. First, it is inherently flexible: the approach can be used to describe any system. Astley and Stammers (1987) point out that over the decades since its inception, HTA has been used to describe each new generation of technological system. Second, it can be used for many ends: from person specification, to training requirements, to error prediction, to team performance assessment, and to system design. Again, Astley and Stammers (1987) point out that although HTA was originally used to develop an understanding of training requirements, it has subsequently been used for a variety of applications. Despite the popularity and enduring use of hierarchical task analysis, and the fact that the analysis is governed by only a few rules, it is something of a craft-skill to apply effectively. Whilst the basic approach can be trained in a few hours, it is generally acknowledged that sensitive use of the method will take some months of practice under expert guidance (Stanton and Young, 1999).

In the large-scale design and development of a new nuclear reactor, Staples (1993) describes how HTA was used as the basis for virtually all of the ergonomics studies. The sub-goal hierarchy was produced through reviews of contemporary operating procedures, discussions with subject matter experts, and interviews with operating personnel from another reactor. Both the hierarchical diagram and the tabular format versions of HTA were produced. The resultant HTA was used to examine potential errors and their consequences, the interface design verification, identification of training procedures, development and verification of operating procedures, workload assessment and communication analysis. Staples argued that HTA is of major benefit in system design as it makes a detailed and systematic assessment of the interactions between human operators and their technical systems possible. As Annett and colleagues have pointed out on many occasions, conducting the HTA helps the analyst become familiar with the processes and procedures so that they can critically assess the crucial aspects of the work. Staples also notes that reference to the HTA for the analysis of all aspects of the system can highlight inconsistencies between training, procedures and system design. Staples draws the general conclusion that the broad application of HTA can make it a very cost-effective approach to system design.

Most books containing descriptions of HTA also contain examples of application areas that it can be, and has been, applied. This serves to demonstrate that HTA has been applied in areas far wider that the training applications for which it was originally devised. Annett (2000) has pointed out the HTA is a general problem solving approach, and performing the analysis helps the analyst understand the nature of both the problem and the domain.

Domain of Application

Generic.

Procedure and Advice

The basic heuristics for conducting a HTA are as follows (Stanton, 2005).

Step 1: Define the purpose of the analysis
Although the case has been made that HTA can be all things to all people, the level or redescription and the associated information collected might vary depending upon the purpose. Examples of different purposes for HTA would include system design, analysis of workload and manning levels, and training design. The name(s), contact details, and brief biography of the analyst(s) should also be recorded. This will enable future analysts to check with the HTA originator(s) if they plan to reuse or adapt the HTA.

Step 2: Define the boundaries of the system description
Depending upon the purpose, the system boundaries may vary. If the purpose of the analysis is to analyse co-ordination and communication in teamwork, then the entire set of tasks of a team of people would be analysed. If the purpose of the analysis is to determine allocation of system function to human and computers, then the whole system will need to be analysed.

Step 3: Try to access a variety of sources of information about the system to be analysed.
All task analysis guides stress the importance of multiple sources of information to guide, check and validate the accuracy of the HTA. Sources such as observation, subject matter experts, interviews, operating manuals, walkthroughs, and simulations can all be used as a means of checking the reliability and validity of the analysis. Careful documentation and recording of the sources of data needs to be archived, so that the analyst or others may refer back and check if they need to.

Step 4: Describe the system goals and sub-goals
As proposed in the original principles for HTA, the overall aim of the analysis is to derive a sub-goal hierarchy for the tasks under scrutiny. As goals are broken down and new operations emerge,

sub-goals for each of the operations need to be identified. As originally specified, it is not the operations that are being described, but their sub-goals. All of the lower level sub-goals are a logical expansion of the higher ones. A formal specification for the statement of each of the sub-goals can be derived, although most analyses do not go to such lengths.

Step 5: Try to keep the number of immediate sub-goals under any superordinate goal to a small number (i.e. between 3 and 10)

There is an art to HTA, which requires that the analysis does not turn into a procedural list of operations. The goal hierarchy is determined by looking for clusters of operations that belong together under the same goal. This normally involves several iterations of the analysis. Whilst it is accepted that there are bound to be exceptions, for most HTAs any superordinate goal will have between three and ten immediate subordinates. It is generally good practice to continually review the sub-goal groupings, to check if they are logical. HTA does not permit single subordinate goals.

Step 6: Link goals to sub-goals, and describe the conditions under which sub-goals are triggered

Plans are the control structures that enable the analyst to capture the conditions which trigger the sub-goals under any superordinate goal. Plans are read from the top of the hierarchy down to the sub-goals that are triggered and back up the hierarchy again as the exit conditions are met. As each of the sub-goals, and the plans that trigger them, are contained within higher goals (and higher plans) considerable complexity of tasks within systems can be analysed and described. The plans contain the context under which particular sub-goals are triggered. This context might include time, environmental conditions, completion of other sub-goals, system state, receipt of information, and so on. For each goal, the analyst has to question how each of its immediate subordinates is triggered. As well as identifying the sub-goal trigger conditions, it is also important to identify the exit condition for the plan that will enable the analyst to trace their way back up the sub-goal hierarchy. Otherwise, the analysis could be stuck in a control loop with no obvious means of exiting.

Step 7: Stop redescribing the sub-goals when you judge the analysis is fit-for-purpose

When to stop the analysis has been identified as one of the more conceptually troublesome aspects of HTA. The proposed P x C (probability versus cost) stopping rule is a rough heuristic, but analysts may have trouble quantifying the estimates of P and C. The level of description is likely to be highly dependent upon the purpose of the analysis, so it is conceivable that a stopping rule could be generated at that point in the analysis. For example, in analysing teamwork, the analysis could stop at the point where sub-goals dealt with the exchange of information (e.g. receiving, analysing and sending information from one agent to another). For practical purposes, the stopping point of the analysis is indicated by underlining the lowest level sub-goal in the hierarchical diagram, or ending the sub-goal description with a double forward slash (i.e., "//") in the hierarchical list and tabular format. This communicates to the reader that the sub-goal is not redescribed further elsewhere in the document.

Step 8: Attribute agents to goals

When the HTA is complete, using a tabular format as shown in Table 9.7, list out the goal hierarchy in the left hand column, then decompose the goals into a goal statement, associated plan, and criterion for successful task completion in the right hand column. The analyst must decide at this point what goals are related to team working and what goals rely only on 'taskwork'. Use this format to systematically attribute agent(s) to the teamwork related goals expressed (in the left hand column).

Step 9: Try to verify the analysis with subject matter experts
It is important to check the HTA with subject matter experts. This can help both with verification of the completeness of the analysis and help the experts develop a sense of ownership of the analysis.

Step 10: Be prepared to revise the analysis
HTA requires a flexible approach to achieve the final sub-goal hierarchy with plans and notes. The first pass analysis is never going to be sufficiently well developed to be acceptable, no matter what the purpose. The number of revisions will depend on the time available and the extent of the analysis, but simple analyses (such as the analysis of the goals of extracting cash from an automatic teller machine) may require at least three interactions, where as more complex analyses (such as the analysis of the emergency services responding to a hazardous chemical incident) might require at least ten iterations. It is useful to think of the analysis as a working document that only exists in the latest state of revision. Careful documentation of the analysis will mean that it can be modified and reused by other analysts as required.

Related Methods

HTA representation is the starting point for the analysis, rather than the end point. The tabular format has enabled a mechanism for extending the analysis beyond the system description provided in the sub-goal hierarchy and plans. These extensions in HTA have enabled the analyst to: investigate design decisions, analyse human-machine interaction, predict error, allocate function, design jobs, analyse teamwork and assess interface design.

Approximate Training and Application Times

According to Annett (2005), a study by Patrick, Gregov and Halliday (2000) gave students a few hours' training with not entirely satisfactory results on the analysis of a very simple task, although performance improved with further training. A survey by Ainsworth and Marshall (1998/2000) found that the more experienced practitioners produced more complete and acceptable analyses. Stanton and Young (1999) report that the training and application time for HTA is substantial. The application time associated with HTA is dependent upon the size and complexity of the task under analysis. For large, complex tasks, the application time for HTA would be high.

Reliability and Validity

There are no data regarding the reliability and validity of HTA used for team task analysis purposes available in the literature. That said, however, subject matter experts have commented favourably on the ecological validity of the method and representation.

Tools Needed

HTA can be carried out using only pencil and paper although there are software tools, such as those developed by the HFI-DTC and others, which can make the processes of developing, editing and reusing the goal and plan structure less laborious.

Example

The HTA(T) was based upon the analysis of the emergency services responses to a hazardous chemical incident. In the scenario analysed, some youths had broken into a farm and disturbed some chemicals in sacking. One of the youths had been taken to the hospital with respiratory problems, whilst the others were still at the scene. The police were sent to investigate the break-in at the farm. They called in the fire service to identify the chemical and clean up the spillage.

The overall analysis shows four main sub-goals: receive notification of an incident, gather information about the incident, deal with the chemical incident, and resolve incident. Only part of the analysis is presented, to illustrate HTA(T). As multiple agencies and people are involved in the team task, they have been identified under each of the sub-goals. Police control, fire control, the hospital and the police officer have all been assigned to different sub-goals.

The overview of the hierarchical task analysis for teams is presented in Figure 9.3. Only some of these goals are further redescribed in Table 9.7, as they are the ones involving teamwork. Any goals that do not involve teamwork do not have to be entered into the table.

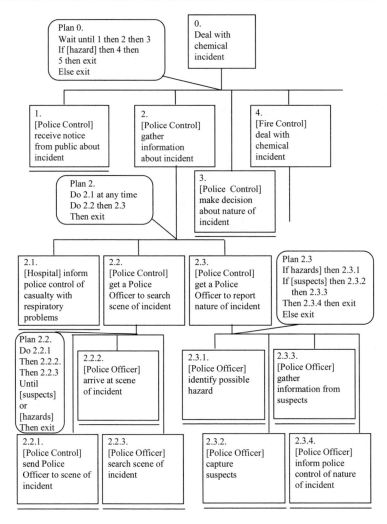

Figure 9.3   HTA(T) of Goals Associated with a Chemical Incident Investigation

Table 9.7   Tabular Form of Selected Teamwork Operations

0. Deal with chemical incident Plan: Wait until 1 then do 2 - If [hazard] then 3 then 4 then exit - else exit	Goal: Deal safely with the chemical incident. Teamwork: This is a multi-agency task involving the police and fire service as well as the hospital with a possible casualty. Plan: Determine nature of incident and then call in appropriate agencies, avoid any further casualties. Criterion measure: Chemical incident cleared up with no further injuries.
2. [Police Control] gather information about incident Plan 2: Do 2.1 at any time if appropriate Do 2.2 then 2.3 Then exit	Goal: Gather information about the nature of the incident. Teamwork: To decide who to send to the site and gather information and liaise with other agencies as necessary. Plan: Send requests to other agencies for information and send a patrol out to the site to search the scene for physical evidence and suspects. Criterion measure: Appropriate response with minimal delay. A hospital may call in about a casualty at any time, but it has to be linked with this incident. The police officer has to find his/her way to the scene of the incident.
2.2. [Police Control] get a Police Officer to search scene of incident Plan 2.2: Do 2.1.1 then 2.2.2 then 2.2.3 Until [suspects] or [hazards] then exit	Goal: To get the officer to search the scene of the incident for evidence of the hazard or suspects. Teamwork: Police control has to direct the officer to the hazard and provide details about the incident. If police control receives information about the incident from other agencies, then this information needs to be passed on to the officer at the scene. Plan: Once at the scene of the incident the officer needs to search for hazards and suspects. Criterion measure: The police officer may have to find a remote location based on sketchy information. The police officer has to search for signs of a break-in and hazards.
2.3. [Police Control] get Police Officer to report nature of incident Plan 2.3: If [suspects] then 2.3.1 If[suspects] then 2.3.2. then 2.3.3 Then 2.3.4. then exit Else exit	Goals: Detailed information on the nature of the incident and the degree of potential hazard present and report this information to police control. Teamwork: Incident details need to be passed on so that the clean-up operation can begin. Plan: If the officer at the scene identifies a hazard then he has to report it to police control, if he identifies a suspect then he has to interview the suspect and report the results to police control. Criterion measure: Any potential hazard needs to be identified, including the chemical ID number Any suspects on the scene need to be identified Suspects need to be questioned about the incident.

Flowchart

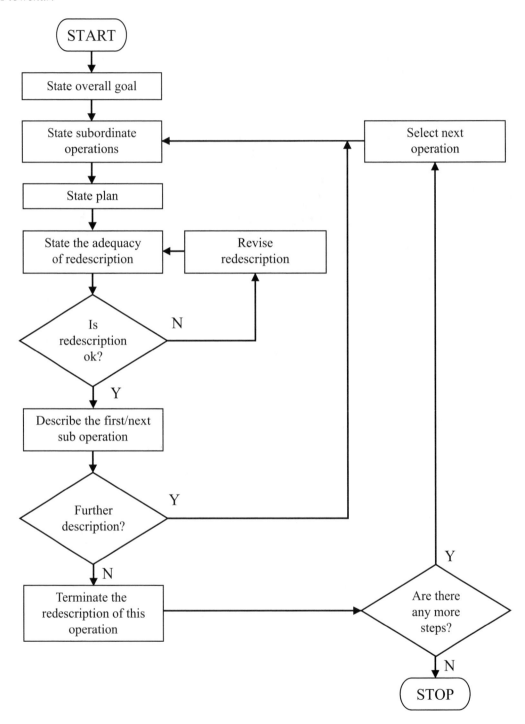

Team Cognitive Task Analysis (TCTA)

Background and Application

Team cognitive task analysis (TCTA; Klein, 2000) is used to describe the cognitive skills and processes that a team or group of actors employ during task performance. TCTA uses semi-structured interviews and pre-defined probes to elicit data regarding the cognitive aspects of team performance and decision making. The TCTA approach is based upon the CDM method that is used to analyse the cognitive aspects of individual task performance. According to Klein (2000), the TCTA method addresses the following team cognitive processes:

1. Control of attention.
2. Shared situation awareness.
3. Shared mental models.
4. Application of strategies/heuristics to make decisions, solve problems and plan.
5. Metacognition.

According to Klein (2000), a TCTA allows the analyst to capture each of the processes outlined above, and also to represent the findings to others. TCTA outputs are used to enhance team performance through informing the development and application of team training procedures, the design of teams and also the design and development of team procedures and processes.

Domain of Application

Generic.

Procedure and Advice (Adapted from Klein, 2000)

Step 1: Specify desired outcome
According to Klein (2000) it is important to specify the desired outcome of the analysis before any data collection is undertaken. The desired outcome is dependent upon the purpose and scope of the analysis effort in question. According to Klein (2000) typical desired outcomes of TCTA include reducing errors, cutting costs, speeding up reaction times, increasing readiness and reducing team personnel. Other desired outcomes may be functional allocation, task allocation, improved overall performance or to test the effects of a novel design or procedure.

Step 2: Define task(s) under analysis
Once the desired outcome is specified, the task(s) under analysis should be clearly defined and described. This is normally dependent upon the focus of the analysis. For example, it may be that an analysis of team performance in specific emergency scenarios is required. Once the nature of the task(s) is defined, it is recommended that a HTA be conducted. This allows the analyst(s) to gain a deeper understanding of the task under analysis.

Step 3: Observational study of the task under analysis
Observational study and semi-structured interviews are typically used as the primary data collection tools in a TCTA. The task under analysis should be observed and recorded. It is recommended that video and audio recording equipment are used to record the task, and that the analyst(s) involved take relevant notes during the observation. Klein (2000) suggests that observers should record

any incident related to the five team cognitive processes presented above (control of attention, shared situation awareness, shared mental models, application of strategies/heuristics to make decisions, solve problems and plan, and metacognition). The time of each incident and personnel involved should also be recorded. An observational transcript of the task under analysis should then be created, including a timeline and a description of the activity involved, and any additional notes that may be pertinent.

Step 4: Perform CDM interviews

The TCTA method involves the use of CDM style interviews with the different team members involved. It is recommended that interviews with each team member be conducted. Interviews are used to gather more information regarding the decision-making incidents collected during the observation phase. Using a CDM (Klein and Armstrong, 2004) approach, the interviewee should be probed regarding the critical decisions recorded during the observation. The analyst should ask the participant to describe the incident in detail, referring to the five cognitive processes outline above. CDM probes should also be used to analyse the appropriate incidents. A set of generic CDM probes are presented in Table 9.8. It may be useful to create a set of specific team CTA probes prior to the analysis, although this is not always necessary.

Table 9.8   CDM Probes (Source: O'Hare et al, 2000)

Goal specification	What were your specific goals at the various decision points?
Cue identification	What features were you looking for when you formulated your decision? How did you know that you needed to make the decision? How did you know when to make the decision?
Expectancy	Were you expecting to make this sort of decision during the course of the event? Describe how this affected your decision-making process.
Conceptual	Are there any situations in which your decision would have turned out differently? Describe the nature of these situations and the characteristics that would have changed the outcome of your decision.
Influence of uncertainty	At any stage, were you uncertain about either the reliability of the relevance of the information that you had available? At any stage, were you uncertain about the appropriateness of the decision?
Information integration	What was the most important piece of information that you used to formulate the decision?
Situation awareness	What information did you have available to you at the time of the decision?
Situation assessment	Did you use all of the information available to you when formulating the decision? Was there any additional information that you might have used to assist in the formulation of the decision?
Options	Were there any other alternatives available to you other than the decision you made?
Decision blocking - stress	Was there any stage during the decision-making process in which you found it difficult to process and integrate the information available? Describe precisely the nature of the situation.
Basis of choice	Do you think that you could develop a rule, based on your experience, which could assist another person to make the same decision successfully? Why/Why not?
Analogy/ generalisation	Were you at any time, reminded of previous experiences in which a similar decision was made? Were you at any time, reminded of previous experiences in which a different decision was made?

Step 5: Record decision requirements

The key decision requirements involved in each incident should be determined and recorded. In a study focusing on Marine Corps command posts (Klein et al, 1996) reported forty decision requirements that included critical decisions, reasons for difficulty, common errors, and cues/

strategies for effective decision making. Klinger and Hahn (2004) describe an approach to the analysis of team decision requirements. The categories proposed include why the decision was difficult, common errors made when making the decision, environmental cues used when making the decision, factors known prior to the decision, strategies and information sources used when addressing the decision and recommendations for better decision making.

Step 6: Identify decision-making barriers
The next step involves identifying any barriers to effective decision making that were evident during the incident under analysis. Barriers to decision making may include the use of inappropriate technology, poor communication, mismanagement of information etc. Each barrier identified should be recorded.

Step 7: Create decision requirements table
A decision requirements table should be created, detailing each critical decision, its associated decision requirements, and strategies for effective decision making in similar scenarios. An extract of a decision requirements table is presented in the example section.

Advantages

1. The TCTA can be used to elicit specific information regarding team decision making in complex systems.
2. The output can be used to inform teams of effective decision-making strategies.
3. Decision-making barriers identified can be removed from the system of process under analysis, facilitating improved team performance.
4. The incidents that the method analyses have already occurred, removing the need for costly, time consuming to construct event simulations.
5. Once familiar with the method, TCTA is easy to apply.
6. CDM has been used extensively in a number of domains and has the potential to be used anywhere.
7. Real life incidents are analysed using the TCTA, ensuring a more comprehensive, realistic analysis than simulation methods.
8. The cognitive probes used in the CDM have been used for a number of years and are efficient at capturing the decision-making process (Klein and Armstrong, in press).

Disadvantages

1. The reliability of such a method is questionable. Klein and Armstrong (2004) suggest that methods that analyse retrospective incidents are associated with concerns of data reliability, due to evidence of memory degradation.
2. The quality of the data collected using such methods is entirely dependent upon the skill of the interviewer and also the participant(s) involved.
3. TCTA is a resource intensive method, including observation and interviews, both of which require significant effort.
4. A high level of expertise and training is required in order to use TCTA to its maximum effect (Klein and Armstrong, 2004).
5. TCTA relies upon interviewee verbal reports in order to reconstruct incidents. The accuracy of verbal reports is questionable, and there are various problems associated with such data, including misrepresentation and glorification of facts.

6. Collecting subjective data post-task performance also has a number of associated problems, such as memory degradation and a correlation with performance.

Example

A study of marine corps command posts was conducted by Klein et al (1996) as part of an exercise to improve the decision-making process in command posts. Three data collection phases were used during the exercise. Firstly, four regimental exercises were observed and any decision-making related incidents were recorded. As a result, over 200 critical decision-making incidents were recorded. Secondly, interviews with command post personnel were conducted in order to gather more specific information regarding the incidents recorded during the observation. Thirdly, a simulated decision-making scenario was used to test participant responses. Klein et al (1996) present 40 decision requirements, including details regarding the decision, reasons for difficulty in making the decision, errors and cues and strategies used for effective decision making. The decision requirements were categorised into the following groups: Building and maintaining situational awareness, managing information and deciding on a plan. Furthermore, a list of thirty 'barriers' to effective decision making were also presented. A summary of the barriers identified is presented in Table 9.9.

Table 9.9　　Summary of Decision-making Barriers (adapted from Klein, 2000)

Decision requirements category	Barriers
Building and maintaining SA	Information presented on separate map-boards. Map-boards separated by location, furniture and personnel. System of overlays archaic and cumbersome. Over-reliance upon memory whilst switching between maps. Erroneous communication.
Managing information	Sending irrelevant messages. Inexperienced personnel used to route information. Commander's critical information requirements (CCIR) concept misapplied.
Deciding on a plan	Communication systems unreliable. Too many personnel to co-ordinate information with.

From the simulated decision-making exercise, it was found that the experienced personnel (colonels and lieutenant colonels) required only five to ten minutes to understand a situation. However, majors took over 45 minutes to study and understand the same situation (Klein et al 1996). In conclusion, Klein et al (1996) reported that there were too many personnel in the command post, which made it more difficult to complete the job in hand. Klein et al (1996) suggested that reduced staffing at the command posts would contribute to speed and quality improvements in the decisions made.

Related Methods

TCTA is based upon observational study of the task under analysis and also semi-structured interview data derived from interviews with the actors involved. The semi-structured interview approach adopted in a TCTA is based upon the CDM method (Klein and Armstrong, 2004) that is used for individual CTA purposes. It is also recommended that an initial HTA of the task(s) under analysis be conducted.

Flowchart

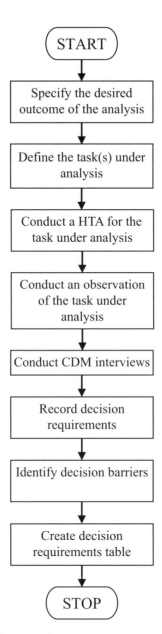

Approximate Training and Application Times

For analysts without experience in the conduct of interviews, the training time associated with the TCTA would be high. For those analysts already skilled in interview techniques, the associated training time would be minimal, requiring only that they become familiar with the CDM probes being used. The typical application time for a CDM type interview is between one and two hours. Since the TCTA requires that CDM interviews are conducted with all of the team members involved, it is estimated that the total application time for TCTA would be high.

Reliability and Validity

There are no data available regarding the reliability and validity of the TCTA approach outlined by Klein (2000). It is apparent that the reliability of such an approach is questionable. Different analysts might elicit very different data for the same scenario. Klein (2003) also suggests that there are concerns associated with the reliability of the CDM due to evidence of memory degradation.

Tools Needed

The observational study and interview components of the TCTA require video (camcorders) and audio (mini-disc recorder) recording equipment in order to record the data collected. It is recommended that Microsoft Excel (or a similar package) is used to analyse and present the data obtained.

Social Network Analysis (SNA)

Background and Applications

Social Network Analysis (SNA) is used to analyse and represent the relationships between groups of agents or teams. A social network is defined as a 'set or team of agents that possess relationships with one another' (Driskell and Mullen, 2004). SNA can be used to demonstrate the type, importance and the number of relationships within a specified group. The output typically provides a graphical depiction and a mathematical analysis of the relationships exhibited within the group under analysis. Depending upon the focus of the analysis, a number of facets associated with the network can be analysed, such as centrality, closeness and betweenness, all of which provide an indication of agent importance within the network in terms of communications. A network density figure can also be derived, which gives an indication of how well the network of agents is distributed. In the analysis of C4i environments Salmon et al (2004), Walker et al (2004) and Baber et al (2004) analysed frequency and direction of communications between agents, agent centrality, sociometric status, network density, and network type in order to determine the importance of each agent within the network and also to classify the type of network involved.

Domain of Application

Generic.

Procedure and Advice

Step 1: Define network or group
The first step in a SNA involves defining the network of agents or group of networks that are to be analysed. For example, in analysing C4i networks, the authors specified a number of different C4i agent networks, including the emergency services (fire and police), the military, civil energy distribution, air traffic control, railway signalling and naval warfare networks.

Step 2: Define scenarios
Typically, networks are analysed over a number of different scenarios. Once the type of network under analysis has been defined, the scenario(s) within which they will be analysed should be

defined. For a thorough analysis of the networks involved, it is recommended that a number of different scenarios be analysed. For example, in the analysis of naval warfare C4i activity (Stanton, Stewart, Harris, Houghton, Baber, McMaster, Salmon, Hoyle, Walker, Young, Linsell, Dymott and Green, in press), the following scenarios were defined and analysed:

1. Air threat scenario.
2. Surface threat scenario.
3. Subsurface threat scenario.

Step 3: Data collection
Once the network and scenario(s) under analysis are defined clearly, the data collection phase can begin. The data collection phase typically involves conducting an observational study of the scenario(s) under analysis. It is recommended that specific data regarding the relationship (e.g. communications) between the agents involved in the scenario is collected. Typically the frequency, direction and content of any communications between agents in the network are recorded. Additional data collection techniques may also be employed in order to gather supplementary data, such as interviews and questionnaires.

Step 4: Construct agent association matrix
Once sufficient data regarding the scenario under analysis is collected, the data analysis component of the SNA can begin. The first step in this process involves the construction of an agent association matrix. The matrix represents the frequency of associations between each agent within the network. An example matrix of association is presented in Table 9.11.

Step 5: Construct social network diagram
Once the matrix of association is completed, the social network diagram should be constructed. The social network depicts each agent in the network and the communications that occurred between them during the scenario under analysis. Within the social network diagram, communications between agents are represented by directional arrows linking the agents involved, and the frequency of communications is presented in numeric form.

Step 6: Calculate agent centrality
Agent centrality is calculated in order to determine the central or key agent(s) within the network. There are a number of different centrality calculations that can be made. For example, agent centrality can be calculated using Bavelas-Leavitt's index. The mean centrality + standard deviation can then be used to define key agents within the network. Those agents who possess a centrality figure that exceeds the mean + standard deviation figure are defined as key agents for the scenario under analysis.

Step 7: Calculate sociometric status
The sociometric status of each agent refers to the number of communications received and emitted, relative to the number of nodes in the network. The mean sociometric status + standard deviation can also be used to define key agents within the network. Those agents who possess a sociometric status figure that exceeds the mean + standard deviation figure can be defined as key agents for the scenario under analysis.

Step 8: Calculate network density
Network density is equal to the total number of links between the agents in the network divided by the total number of possible links. Low network density figures are indicative of a well distributed network of agents. High density figures are indicative of a network that is not well distributed.

Advantages

1. SNA can be used to determine the importance of different agents within a team or group of agents.
2. The SNA offers a comprehensive analysis of the network in question. The key agents within the network are identified, as are the frequency and direction of communications within the network. Further classifications include network type and network density. There are also additional analyses that can be calculated, such as betweenness, closeness and distance calculations.
3. Networks can be classified according to their structure. This is particularly useful when analysing networks across different domains.
4. SNA is suited to the analysis of C4i scenarios.
5. The method has been used extensively in the past for the analysis of various social networks.
6. The method is simple to learn and easy to use.
7. The Agna SNA software package reduces application time considerably.
8. SNA is a generic method that could potentially be applied in any domain involving team-based or collaborative activity.

Disadvantages

1. For large, complex networks, it may be difficult to conduct a SNA. Application time is a function of network size, and large networks may incur lengthy application times.
2. The data collection phase involved in a typical SNA is resource intensive.
3. Some knowledge of mathematical methods is required.
4. It is difficult to collect comprehensive data for a SNA. For example, a dispersed network of ten agents would require at least 10 observers in order to accurately and comprehensively capture the communications made between all agents.
5. Without the provision of the Agna SNA software package, the method may be time consuming to apply.

Example

The following example is taken from a SNA of a civil energy distribution scenario (Salmon et al, 2004). The scenario involved the return to service of a high voltage circuit at a specific substation and Network Operations Centre (NOC). The agents involved in the scenario are presented in Table 9.10.

Table 9.10   Agents Involved in the Return to Service Scenario

Role of agent A	NOC control room operator
Role of agent B	SAP/AP at Tottenham substation
Role of agent C	SAP/AP at Waltham Cross substation
Role of agent D	SAP/AP at Brimsdown substation
Role of agent E	Overhead line party contact
Role of agent F	WOK control room operator

From the list of agents identified for the scenario, a matrix of association can be constructed. This matrix shows whether or not an agent within the system can be associated with any other agent, specifically through frequency of communications. The association matrix for the switching scenario is presented in Table 9.11.

Table 9.11   Agent Association Matrix

	A	B	C	D	E	F
A	0	2	2	2	1	4
B	8	0	0	0	0	1
C	4	0	0	0	0	0
D	8	0	0	0	0	0
E	1	0	0	0	0	0
F	0	1	0	0	0	0

Finally, a social network diagram is created. The social network diagram illustrates the proposed association between agents involved in the scenario. The numbers associated with the links between the agents in the system indicate the strength of association. The strength of association is defined by the number of occasions on which agents exchanged information. The direction of association is represented by directional arrows. The social network diagram is presented in Figure 9.4.

There are a number of ways to analyse social networks. In this case, agent centrality, sociometric status and network density were calculated. Agent centrality was calculated using Bavelas-Leavitt's index. Table 9.12 shows the centrality for the agents in this incident. The mean centrality was calculated as 3.13. A notion of 'key' agents can be defined using the mean + 1 standard deviation (i.e., 3.13 + 0.74 = 3.87). Using this rule, the B-L centrality calculation indicates that the NOC operator and the SAP/AP at Tottenham substation are the key agents in the network. Table 9.13 shows the sociometric status for each agent involved in the scenario. From the calculation, a mean status of 2.26 (±3.82) was found. The value of mean + one standard deviation, i.e. 2.26 + 3.82 = 6.08, is used to define 'key' agents in this network. Again, the sociometric status analysis indicates that the NOC operator is the key agent within the network. An overall measure of network density was also derived by dividing the links actually present in the scenario, by all of the available links. For the Tottenham scenario, the overall network density is calculated as 0.2 (6 links present divided by 30 possible links). This figure is suggestive of a well distributed, (and therefore less dense) network of agents.

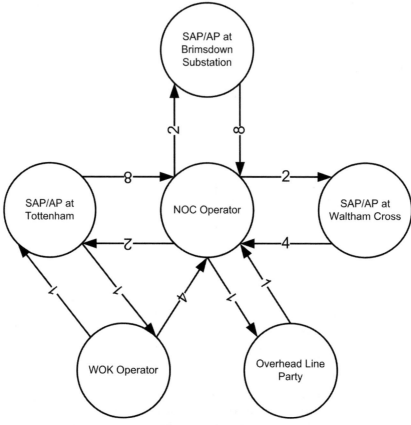

Figure 9.4   Return to Service Social Network Diagram

Table 9.12   Agent Centrality (B-L Centrality)

Agent	B-L Centrality
NOC operator	4.72
SAP/AP at Tottenham	3.25
SAP/AP at Waltham Cross	2.73
SAP/AP at Brimsdown	2.73
Overhead line party	2.73
WOK operator	2.6

Table 9.13   Agent Sociometric Status

Agent	Sociometric status
NOC operator	6.4
SAP/AP at Tottenham	2.4
SAP/AP at Waltham Cross	1.2
SAP/AP at Brimsdown	2.0
Overhead line party	0.4
WOK operator	1.2

Flowchart

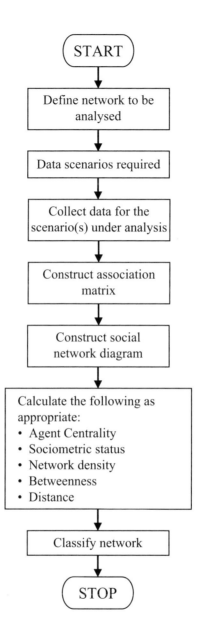

Related Methods

SNA is based upon observational data of the scenario under analysis. Additional HF data collection methods, such as interviews and questionnaires might also be used to gather supplementary data.

Approximate Training and Application Times

The training time associated with the SNA method is typically low. Although some knowledge of mathematical analysis is required, the basic SNA procedure is a simple one. The associated application time is also minimal, and can be reduced considerably with the provision of the AGNA

SNA software support package, which can be used for the data analysis part of an SNA. The application time is of course dependent upon the size and complexity of the network under analysis, and small simple networks may only incur a limited application times. However, larger more complex networks would incur a considerable application time. In a recent study of C4i activity in the energy distribution domain (Salmon et al, 2004) the SNA conducted typically took around one to three hours.

Reliability and Validity

No data regarding the reliability and validity of the SNA method are available.

Tools Needed

Once the initial data collection phase is completed, a SNA can be conducted using pen and paper. The tools required during the data collection phase for a SNA would be dependent upon the type of data collection techniques used. Observational analysis, interviews and questionnaires would normally require visual and audio recording equipment (video cameras, audio recorder, PC, etc.). For the data analysis component, various forms of software exist on the internet.

Questionnaires for Distributed Assessment of Team Mutual Awareness

Background and Applications

Macmillan, Paley, Entin and Entin (2004) describe a set of self-rating questionnaires designed to assess the team member mutual awareness. Based upon a model of team mutual awareness, the methodology proposed by MacMillan et al (2004) comprises three questionnaires: the task mutual awareness questionnaire, workload awareness questionnaire and teamwork awareness questionnaire. The task mutual awareness questionnaire involves participants recalling salient events that occurred during the task under analysis and then describing the tasks that they were performing during these events and also the tasks that they think the other team members were performing during these events. The team workload awareness questionnaire is a subjective MWL assessment method based upon the NASA TLX (Hart and Staveland, 1988) and is used to elicit subjective ratings of team member MWL on the following dimensions: mental demand, temporal demand, performance effort and frustration. Team members also provide an overall rating of other team member MWL and also a rating of each TLX dimension for the team as a whole. The teamwork awareness questionnaire is used to rate the team on four components of teamwork processes. Team members provide subjective ratings of the team's performance on the following team behaviours: communication, back-up, co-ordination and information management, and leadership/team orientation. Each of the questionnaires is administered post-trial in order to gain a measure of 'team mutual awareness'.

Procedure and Advice

Step 1: Define task(s) to be analysed
The first step is to clearly define the task or set of tasks that are to be analysed. This allows the analyst(s) to gain a clear understanding of the task content, and also allows for the modification of the behavioural rating scale, whereby any behaviours missing from the scale that may be evident during the task are added. It is recommended that a HTA is conducted for the task(s) under analysis. This allows the analysts involved to gain a thorough understanding of the task(s) under analysis.

Step 2: Select team(s) to be observed
Once the task(s) under analysis are clearly defined and described, and the analyst(s) have gained a full understanding of the task(s) under analysis, the participants that are to be observed can be selected. This may be dependent upon the purpose of the analysis. Typically, the team(s) under analysis are defined by the nature of the task(s) under analysis.

Step 3: Brief participants
In most cases, it is appropriate to brief the participants involved regarding the purpose of the study and also the techniques used during the procedure. The participants involved should be instructed in the completion of each of the three questionnaires. It may be useful to conduct a walk-through of an example analysis using the three questionnaires. This procedure should continue until all of the team members fully understood how the techniques work and also what is expected of them as participants in the trial.

Step 4: Begin task performance
The questionnaires are typically administered post-trial. The team should be instructed to perform the task under analysis as normal.

Step 5: Completion of task mutual awareness questionnaire
Once task performance is completed, the data collection phase can begin. The task mutual awareness questionnaire involves the participant recalling salient events that occurred during the task performance. Once an appropriate event is recalled, participants are required to describe the tasks that they were performing during the recalled event, and those tasks that they thought the other team members were performing. An appropriate SME is then used to classify the responses into task categories.

Step 6: Completion of team workload awareness questionnaire
The team workload awareness questionnaire involves participants rating their own workload across the five NASA-TLX workload dimensions: mental demand, temporal demand, performance, effort and frustration. The participant should then rate the other team member's workload and also the overall team's workload across the five dimensions described above.

Step 7: Completion of teamwork awareness questionnaire
In completing the teamwork awareness questionnaire, team members subjectively rate team performance on four teamwork behaviours: communication, co-ordination and information management, and leadership/team orientation.

Step 8: Calculate questionnaire scores
Once all of the questionnaires are completed by all of the team members, the data analysis phase can begin. Each questionnaire has its own unique scoring procedure. In scoring the mutual awareness questionnaires, the task category reported by each team member is compared to the task category that they were performing as reported by the other team members. The number of category matches for each individual are then summed, and a percentage agreement (congruence score) is computed for each item. In scoring the mutual awareness workload questionnaire, a convergence measure that reflects the difference between each team member's self-reported workload and the estimate of his workload provided by the other team members is calculated. Scoring of the teamwork awareness questionnaire involves calculating a mean score of each rating across the team. According to MacMillan et al (2004), this score reflects how well the team are performing. Agreement scores within the team should also be calculated.

Flowchart

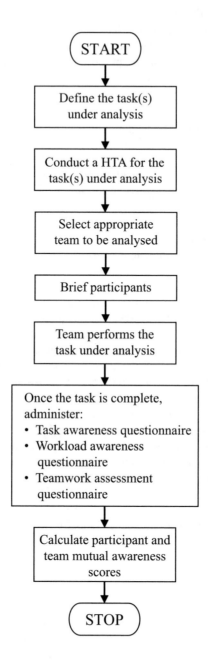

Advantages

1. The questionnaire techniques used are quick, low cost and easy to apply.
2. Minimal training is required in order to use the technique effectively.
3. A number of measures are provided, including team and individual workload.

Disadvantages

1. Each technique uses subjective ratings provided by participants once the task is complete. There are a number of problems associated with this form of data collection. Participants are not efficient at recalling mental events and have a tendency to forget certain aspects (such as low workload periods of the task). There is also a tendency for participants to correlate workload measures with task performance.
2. There is limited evidence of the technique usage in the literature.
3. There is limited validation evidence associated with the technique.

Related Methods

The team mutual awareness methodology uses three subjective self-rating questionnaires. The team workload awareness questionnaire is based upon the NASA-TLX workload assessment method.

Training and Application Times

It is estimated that the training times for the three questionnaires would be minimal. The application time for each questionnaire is also estimated to be low. MacMillan et al (2004) report that several minutes of introductory training is required for each questionnaire, and that each questionnaire takes around five minutes to complete, although this is dependent upon the size of the teams under analysis.

Reliability and Validity

MacMillan et al (2004) report that the validity of the measures is supported by their correlation to team performance and that the measures possess face validity due to their focus upon those observable aspects of team performance that the team members define as important.

Tools Needed

The questionnaires can be applied using pen and paper. MacMillan et al (2004) have also developed software versions of the three questionnaires.

Team Task Analysis (TTA)

Background and Applications

Team Task Analysis (TTA) is used to describe and analyse tasks performed by teams within complex, dynamic systems, such as infantry operations and C4i activity within the military domain. The TTA method is used to describe the tasks performed and also identify the associated knowledge, skills and abilities required for effective task performance. According to Baker, Salas and Bowers (1998) TTA refers to the analysis of a teams tasks and also the assessment of a teams teamwork requirements (knowledge, skills and abilities) and TTA forms the foundation for all team resource management functions. TTA is typically used to inform the design and development of team training interventions, such as Crew Resource Management (CRM) training, the design of teams and their associated processes, and also for team performance evaluation. TTA defines the following aspects of team-based activity:

- *Teamwork.* Refers to those tasks related to the team's goals that involve interaction or collaboration between the actors within the team or network; and
- *Taskwork.* Refers to those tasks that are performed individually by the actors within the team.

According to Burke (2005), the TTA procedure has not yet been widely adopted by organisations, with the exception of the US military and aviation communities. Although a set procedure for TTA does not exist, Burke (2003) attempted to integrate the existing TTA literature into a set of guidelines for conducting a TTA.

Domain of Application

Generic.

Procedure and Advice (Adapted from Burke 2005)

Step 1: Conduct requirements analysis
Firstly, a requirements analysis should be conducted. This involves clearly defining the task scenario to be analysed, including describing all duties involved and also conditions under which the task is to be performed. Burke (2005) also suggests that when conducting the requirements analysis, the methods of data collection to be used during the TTA should be determined. Typical TTA data collection methods include observational study, interviews, questionnaires, and surveys. The requirements analysis also involves identifying the participants that will be involved in the data collection process, including occupation and number.

Step 2: Task identification
Next, the tasks involved in the scenario under analysis should be defined and described clearly. Burke (2005) recommends that interviews with SMEs, observation and source documents should be used to identify the full set of tasks. Once each individual task step is identified, a task statement should be written (for component task), including the following information:

1. Task name.
2. Task goals.
3. What the individual has to do to perform the task.
4. How the individual performs the task.
5. Which devices, controls, interfaces are involved in the task.
6. Why the task is required.

Step 3: Identify teamwork taxonomy
Once all of the tasks involved in the scenario under analysis have been identified and described fully, a teamwork taxonomy should be selected for use in the analysis (Burke, 2005). According to Burke (2005) several teamwork taxonomies exist in the literature. A generic teamwork taxonomy is presented in Table 9.14.

Step 4: Conduct a co-ordination analysis
Once an appropriate teamwork taxonomy is selected, a co-ordination demands analysis should be conducted. The TTA involves classifying the tasks under analysis into teamwork and taskwork

activity and then rating each teamwork task step for the level of co-ordination between team members for each behaviour identified in the teamwork taxonomy.

Table 9.14 Teamwork Taxonomy (Source: Burke, 2005)

Co-ordination Dimension	Definition
Communication	Includes sending, receiving, and acknowledging information among crew members.
Situational Awareness (SA)	Refers to identifying the source and nature of problems, maintaining an accurate perception of the aircraft's location relative to the external environment, and detecting situations that require action.
Decision Making (DM)	Includes identifying possible solutions to problems, evaluating the consequences of each alternative, selecting the best alternative, and gathering information needed prior to arriving at a decision.
Mission analysis (MA)	Includes monitoring, allocating, and co-ordinating the resources of the crew and aircraft; prioritizing tasks; setting goals and developing plans to accomplish the goals; creating contingency plans.
Leadership	Refers to directing activities of others, monitoring and assessing the performance of crew members, motivating members, and communicating mission requirements.
Adaptability	Refers to the ability to alter one's course of action as necessary, maintain constructive behaviour under pressure, and adapt to internal or external changes.
Assertiveness	Refers to the willingness to make decisions, demonstrating initiative, and maintaining one's position until convinced otherwise by facts.
Total Co-ordination	Refers to the overall need for interaction and co-ordination among crew members.

Step 5: Determine relevant taskwork and teamwork tasks
The next step in the TTA procedure involves determining the relevance of each of the component tasks involved in the scenario under analysis, including both teamwork and taskwork tasks. Burke (2005) recommends that a likert scale questionnaire is used for this step and that the following task factors should be rated:

1. Importance to train;
2. Task frequency;
3. Task difficulty;
4. Difficulty of learning; and
5. Importance to job

It is recommended that the task indices used should be developed based upon the overall aims and objectives of the TTA.

Step 6: Translation of tasks into KSAOs
Next, the knowledge, skills, abilities and attitudes (KSAOs) for each of the relevant task steps should be determined. Normally, interviews or questionnaires are used to elicit the required information from an appropriate set of SMEs.

Step 7: Link KSAOs to team tasks
The final step of a TTA is to link the KSAOs identified in step 6 to the individual tasks. According to Burke (2003) this is most often achieved through the use of surveys completed by SMEs.

Advantages

1. TTA goes further than individual task analysis methods by specifying the knowledge, skills and abilities required to complete each task step.
2. The output from TTA can be used in the development of team training procedures such as crew resource management training programs, and also in the design of teams and their associated procedures.
3. The TTA output states which of the component tasks involved are team based and which tasks are performed individually.

Disadvantages

1. TTA is a time consuming method to apply.
2. Appropriate SMEs and domain experts are required throughout the procedure. Access to sufficient SMEs is often difficult to obtain.
3. There is no rigid procedure for the TTA method. As a result, the reliability of the method may be questionable.
4. Great skill is required on behalf of the analyst in order to elicit the required information throughout the TTA procedure.

Flowchart

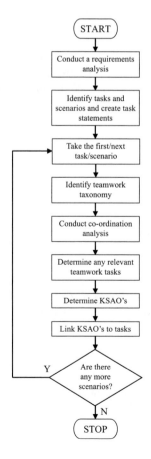

Related Methods

There are a number of different approaches to team task analysis, such as TTRAM, CUD and SNA. TTA also utilises a number of traditional HF data collection techniques, such as observational study, interviews, questionnaires and surveys.

Approximate Training and Application Times

Due to the exhaustive nature of the TTA procedure outlined above, it is estimated that the associated training and application times would be high. The application time includes the data collection procedure, the CDA and the KSAO identification phases, all of which are time consuming when conducted on their own.

Tools Needed

The tools required for conducting a TTA are dependent upon the methodologies employed during the procedure. TTA can be conducted using pen and paper, and a visual or audio recording device. A PC with a word processing package such as Microsoft Word is normally used to transcribe and sort the data.

Team Workload Assessment

Background and Applications

Although there are numerous techniques available for the assessment of individual operator MWL, the concept of measuring the MWL of a team or network of actors has received only minimal attention. Bowers and Jentsch (2004) describe an approach designed to measure both team and team member MWL that uses a modified version of the NASA-TLX (Hart and Staveland, 1988) subjective workload assessment method. In its present usage, the NASA-TLX is administered post-trial to team members who are then asked to provide subjective ratings for each of the NASA-TLX MWL dimensions and also ratings for each of the dimensions for the team as a whole.

Domain of Application

Generic.

Procedure and Advice

Step 1: Define task(s)
The first step in a team workload analysis (aside from the process of selecting the team(s) to be analysed, gaining access to the required systems and personnel) is to define the task(s) under analysis. The type of tasks analysed are dependent upon the focus of the analysis. For example, when assessing the effects on operator workload caused by a novel design or a new process, it is useful to analyse a set of tasks that are as representative of the full functionality of the interface, device or procedure as possible. To analyse a full set of tasks will often be too time consuming and labour intensive, and so it is pertinent to use a set of tasks that use all aspects of the system under analysis.

Step 2: Conduct a HTA for the task(s) under analysis
Once the task(s) under analysis are defined clearly, a HTA should be conducted for each task. This allows the analyst(s) and participants to understand the task(s) fully.

Step 3: Brief participants
Before the task(s) under analysis are performed, all of the participants involved should be briefed regarding the purpose of the study and the NASA-TLX method. It is recommended that participants are given a workshop on MWL and MWL assessment. It may also be useful at this stage to take the participants through an example team MWL assessment, so that they understand how the method works and what is required of them as participants.

Step 4: Conduct pilot run
Before the 'real' data collection procedure begins, it is useful to conduct a pilot run. The team should perform a small task, and then complete a NASA-TLX for themselves and for the team as a whole. This acts as a 'pilot run' of the procedure and highlights any potential problems in the data collection procedure.

Step 5: Performance of task under analysis
The NASA-TLX is typically administered post-trial. The team should be instructed to perform the task or scenario in question as normal.

Step 6: Weighting procedure
When the task under analysis is complete, the weighting procedure can begin. The WEIGHT software presents fifteen pair-wise comparisons of the six sub-scales (mental demand, physical demand, temporal demand, effort, performance and frustration level) to the participant. Participants should be instructed to select, from each of the fifteen pairs, the sub-scale that contributed the most to the workload of the task. The WEIGHT software then calculates the total number of times each sub-scale was selected by the participant. Each scale is then rated by the software based upon the number of times it is selected by the participant. This is done using a scale of 0 (not relevant) to 5 (more important than any other factor).

Step 7: NASA-TLX rating procedure
Participants should be presented with the interval scale for each of the TLX sub-scales. Participants are asked to provide a subjective rating for each sub-scale, between 1 (Low) and 20 (High), in response to the associated sub-scale questions. This is based entirely on the participant's subjective judgement. Participants should be instructed to complete a TLX for themselves and also for the team as a whole.

Step 8: TLX score calculation
A workload score is then calculated for each team member and also for the team as a whole. This is calculated by multiplying each rating by the weight given to that sub-scale by the participant. The sum of the weighted ratings for each task is then divided by 15 (sum of weights). A workload score of between 0 and 100 is then provided for the task under analysis.

Advantages

1. Offers a quick and easy approach for measuring team and team-member MWL.
2. The method is low cost and easy to apply requiring only minimal training.
3. The NASA-TLX method is the most commonly used MWL assessment method available and has been subjected to numerous validation studies.

4. The NASA TLX sub-scales are generic, so the method can be applied in any domain.
5. Offers a multi-dimensional assessment of workload.
6. Team MWL ratings can be compared across team member to ensure reliability.

Disadvantages

1. The extent to which team members can provide an accurate assessment of overall team workload is questionable and requires further testing.
2. A host of problems are associated with collecting data post-trial. Participants may have forgotten high or low workload aspects of the task and workload ratings may also be correlated with task performance e.g. subjects who performed poorly on the primary task may rate their workload as very high and vice versa.
3. Bowers and Jentsch (2004) report that the approach is cumbersome and also highlight the fact that the method that does not provide separate estimates for teamwork vs. task-work.

Training and Application Times

Due to the simplistic nature of the NASA-TLX method, the training time associated with the method is estimated to be very low. Similarly, the application time associated with the method is also estimated to be very low. Bowers and Jentsch (2004) report that the individual and team measures take about ten minutes each to complete.

Reliability and Validity

There is limited reliability and validity data available regarding this approach to the assessment of MWL. The reliability of such an approach certainly is questionable. The extent to which individuals can accurately provide a measure of team workload is also questionable. Bowers and Jentsch (2004) describe a study designed to test the validity of the approach whereby team performance was compared to MWL ratings. It was found that the lowest individual MWL rating was the best predictor of performance, in that the higher the lowest reported individual MWL rating was, the poorer the team's performance was. It is apparent that such approaches to the assessment of team MWL require further testing in terms of reliability and validity. How to test the validity of such methods is also a challenge, as there are problems associated with associating workload and performance. That is, it may be that team performance was poor and team members rated the overall team workload as high, due to a correlation with performance. However, this may not be the case, and it may be that teams with low workload perform poorly, due to factors other than workload.

Tools Needed

The NASA-TLX can be applied using pen and paper.

Flowchart

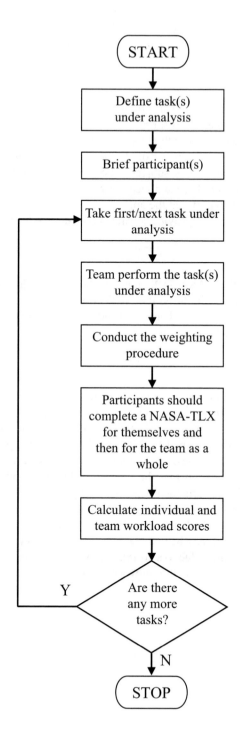

Related Methods

The team MWL assessment method uses the NASA-TLX subjective MWL assessment method. A number of other multi-dimensional subjective MWL assessment methods exist, such as the SWAT (Reid and Nygren, 1988) and the workload profile method (Tsang and Velazquez, 1996).

Task and Training Requirements Analysis Methodology (TTRAM)

Background and Applications

The task and training requirements analysis methodology (TTRAM; Swezey, Ownes, Burgondy and Salas, 2000) method comprises a number of techniques that are used to identify team-based task training requirements and also to evaluate any associated training technologies that could potentially be used in the delivery of team training. The method was developed for the military aviation domain and according to Swezey et al (2000) has shown to be effective at discriminating tasks that are prone to skill decay, tasks that are critical to mission success, tasks that require high levels of teamwork (internal and external) and tasks that require further training intervention. The TTRAM technique is used to identify current training and practice gaps, and then to determine potential training solutions designed to address the training and practice gap identified. In order to identify the current training and practice gaps, a skill decay analysis and a practice analysis is conducted and a skill decay index score and a practice effectiveness index score are derived. The two scores are then compared in order to identify practice and training gaps. For example, a task high skill decay index score compared to a low practice effectiveness index score would demonstrate a requirement for additional training and practice for the task under analysis.

Domain of Application

Military aviation

Procedure and Advice (Adapted from Swezey et al, 2000)

Step 1: Perform a task analysis for the scenario or set of tasks under analysis
It is recommended that a task analysis for the task or set of tasks under analysis should act as the initial input to the TTRAM analysis. For this purpose, it is recommended that a HTA is the most suitable. A number of data collection procedures may be used to collect the data required for the HTA, including interviews with SMEs and observational study of the task or scenario under analysis.

Step 2: Conduct skill decay analysis
The skill decay analysis is conducted in order to identify those tasks that may be susceptible to skill degradation without sufficient training or practice (Swezey et al, 2000). The skill decay analysis involves identifying the difficulty associated with each task, identifying the degree of prior learning associated with each task, and determining the frequency of task performance. A skill decay index score is then calculated from these three components. Each component is described further below:

Task difficulty. The analyst should rate each task in terms of its associated difficulty, including difficulty in performing the task and also in acquiring and retaining the required skills. Task difficulty is rated as low (1), medium (2) or high (3). Swezey et al (2000) suggest that task difficulty be assessed via SME interviews and a behaviourally anchored rating scale (BARS). The BARS is presented in Table 9. 15

Degree of prior learning. The analyst should assess the degree of prior learning associated with each task under analysis. SMEs and BARS are also used to gather these ratings. The degree of prior learning for a task is rated as low (3), medium (2) or high (1). The degree of prior learning BARS is presented in Table 9. 16.

Frequency of task performance. The analyst should rate the frequency of performance of each task. This is rated as infrequent, frequent or very frequent. The frequency of task performance assessment scale is shown in Table 9.17.

Table 9.15   Task Difficulty BARS (Source: Swezey et al 2000)

Question: How difficult is this task to perform?	
Difficulty levels	Associated task characteristics
Low	Virtually no practice is required. Most trained individuals (i.e. 90%) will be able to perform this task with minimal exposure or practice on the operational equipment. Consists of very few procedural steps, and each step is dependent upon preceding steps.
Medium	Individuals can accomplish most of the activity subsequent to baseline instruction. The majority of trained individuals (i.e. 60%) will be able to perform this task with minimal exposure or practice on the operational equipment. This activity does require moderate practice to sustain competent performance at the desired level of proficiency. Consists of numerous complex steps
High	Requires extensive instruction and practice to accomplish the activity. Very few trained individuals (i.e. 10%) will be able to perform this task with minimal exposure or practice on the operational equipment. Consists of a large number of complex steps, and there is little if any dependency among the task steps

Table 9.16   Degree of Prior Learning BARS (Source: Swezey et al 2000)

Question: What level of training is required to maintain an adequate level of proficiency on this task?	
Proficiency levels	Associated task characteristics
Low	A high level of training is required to maintain proficiency on this task. Individual cannot be expected to perform the task without frequent recurrency training. Individual fails to meet task performance standards without frequent recurrency training
Medium	A moderate level of training is required to maintain proficiency. Individual can perform the task in the trainer under a restricted set of task conditions; however, needs more practice in the actual job setting under varying task conditions and under supervision. Individual meets minimum performance standards without frequent recurrency training
High	Minimal training is required to maintain proficiency. Individual can perform the task completely and accurately without supervision across varying task conditions; has achieved mastery level proficiency Individual exceeds performance standards

Table 9.17 Frequency of Task Performance BARS (Source: Swezey et al 2000)

Question: How often is this task performed in the context of your job (across different missions)? Do not factor in time spent training: limit responses to the frequency with which the task is inherently performed as part of the operational setting	
Frequency levels	Associated task characteristics
Infrequent	Extremely little time is spent performing the task Task is infrequently performed
Frequent	A moderate amount of time is spent performing this task Task is performed frequently
Very frequent	This task comprises a large amount of time Task is performed very frequently

Step 3: Compute skill decay index
Once ratings for task difficulty, degree of prior learning and frequency of task performance are obtained, the skill decay index score should be calculated. The skill decay is calculated by summing the individual scores for each of the three components, task difficulty, degree of prior learning and frequency of task performance. A skill decay index score between 3 and 9 is derived.

Step 4: Conduct practice analysis
The practice analysis is conducted in order to determine the current levels of task and skill practice associated with the task under analysis. The practice analysis comprises of the following:

1. Amount of practice. The amount of practice associated with each task is determined using SME interviews and rated on a scale of 1 (low) to 3 (high).
2. Frequency of practice. The frequency in which the tasks are practiced is rated as high, medium or low.
3. Quality of practice. The quality of the practice undertaken for each task is also rated using a scale of high (3), medium (2) and low (1). A team skill training questionnaire and a simulator capability and training checklist are also used. The team skill training questionnaire is presented in Table 9. 18.
4. Simulator capability. The analyst is also required to assess the capability of any simulators used in the provision of practice.

Table 9.18 Team Skill Training Questionnaire (Source: Swezey et al 2000)

Extent to which training allows team members to practice co-ordinated activities required by the task (both internal and external to the simulator)	
Extent to which training provides practice for improving the effectiveness of communication among crew members	
Extent to which training incorporates objective measures for evaluating crew performance	
Level of feedback provided by training on how well the aircrew performed as a team	

Step 5: Compute practice effectiveness index
Once the ratings for the four components outlined above are determined, the practice effectiveness index score is calculated. The practice effectiveness index score is derived by summing the four values derived for practice analysis components (amount of practice, frequency of practice,

quality of practice and simulator capability) during step 4. For each task that is using the TTRAM technique, a skill decay index score and a practice effectiveness index score should be derived.

Step 6: Compare skill decay index and practice effectiveness index scores
The next step involves comparing the associated skill decay index and practice effectiveness scores for each of the tasks under analysis. Those tasks with higher skill decay index scores possess a greater potential for skill degradation, whilst those tasks with higher practice effectiveness scores indicate too great a level of task support.

Step 7: Identify training gaps
Once the analyst has determined those tasks that are not adequately supported by training or practice and that have the potential for skill decay, the nature of the training gaps should be determined. According to Swezey et al (2000), gaps represent areas of task practice or training in which task skills are not addressed, or are inadequately addressed by current training schemes.

Step 8: Identify potential training intervention
For each training gap specified, the analyst should attempt to determine potential training solutions, such as simulations and computer-based training interventions.

Step 9: Perform training technology analysis
The training technology analysis is conducted in order to identify alternative and appropriate training or practice interventions for those training gaps identified. The training technology analysis involves the following components:

1. Identification of task skill requirements. A behavioural classification system (Swezey et al, 2000) is used to categorise tasks in terms of their underlying process.
2. Identification of task criticality level. SMEs should be used to rate the criticality of each task under analysis. A task criticality assessment scale is used for this purpose (Table 9. 19).
3. Identification of task teamwork level. The extent to which the task requires co-ordinated activity and interaction amongst individuals is also assessed using SMEs. A teamwork assessment scale is used for this purpose (Table 9.20).
4. Specification of training media and support recommendations.

Table 9.19   Task Criticality Table (Source: Swezey et al 2000)

Question: How critical is this task to successful mission performance?	
Criticality levels	Associated task characteristics
Low	Errors are unlikely to have any negative consequences to overall mission success Task is not a critical/important component of the overall duty/mission Task can be ignored for long periods of time
Medium	Errors or poor performance would have moderate consequences and may jeopardise mission success Task is somewhat critical/important to overall duty/mission Task requires attention, but does not demand immediate action
High	Errors would most likely have serious consequences, failing to execute the task correctly would lead to mission failure Task is a critical/important component of the overall duty/mission Task requires immediate attention and action

Table 9.20 Teamwork Assessment Scale (Source: Swezey et al 2000)

Question: What level of teamwork is required in order to perform this task? Assign two ratings: one for internal crew member teamwork, and a second for external teamwork	
Criticality levels	Associated task characteristics
Low	Task can be accomplished on the basis of individual performance alone; the task can be performed in isolation of other tasks Virtually no interaction or co-ordination among team members is required Task can be performed in parallel with other team member tasks
Medium	Requires a moderate degree of information exchange about internal/external resources, and some task interdependencies among individuals exist Some co-ordination among team members is required if the task is to be successfully completed Some sequential dependencies among sub-tasks are required
High	Involves a dynamic exchange of information and resources among team members Response co-ordination and sequencing of activities of activities among team members is vital to successful task performance (activities must be synchronised and precisely timed Actions are highly dependent upon the performance of other team members

Flowchart

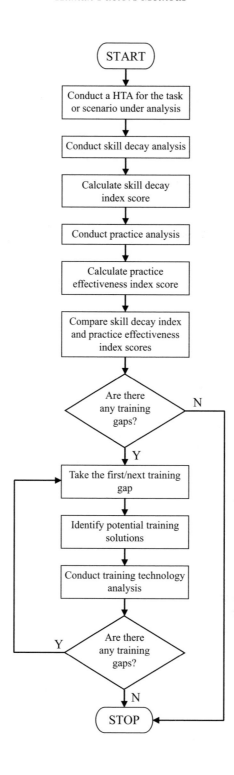

Advantages

1. The output of a TTRAM analysis is extremely useful for a number of different purposes. Tasks prone to skill decay are identified and training solutions are offered. Training gaps are also identified as are the underlying skills associated with each task. TTRAM also rates the level of teamwork required for task steps.
2. The TTRAM procedure is very exhaustive.

Disadvantages

1. TTRAM is time consuming in its application.
2. SMEs are required for a TTRAM analysis. Access to these may prove difficult.
3. Resource intensive.

Related Methods

The TTRAM technique uses a number of different approaches, including interviews, BARS, classification schemes and checklists.

Training and Application Times

The training time associated with the TTRAM technique is estimated to be high. It is estimated that a practitioner with no prior experience of the techniques used would require in excess of one to two days' training for the method. The application time for the technique would also be high, considering that the method uses a number of interviews, as well as a number of rating scales and checklists.

Reliability and Validity

No data regarding the reliability and validity of the TTRAM technique are offered by the authors.

Tools Needed

The tools required for a TTRAM analysis would include those required for any interview type analysis, such as a PC with Microsoft Excel, and video and audio recording equipment. Each of the TTRAM behavioural rating scales would also be required, along with the task process classification scheme. The analyst would also require some access to the simulators, simulations and software that are used for training purposes in the establishment under analysis.

Chapter 10

Interface Analysis Methods

Interface analysis methods are used to assess the man-machine interface of a particular system, product or device. Interface analysis methods can be used to assess a number of different aspects associated with a particular interface, including usability, user satisfaction, error, layout, labelling, and the controls and displays used. The output of interface analysis methods is then typically used to improve the interface in question through redesign. Such methods are used to enhance the performance of the design by improving its usability, user satisfaction, and reducing user errors and interaction time. ISO9241-11 requires that the usability of software is considered along three dimensions: effectiveness (how well does the product's performance meet the tasks for which it was designed?); efficiency (how much resource, e.g., time or effort, is required to use the product to perform these tasks?) and attitude (e.g., how favourably do users respond to the product?). It is important to note that it is often necessary to conduct separate evaluations for each dimension rather than using one method and hoping that it can capture all aspects.

According to ISO13407, it is important to apply interface analysis methods throughout a product's life cycle, either in the design stage to evaluate design concepts or in the operational stage to evaluate effects on performance. In particular, this Standard calls for the active involvement of users in the design process in order to gain an appropriate understanding of requirements and an appropriate allocation of function between users and the technology. It assumes that the design process is both multidisciplinary and iterative. This suggests that there is a need to have a clear and consistent set of representations that can be shared across the design team and revised during the development of the design. In this chapter, we review methods that can fulfil these requirements. Most of the methods considered in this review require at least some form of interface, ranging from paper-based functional diagrams to the operational product itself, and most methods normally use end users of the system, product or device under analysis.

A number of different types of interface analysis method are available, such as usability assessment, error analysis, interface layout analysis and general interface assessment methods. Indeed it could be argued that the interface analysis category covers a number of methods described previously in this review, such as HEI. Usability assessment methods are used to assess the usability (effectiveness, learnability, flexibility and attitude) of a particular interface. As Baber (2005) notes, a significant element of evaluation lies in defining an appropriate referent model; it is not sufficient to simply conduct an evaluation of a product in isolation because that does not provide adequate grounds for making a judgement of the quality. Consequently, it is necessary to either make a comparison with another product or to define a target against which to make a judgement. Some questionnaire methods such as SUMI, QUIS and SUS provide scores that can be judged against some notion of a 'baseline'. Typically these are completed by potential end users based upon user trials with the device or system under analysis. Checklists such as Ravden and Johnson's (1989) HCI usability checklist are also used to assess the usability of an interface.

The layout of an interface can also be assessed using methods such as link and layout analysis. As the names suggest, these methods are used to assess the layout of the interface and its effects upon task performance. More general interface analysis methods such as heuristic evaluation and user trials are used to assess the interface as a whole, and are flexible in that the focus of the analysis is determined by the analyst(s). The advantages associated with the use of interface analysis methods lie in their simplistic nature and the usefulness of their outputs. Most of the interface analysis methods are simple to apply, requiring minimal time and costs and also require only minimal training. The utility of the outputs is also ensured, as most approaches offer interface redesigns based upon end-user opinions. The only significant disadvantages associated with the use of interface analysis methods are that the data analysis procedures may be time consuming and laborious and also that much of the data obtained is subjective. A brief description of the interface analysis methods considered in this review is given below.

Checklists offer a simplistic and low-cost approach to interface assessment. When using a checklist, the analyst checks the product or system interface against a pre-defined set of criteria in order to evaluate its usability. Conducting a checklist analysis is a matter of simply inspecting the device against each point on the chosen checklist. A number of checklists are available, including Ravden and Johnson's (1989) HCI checklist and Woodson, Tillman and Tillman's (1992) human engineering checklists. Heuristic analysis is one of the simplest interface analysis methods available, involving simply obtaining analyst(s)' subjective opinions based upon their interactions with a particular device or product. In conducting a heuristic analysis, an analyst or end user should perform a user trial with the device or product under analysis and make observations regarding the usability, quality, and error potential of the design. Interface surveys (Kirwan and Ainsworth, 1992) are a group of surveys that are used to assess the interface under analysis in terms of controls and displays used, their layout, labelling and ease of use. Each survey is completed after a user trial and conclusions regarding the usability and design of the interface are made.

Link analysis is used to evaluate and redesign an interface in terms of nature, frequency and importance of links between elements of the interface in question. A link analysis defines links (hand or eye movements) between elements of the interface under analysis. The interface is then redesigned based upon these links, with the most often linked elements of the interface relocated to increase their proximity to one another. Layout analysis is also used to evaluate and redesign the layout of the interface in question. Layout analysis involves arranging the interface components into functional groupings, and then organising these groups by importance of use, sequence of use and frequency of use. The layout analysis output offers a redesign based upon the user's model of the task.

The software usability measurement inventory (SUMI), the questionnaire for user interface satisfaction (QUIS) and the system usability scale (SUS) are all examples of usability questionnaires. Typically, participants perform a user trial with the system or device under analysis and then complete the appropriate questionnaire. Overall usability scores and specific sub-scale scores for the system or device under analysis are then calculated.

Repertory grid analysis has also been used as an interface analysis method (Stanton and Young, 1999) and involves assessing user perceptions of the interface under analysis. A grid consisting of elements, constructs and opposites is formed and used to rate the interface elements. Walkthrough analysis is a very simple procedure used by designers whereby experienced system operators or analysts perform a walkthrough or demonstration of a task or set of tasks using the system under analysis in order to provide an evaluation of the interface in question. User trials involve the potential system or device end users performing trials with the interface under analysis and providing an assessment in terms of usability, user satisfaction, interaction times, and error. A summary of the interface analysis methods reviewed is presented in Table 10.1.

Table 10.1 Summary of Interface Analysis Methods

Method	Type of method	Domain	Training time	App time	Related methods	Tools needed	Validation studies	Advantages	Disadvantages
Checklists	Subjective interface analysis	Generic	Low	Low	User trials	Pen and paper	Yes	1) Easy to use, low cost, requires little training. 2) Based upon established knowledge of human performance. 3) Offers a direct assessment of the system or device under analysis.	1) Context is ignored when using checklists. 2) Data is subjective. 3) Inconsistent.
Heuristic evaluation	Subjective interface analysis	Generic	Low	Low	User trials	Pen and paper	Yes	1) Easy to use, low cost, requires little training. 2) Output is immediately useful.	1) Poor reliability and validity statistics. 2) Data is subjective. 3) Unstructured approach.
Interface surveys	Survey	Generic	Low	High	Surveys User trials	Pen and paper	No	1) Easy to use, low cost, requires little training. 2) Potentially exhaustive. 3) Based upon traditional HF guidelines and standards.	1) Time consuming in application. 2) Surveys are dated. 3) Requires operational system.
Link analysis	Layout analysis	Generic	Low	Low	Observation HTA	Pen and paper	Yes	1) Easy to use, low cost, requires little training. 2) Output is very useful, offering a logical redesign of the interface in question. 3) Can be used throughout the design process in order to evaluate design concepts (can be applied to functional diagrams).	1) Preliminary data collection involved e.g. observation, HTA etc. 2) Does not consider cognitive processes. 3) Output is not easily quantifiable.

Table 10.1 (continued)

Method	Type of method	Domain	Training time	App time	Related methods	Tools needed	Validation studies	Advantages	Disadvantages
Layout analysis	Layout analysis	Generic	Low	Low	Observation HTA	Pen and paper	Yes	1) Easy to use, low cost, requires little training. 2) Offers a redesign of the interface based upon importance, frequency and sequence of use. 3) Can be used throughout the design process in order to evaluate design concepts (can be applied to functional diagrams).	1) Poor reliability and validity statistics. 2) Preliminary data collection involved e.g. observation, HTA etc. 3) May be difficult to use when considering complex interfaces.
QUIS – Questionnaire for User Interface Satisfaction	Usability questionnaire	HCI	Low	Low	Questionnaires User trials	Pen and paper	Yes	1) Quick and easy to use involving little training and cost. 2) Output offers an assessment of the usability of the interface in question.	1) May require substantial development to be used in the analysis of C4i. 2) Data is subjective.
Repertory Grid analysis	Usability questionnaire	Product design	Med	High	N/A	Pen and paper	Yes	1) Structured, thorough procedure. 2) Easy to use. 3) Assesses end-user opinions.	1) Procedure is a long and drawn out one. 2) Does not always produce usable factors. 3) Reliability and validity questionable.

Table 10.1 (continued)

Method	Type of method	Domain	Training time	App time	Related methods	Tools needed	Validation studies	Advantages	Disadvantages
SUMI – Software Usability Measurement Inventory	Usability questionnaire	HCI	Low	Low	Questionnaires User trials	Pen and paper	Yes	1) Quick and easy to use involving little training and cost. 2) Output offers an assessment of the usability of the interface in question. 3) Encouraging reliability and validity statistics.	1) May require substantial development to be used in the analysis of C4i. 2) Data is subjective. 3) Only available commercially, costing over one thousand Euros.
SUS – System Usability Scale	Usability questionnaire	Generic	Low	Low	Questionnaires User trials	Pen and paper	Yes	1) Quick and easy to use involving little training and cost. 2) Offers a usability score for the device under analysis.	1) Output is limited. 2) Unsophisticated. 3) Data is subjective.
User Trials	User trial	Generic	Low	High	Questionnaires Workload SA Assessment methods	Pen and paper	No	1) Can be used to assess anything from workload to usability. 2) Powerful insight into how the end product will potentially be used.	1) Can be time consuming. 2) Requires access to end users.
Walkthrough analysis	Task analysis	Generic	Low	Low	Talkthrough analysis	Pen and paper	No	1) Quick and easy to use involving little training and cost. 2) Allows the analyst(s) to understand the physical actions involved in the performance of a task. 3) Very flexible.	1) SMEs required. 2) Access to the system under analysis is required. 3) Reliability is questionable.

Checklists

Background and Applications

Checklists offer a quick, easy and low-cost approach to interface assessment. Typical checklist approaches involve analysts checking features associated with a product or interface against a checklist containing a pre-defined set of criteria. Checklist style evaluation can occur throughout the life cycle of a product or system, from paper drawings to the finished product. A number of specific HF checklists exist, such as Ravden and Johnson's (1989) HCI checklist, the Human Engineering Design checklist and various Woodson, Tillman and Tillman (1992) checklists. Checklists can be used to evaluate the usability and design of a device or system in any domain. In the past, checklists have been used to evaluate product usability in the HCI (Ravden and Johnson, 1990), automotive (Stanton and Young, 1999) and air traffic control domains. When using checklists, the analyst using the checklist should have some level of skill or familiarity with the device under evaluation. Performing a checklist analysis is a matter of simply inspecting the device against each point on an appropriate checklist. Checklists are also very flexible in that they can be adapted or modified by the analyst according to the demands of the analysis. For example, Stanton and Young (1999) used a section of Ravden and Johnson's HCI checklist in order to evaluate the design of in-car radios.

Domain of Application

Generic. Although checklist methods originated in the HCI domain, they are typically generic and can be applied in any domain.

Procedure and Advice

Step 1: Select appropriate checklist
Firstly, the analyst must decide which form of checklist is appropriate for the product or system under analysis. The checklist used may be simply an existing one or the analyst may choose to adapt an existing checklist to make it more appropriate for the system under analysis. Stanton and Young (1999) used a portion of Ravden and Johnson's (1989) HCI checklist for in-car entertainment systems. One of the main features of checklists is that they are very flexible. Checklists can be adapted or modified according to the demands of the analysis. Alternatively, if a suitable checklist is not available, the analyst may choose to create a new checklist specifically for the system/ product in question.

Step 2: Check item on checklist against product
The analyst should take the first point on the checklist and check it against the product or system under analysis. For example, the first item in Ravden and Johnson's checklist asks. 'Is each screen clearly identified with an informative title or description'? The analysts should then proceed to check each screen and its associated title and description. The options given are 'Always', 'Most of the time', 'Some of the time' and 'Never'. Using subjective judgement, the analyst should rate the device under analysis according to the checklist item. Step 2 should be repeated until each item on the checklist has been dealt with.

Flowchart

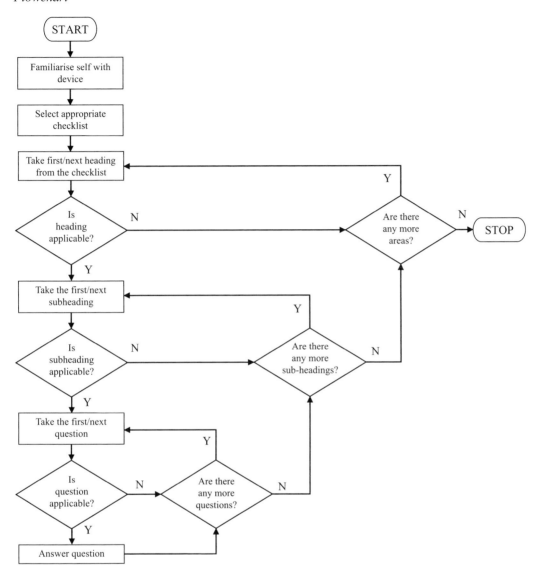

Advantages

1. Checklists are quick and simple to apply, and incur only a minimal cost.
2. Checklists offer an immediately useful output.
3. Checklists are based upon established knowledge about human performance (Stanton and Young, 1999).
4. The method requires very little training.
5. Resource usage is very low.
6. Checklists are very adaptable and can easily be modified in order to use them for other devices/systems. Stanton and Young (1999) suggest that the Ravden and Johnson checklist

(1989), originally designed for HCI, is easily adapted to cater for the usability of other devices, such as in-car stereos.

7.   A number of different checklists are available to the HF practitioner.

Disadvantages

1.   A checklist type analysis does not account for errors or cognitive problems associated with the device.
2.   Context is ignored by checklists.
3.   Checklist data is totally subjective. What one analyst classes as bad design may be classed as suitable by another.
4.   Low consistency.
5.   Not a very sophisticated approach to system evaluation.

Example

The following example (Table 10.2) is an extract of a checklist analysis of a Sony Ericsson t68i mobile phone using Ravden and Johnson's HCI checklist.

Table 10.2   Extract of Checklist Analysis

Section 1: Visual Clarity

Key: A = Always, M = Most of the time, S = Some of the time, N = Never

Section 1: Visual Clarity	A	M	S	N	Comments
1. Is each screen clearly identified with an informative title or description?				✓	Some screens lack titles
2. Is important information highlighted on the screen? (e.g. cursor position, instructions, errors)			✓		
When the user enters information on the screen, is it clear: Where the information should be entered? In what format it should be entered?				✓	
4. Where the user overtypes information on the screen, does the system clear the previous information, so that it does not get confused with the updated input?					N/A
5. Does information appear to be organised logically on the screen? (e.g. menus organised by probable sequence of selection, or alphabetically)			✓		
6. Are different types of information clearly separated from each other on the screen? (e.g. instructions, control options, data displays)				✓	Different information is often grouped into lists
7. Where a large amount of information is displayed on one screen, is it clearly separated into sections on the screen?			✓		
8. Are columns of information clearly aligned on the screen? (e.g. columns of alphanumerics left justified, columns of integers right justified)					
9. Are bright or light colours displayed on a dark background, and vice versa?			✓		
10. Does the use of colours make the displays clear?			✓		
11. Where colour is used, will aspects of the display be easy to see if used on a monochrome or low resolution screen, or if the user is colour blind?					
12. Is the information on the screen easy to see and read?					
13. Do screens appear uncluttered?			✓		
14. Are schematic and pictorial displays (e.g. figures and diagrams) clearly drawn and annotated?			✓	✓	
15. Is it easy to find the required information on a screen?			✓		Easy to get lost in menu system

Related Methods

There are a number of checklists available to the human factors practitioner, such as Woodson, Tillman and Tillman's (1992) human engineering checklists, and Ravden and Johnson's (1989) HCI checklist.

Approximate Training and Application Times

Checklists require only minimal training time. Similarly, the application time associated with checklist techniques is minimal. In an analysis of twelve ergonomics methods, Stanton and Young (1999) report that checklists are one of the quickest techniques to train, practise and apply.

Reliability and Validity

Whilst Stanton and Young (1999) report that checklists performed quite poorly on intra-rater reliability, they also report that inter-rater reliability and predictive validity of checklists was good.

Tools Needed

Checklists can be applied using pen and paper only, however, for a checklist analysis, the analyst must have access to some form of the device under analysis. This could either be the finished article, paper drawings or a prototype version. An appropriate checklist is also required.

Heuristic Analysis

Background and Applications

Heuristic analyses methods offer a quick and simple approach to interface evaluation. Heuristic analysis involves analysts providing subjective opinions based upon their interaction with a particular design, device or product. Heuristic analysis is a flexible approach that can be used to assess a number of features associated with a particular product or interface, including usability, error potential, MWL and overall design quality. To conduct a heuristic analysis, an analyst or team of analysts perform a series of interactions with the product or interface under analysis, recording their observations as they proceed. Heuristic type analyses are typically conducted throughout the design process in order to evaluate design concepts and propose remedial measures for any problems encountered. The popularity of heuristic analysis lies in its simplicity and the fact that it can be conducted easily and with only minimal resource usage, at any stage throughout the design process.

Domain of Application

Generic.

Procedure and Advice

Step 1: Define tasks under analysis
The first step in a heuristic analysis is to define a representative set of tasks or scenarios for the system or device under analysis. It is recommended that heuristic analyses are based upon the

analyst performing an exhaustive set of tasks with the device in question. The tasks defined should then be placed in a task list. It is normally useful to conduct a HTA for this purpose, based on the operation of the device in question. The HTA then acts as a task list for the heuristic analysis.

Step 2: Define heuristic list
In some cases it may be fruitful to determine which aspects are to be evaluated before the analysis begins. Typically, usability (ease of use, effectiveness, efficiency and comfort) and error potential are evaluated.

Step 3: Familiarisation phase
To ensure that the analysis is as comprehensive as possible, it is recommended that the analysts involved spend some time to familiarise themselves with the device in question. This might involve consultation with the associated documentation (e.g. instruction manual), watching a demonstration of the device being operated, or being taken through a walkthrough of device operation.

Step 4: Perform task(s)
Once familiar with the device under analysis, the analyst(s) should then perform each task from the task list developed during steps 1 and 2 and offer opinions regarding the design and the heuristic categories required. During this stage, any good points or bad points associated with the participants' interactions with the device should be recorded. If the analysis concerns a design concept, then a task walkthrough is sufficient. Each opinion offered should be recorded.

Step 5: Propose remedies
Once the analyst has completed all of the tasks from the task list, remedial measures for any of the problems recorded should be proposed and recorded.

Advantages

1. Heuristic analysis offers a quick, simple and low-cost approach to usability assessment.
2. Due to its simplicity, only minimal training is required.
3. Heuristic analysis can be applied to any form of product, including paper-based diagrams, mock-ups, prototype designs and functional devices.
4. The output derived is immediately useful, highlighting problems associated with the device in question.
5. Very low resource usage.
6. Can be used repeatedly throughout the design life cycle.

Disadvantages

1. Poor reliability, validity and comprehensiveness.
2. Requires SMEs in order for the analysis to be worthwhile.
3. Subjective.
4. Totally unstructured.
5. Consistency of such a technique is questionable.

Example

The following example is taken from Stanton and Young (1999). Heuristic analyses of Ford and Sharp in car radio devices were conducted in order to assess the interface in terms of ease of skill acquisition, effectiveness on task, comfort/satisfaction and flexibility on task. The following heuristic analysis notes were recorded:

Ford radio

- Large on/off/volume button is very good.
- Preset buttons are large and clear; their positioning along the bottom of the unit is very good.
- Rocker seek button is satisfactory, good size and well located.
- Menu button a little small and awkward, also does not react enough when operated – could be more sensitive.
- News/TA buttons are well labelled and easy to operate.
- Pressing tape buttons for autoreverse function is a little unconventional, but a good way of saving buttons.
- Excellent idea to maintain FF/RWD buttons regardless of which side of the tape is playing.
- CD, AM/FM and Dolby buttons are well labelled and easy to use.
- Eject button is clear, easy to use and well positioned in relation to cassette door.
- Very good consistency – all buttons have uniform size and labelling.
- PTY function is not very good; allocating generic titles to stations does not work very well.
- Display is well positioned and easy to read – informative and clear.
- RDS functions are a little obscure – required to read manual before initial operation.

Sharp radio

- On/off/volume control is a bit small and awkward, combined with difficult balance control.
- Pushbutton operation would be more satisfactory for On/Off, as volume stays at preferred level.
- Fader control is particularly small and awkward.
- Both of the above points are related to the fact that a single button location has multiple functions – this is too complex.
- Treble and Bass controls also difficult and stiff; although these functions are rarely adjusted once set.
- Station pre-set buttons are satisfactory; quite large and clear.
- Band selector button and FM Mono-Stereo button should not have two functions on each button – could result in confusion if the wrong function occurs. These buttons are the only buttons on the radio which are not self explanatory – the user must consult the manual to discover their function.
- Tuning seek and tuning scan buttons are easier to understand and use, although there are still two functions on one button.
- Auto-reverse function is not obvious, although it is an accepted standard.
- Illumination – is daytime/night time illumination satisfactory? A dimmer control would probably aid matters.

Flowchart

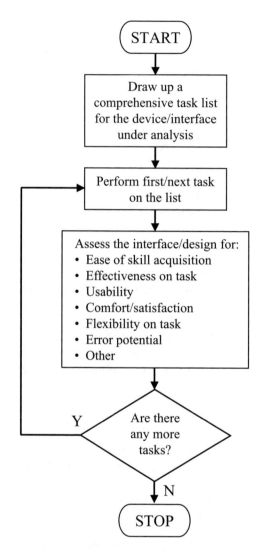

Approximate Training and Application Times

The method requires very little, if any at all, training and the associated application time is also typically low.

Reliability and Validity

In conclusion to a comparison of twelve HF methods, Stanton and Young (1999) report that the unstructured nature of the method led to very poor results for reliability and predictive validity. Both intra- and inter-analyst reliability for the method are questionable, due to its unstructured nature.

Tools Needed

A heuristic analysis is conducted using pen and paper only. The device under analysis is required in some form e.g. functional diagrams, the actual device or paper drawings.

Interface Surveys

Background and Application

Kirwan and Ainsworth (1992) describe the interface survey method, which is used to assess the physical aspects of man-machine interfaces. The method involves the use of survey-based analysis to consider the following interface aspects:

- Controls and displays.
- Labelling.
- Coding consistency.
- Operator modification.
- Sightline.
- Environmental aspects.

The interface surveys are used to pinpoint design inadequacies for an interface or design concept. A brief summary of each of the survey methods is given below:

Control and display survey
A control and display survey is used to evaluate the controls and displays provided by a particular interface. According to Kirwan and Ainsworth (1992), the analyst should first record all of those parameters that can be controlled and displayed, and then create a list containing a description of each control used. Developing this list involves examining each control, recording exactly what the control is controlling, its location, type of control, and any other relevant details, such as movement (e.g. up/down, rotary, left to right etc). Likewise, each display should be investigated in the same manner e.g. display type, what is being displayed, location etc. According to Kirwan and Ainsworth (1992) the list should then be sorted into a hierarchical list containing the system, sub-system and parameter. The control and display list can then be used as a checklist to ensure that the system user is presented with adequate information and provided with the appropriate controls in order to perform the task. If required (depending upon the scope of the analysis) the appropriate guidelines or standards can also be applied, in order to check that the system controls and displays adhere to the relevant guidelines/standards.

Labelling surveys
Labelling surveys are used to examine the labelling provided by the interface under analysis. According to Kirwan and Ainsworth (1992) the following aspects of each label are recorded: reference, wording, size, position, and colour. It may also be useful to make a subjective judgement on the clarity and ease of identification of each label identified. Any missing or confusing labels should also be recorded. Again, depending upon available resources, the labels identified can also be compared to the associated labelling standards and guidelines for the system under analysis. An extract of a labelling survey is presented in Table 10.4.

Coding consistency survey
Coding surveys are used to analyse any coding used on the interface under analysis. Typical types of coding used are colour coding (e.g. green for go, red for stop), positional coding, size coding and shape coding (Kirwan and Ainsworth, 1992). The coding analysis is used to highlight ambiguous coding and also where any additional coding may be required (Kirwan and Ainsworth, 1992). The analyst should systematically work through the interface, recording each use of coding, its location, the feature that is coded, description, relevance, instances where coding could be used but is not, instances of counteracting coding and any suggested revisions in terms of coding to the interface.

Operator modification survey
The end users of systems often add temporary modifications to the interface in order to eradicate design inadequacies. Typically, operators use labels or markings to highlight where specific controls should be positioned or place objects such as paper cups over redundant controls. The modifications made by the end users offer an intriguing insight into the usability of the interface, often highlighting bad design, poor labelling, and simpler procedures (i.e. missing out one or two actions). Kirwan and Ainsworth (1992) suggest that such information can be gathered quickly through a survey of the operational system. The information gathered can be used to inform the design of similar systems or interfaces. Conducting an operator modification survey simply involves observing a representative set of tasks being performed using the system under analysis, and recording any instances of operator modification. The use of interviews is also useful, to help understand why the modification occurred in the first place.

Sightline surveys
A sightline survey involves an analysis of operator sightlines in terms of distance, angle and obstructions. Typically a line is drawn from the operator's eye position to the display under analysis. If the line is interrupted, then the obstruction should be recorded. Distance and angle of the sightline are also typically recorded. The output of a sightline survey can be presented in tabular or diagrammatic form.

Environmental survey
According to Kirwan and Ainsworth (1992) environmental surveys measure the state of the ambient environment e.g. noise, illumination, temperature and humidity levels.

Domain of Application

Generic.

Procedure and Advice

Step 1: Select appropriate survey(s) and prepare data collection sheets
The first step in an interface survey type analysis is to select the appropriate surveys that will be used during the analysis effort. This is dependent upon the focus of the analysis. Once the appropriate surveys are selected, data collection sheets should be created for each of the chosen surveys.

Step 2: Data collection
The data collection phase involves completing each survey for the system under analysis. There are a number of ways to accomplish this. Access to the system under analysis is normally required, although Kirwan and Ainsworth (1992) suggest that the relevant data can sometimes be collected

from drawings of the system under analysis. It is recommended that a walk-through of the system under analysis is conducted, involving as representative a set of tasks of the full functionality of the system as possible. Observational study of task performance with the system under analysis is also very useful. For the operator modification surveys, interviews with system operators are required and for the environmental survey, on-line access to the operating system is required.

Step 3: Complete appropriate surveys
Once the data collection phase is complete, the appropriate surveys should be completed and analysed accordingly. The results are normally presented in tabular form.

Step 4: Propose remedial measures
Once the surveys are completed, it is often useful to propose any remedial measures designed to remove any problems highlighted by the surveys. Such recommendations might offer countermeasures for the system under analysis in terms of design inadequacies, error potential, poor coding, operator modifications etc.

Advantages

1. Each of the surveys described is easy to apply, requiring very little training.
2. The surveys are generic and can be applied in any domain.
3. The output of the surveys offers a useful analysis of the interface under analysis, highlighting instances of bad design and problems arising from the man-machine interaction.
4. Standards and guidelines can be used in conjunction with the techniques in order to ensure comprehensiveness.
5. If all of the surveys are applied, the interface in question is subjected to a very exhaustive analysis.

Disadvantages

1. The application of the surveys is time consuming.
2. It is questionable whether such dated survey methods will be useful in the analysis of contemporary complex, dynamic systems.
3. An operational system is required for most of the methods. The use of such methods during the design process would be limited.
4. Reliability is questionable.
5. Whilst the surveys address the design inadequacies of the interface, no assessment of performance is given.

Example

Control and display and labelling surveys were conducted on the auto-pilot panel of a civil aircraft (Marshall et al, 2003) to examine their potential for use in the identification of design induced pilot error. Extracts of each survey are presented in Table 10.3 and Table 10.4.

Related Methods

Interface surveys are conducted on the basis of observational study and walkthrough analysis data of the task under analysis. Additionally, interviews are often used to inform interface survey analysis.

Approximate Training and Application Times

The training time for each of the surveys is estimated to be very low. However, the application time of survey methods such as control and display survey and sightline survey is estimated to be very high. For example, a control and display survey involves recording each control and display used by the interface and then recording certain features regarding each control or display. This is a very time consuming and laborious process.

Reliability and Validity

No data regarding the reliability and validity of the method are presented in the literature. There may be problems associated with the intra- and inter-rater reliability of the method. For example, different analysts may derive different results for the same interface, and also the same analyst may derive different results when using the method for the same device or system on different occasions.

Table 10.3   Extract of Control and Display Survey for Aircraft X Autopilot Panel

Control			Parameter	Display		
Name	Type	Comments		Name	Type	Comments
Speed/Mach selector	Rotary knob	Speed/MACH knob is very similar to the heading knob. Potentially could be confused with each other	Airspeed	Speed/Mach window	Digital Numerical	Window is very small and located in close proximity to the airspeed window. It is possible that the two may be confused
Heading/Track selector knob	Rotary knob		Heading	Heading/Track window	Digital Numerical	Window is very small and located in close proximity to the heading window. It is possible that the two may be confused

Tools Needed

Most of the surveys described can be applied using pen and paper. The environmental survey requires the provision of equipment capable of measuring the relevant environmental conditions, including noise, temperature, lighting and humidity levels. The sightline survey requires the appropriate measurement equipment, such as a tape measures and rulers.

Table 10.4   Extract of Labelling Survey for Aircraft X Autopilot Panel

Label	Description	Clarity	Error potential
Speed/Mach selector knob	Blue triangle within rotary knob	Label is clear, No description of control included within the label	Control is easily confused with other knobs in close proximity e.g. speed/Mach selector knob
Heading/Track selector knob	No Label White rotary knob Same knob as the heading/track selector knob	N/A No description of control	Control is easily confused with other knobs in close proximity e.g. heading/track selector knob
Localiser	White 'LOC' text located within black push button control	Very clear LOC easily translated into localiser	Control is similar in form to a number of others. However, the label is clear and identification of the control is immediate

Flowchart

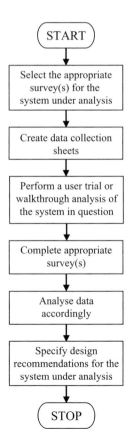

Link Analysis

Background and Applications

Link analysis is an interface evaluation method that is used to identify and represent 'links' in a system between interface components and operations and to determine the nature, frequency and importance of these links. Links are defined as movements of attentional gaze or position between parts of the system, or communication with other system elements. For example, if an actor is required to press button A and then button B in sequence to accomplish a particular task, a link between button's A and B is recorded. Link analysis uses spatial diagrams to represent the links within the system or device under analysis, with each link represented by a straight line between the 'linked' interface elements. Specifically aimed at aiding the design of interfaces and systems, link analyses' most obvious use is in the area of workspace-layout optimisation (Stanton and Young, 1999) i.e. the placement of controls and displays according first to their importance, then to their frequency of use, then to their function within the system and finally to their sequence of use. Link analysis was originally developed for use in the design and evaluation of process control rooms (Stanton and Young, 1999) but it can be applied to any system where the user exhibits hand or eye movements, including driving, control room operation, aviation, and air traffic control. When conducting a link analysis, establishing the links between system/interface components is normally achieved through a walkthrough or observational study of the task(s) under analysis. The output of a link analysis is normally a link diagram and also a link table (both depict the same information). The link diagram and table can be used to suggest revised layouts of the components for the device, based on the premise that links should be minimised in length, particularly if they are important or frequently used.

Domain of Application

Generic.

Procedure and Advice

Step 1: Define task(s) under analysis
The first step in a link analysis involves clearly defining the task(s) under analysis. When using link analysis to evaluate the interface layout of a particular device or system, it is recommended that a set of tasks that are as representative of the full functionality of the device or system are used. It is normally useful to conduct a HTA for normal operation of the device or system in question at this stage, as the output can be used to specify the tasks that are to be analysed and also allows the analyst(s) involved to gain a deeper understanding of the tasks and the device under analysis.

Step 2: Task analysis/list
Once the task(s) under analysis are clearly defined, a task list including (in order) all of the component task steps involved should be created. The task list can be derived from the HTA. Typically a link analysis is based upon the bottom-level tasks or operations identified in the HTA developed during step 1.

Step 3: Data collection
The analyst should then proceed to collect data regarding the tasks under analysis. This normally includes performing a walkthrough of the task steps contained in the task list and also observational

study of the task(s) in question. The analyst should record which components are linked by hand/eye movements and how many times these links occur during the tasks performed.

Step 4: Construct link diagram

Once the data collection phase is complete, construction of the link diagram can begin. This involves creating a schematic layout of the device/system/interface under analysis and adding the links between interface elements recorded during the data collection phase. Links are typically represented in the form of lines joining the linked interface elements or components. The frequency of the links is represented by the number of lines linking each interface element e.g. seven lines linking interface elements A and B represents a total of seven links between the two interface elements during the tasks under analysis.

Step 5: Link table

The link diagram is accompanied by a link table, which displays the same information as the link diagram, only in a tabular format. Components take positions at the heads of the rows and columns and the numbers of links are entered in the appropriate cells.

Step 6: Redesign proposals

Although not compulsory as part of a link analysis, a redesign for the interface under analysis is normally offered, based upon the links defined between the interface elements during the analysis. The redesign is based upon reducing the distance between the linked interface components; particularly the most important and frequently used linked components.

Advantages

1. Link analysis is a very simple method that requires only minimal training.
2. Link analysis is a quick method that offers an immediately useful output.
3. Link analysis output helps to generate design improvements.
4. Link analysis has been used extensively in the past in a number of domains.
5. Link analysis output prompts logical redesign of system interfaces.
6. Link analysis can be used throughout the design process to evaluate and modify design concepts.

Disadvantages

1. A link analysis requires preliminary data collection, including observational study and a walkthrough analysis of the task(s) under analysis.
2. The development of a HTA adds considerable time to the analysis.
3. Link analysis only considers the basic physical relationship between the user and the system. Cognitive processes and error mechanisms are not accounted for.
4. Link analysis output is not easily quantifiable.

Flowchart

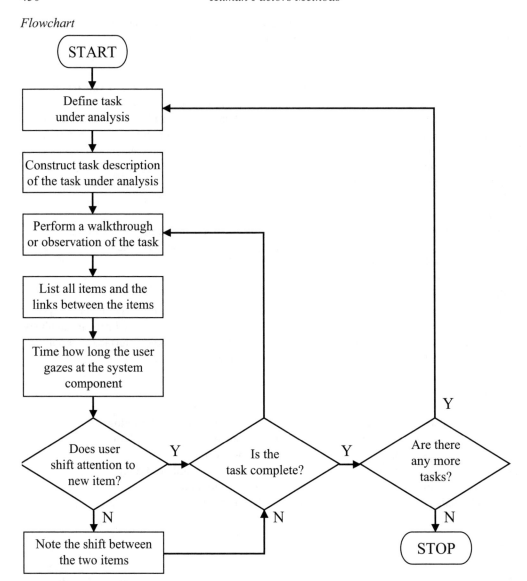

Example

The following example presents the results of a link analysis performed on the SHARP RG-F832E In-Car Radio (Stanton and Young, 1999).

Task List
- Switch unit on
- Adjust Volume
- Adjust Bass
- Adjust Treble
- Adjust Balance
- Choose new Pre-set

- Use Seek, then Store station
- Use Manual search, then store station
- Insert Cassette
- Autoreverse, then Fast Forward
- Eject cassette and switch off

Table 10.5   Table Showing Ford In-Car Radio Components and Functions (Stanton and Young, 1999)

A = On/Off/Volume/Balance/Fader	H = Tape Eject Button
B = Treble Bass	I = Cassette Compartment
C = Station Preset Buttons	J = Fast Wind/Programme Buttons
D = FM Mono Stereo Button	K = Tuning Up/Down Buttons
E = DX-Local Button	L = Tuning Scan/Seek Buttons
F = Band Selector Button	M = Tuning Scan/Seek Buttons
G = ASPM/Preset Memory Scan Button	

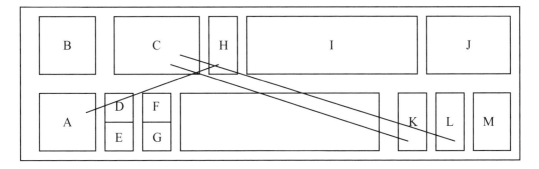

Figure 10.1   Link Diagram for Ford In-Car Radio (Stanton and Young, 1999)

Table 10.6   Link Table for Ford In-Car Radio (Stanton and Young, 1999)

	A	B	C	D	E	F	G	H	I	J	K	L	M
A	X												
B		X											
C			X										
D				X									
E					X								
F						X							
G							X						
H	1							X					
I									X				
J										X			
K		1									X		
L		1										X	
M													X

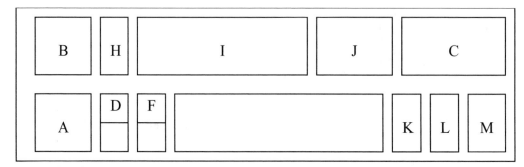

Figure 10.2   Revised Design for Ford In-Car Radio (Stanton and Young, 1999)

Related Methods

A link analysis normally requires an initial task description to be created for the task under analysis, such as a HTA. Also, an observation or walkthrough analysis of the task(s) under analysis should be performed in order to establish the links between components in the system.

Approximate Training and Application Times

In conclusion to a comparison of twelve ergonomics methods, Stanton and Young (1999) report that the link analysis method is relatively fast to train and practise and also that execution time is moderate compared to the other methods (e.g. SHERPA, layout analysis, repertory grids, checklists and TAFEI).

Reliability and Validity

In conclusion to the comparison study described above, Stanton and Young (1999) reported that link analysis performed particularly well on measures of intra-rater reliability and predictive validity. They also reported, however, that the method was let down by poor inter-rater reliability.

Tools Needed

When conducting a link analysis the analyst should have the device under analysis, pen and paper, and a stopwatch. For the observation part of the analysis, a video recording device is required. An eye tracker device can also be used to record fixations during the task performance.

Layout Analysis

Background and Applications

Layout analysis is similar to link analysis in that it is based on spatial diagrams of the product and its output directly addresses interface design. Layout analysis is used to analyse existing designs and suggests improvements to the interface arrangements based on functional grouping. The theory behind layout analysis is that the interface should mirror the user's structure of the task and the conception of the interface as a task map greatly facilitates design (Easterby, 1984). A layout analysis begins by simply arranging all of the components of the interface into functional groupings. These groups are then organised by their importance of use, sequence of use and frequency of use. The components within each functional group are then reorganised, once more this is done according to importance, sequence and frequency of use. The components within a functional group will then stay in that group throughout the analysis and they cannot move anywhere else in the reorganisation stage. At the end of the process, the analyst has redesigned the device in accordance with the user's model of the task based upon importance, sequence and frequency of use.

Domain of Application

Generic.

Procedure and Advice

Step 1: Schematic diagram
First, the analyst should create a schematic diagram for the device under analysis. This diagram should contain each (clearly labelled) interface element.

Step 2: Arrange interface components into functional groupings
The analyst begins by arranging the interface components into functional groupings. Each interface element should be grouped according to its function in relation to the device under analysis. For example, the interface components of a Ford In-Car Radio were arranged into the functional groups *radio* and *cassette* (Stanton and Young, 1999). This part of the analysis is based entirely upon the subjective judgement of the analyst involved.

Step 3: Arrange functional groupings into importance of use
Next, the analyst should arrange the functional groupings into importance of use. The analyst may want to make the most important functional group the most readily available on the interface. Again this is based entirely on the analyst's subjective judgement.

Step 4: Arrange functional groupings into sequence of use
The analyst should then repeat step 3, only this time arranging the functional groupings based upon their sequence of use.

Step 5: Arrange functional groupings into frequency of use
The analyst should then repeat step 3, only this time arranging the functional groupings based upon their frequency of use. At the end of the process, the analyst has redesigned the device according to the end users' model of the task (Stanton and Young, 1999).

Step 6: Redesign the interface
Once the functional groups have been organised based upon their importance, sequence and frequency of use, the interface should be redesigned. The analyst should base the interface redesign upon the three categories (importance, sequence, frequency of use). For example, the analyst may wish to make the most important and frequently used aspect of the interface the most readily available.

Flowchart

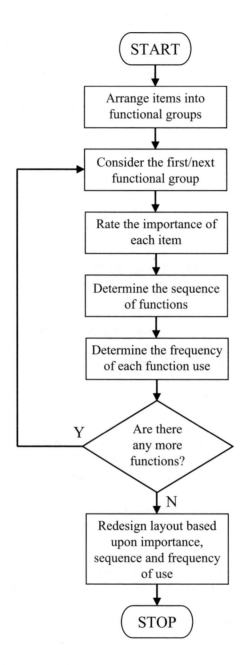

Advantages

1. Layout analysis offers a quick, easy to use and low-cost approach to interface design and evaluation.
2. Low resource usage.
3. Layout analysis requires only minimal training.
4. Can be applied to paper diagrams of the device/interface under analysis.

5. The output provided by the method is immediately useful, offering a redesign of the interface under analysis based upon importance, sequence and frequency of use of the interface elements.

Disadvantages

1. Poor reliability and validity (Stanton and Young, 1999).
2. The output of the method is very limited i.e. it only caters for layout. Errors, MWL and task performance times are ignored.
3. Literature regarding layout analysis is extremely sparse.
4. If an initial HTA is required, application time can rise dramatically.
5. Conducting a layout analysis for complex interfaces may be very difficult and time consuming.

Example

The following layout analysis was conducted on a SHARP RG-F832E In-Car Radio (Stanton and Young, 1999)

Initial design

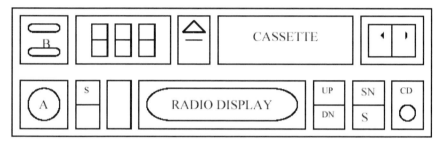

Functional groupings

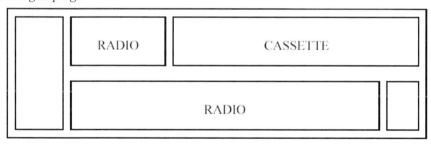

Importance of use

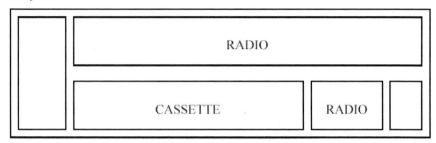

Sequence of use

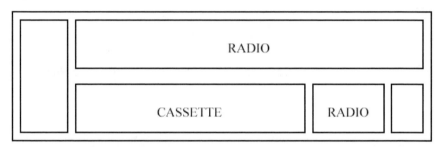

Within functional groupings

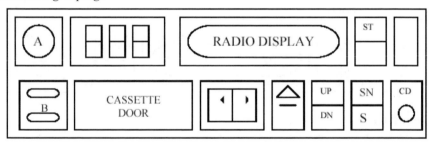

Redesign based upon importance, frequency and sequence of use

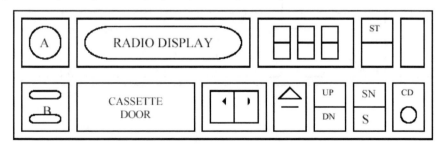

Related Methods

Layout analysis is very similar to link analysis in its approach to interface design.

Approximate Training and Application Times

In conclusion to a comparison study of 12 ergonomics methods, Stanton and Young (1999) report that little training is required for layout analysis and that it is amongst the quickest of 12 methods to apply. It is therefore estimated that the training and application times associated with the method are low. However, if an initial HTA is required, the application time would rise considerably.

Reliability and Validity

In conclusion to a comparison study of twelve ergonomics methods, Stanton and Young (1999) report poor statistics for intra-rater reliability and predictive validity for layout analysis.

Tools Needed

A layout analysis can be conducted using pen and paper, providing the device or pictures of the device under analysis are available.

Questionnaire for User Interface Satisfaction (QUIS)

Background and Applications

The questionnaire for user interface satisfaction (QUIS) is a questionnaire method that is used to assess user acceptance and opinions of human-computer interfaces. The QUIS method is used to elicit subjective user opinions on all usability related aspects of an interface, including ease of use, system capability, consistency and learning. There are a number of different versions of the QUIS method available. QUIS uses questions relating to the use of human-computer interfaces. Each question has an associated rating scale, typically ascending from 1 to 10. Examples of the QUIS statements are presented in Figure 10.3 (Source: Chin, Diehl and Norman, 1988).

Organisation of information on screen

Confusing   Very clear

0	1	2	3	4	5	6	7	8	9

Learning to operate the system

Difficult   Easy

0	1	2	3	4	5	6	7	8	9

Computer keeps you informed about what it is doing

Never   Always

0	1	2	3	4	5	6	7	8	9

Figure 10.3   Example QUIS Statements

Procedure and Advice

Step 1: Identify user sample
The first step in a QUIS analysis is to identify the user sample that will be used in the analysis. It is recommended that the user sample used represents a portion of the typical users of the software system or type of software system under analysis. It may be most pertinent to use a sample of end users of the system in question.

Step 2: Define representative task list for the system under analysis
Once the participant sample has been defined, the analyst(s) should develop a representative task list for the software system under analysis. This task list should be exhaustive, representing every possible task that can be performed using the system under analysis. This task list represents the set of tasks that the participants will perform during the analysis. If the task list is too great (i.e. requires more time to complete than is allowed by the scope of the analysis), then the analyst should pick as representative a set of tasks as possible. It is recommended that a HTA for the software system under analysis be used to develop the task list.

Step 3: QUIS briefing session
Before the task performance step of the QUIS analysis, the participants should be briefed regarding the purpose of the analysis and how to complete the QUIS questionnaire. It may be useful for the analyst(s) to run through the task list and the QUIS questionnaire, explaining any statements that may cause confusion. In some cases, a demonstration of the tasks required may be pertinent. The participants should be encouraged to ask any questions regarding the completion of the QUIS questionnaire and the task list at this point.

Step 4: Task performance
Once the participant sample and task list have been defined, and the participants fully understand the tasks that they are required to perform and also how to complete the QUIS questionnaire, the task performance can begin. The participants should now be given the task list and instructed to perform, as normal, the tasks in the order that they are specified using the system under analysis. It is important that no conferring between participants takes place during the task performance, and also that no help is administered by the analyst(s). The task performance should go on as long as is required for each participant to complete the required task list.

Step 5: Administer QUIS questionnaire
QUIS is normally administered post-trial. Once all of the participants have completed the task list for the software system under analysis, the QUIS questionnaire should be administered. After a brief demonstration of how to complete the QUIS questionnaire, the participants should be instructed to complete the questionnaire, basing their responses on the tasks that they have just carried out with the interface in question. Again, no conferring between participants is permitted during this step, although the analyst(s) may assist the participants with statements that they do not understand.

Step 6: Calculate global and sub-scale QUIS scores
Once all of the QUIS questionnaires are completed and handed in, the scoring process begins. The analyst may choose to calculate a global QUIS score and scores for each of the separate QUIS sub-scales (e.g. system capability, learning, screen, terminology and system information). These scores can then be averaged across participants in order to obtain mean scores for the system under analysis.

Advantages

1. QUIS is a very quick and easy method to use, requiring only minimal training.
2. The output of QUIS is immediately useful, offering an insight into the system users' attitudes regarding the usability of the interface under analysis.
3. If the correct sample is used, the data obtained is potentially very powerful, offering an end-user rating of system usability.
4. Once an operational system is available, the speed, ease and usefulness of QUIS allow it to be used repeatedly throughout the design lifecycle to evaluate and modify design concepts.
5. Encouraging reliability and validity statistics.
6. The QUIS can be modified to suit analysis needs. For example, QUIS statements can be added and removed in order to make the analysis more suitable for the software system under analysis.
7. Can be used effectively even with small sample sizes.

Disadvantages

1. QUIS is limited to the analysis of HCI devices.

Related Methods

The QUIS method is a questionnaire method used for the analysis of HCI interfaces. There are a number of similar methods which use attitude scales to assess the usability of a device or system, such as CUSI, SUMI, the system usability scale (SUS) method and the WAMMI method.

Approximate Training and Application Times

The training time for the QUIS method is very low, with little or no training required. In terms of application time, it is estimated that the QUIS questionnaire would take between five and twenty minutes to complete. However, the total time for a QUIS analysis is dependent upon the length of the task performance stage i.e. the number of tasks that the participants are required to perform before they complete the QUIS questionnaire. It is estimated that the total application time for QUIS is low, and that even in scenarios where the task list is very large, the total application time would probably not exceed two hours.

Reliability and Validity

Chin et al (1988) report a number of studies designed to assess the reliability and validity of the QUIS questionnaire. In a study using QUIS versions 3.0 and 4.0 to assess the interactive batch run IBM mainframe and an interactive syntax-directed editor programme environment, QUIS was found to have a high level of reliability (Version 3.0, .94, Version 4.0, .89, Cronbach's alpha). In another study, QUIS version 5.0 was used by participants to evaluate a product that they liked, a product that they disliked, MS-DOS, and another comparable software product (e.g. WordStar™, WordPerfect™, Lotus™, Dbase™ etc). Overall reliability was reported as .94 (Cronbach's alpha). Establishing the validity of the method has proved more difficult, and there is limited data regarding this available in the literature. According to Chin et al (1988) there are two reasons for the difficulty in establishing the validity of the method. Firstly, there is a lack of theoretical constructs regarding HCI with which to test QUIS, and secondly, there is a lack of established questionnaires that are available for cross-validating purposes.

Tools Needed

QUIS is normally applied using pen and paper. An operational version of the interface under analysis is also required for the task performance component of the QUIS analysis. A computerised version of QUIS is also available.

Flowchart

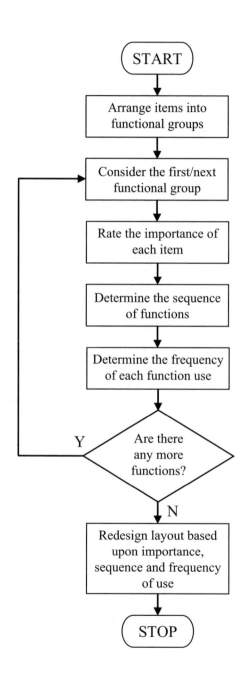

Repertory Grid Analysis

Background and Applications

The repertory grid method is an interview-based method that can be used to analyse participant perceptions or views regarding a set of similar products, systems or devices. Repertory grid analysis can be used either in the early design life cycle in order to provide an insight into how potential users think about the product in question, and to specify product requirements and design preferences, or to evaluate existing product designs in terms of user attitudes. The method was originally developed as a technique for analysing personality and according to Baber (2004a) was originally used to study patient interaction with other people e.g. for examining responses to authority or attachment. Repertory grids have since been employed for a number of different purposes, including for product evaluations of in-car radio players (Stanton and Young, 1999), and microwave ovens (Baber 1996), the evaluation of different text types (Dillon and McKnight, 1990), the evaluation of consumer behaviour (Baber, 1996) and for the evaluation of collaboration (Shuler, 1990). Furthermore, Baber (1996) suggests that the repertory grid method has the potential to be used for a wide range of purposes. The method involves presenting a single participant with a set of similar products or proposed product designs and eliciting constructs and contrasts for these items. Each construct and contrast is then analysed in relation to each product under analysis, and a set of factors for the product group is specified. The output of a repertory grid can either be qualitative or quantitative.

Domain of Application

Generic.

Procedure and Advice

The following procedure is adapted from Baber (2004a).

Step 1: Determine products/devices to be compared
The first step in a repertory grid analysis is to determine which products or devices will be compared. If the analysis is based upon an early design concept, a number of different design concepts may be compared. If the analysis based upon the evaluation of existing products or devices, then each item should possess a common feature of some sort. It is useful at this stage to provide a description that caters for all of the items together, in order to clarify the relation between the items. Baber (2004a) described a repertory grid analysis of 'wearable technology items'. The three items compared in this analysis were wristwatches, head-mounted displays and GPS units.

Step 2: Brief the participant
Once the items under analysis are defined, the participant should be briefed regarding their role in the analysis i.e. inform the participant that they are required to select one item and a short word or phrase to justify that item's selection.

Step 3: Determine constructs
Using the objects under analysis (or photographs of them), the analyst should present each item to the participant, along with a short description. The participant should then be encouraged to decide which of the two items are the most similar, and then to describe how the third item is

different. According to Baber (2004a) it is crucial that the participant provides a reason for their selection(s), and it is also useful for the analyst and participant to agree on a short word or phrase that describes the construct for the triad. Step 3 should be repeated until no further constructs are generated. Baber (1996) suggests that this step is repeated until the participant is unable to offer any new constructs.

Step 4: Construct repertory grid table
Once all of the constructs are noted, the analyst should construct the repertory grid table. Each product or device should appear across the top row, and the constructs should appear down the right hand column of the table.

Step 5: Define contrasts or opposites
Next, the analyst has to gather a contrast or opposite for each construct identified from the participant. This involves probing the participant for an opposite for each construct in the repertory grid table. Table 10.7 displays the constructs and their contrasts identified by Stanton and Young (1999) in a product evaluation of two in-car radio players.

Table 10.7   Constructs and Contrasts for two In-Car Radio Players (Source: Stanton and Young, 1999)

Constructs	Contrasts
Mode dependent	Separate functions
Push-button operation	Knob-turn operation
Bad labelling	Clear labelling
Easy controls	Fiddly controls
Poor functional grouping	Good functional grouping
Good illumination	Poor illumination

Step 6: Relate constructs to items
Next, the participant should be asked to state whether or not each construct 'fits' each item or product i.e. does radio A have bad labelling, or good labelling? Only a 'yes' or 'no' answer should be given by the participant. Each 'yes' response is represented by a '1' in the repertory grid table. Each 'no' is represented by a '0' in the repertory grid table.

Step 7: Review repertory grid table
Step 7 acts as a check that each construct in the repertory grid table is scored correctly. The analyst simply takes the participant through each product and construct in the repertory grid table and ensures that the participant agrees with the scores given.

Step 8: Perform first pass analysis
The 'first pass' (Baber, 2004a) involves constructing a template in order to determine the membership of the group. For each product or device included in the analysis, the columns should be summed (0's and 1's). The value for each column is then entered in the appropriate column at the foot of the table. To convert these totals into a template, the analyst should define a numerical cut-off point in the totals. Each column total equal to or below the cut-off point is assigned a 0, whilst each column total above the cut-off total is assigned a 1. The template values should then be added to their appropriate columns, underneath the relevant column totals.

Step 9: Compare template with constructs
Once the template is entered into the repertory grid table, the analyst should compare the template with each construct. To do this, the template is overlaid upon each construct line in the repertory grid table. For all those cases where the template value matches the corresponding construct value, a 1 should be added to the score. If there are fewer than ½ matches, then a – score is assigned and the analyst proceeds to step 10. If not, the total should be calculated and entered into the table. Once the table is complete, the analyst should proceed to step 11.

Step 10: Reflection phase
If the construct value is not matched to the template value, then the analyst should reverse the construct/ contrast. The reflection phase is used to remove any negative scores from the repertory grid.

Step 12: Define groups
Next, the analyst should define the groups of constructs. The method assumes binomial distribution of responses, i.e., a statistical majority is required before a group can be defined.

Step 13: Name factors
The participant is then asked to provide names for any factors that have been identified i.e. in an analysis of microwave ovens (Baber, 1996), the group of constructs touch pad, digital clock, > 90 minute timer, memory and delay start were named 'technical sophistication'.

Step 14: Discuss products
The factors, and their names, are then used to discuss the products.

Example (Source: Baber, 1996)

The following example is a repertory grid analysis of the factors influencing consumer decisions involved in the selection of a microwave oven (Baber, 1996). Eight microwave ovens were used, along with one female participant.
    The construct elicitation phase was conducted using photographs of the products combined with additional details provided by the manufacturers. The subject was presented with three photographs and asked to provide a construct to define a pair. The resultant constructs and their contrasts are shown in Table 10.8.

Table 10.8   Constructs and Contrasts for Microwave Ovens (adapted from Baber, 1996)

Construct	Contrast
Dials	Touch pad
<800W	>800W
Clock	No clock
White	Black
Timer (90 min)	<90min
Memory	No memory
Grill	No grill
<5 settings	>5 settings
Defrost	No defrost
Button (door)	Lever (door)
<£130	>£130
Fitted plug	No plug
Delay start	No delay
<0.8ft3 capacity	>0.8ft3 capacity

The participant then rated each item and associated construct. A 1 value represents an agreement between the item and construct, whilst a 0 value represents an agreement between the item and its contrast. Next, each column is summed and a template is created. The cut-off point defined for this analysis is 7. Therefore, all those scores above 7 are scored as 1, whilst all those equal to or less than 7 are scored as 0. The template is then overlaid and the number of matches between the values in the repertory grid table and the template are calculated. Column Fla in Table 10.9 shows the total number of matches or 'hits'. If there are more hits than misses then a negative score is placed in the Fla column. If there are more hits than misses, then a positive score is assigned. If there are an equal number of hits and misses, then 0 is entered into the column. Table 10.9 shows the initial repertory grid table and first pass analysis.

Table 10.9   Initial Repertory Grid Table and First Pass Analysis

Item number										
1	2	3	4	5	6	7	8	Construct	Contrast	Fla
1	1	1	0	0	0	0	0	Dials	Touch pad	-7
1	1	1	1	0	1	0	1	<800W	>800W	4
0	0	0	1	1	1	1	1	Clock	No clock	7
1	1	1	1	1	1	0	1	White	Black	5
0	0	0	1	1	1	1	1	Timer (90 min)	<90min	7
0	0	0	1	1	1	0	1	Memory	No memory	8
0	0	0	0	0	0	0	1	Grill	No grill	5
1	1	0	0	1	0	0	1	<5 settings	>5 settings	0
0	0	0	0	1	1	1	1	Defrost	No defrost	6
1	0	1	1	1	1	1	0	Button (door)	Lever (door)	0
1	1	1	1	0	0	0	0	<£130	>£130	-6
0	0	1	1	0	0	0	0	Fitted plug	No plug	0
0	0	0	1	1	1	1	1	Delay start	No delay	7
1	1	1	1	0	1	0	1	<0.8ft3 capacity	>0.8ft3 capacity	0
7	6	7	10	8	9	5	10	<0.8ft3 capacity	>0.8ft3 capacity	

Next, the 'reflection phase' is used to remove any negative scores from the repertory grid table (Baber, 1996). This is achieved by reversing the construct/contrast. Table 10.10 shows the repertory grid after the reflection phase.

Table 10.10   Modified Repertory Grid Table

Item number										
1	2	3	4	5	6	7	8	Construct	Contrast	Fla
1	1	1	0	0	0	0	0	Dials	Touch pad	7
1	1	1	1	0	1	0	1	<800W	>800W	4
0	0	0	1	1	1	1	1	Clock	No clock	7
1	1	1	1	1	1	0	1	White	Black	5
0	0	0	1	1	1	1	1	Timer (90 min)	<90min	7
0	0	0	1	1	1	0	1	Memory	No memory	8
0	0	0	0	0	0	0	1	Grill	No grill	5
1	1	0	0	1	0	0	1	<5 settings	>5 settings	0
0	0	0	1	1	1	1	1	Defrost	No defrost	6
1	0	1	1	1	1	1	0	Button (door)	Lever (door)	0
1	1	1	1	0	0	0	0	<£130	>£130	6
0	0	1	1	0	0	0	0	Fitted plug	No plug	0
0	0	0	1	1	1	1	1	Delay start	No delay	7
1	1	1	1	0	1	0	1	<0.8ft3 capacity	>0.8ft3 capacity	0
7	6	7	10	8	9	5	10	<0.8ft3 capacity	>0.8ft3 capacity	
0	0	0	1	1	1	0	1			

Once the reflection phase is complete, common constructs are extracted from the repertory grid. According to Baber (1996) binomial theorem is used to determine the probability of matches between reference and construct rows occurring by chance. The following sets of related constructs were extracted in this case.

F1=   Touch pad
       Digital clock
       >90 min timer
       Memory
       Delay start

A further four passes were conducted, and the following four factors were defined.

F3=   Power settings, plug
F4=   <800W, defrost, <£130
F5=   <0.8ft2 capacity
F6=   White, grill

Following this, a label for each construct group factor was provided by the subject. Table 10.11 shows the construct groups and their labels.

Table 10.11   Construct Groups and their Labels

Pass	No. reflections	Constructs	Factor label
1	1	Touch pad	
		Digital clock	
		>90 min timer	
		Memory	
		Delay start	'technical sophistication'
2	0	Lever/push button	'door operation'
3	1	Power settings	
		Fitted plug	'electrics'
4	2	<800W	
		Defrost	
		<£130	'buying points'
5	0	<0.8ft3 capacity	'size'
6	0	White	
		Grill	'appearance'

The resultant groupings reflect the participant's consideration of the products used in the analysis (Baber, 1996).

Advantages

1. Structured and thorough procedure.
2. The method is generic and can be applied in any domain for any product, system or device.
3. A very easy method to use.
4. Can be used in the early design lifecycle in order to determine user opinions on what the design should include, or with existing products for evaluation purposes.

5. Repertory grid analysis output is very useful, providing an insight into user perceptions and attitudes.
6. Little training required.

Disadvantages

1. The repertory grid procedure is a long and drawn out one.
2. Tedious and time consuming in its application.
3. According to Baber (1996), repertory grid analysis does not always produce usable factors.
4. If quantitative analysis is required, additional training is also needed.
5. The reliability and validity of the method is questionable.
6. Knowledge of statistics is required.

Flowchart

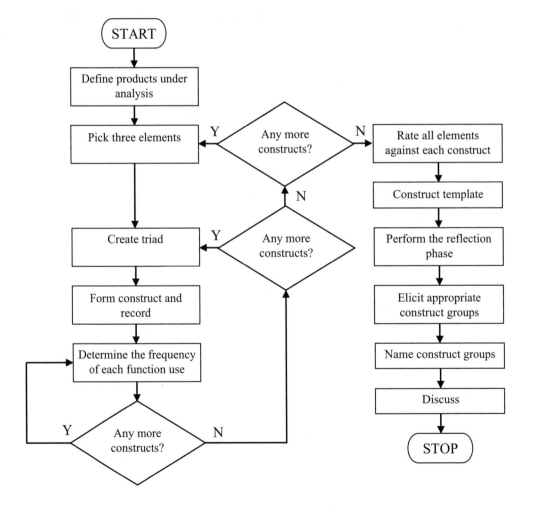

Related Methods

The repertory grid analysis method is an interview-based knowledge elicitation technique. According to Baber (2004a) there are numerous techniques available to the HF practitioner for knowledge elicitation purposes.

Approximate Training and Application Times

Stanton and Young (1999) report a moderate training and application time for the repertory grid method. According to Baber (2004a) analysts can become proficient users of the method within two to three hours. However, both Stanton and Young (1999) and Baber (2004a) suggest that further practice for the repertory grid method is very useful. For its application time, Baber (1996) reports that time taken for the construct elicitation phase depends upon a number of variables, such as the willingness of the subject, the similarity between the items and the number of items used. However, Baber (1996) suggests that the method is a very quick one to use, with an example based upon a repertory grid analysis of the factors influencing consumer decisions involved in the selection of a microwave oven (see example section) taking only 30 minutes to complete (analysis, reflection and factoring).

Reliability and Validity

Baber (1996) reports that the issue of reliability with the method requires consideration and that it is very difficult to determine an appropriate measure of reliability for repertory grids. In a study comparing 12 ergonomics methods when used for product evaluation purposes, Stanton and Young (1999) report a reasonable level of validity for the method. From the same study, an acceptable level of intra-rater reliability was reported, along with a poor level of inter-rater reliability. It is apparent then, that the reliability and validity of the repertory grid method is questionable, and that further testing is required.

Tools Needed

The repertory grid method can be conducted using only pen and paper.

Software Usability Measurement Inventory (SUMI)

Background and Applications

The software usability measurement inventory (SUMI, Kirakowski, 1996) is a questionnaire method that uses 50 attitude scale statements in order to measure the usability of software systems. The method was developed as part of a CEC supported ESPIRIT project 5429, entitled 'measuring usability of systems in context' (MUSIC; Kirakowski, 1996) one of the main aims of which was to develop questionnaire methods for assessing usability (Kirakowski, 1996). SUMI comprises 50 attitude statements, each with a three-point response scale of 'agree', 'don't know' or 'disagree'. A number of example SUMI statements are presented below (Source: Kirakowski 1996).

- This software responds too slowly to inputs.
- The instructions and prompts are helpful.

- The way that system information is presented is clear and understandable.
- I would not like to use this software everyday.

According to Kirakowski (1996) SUMI can be applied to any software system that has a display, a keyboard (or other data entry device) and a peripheral memory device such as a disk drive. When using SUMI, the sample group are given a representative set of tasks to perform with the system under analysis and then are asked to complete the SUMI questionnaire. In scoring the participant responses, Kirakowski (1996) reports that the SUMI method provides the following results:

Global usability score. Represents an overall rating of the system's usability.
The following five usability sub-scale scores:

- *Affect.* Represents the user's general reaction to the software.
- *Efficiency.* Represents the degree to which the user feels that the software has assisted them in their task.
- *Helpfulness.* Represents the degree to which the software is self-explanatory.
- *Control.* Represents the extent to which the user feels in control.
- *Learnability.* Represents the speed with which the user has been able to master the system.
- *Item consensual analysis.* Represents a method of questionnaire analysis that was developed especially for the SUMI questionnaire. The item consensual analysis involves using a database to generate expected response patterns for each SUMI item. The expected response patterns are then compared to the actual response patterns in order to determine those aspects that are unique to the system under analysis, and also those aspects that require further development.

SUMI has been extensively used in the past for a number of different purposes. Kirakowski (1996) describes the following uses of SUMI:

- Assessing new products during product evaluation.
- Product comparisons.
- To set targets for future application development.
- To set verifiable goals for quality of use attainment.
- To track achievement of targets during product development.
- To highlight the good and bad points of interfaces.

Procedure and Advice

Step 1: Identify user sample
The first step in a SUMI analysis is to identify the user sample that will be used in the analysis. Kirakowski (1996) suggests that a minimal sample size of 10-12 participants should be used. It is recommended that the user sample used in the analysis represent a portion of the typical users of the software system or type of software system under analysis.

Step 2: Define representative task list for the system under analysis
Once the participant sample has been defined, the analyst(s) should develop a representative task list for the software system under analysis. This task list should be exhaustive, representing every possible task that can be performed using the system under analysis. This task list represents the set of tasks that the participants will perform during the analysis. If the task list is too great (i.e.

requires more time to complete than is allowed by the scope of the analysis), then the analyst should pick as representative a set of tasks as possible. It is recommended that a HTA for the software system under analysis be used to develop the task list.

Step 3: SUMI briefing session
Before the task performance step of the SUMI analysis, the participants should be briefed regarding the purpose of the analysis and how to complete the SUMI questionnaire. It may be useful for the analyst(s) to quickly run through the task list and the SUMI questionnaire, explaining any statements that may cause confusion. In some cases, a demonstration of the tasks required may be pertinent. The participants should be encouraged to ask any questions regarding the completion of the SUMI questionnaire and the task list at this point.

Step 4: Task performance
Once the participant sample and task list have been defined, and the participants fully understand the tasks that they are required to perform and also how to complete the SUMI questionnaire, the task performance can begin. The participants should now be given the task list and asked to begin performing the tasks in the order that they are specified. It is important that no conferring between participants takes place during the task performance, and also that no help is administered by the analyst(s). The task performance should go on as long as is required for each participant to complete the required task list.

Step 5: Administer SUMI questionnaire
Once all of the participants have completed the task list for the software system under analysis, the SUMI questionnaire is administered. After a brief demonstration of how to complete the SUMI questionnaire, the participants should be instructed to complete the questionnaire. Again, no conferring between participants is permitted during this step, although the analyst(s) may assist the participants with statements that they do not understand.

Step 6: Calculate global SUMI score
Once all of the SUMI questionnaires are completed and handed in, the scoring process begins. The first score to be calculated for the software system under analysis is a global SUMI score for each participant. The global score represents an overall subjective rating of the system's usability.

Step 7: Calculate SUMI subscale scores
Next, the analyst(s) should calculate the SUMI subscale scores for each participant. Scores for efficiency, affect, helpfulness, control and learnabilty should be calculated for each participant.

Step 8: Perform item consensual analysis
Next, the analyst should use the SUMI database to generate expected response patterns for each SUMI item. These should then be compared to the actual responses gained during the analysis.

Advantages

1. SUMI is a very quick and easy method to use, requiring almost no training.
2. The output of SUMI is very useful, offering an insight into the system users' attitudes regarding the system's usability.
3. If the correct sample is used, the system's potential users are in effect rating the usability of the system.

4. Once an operational system is available, the speed, ease and usefulness of SUMI mean that it can be used again and again to evaluate and modify the design concept.
5. Encouraging reliability and validity statistics.
6. SUMI statements can be added and removed in order to make the analysis more suitable for the software system in question.
7. Can be used effectively even with small sample sizes.8.
8. The scoring process is computerised.
9. SUMI is recognised by the ISO as a method for testing user satisfaction.

Disadvantages

1. Developed specifically for software systems containing a display, a data input device and a peripheral memory device. If the system under analysis does not possess all of these facets, some modification of the SUMI statements would be required.
2. The method is only available commercially, and costs over one thousand Euros to purchase.

Example (Adapted from Kirakowski, 1996)

Kirakowski (1996) describes three examples of the successful application of the SUMI method.

Analysis A – SUMI was used by a company to evaluate the existing software systems that were currently in use in their offices. The results of the SUMI analysis highlighted the software that needed to be replaced.

Analysis B – SUMI was used by a company who were about to purchase a new data entry system, to evaluate the two possible systems. The company wished to involve the end users in the selection process. A number of staff were used to evaluate both of the systems using the SUMI method. Low learnability profile scores for the chosen system prompted the company to bid for an improved training and support system for the software.

Analysis C – SUMI was used by a company to evaluate a new GUI version of a software package and the old version. In most of the SUMI sub-scales, the new interface was rated as worse than the old one. The company checked this and discovered that the interface for the new system became too complicated and also took too long to operate. As a result, the release of the new version was postponed and a further redesign based upon the SUMI evaluation results was undertaken.

Related Methods

The SUMI method is a questionnaire technique used for the assessment of the software systems. There are a number of similar methods which use attitude scales to assess the usability of a device or system, such as CUSI, which SUMI is based upon, the questionnaire for user interface (QUIS) method, the system usability scales (SUS) method and the WAMMI method.

Approximate Training and Application Times

The training time for the SUMI method is very low, with little or no training required. In terms of application time, according to Kirakowski (1996), the SUMI questionnaire should take no longer than five minutes to complete. At worst case, it is estimated that the application time for the SUMI questionnaire is ten minutes. Of course, the total time for a SUMI analysis is dependent upon the length of the task performance stage. The time associated with task performance is dependent upon the length of the task list used. It is estimated that the total application time for SUMI is very low, and that even in scenarios where the task list is very large, the total application time would not exceed two hours.

Flowchart

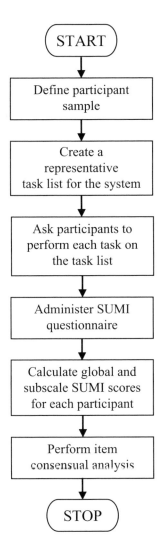

Reliability and Validity

Kirakowski (1996) describes a study reported by Kennedy (1992), where SUMI was used to compare two address book type databases. The first version of the database was an older version that used 'old-fashioned' language and concepts, whilst the second version was a more modern database that used a more user-orientated language and concepts. The two versions were thus labelled the 'unfriendly' and 'friendly' versions. An expert user group (experienced with similar databases) and a casual user group (no experience) conducted a small set of commands using one of the database versions. Upon completion of the designated task(s) participants completed a SUMI questionnaire. The results demonstrated that SUMI was able to differentiate between different levels of usability. The friendly version was rated as more usable by the expert group than the casual group, and both groups rated the friendly version as more efficient. Both groups also disliked the unfriendly version in terms of effect. The casual group rated the friendly version as more helpful than the expert group did.

Tools Needed

SUMI is typically applied using pen and paper. The software system under analysis is also required for the task performance component of the SUMI analysis. The SUMI method is available as an MS windows compliant software application.

System Usability Scale (SUS)

Background and Applications

The system usability scale (SUS) offers a very quick and simple to use questionnaire designed to assess the usability of a particular device or product. The SUS consists of ten usability statements that are rated on a likert scale of 1 (strongly agree with statement) to 5 (strongly disagree with statement). Answers are coded and a total usability score is derived for the product or device under analysis.

Domain of Application

Generic.

Procedure and Advice

Step 1: Create exhaustive task list for the device under analysis
Initially, the analyst(s) should develop an exhaustive task list for the product or device under analysis. This should include every possible action associated with the operation of the device. If this is not possible due to analysis time constraints, then the task list should be as representative of the full functionality of the device as possible. A HTA is normally used for this purpose.

Step 2: User trial
Next, the participant(s) should complete a thorough user trial for the device or product under analysis. The participant(s) should be instructed to perform every task on the task list given to them.

Step 3: Complete SUS questionnaire
Once the participant(s) have completed the appropriate task list, they should be given the SUS questionnaire and instructed to complete it, based upon their opinions of the device under analysis.

Step 4: Calculate SUS score for the device under analysis
Once completed, the SUS questionnaire score is calculated in order to derive a usability score for the device under analysis. Scoring an SUS questionnaire is a very simple process. Each item in the SUS scale is given a score between 0 and 4. The items are scored as follows (Stanton and Young 1999):

- The score for odd numbered items is the scale position e.g. 1, 2, 3, 4 or 5 minus 1.
- The score for even numbered items 5 minus the associated scale position.
- The sum of the scores is then multiplied by 2.5.
- The final figure derived represents a usability score for the device under analysis and should range between 0 to 100.

Advantages

1. Very easy to use, requiring only minimal training.
2. Offers an immediately useful output in the form of a usability 'rating' for the device under analysis.
3. Very useful for canvassing user opinions of devices or products.
4. The scale is generic and so the scale can be applied in any domain.
5. The SUS scale is very useful when comparing two or more devices in terms of usability.
6. Its simplicity and speed of use mean that it is a very suitable method to use in conjunction with other usability assessment techniques.
7. Very quick in its application.
8. The scale can be adapted to make it more suitable for other domains.

Disadvantages

1. The output of the SUS is very limited.
2. Requires an operational version of the device or system under analysis.
3. Unsophisticated.

Example

Stanton and Young (1999) conducted a study comparing twelve ergonomics methods, one of which was the SUS technique. The SUS scale was used to rate the usability of two in-car radio cassette players, the Ford 7000 RDS-EON and the SHARP RG-F832E. SUS results for both devices are presented below.

Ford radio SUS scoring

Odd numbered items score = Scale position - 1
Item 1. 5 − 1 = 4
Item 3. 5 − 1 = 4
Item 5. 4 − 1 = 3
Item 7. 4 − 1 = 3
Item 9. 5 − 1 = 4
Total for odd-numbered items = 18
Grand total = 34
SUS usability score = grand total X 2.5
        = 34 X 2.5
        = **85**

Even numbered items score = 5 − scale position
Item 2. 5 − 2 = 3
Item 4. 5 − 1 = 4
Item 6. 4 − 1 = 3
Item 8. 4 − 2 = 2
Item 10. 5 − 3 = 2
Total for even-numbered items = 14

SHARP radio SUS scoring

Odd numbered items score = Scale position - 1
Item 1. 4 − 1 = 3
Item 3. 5 − 1 = 4
Item 5. 3 − 1 = 2
Item 7. 5 − 1 = 4
Item 9. 4 − 1 = 3
Total for odd-numbered items = 16

Even numbered items score = 5 − scale position
Item 2. 5 − 1 = 4
Item 4. 5 − 1 = 4
Item 6. 5 − 2 = 3
Item 8. 5 − 1 = 4
Item 10. 5 − 1 = 4
Total for even-numbered items = 19

Grand total = 35
SUS usability score = grand total X 2.5
      = 35 X 2.5
      = **87.5**

Flowchart

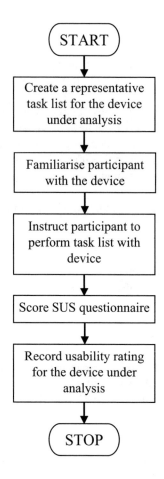

Related Methods

There are a number of other usability questionnaires available, such as SUMI, QUIS and WAMMI.

Training and Application Times

Both the training and application times for the SUS method are very low. Since the SUS scale uses only ten questions, it is very quick to train and apply. In conclusion to a study designed to compare twelve ergonomics techniques, Stanton and Young (1999) report that questionnaire methods such as the SUS are the quickest to train and apply.

In a comparison of twelve ergonomics techniques, SUS was tested in an analysis of two in-car radio cassettes (Stanton and Young, 1999). In conclusion, the SUS method failed to achieve a significance level for intra-rater reliability and predictive validity. Inter-rater reliability was also rated as moderate (on the method's second application trial) (Stanton and Young, 1999).

Tools Needed

The SUS method can be applied using pen and paper. The device or product under analysis is also required.

User Trials

Background and Applications

Employing user trials to test products or devices offers a simplistic and flexible means of evaluating a new product or design. User trials involve product or system end-users performing a series of tasks with a new product or device in order to evaluate various features associated with the usability of the product in question. User trials are perhaps most appealing as they provide an indication of how the end users will use the operational product or device. Salvendy (1997) suggests that user testing with real users is the most fundamental usability method available, as it provides direct information about how the potential end users will use the interface under analysis, and what problems they may encounter. The flexible nature of user trials allows them to be used to assess a wide range of features associated with a particular device, including usability, MWL, SA, error potential, task performance times and user reactions. The output of a user trial is typically used to generate a set of design recommendations or remedial measures for the product or device under analysis.

Domain of Application

Generic.

Procedure and Advice

Step 1: Specify desired outcomes of the user trial
The first step in conducting a user trial involves specifying the desired outcomes of the analysis. The analyst(s) should clearly define what it is that they wish to assess through the user trial.

Step 2: Define task(s) under analysis
Next, the analyst(s) should define the task(s) that the user will conduct with the system or device under analysis. It is recommended that an exhaustive task list is generated, including all of the tasks that can be performed when using the device or system under analysis. If the task list becomes too great and the analysis cannot cover all of the tasks specified due to time and financial constraints, it is recommended that the task list used is as representative of the device or system's functions as possible.

Step 3: Conduct a HTA for the task(s) under analysis
Once a representative set of tasks for the system or device under analysis are defined, they should be described using a HTA. HTA involves breaking down the task under analysis into a hierarchy of goals, operations and plans. Tasks are broken down into hierarchical set of tasks, sub-tasks and plans. The HTA is useful as it gives the analysts a clear description of how the task(s) should be carried out and can also be used to develop a procedural list for the user trial.

Step 4: Create procedural list for the task(s) under analysis
The HTA should be used in order to create a procedural list for the task(s) under analysis. The procedural list should describe the required task steps, their sequence and the interface components used.

Step 5: Select appropriate participants
Once the task(s) under analysis are clearly defined and described, the appropriate participants who are to take part in the user trials should be selected. The participants used should represent the potential end users for the system or product under analysis.

Step 6: Brief participants
The selected participants should then be briefed regarding the purpose of the analysis and also the system or product under analysis. The participants should fully understand the purpose of the user trial and functions of the system or product under analysis before the user trial can proceed. It is useful at this stage for participants to familiarise themselves with the system or product under analysis. This might involve allowing participants to consult any documentation (e.g. user manual) associated with the system or product.

Step 7: Demonstration of task(s) under analysis
Next, the participants should be given a demonstration or walkthrough of the task(s) under analysis. It is normally useful for the analyst to walk the participants through a procedural list of the task(s) under analysis. The analyst(s) should verbally describe each action and physically perform any interactions with interface components. The participants should be encouraged to ask questions regarding the task(s) during this step.

Step 8: Run user trial
Once the participants fully understand the task(s) under analysis and what is required of them as participants, they should be instructed to begin the first task. It is important that they are given no assistance or feedback during task performance. It is also recommended that the user trials are recorded using video and audio recording equipment. This allows the analyst(s) to consult the recordings of the user trials during the data analysis stage, in order to ensure comprehensiveness.

Step 9: Administer appropriate usability, workload and SA questionnaires
Once task performance is complete, participants should be instructed to complete appropriate MWL (e.g. NASA-TLX), SA (e.g. SARS) and usability questionnaires (e.g. SUMI). The questionnaires used are dependent upon the nature of the analysis.

Step 10: Interview participants
Upon completion of the trial, participant interviews should be conducted. Depending upon the nature of the analysis, the interviews can be used to assess a number of factors, such as user opinions of the system or device under analysis and errors made during the trial.

Step 11: Debrief participants
Next, the participants should be given a debriefing interview, in order to provide feedback regarding their performance during the trial and to gather the users' feedback regarding the system under analysis.

Step 12: Analyse data
Once the user trial and interviews are complete, the analyst(s) should analyse the data accordingly, in line with the outcomes specified prior to the analysis. Typically measures of usability, MWL, SA and errors are analysed statistically in order to assess their significance.

Step 13: Determine design recommendations
Once the data is analysed, the analyst(s) should develop a set of design recommendations based upon the findings of the user trials. These design recommendations should then be used to redevelop the system or device in question.

Advantages

1. User trials offer a simplistic and flexible approach to usability evaluation.
2. Potentially a user trial can be used to assess multiple features associated with a system or product's usability, including error, MWL, situation awareness and performance time.
3. When using user trials, the system is evaluated based upon the potential end users' performance. End-user opinions and advice are elicited during the user trial.
4. Design recommendations are based upon interviews with the system end users.
5. A user trial gives the designers a powerful insight into how the system under analysis will be used.
6. If used throughout the design process, user trials ensure that the end users of the system under analysis are considered.
7. Once the appropriate personnel are gathered, the user trial is simple to conduct.

Disadvantages

1. Time consuming to conduct.
2. Large amounts of data are collected, ensuring a lengthy data analysis process.
3. It may be difficult to gain access to the required personnel or end users. For example, when conducting a user trial for military applications, it may prove difficult to gain access to the appropriate military personnel for the required duration.
4. Often the end users may be biased towards the old system or procedure.

Related Methods

User trials are similar to heuristics evaluation. Depending upon the nature of the analysis, a user trial may utilise a number of other HF methods, such as MWL assessment methods (primary and secondary task performance measures, subjective rating methods), usability metrics (SUMI, SUS, QUIS), checklists (Ravden and Johnson, 1989) and SA measurement methods (SAGAT, SART, SARS). Interviews, questionnaires and observations are also typically used during a user-trial analysis.

Flowchart

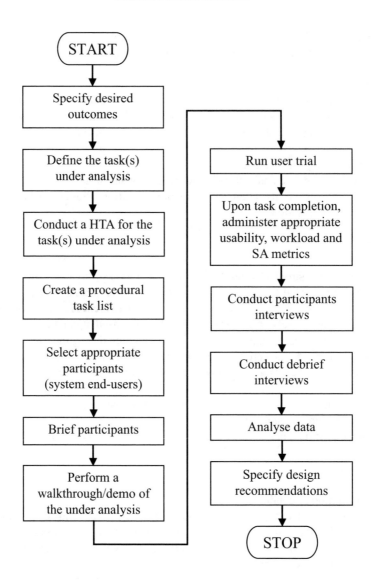

Training and Application Times

The training time associated with user trials is minimal, provided that the analyst(s) has a working knowledge of the methods that are employed as part of the user trial (workload assessment, usability metrics, interviews etc). If the analyst has no prior knowledge of the methods that are to be applied, it is estimated that the training time would be high. The application time associated with user trial is also estimated to be high, involving defining the task(s), conducting a HTA, conducting the user trials and associated interviews and analysing the data gathered.

Reliability and Validity

There are no data regarding the reliability and validity of user trials available in the literature.

Tools Needed

A simple user trial can be conducted using pen and paper. However, more sophisticated user trials may require video (video recorder) and audio (mini-disc recorder) recording equipment and the appropriate analysis software (Observer™, SPSS™ and Microsoft Excel™).

Walkthrough Analysis

Background and Applications

Walkthrough analysis is a very simple procedure used by designers whereby experienced system operators perform a walkthrough or demonstration of a task or set of tasks using the system under analysis. Walkthroughs are typically used early in the design process to envisage how a design concept would work and also to evaluate and modify the design concept. They can also be used on existing systems to demonstrate to system designers how a process is currently performed, highlighting flaws, error potential and usability problems. The appeal in walkthrough type analysis lies in the fact that the scenario or task under analysis does not necessarily have to occur. One of the problems of observational study is that the required scenario simply may not occur, or if it does, the observation team may have to spend considerable time waiting for it to occur. Walkthrough analysis allows the scenario to be 'acted out' removing the problems of gaining access to systems and personnel and also waiting for the scenario to occur. A walkthrough involves an operator walking through a scenario, performing (or pretending to perform) the actions that would occur, explaining the function of each control and display used. The walkthrough is also verbalised and the analyst(s) can stop the scenario and ask questions at any point. Walkthrough analysis is particularly useful in the initial stages of task analysis development.

Domain of Application

Generic.

Procedure and Advice

There are no set rules for a walkthrough analysis. The following procedure is intended to act as a set of guidelines for conducting a walkthrough analysis of a proposed system design concept.

Step 1: Define set of representative scenarios
Firstly, a representative set of tasks or scenarios for the system under analysis should be defined. As a general rule, the set of scenarios used should cover every aspect of the system and its interface at least once. The personnel involved in each scenario should also be defined. If the required personnel cannot be gathered for the walkthrough, then members of the design team can be used.

Step 2: Conduct HTA for the scenario(s) under analysis
Once a representative set of tasks for the system or device under analysis are defined, they should be described using a HTA. HTA involves breaking down the tasks under analysis into a hierarchy of goals, operations and plans. Tasks are broken down into a hierarchical set of tasks, sub-tasks and plans. The HTA is useful as it gives the analysts a clear description of how the task(s) should be carried out and also defines the component task steps involved in the scenario(s) under analysis.

Step 3: Perform walkthrough
The analyst team then simply take each scenario and perform a verbalised walkthrough using the system design under analysis. It is recommended that the analyst uses the HTA to determine the component task steps involved. The scenario can be frozen at any point and questions asked regarding controls, displays, decisions made, situation awareness, error occurrence etc. The walkthrough should be recorded using video recording equipment. Any problems with the design concept encountered during the walkthrough should be recorded and design remedies offered and tested.

Step 4: Analyse data
Once the walkthrough has been performed, the data should be analysed accordingly and used with respect to the goals of the analysis. Walkthrough data is very flexible and can be used for a number of purposes, such as task analysis, constructing timelines and evaluating error potential.

Step 5: Modify design
Once the walkthrough is complete and the data is analysed, the design can be modified based upon the remedial measures proposed as a result of the walkthrough. If a new design is proposed, a further walkthrough should be conducted in order to analyse the new design.

Advantages

1. When used correctly, a walkthrough can provide a very accurate description of the task under analysis and also how a proposed system design would be used.
2. Walkthrough analysis allows the analyst to stop or interrupt the scenario in order to query certain points. This is a provision that is not available when using other methods such as observational analysis.
3. A walkthrough analysis does not necessarily require the system under analysis.
4. Walkthrough analysis is a simple, quick and low-cost method.
5. Walkthrough analysis would appear to be a very useful tool in the analysis of distributed (team-based) tasks.
6. Walkthrough analysis can provide a very powerful assessment of a design concept.

Disadvantages

1. For the analysis to be fruitful, experienced operators for the system under analysis are required.
2. Reliability of the method is questionable.

Related Methods

The walkthrough method is very similar to verbal protocol analysis and observational analysis.

Approximate Training and Application Times

There is no training as such for walkthrough analysis, and the associated application time is dependent upon the size and complexity of the task or scenario under analysis. The application time for walkthrough analysis is typically very low.

Reliability and Validity

No data regarding the reliability and validity of the walkthrough method are available.

Flowchart

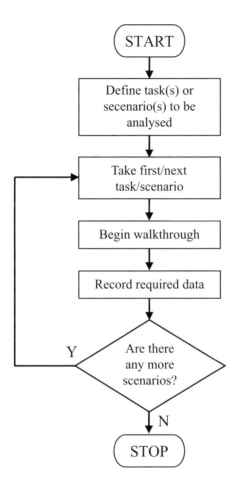

Tools Needed

A walkthrough analysis can be conducted using pen and paper. Some form of the device or system under analysis is also required (e.g. mock-up, prototype, operational device). It is also recommended that video and audio recording equipment are used to record the walkthrough.

Chapter 11

Design Methods

Design methods are a general classification used for the purposes of this book. A design method in this case merely implies that the method is one that is used by designers during the early design lifecycle of a particular system, device or product. According to Wilson and Corlett (1995) ergonomics methods are used to assist the development stages of the design or redesign of equipment, workplaces, software, jobs and buildings. Wilson and Corlett (1995) suggest that the ergonomics methods should be used to develop ergonomically sound concepts, prototypes and final designs. When designing products or systems, designers may utilise a number of design methods in order to inform and evaluate the design process. There are a number of different types of design methods available, such as interface design methods and group design methods. These design methods are often used to provide structure to the design process, and also to ensure that the end user of the product or system in question is considered throughout the design process. Contrary to the wider goal of HFI, HF intervention is typically requested once a design is complete and problems begin to be unearthed by the end users of the new system. Usability, error, workload, and situation awareness analyses are then conducted, and design recommendations are offered. Ironically these recommendations are often ignored due to the high costs associated with redesign. The design methods reviewed in this chapter represent those techniques that are used during the actual design process of a system or product, and not those techniques that may be used to highlight design flaws 'after the fact'. A brief description of the design methods considered is given below.

Allocation of function analysis is used by system designers to determine whether jobs, tasks, system functions etc., are allocated to human or technological agents within a particular system. Focus group approaches use group interviews to discuss and assess user opinions and perceptions of a particular design concept. In the design process, design concepts are evaluated by the focus group and new design solutions are offered. Scenario based design involves the use of imaginary scenarios or storyboard presentations to communicate or evaluate design concepts. A set of scenarios depicting the future use of the design concept are proposed and performed, and the design concept is evaluated. Scenarios typically use how, why and what if questions to evaluate and modify a design concept. Mission analysis is a method that is used during the design of military cockpit environments. End-user tasks and requirements are evaluated and translated into a set of design requirements for the cockpit in question. Task centred system design (TCSD) is a quick and easy approach to evaluating system design involving the identification of the potential users and tasks associated with the design concept and evaluating the design using design scenarios and a walkthrough type analysis. The method offers a redesign of the interface or system design under analysis as its output. Focus groups are also often used during the design process. A summary of the system design methods reviewed is presented in Table 11.1.

Table 11.1   Summary of System Design Methods

Method	Type of method	Domain	Training time	App time	Related methods	Tools needed	Validation Studies	Advantages	Disadvantages
Allocation of functions analysis	Systems design	Generic	High	High	Pen and paper	Pen and paper	Yes	1) Ensures that tasks are conducted by the most efficient system component. 2) Provides a structure to the automation decision process. 3) Ensures that automation selection is audited.	1) Time consuming in application. 2) A multi-disciplinary team of various experts is required.
Focus groups	Group design	Product design	Low	High	Group design methods Observation Interview	Pen and paper Video and audio recording equipment	No	1) Flexible design method, able to consider any aspect of system design. 2) Powerful design method.	1) Assembling the focus group is difficult. 2) If the chemistry is wrong, then the data may suffer. 3) Reliability and validity is questionable.
Mission Analysis	Systems design	Aviation	High	High	HTA	Pen and paper	No	1) Specifies design and information requirements. 2) Potentially exhaustive.	1) Time-consuming procedure. 2) Labour intensive. 3) Used for cockpit design.
Scenario based design	Design	Generic	Low	Med	Group design methods Observation Focus groups	Pen and paper Video and audio recording equipment	No	1) Flexible design method, able to consider any aspect of system design. 2) Quick and easy, offering useful outputs. 3) Designers can see how the end product may be used.	1) Unsophisticated. 2) A multi-disciplinary team of various experts is required.
TCSD – Task Centred System Design	Systems design	Generic	Low	High	Design methods Observation	Pen and paper	No	1) Simple to conduct, offering an immediately useful output. 2) Facilitates design modifications.	1) Unsophisticated. 2) Time consuming.

Allocation of Function Analysis

Background and Applications

The emergence of system automation and an increase in technological capability has resulted in agent and artefact roles within complex, dynamic systems becoming ill defined and somewhat opaque. It is now entirely feasible that human operators and technological artefacts can perform a variety of tasks within complex, dynamic systems equally as well as each other. Allocation of function analysis is used during the design process in order to allocate jobs, tasks, functions and responsibility to the man or machine for the system in question (Marsden and Kirby, 2005). Allocation of function involves the design team considering each task and the relative advantages and disadvantages associated with that task being performed by the man, or by the machine. Allocation of functions analysis is particularly important when considering system automation.

Domain of Application

Generic.

Procedure and Advice (Adapted from Marsden and Kirby, 2005)

Step 1: Define the task(s) under analysis
The first step in an allocation of functions analysis is to define the task(s) that are to be considered during the analysis. It is recommended that an exhaustive set of tasks for the system under analysis are considered. However, it may be that a number of the tasks are already allocated to either the man or machine and so only those tasks that require functional allocation should be considered.

Step 2: Conduct a HTA for the task(s) under analysis
Once the tasks under analysis are defined, a HTA should be conducted for each task or scenario. HTA involves breaking down the task under analysis into a hierarchy of goals, operations and plans. Tasks are broken down into a hierarchical set of tasks, sub-tasks and plans. It is recommended that each bottom level task step in the HTA is considered during the allocation of functions analysis.

Step 3: Conduct stakeholder analysis for allocation of functions
According to Marsden and Kirby (2005) a stakeholder analysis is conducted in order to identify stakeholder satisfaction and dissatisfaction caused by changes in the computer systems in the system or type of system under analysis. Observational study is required in order to conduct the stakeholder analysis. The stakeholder analysis involves determining the current knowledge and skills of the existing stakeholders and the potential of stakeholders to develop new knowledge and skills (Marsden and Kirby, 2005). Marsden and Kirby (2005) also suggest that the analyst should consider a number of aspects of work that are important to the stakeholders involved, such as the development of new skills, enjoying interaction with other people and having a variety of work to do.

Step 4: Consider human and computer capabilities
Next, the analyst(s) should consider each bottom level task step in the HTA and the associated advantages and disadvantages of allocating that task to the human operator or to the machine or system. The capability of the personnel and the technological artefacts involved should be considered with respect to the each task step in the HTA. Marsden and Kirby (2005) recommend that each task step should be allocated to human only (H), the human and computer with the human

in control (H-C), the human and computer with the computer in control (C-H), or the computer only (C).

Step 5: Assess impact of allocation of function on task performance and job satisfaction
Once the tasks have been allocated, the analyst(s) should review each allocation and determine the effects upon task performance and job satisfaction (Marsden and Kirby, 2005). The analysts should consider error potential, performance time gains/losses, impact upon cost, MWL and the job satisfaction criteria highlighted earlier in the analysis. For any allocations that have a significant negative effect upon task performance and job satisfaction, the analyst(s) should determine an alternative allocation of function. The alternative allocation of functions for the task step in question should then be compared, and the most suitable allocation selected.

Example (Adapted from Marsden and Kirby, 2005)

The following example for a decision support system in a brewery context is taken from Marsden and Kirby (2005):

> *1: to check the desirability of trying to meet a potential increase in demand:*

- forecast demand
- review regular sales
- review demand from pub chains
- review potential demand from one-off events
- produce provisional resource plan
- calculate expected demand for each type of beer
- make adjustment for production minima and maxima
- check feasibility of plan
- do materials explosion of ingredients
- do materials explosion of casks and other packaging
- check material stocks
- calculate materials required
- negotiate with suppliers
- check staff availability
- check ability to deliver beer to customers
- review potential impact
- review impact of plan on cash flow
- review impact of plan on staff
- review impact on customer relations
- review impact on supplier relations.

Function allocations analysis based on stakeholder analysis of the socio-technical system (Source: Marsden and Kirby, 2005).

1: to check the desirability of trying to meet a potential increase in demand:

- forecast demand H
- review regular sales H
- review demand from pub chains H
- review potential demand from one-off events H
- produce provisional resource plan H-C
- calculate expected demand for each type of beer   H-C
- make adjustment for production minima and maxima   C
- check feasibility of plan   H-C
- do materials explosion of ingredients   H-C
- do materials explosion of casks and other packaging   C
- check material stocks   H-C
- calculate materials required   C
- negotiate with suppliers   H
- check staff availability   H
- check ability to deliver beer to customers   H
- review potential impact   H
- review impact of plan on cash flow H
- review impact of plan on staff   H
- review impact on customer relations   H
- review impact on supplier relations   H.

Advantages

1. Allocation of functions analysis is a simplistic procedure that allows tasks to be allocated appropriately within the system or device under analysis.
2. Analysis of functions allows the designers to ensure that the tasks are carried out by the most efficient system component.
3. According to Marsden and Kirby (2005) allocation of functions analysis provides a structure to the automation decision process and also ensures that automation decisions are traceable.
4. Provided that the appropriate personnel are used, the procedure is a simple and straightforward one.

Disadvantages

1. The procedure can be laborious and time consuming, particularly for complex systems or devices.
2. A multi-disciplinary team of HF specialists, potential end users, and designers are required in order to conduct the analysis properly. It may be difficult to assemble such a team.

Related Methods

An allocation of functions analysis uses HTA as its primary input. A stakeholder analysis is also conducted during the allocation of functions analysis.

Approximate Training and Application Times

According to Marsden and Kirby (2005) an allocation of function analysis requires several skills on behalf of the analyst(s). The analyst(s) should be proficient in task analysis techniques and stakeholder analysis techniques. It is therefore estimated that the training time for the method is considerable in cases where the analyst has no prior experience of the techniques used. The application time for an allocation of function analysis is also estimated to be high.

Flowchart

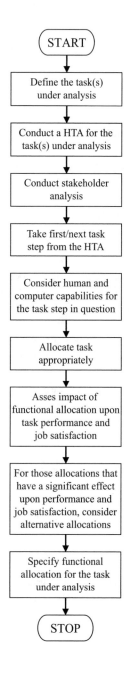

Reliability and Validity

There are no data regarding the reliability and validity of the allocation of functions analysis.

Tools Needed

Allocation of functions analysis can be conducted using pen and paper. It is also useful to have some form of the system under analysis (e.g. mock-up, functional diagrams, prototype, operational system).

Focus Groups

Background and Applications

Focus groups offer a flexible approach that can be used to assess a wide range of features associated with a system or device, including user opinions and reactions, system usability, error occurrence and potential, MWL and situation awareness. A focus group is a group interview approach that involves using a group of appropriate participants (e.g. SMEs, potential end users or an existing user population) to discuss a particular design, prototype or operational system. Focus groups were originally used for market research purposes, and have since been applied for a wide range of different purposes in a number of different domains. A typical focus group involves a group of appropriate participants and one to two moderators who facilitate the discussion to meet pre-specified objectives. The output of a focus group is normally a list of agreed and disagreed statements. Hypponen (1999) suggests that focus groups are used to gather raw data regarding user needs in the concept development phase of a design and that they can also be used to clarify issues during the design. Focus groups can also be used as an evaluation tool in order to evaluate existing system design with regard to error occurrence, usability, MWL and situation awareness.

Domain of Application

Generic.

Procedure and Advice

There are no set rules for conducting a focus group type analysis. The following procedure is intended to act as a set of guidelines to consider when conducting a focus group type analysis.

Step 1: Define aims and objectives
The first step in conducting a focus group is to clearly define the overall aims and objectives of the focus group. This involves stating explicitly the purpose of the focus group i.e. to discuss the C4i Gold command interface design concept.

Step 2: Determine key discussion topics
Once the overall aim of the focus group has been defined, it should be divided into specific areas that are to be the topic of discussion during the focus group. Using the example above, the 'C4i Gold command interface design concept', this could be split into the following key discussion areas: interface layout, probability of error, task times, usability, design flaws and design remedies.

The key discussion points should be placed in a logical order and this order should be adhered to during the focus group.

Step 3: Assemble focus group
Assembling the correct personnel for a focus group is crucial. For the example outlined above, the focus group would require a number of different personnel, including the following:

1. Human factors experts.
2. Military personnel.
3. Experienced command and control system operators.
4. Project manager.
5. HRA/HEI specialist.
6. Usability specialist.
7. Designers.
8. Data recorder.
9. Controllers from different domains (such as ATC, Police, Ambulance).

Focus group participants are normally made up of end users of the device or system under analysis. It is often useful to recruit participants via advertising or group email.

Step 4: Administer demographic questionnaire
A simple demographic questionnaire is normally administered at the beginning of a focus group in order to gather information regarding participant age, gender, occupation, experience etc.

Step 5: Introduce design concept
Once the demographic questionnaires have all been completed, the starting point of the focus group session is to introduce to the group the design concept that is to be the topic of discussion. This would normally take the form of a presentation. Once the presentation is finished, the focus group leader should introduce the first topic of discussion. It is recommended that the focus group is recorded either using audio or video recording equipment.

Step 6: Introduce first/next topic
The first topic of discussion should be introduced clearly to the group, including what the topic is, why it is important and what is hoped to be achieved by discussing that certain topic. The actual topic should be discussed thoroughly until it is exhausted and a number of points are agreed upon. Step 6 should be repeated until all of the chosen discussion points have been discussed fully.

Step 7: Transcribe data
Once the focus group session has been completed, the data requires transcribing. The analyst should use an audio or video recording of the focus group session in order to do this.

Step 8: Analyse data
Once transcribed, the data should then be analysed accordingly. Focus group data can be analysed in a number of ways and is dependent upon the focus of the analysis. Typically, the data output from a focus group session is a set of agreed upon statements regarding the design concept.

Advantages

1. Focus groups offer a flexible approach that can be used for a wide range of purposes, ranging from user reactions and opinions to the error potential of a particular system or device.
2. The make up of the focus group is entirely up to the analyst(s) involved. A correctly assembled focus group can provide a very powerful input into the design process.
3. The analyst(s) has complete control of the focus and direction of the analysis and can change this at any time.
4. Very powerful data can be elicited from a focus group type analysis.
5. Focus group type interviews allow the analyst to quickly survey a great number of opinions.
6. Participants discuss issues more freely in a group context.

Disadvantages

1. Assembling the desired focus group is a very difficult thing to do. Getting such a diverse group of experts together at the same location and at the same time is a very difficult. Similarly, recruiting participants is also difficult.
2. Focus group data is difficult to treat statistically.
3. The chemistry within the focus group has a huge effect upon the data collected.
4. The reliability and validity of focus groups is questionable.
5. Large amounts of data are gathered. This is time consuming to transcribe and analyse.
6. Focus group data can be subject to bias.

Related Methods

Focus groups use a semi-structured group interview approach and also typically employ questionnaires or surveys as part of the data collection procedure.

Approximate Training and Application Times

There are no training times associated with a focus group type analysis. Typical focus group session duration is between 90 minutes and two hours. However, this is dependent upon the requirements of the focus groups and it is not unheard for focus group sessions to last days at a time.

Reliability and Validity

Whilst no data regarding the reliability and validity of focus groups is available in the literature, it is apparent that it could be questionable.

Tools Needed

The tools required to conduct a focus group analysis include pen and paper, a video recording device, such as a video recorder and/or an audio recording device, such as a cassette recorder. A PC with a word processing package such as Microsoft Word is required to transcribe the data collected.

Flowchart

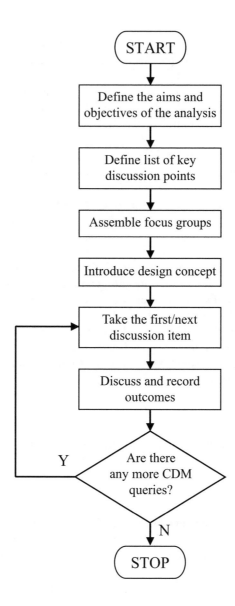

Mission Analysis

Background and Application

The mission analysis technique (Wilkinson, 1992) is a cockpit design methodology that is used to generate cockpit design requirements based upon an analysis of operational procedures and requirements. The technique was developed by BAe systems and has been used on the European Fighter Aircraft (EFA) project. The technique involves the breakdown of representative flight missions into flight segments and operational modes and the specification of function, information and control requirements within the cockpit (Wilkinson, 1992). Whilst developed for use in the aviation domain, the actual procedure used is generic, allowing the technique to be applied to the interface design process in other domains.

Domain of Application

Military aviation.

Procedure and Advice

The following procedure is adapted from Wilkinson (1992).

Step 1: Compile mission profiles list
The first step in a mission analysis is to create a set of mission profiles for the system under analysis. The analyst should identify a set of representative mission profiles for the system. These mission profiles should be comprehensive, covering all aspects of future use of the system.

Step 2: Select forcing mission
As it would be too resource intensive to analyse the full set of missions outlined in the mission profiles, a 'forcing mission' is selected. A single mission profile that involves the use of all of the potential design elements of the cockpit should be chosen. Care should be taken in choosing the appropriate mission profile, as it is this 'forcing mission' that is used to establish the initial cockpit design.

Step 3: Conduct a HTA for the selected 'forcing mission'
Once the appropriate mission profile or 'forcing mission' is selected, a HTA should be conducted. This allows the analyst to describe the forcing mission in detail, including each of the tasks and task steps involved.

Step 4: Breakdown mission into set of mission phases
Next, the analyst should consult the HTA and divide the forcing mission profile into a set of mission phases. Wilkinson (1992) proposes the following set of mission phases for a mission profile:

1. Ground procedures.
2. Take off.
3. Navigation.
4. Combat.

Step 5: Identify operation modes
According to Wilkinson (1992), each phase of flight comprises several modes of operation. The analyst should identify the modes of operation associated with the mission phases identified during step 4. Wilkinson (1992) divided beyond visual range combat flight into the following modes:

1. Target detection and identification.
2. Evaluation, prioritisation and decision.
3. Pre-launch manoeuvre.
4. Launch weapons.
5. Post-launch manoeuvre.

Step 6: Divide each flight mode into list of task steps
Next, the analyst should take each flight segment or mode and using the HTA, describe the tasks that are involved in each flight segment. These tasks should then be divided into the following categories:

1. Primary tasks – the tasks that characterise each segment and are performed sequentially, requiring the pilots' foreground attention.
2. Intermittent tasks – the tasks that are performed by the pilot as and when required or when the system requests.
3. Continuous tasks – tasks that are performed continuously and concurrently (mainly monitoring) and are preferably carried out by the system, alerting the pilot only when necessary.

Step 7: Determine task function requirements
For each of the tasks identified in steps 5 and 6, the analyst is then required to determine a set of task function requirements. In order to do this, the functions required to perform the task should be specified. The function categories used are presented below (Source: Wilkinson, 1992).

1. Manual – Purely visual, verbal or mental.
2. Manual augmented – e.g. Fly-by-Wire.
3. Manual augmented – Automatically limited e.g. anti-skid braking.
4. Automatic – Manually limited e.g. Autopilot attitude hold mode.
5. Automatic – Manual Sanction e.g. Target nomination.
6. Automatic Autonomous – e.g. systems status monitoring.

Step 8: Determine task/control requirements
Finally, the analyst should specify the information presentation and control function requirements for each task. The requirements depict how the pilot would perform the task or monitor the automated performance of the task. Therefore, the controls and displays required should be specified. It is these requirements that act as the primary output of the mission analysis, and that the design aims to cater for. It is recommended that the information presentation requirements include a specification of content (what information is required), format (in what format would the information best be presented) and type of display used. The control function requirements should at least specify the function of control required, the location of the control and the type of control required.

Advantages

1. The output of a mission analysis clearly specifies the system requirements to the designers.
2. An exhaustive analysis of the potential user requirements of the system is conducted, including an analysis of user requirements and an analysis of the system's future use.
3. The design team can use the mission analysis output to guide the design, ensuring that all requirements are catered for.

Disadvantages

1. The procedure involved in a mission analysis appears to be very time consuming and laborious.

2. The selection of a representative mission profile is crucial. It may be that elements of system usage are not catered for by the analysis, due to the selection of an inappropriate mission profile.
3. No data regarding the reliability and validity of the technique are available in the literature.

Flowchart

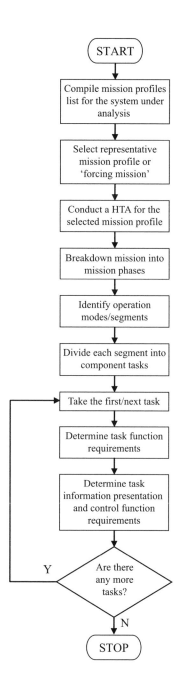

Related Methods

The mission analysis technique uses task analysis techniques, such as HTA in its application

Training and Application Times

It is estimated that the training time for the mission analysis technique would be low, provided that the analyst in question possessed sufficient domain expertise. It is apparent that a considerable amount of knowledge regarding the system under analysis is required. For example, when applying the mission analysis in an aviation context, knowledge regarding the types of mission, the tasks involved, and the level of automation available in the cockpit is required. The application time for the mission analysis technique is estimated to be high.

Reliability and Validity

No data regarding the reliability and validity of the technique are available in the literature.

Tools Needed

The mission analysis technique can be applied using pen and paper.

Scenario Based Design

Background and Applications

Design scenarios offer a flexible approach to system or device design by adopting a storybook style approach to help designers and design teams propose, evaluate and modify design concepts. According to Go and Carroll (2003) a scenario is a description that contains actors, assumptions about the environment, goals and objectives, sequences of actions and events. Scenario analyses are used throughout the design cycle to develop and present new system designs in future contexts. Scenario analyses typically involve the use of sketch storyboards depicting a proposed future operation of the device/system in question. At its most basic level, a scenario type analysis involves proposing a design concept and querying the design using who, what, when, why and how type questions (Go and Carroll, 2003). Once a scenario is created, design ideas and changes can be added to the storyboard and the design is modified as a result. Scenarios are also used to communicate design concepts to other organisations or design teams. One of the main reasons for using scenario analysis is that it is much cheaper to sketch and act out a future scenario than it is to develop a simulation, mock-up or prototype version of one. Scenario type analyses are a powerful design tool that have been applied to the design process in a number of different domains, such as HCI, requirements engineering, object oriented design, systems design and strategic planning (Go and Carroll, 2003). The appeal of scenario based design lies in the method's flexibility, whereby the focus and nature of the analysis is based entirely upon the analyst(s)' requirements, and the direction of the analysis is entirely up to the analysis team.

Domain of Application

Generic.

Procedure and Advice

There are no set rules for scenario type analysis. A rough guide proposed by the author is presented below.

Step 1: Determine representative set of scenarios
The first step in a scenario analysis is to develop and describe a representative set of scenarios for the system under analysis. Each scenario should be described fully, including the scenario aims, objectives and activities as well as any input devices, displays or interfaces used in the scenario. The personnel involved, the context within which the scenario may take, individual goals, actions and possible outcomes should also be stipulated. A scenario description table should be constructed at this point, containing all of the relevant information regarding the scenario, such as goals, objectives, task steps, input devices, output devices etc.

Step 2: Scenario observation
Scenarios are normally based upon an observation of similar scenarios to the scenario under analysis. The analyst(s) should record and observe the scenario under analysis. If the system or design concept does not yet exist, the scenario should be 'made-up' from scratch using methods such as group brainstorming. Any novel scenarios observed or elicited that were not expressed in step 1 should also be added to the scenario description table. Interviews and questionnaires may also be used to elicit information regarding potential scenarios.

Step 3: Act out the scenario
The analyst or team of analysts should then create the scenario in the form of a storyboard. The scenario should be based upon the system being designed, with future contexts and situations being added to the scenario as the analysis progresses. Team members should offer intervention, proposing different contexts and events, such as 'what would happen if' and 'how would the operator cope if ...'. This allows the scenario team to evaluate every possibility that occurs with the design concept. Problem scenarios are particularly useful for evaluating a design concept. This part of the scenario analysis is the most crucial and should involve maximum experimentation with the proposed design concept. All assumptions and resultant design modifications should be recorded. The process should continue until the design team is satisfied that all possible scenarios have been exhausted and the end design is complete.

Advantages

1. Scenario analyses offer a quick and easy approach of evaluating a particular design concept in future contexts. This can help highlight any design flaws and future problems associated with the initial design.
2. Scenario analysis is a very flexible method.
3. Scenario analyses can provide a format for communicating design concepts and issues between designers and design teams.
4. Quick, low cost and easy to apply.
5. Scenario analysis output is immediately useful, giving a sketch drawing of the design in action and also highlighting any problems that may be encountered.
6. Any number of scenarios can be evaluated, ranging from 'normal' to 'worse case' scenarios.

Disadvantages

1. Scenarios are not very precise and many potential scenarios may be missed or left out by the analysis team.
2. Could be time consuming for large scenarios.
3. To reap the full benefit of a scenario analysis, a multi-discipline team needs to be put together. This is often difficult to achieve.

Flowchart

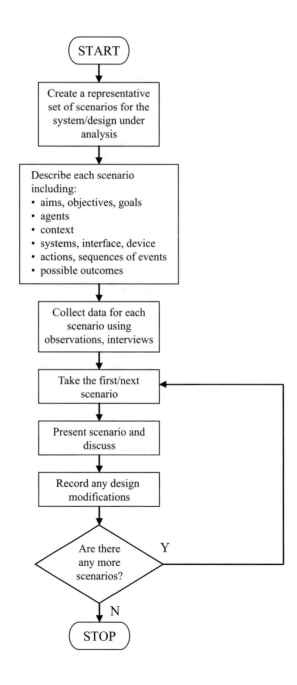

Related Methods

Scenario analysis involves the collection of data using traditional HF data collection procedures such as observational study, interviews and questionnaires. Scenario methods are also similar to role-play methods, which are also used by designers to visualise potential product use.

Approximate Training and Application Times

The method is simple to use and so training time is estimated to be very low. Application time can vary, as there are no set end points to a scenario and new scenarios can be added to existing ones at any point. The size of the scenario also has an effect upon the length of the analysis.

Reliability and Validity

The reliability of the method is questionable. Scenario teams may fail to capture all of the potential future scenarios of a design in a scenario analysis. Similarly, the method may produce inconsistent results for the same design, when applied by different teams.

Tools Needed

Scenarios are typically conducted using pen and paper. For the data collection part of scenario analysis, it is recommended that visual and/or audio recording equipment is used.

Task-Centred System Design

Background and Applications

Task-Centred System Design is a simple, low-cost and resource efficient approach to evaluating system design concepts. It involves the identification of the potential users, the tasks associated with the design concept and evaluating the design using design scenarios and a walkthrough type analysis. The method's main appeal lies in its quick and easy application and the immediate usefulness of its output. The method offers a redesign of the interface or system design under analysis as its output. TCSD is both easy to learn and apply. Greenberg (2003) divides the TCSD procedure into four main phases:

1. Identification phase: Involves specifying potential system users and example tasks.
2. User-centred requirements analysis: involves determining which user groups and which tasks will be catered for by the design.
3. Design through scenarios: involves the assessment and modification of the design concept through use of design scenarios or storybooks.
4. Evaluation: involves the evaluation of the design concept via walkthrough type analysis.

A typical TCSD involves gathering data from an existing design and redesigning the system using design scenarios and system task walkthroughs.

Domain of Application

Generic.

Procedure and Advice

Step 1: Identification of potential users
The first step in a TCSD analysis is to identify the potential end users of the design under analysis. Specific user groups should be described. Observation and interviews are normally used to gather this data. The analyst should produce a representative list of user groups.

Step 2: Specification of example tasks
Once the specific user groups have been defined, a representative set of tasks for the system under analysis should be defined. This data is also collected through observation and interviews. The data for steps 1 and 2 are normally collected at the same time i.e. observing different users performing different tasks. Once the set of representative tasks is defined fully, each individual task should be given a task description. Greenberg (2003) suggests that each task description should adhere to the following five rules:

1. Description should describe what the user wants to do but not how they will do it.
2. Description should be very specific.
3. Description should describe a complete job.
4. Description should identify the users and reflect their interests.
5. When put together as a set of task descriptions, a wide range of users and task types should be described.

Once the list of tasks is complete, they should be checked and verified by the system end users. Task descriptions that are incomplete should be rewritten.

Step 3: Determine system users
The next step forms the first part of phase 2, the user-centred requirements analysis. Typically, system design cannot cater for all possible users. Step 3 involves determining which users or user groups the proposed design will cater for. Greenberg (2003) suggests that users should be put into typical user types or groups. Greenberg also suggests that the different user types or groups should be categorised as *absolutely must include, should include if possible* and *exclude*. For example, for a military command and control system design concept, the user groups falling into the absolutely must include group would be Gold command users, silver command users and bronze command personnel (foot soldiers, infantrymen).

Step 4: Determine system tasks
The next task in the TCSD process involves clearly specifying which tasks the system design will cater for. Similar criteria to that used in step 3 (absolutely must include, should include if possible and exclude) are used (with the addition of a 'could include' category) to categorise each task described in step 2.

Step 5: Generate design scenarios
Once steps 1 to 4 are complete, the analyst(s) should have a set of clearly defined end users and a set of tasks that the design will cater for. The actual design of the system can now begin. To do this, the TCSD informs the design process via the use of design scenarios or storybooks. A number of different design scenarios should be created, each one exploring how the design could cope with the scenario under analysis. Whilst no guidelines are offered regarding which scenarios and how many, it is recommended that a scenario involving each of the 'absolutely must include', 'should include if possible' and 'could include' tasks identified in step 4 should be created.

Step 6: Evaluate and modify design concept using scenario

Once a set of design scenarios have been specified, they should be used to continually evaluate and modify the design concept. Each scenario should be taken individually and applied to the system design, with team members questioning the efficiency of the design with respect to the events that unfold during each scenario. This is a continuous process, with each design scenario effectively testing the design concept. This process should continue until the team are happy with the system design.

Step 7: Perform task walkthrough

Once all of the scenarios have been applied to the design and the design team are happy with the end design concept, the design is tested further and more thoroughly using a walkthrough analysis. Depending upon resources available (time, money) SMEs or members of the design team can be used. However, walkthroughs using SMEs or system operators would produce more valid results. Essentially, the walkthrough involves role-playing, putting oneself in the mind and context of the user (Greenberg 2003). Lewis and Reiman (1993) propose the following procedure for performing task-centred walkthroughs.

1. Select one of the task scenarios.
2. For each of the users/actions in the task ask:
3. Can you build a believable story that motivates the user's actions?
4. Can you rely on the user's expected knowledge and training about the system?
5. If you cannot, you have located a problem in the interface.
6. Note the problem and any comments or solutions that come to mind.
7. Once a problem is identified, assume it has been repaired.
8. Go to the next step in the task.
9. Once all of the scenarios have been subjected to a walkthrough, the end design should be complete.

Advantages

1. TCSD is a simplistic method to use that immediately informs system design.
2. Design modifications occur naturally throughout the analysis.
3. Considers the end users and the set of tasks that the design is required to support.
4. The use of design scenarios allows the design to be evaluated as it would be used.
5. Correctly assembled TCSD teams can be very powerful.
6. The design concept is evaluated and modified as a result of a TCSD analysis.
7. Not as resource intensive as other methods.

Disadvantages

1. Validity and reliability of the method is questionable.
2. The use of such a simplistic method in the design of a miltary command and control may be questioned.
3. Whilst the method's simplicity is the main advantage associated with its use, this leads to criticisms regarding depth of the analysis.
4. Although TCSD is not as resource intensive as other methods, it is still a time consuming method to apply.
5. Assembling the TCSD team may prove difficult. For example, a TCSD analysis for the design of a military command and control system would require numerous specialists

(human factors, military, design, system operators etc). Getting such a team together in one place at one time could prove very difficult.

6. TCSD generates huge amounts of data.

Example

The following example (Table 11. 2, Table 11.3 and Table 11.4) is adapted from a TCSD analysis of a catalogue based department store (Greenberg, 2003). As the end output of TCSD is typically very large, only extracts of the analysis are shown below. The example is based upon the evaluation and redesign of an in-store computer ordering system. For a more detailed example, the reader is referred to Greenberg (2003).

Table 11.2   User Types

Customers	Sales Clerks
First time v's Repeat customers	Experienced and trained
Computer knowledgeable v's Computer naive	New staff member; has passed introductory training session
Typists v's Non-typists	
Willing to use the computer v's Unwilling	
People with disabilities who may have trouble with fine motor control	

Table 11.3   Tasks to be Catered for by the End Design

Choosing merchandise	Pay by	Reviewing cost	Merchandise pickup
One item	Cash	Individual item cost	Immediate
Multiple items	Credit or debit card	Total costs	Delivery
Modifying the selected list of items	Invoice	Comparison shopping	

Table 11.4   Example TCSD Walkthrough

Task step	Knowledge? Believable? Motivated?	Comments/Solutions?
a. Enters store	Okay	Finding paper catalogues is not a problem in the current store
b. Looks for catalogue	Okay if paper catalogue is used, but what if the catalogue is on-line	However, we were not told if the paper catalogue would still be used or if the catalogue would be made available on-line. Note – ask cheap shop about this. If they are developing an electronic catalogue, we will have to consider how our interface will work with it. For now, we assume that only a paper catalogue is used.
c. Finds red JPG stroller in catalogue	Okay	The current paper catalogue has proven itself repeatedly as an effective way for customers to browse cheap shop merchandise and to locate products.
d. Looks for computer	Modest problem	As a first-time customer, Fred does not know that he needs to order through the computer. Unfortunately, we do not know how the store plans to tell customers that they should use the computer. Is there a computer next to every catalogue or are there a limited number of computers on separate counters? Are there signs telling Fred what to do? Note: Ask cheap shop about the store layout and possible signage. Possible solution: Instead of screen 1, a start-up screen can clearly indicate what the computer is for (e.g., 'Order your items here' in large letters).

Flowchart

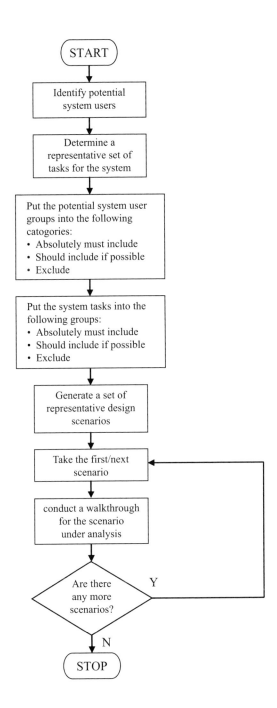

Related Methods

In conducting a TCSD analysis, a number of different human factors methods can be utilised. Observational methods and interviews are typically used to collect data regarding the system users and the type of tasks that the system caters for. Design scenarios and walkthrough analysis are also used to evaluate the design concept. Greenberg (2003) suggests that to make a TCSD analysis more comprehensive, heuristic type analysis is often used.

Approximate Training and Application Times

The training time for the TCSD method would be minimal. The application time, including observations, interviews, the generation of scenarios and the application of walkthrough type analysis would be high.

Reliability and Validity

The reliability of the TCSD method is questionable. Greenberg (2003) suggests that it is not a precise method and that tasks or user groups are likely to be overlooked. Indeed, it is apparent that when used by different analysts, the method may offer strikingly different results. The validity of such a method therefore becomes rather hard to define.

Tools Needed

TCSD can be conducted using pen and paper. However, for the observational analysis, it is recommended that visual and/or audio recording devices are used.

Chapter 12

Performance Time Prediction Methods

The temporal nature of task performance is an important feature of activity in complex systems. Data regarding the duration of the component task steps involved in activity is used for a number of reasons, including the design and development of processes and procedures, performance evaluation and performance prediction. Task performance time prediction is used in the design of systems and processes in order to determine whether proposed design concepts offer performance time reductions, and also to offer performance times associated with a particular task or set of tasks. Predicted task performance times are compared to existing performance times in order to evaluate the impact of proposed design concepts. Predicted task performance times are also evaluated in order to ensure that task performance with the proposed design meets the associated performance time constraints or requirements. According to Card, Moran and Newell (1983) it is useful for system designers to possess a model enabling the prediction of how much time it takes to accomplish a given task. The prediction of performance times associated with operator tasks was first attempted in the HCI domain (Card, Moran and Newell, 1983). The GOMS family of techniques included the Keystroke Level Model (KLM), which offered a set of standard times for operator actions, such as button press, mental operation and homing (in on a key or button). Operator tasks are broken down into unit-tasks and standard times are assigned to each unit-task. These unit-task times are then summed to calculate the total performance time. Although initially developed for the HCI domain, the method has been used elsewhere. For example, Stanton and Young (1998) used KLM to predict the performance time for the operation of two in-car stereo/radio devices. Baber (2004) describes the potential of critical path analysis (CPA) for predicting task performance times. Timeline analysis methods have also been used to predict performance time. According to Kirwan and Ainsworth (1992), the American National Standards Institute defines timeline analysis as:

> An analytical technique for the derivation of human performance requirements which attends to both the functional and temporal loading for any given combination of tasks.

Typically, observational data is used to construct graphically the performance times associated with operator tasks. Timeline type analysis seems to be potentially suited to analysing team performance times. Kirwan and Ainsworth (1992) also suggest that timelines are useful in assessing task allocation and identifying communications requirements. A summary of the performance time assessment methods reviewed is presented in Table 12.1.

Table 12.1   Summary of Performance Time Assessment Methods

Method	Type of method	Domain	Training time	App time	Related methods	Tools needed	Validation studies	Advantages	Disadvantages
CPA – Critical Path Analysis	Task analysis	HCI	Med	Med	KLM	Pen and paper	Yes	1) Considers parallel task activity. 2) Can be used to assess or predict task performance times. 3) More efficient than KLM.	1) Can be tedious and time consuming for large, complex tasks. 2) Only models error-free performance. 3) Times are not available for all actions.
KLM – Keystroke Level Model	Performance time assessment + prediction	HCI	Low	Low	NGOMSL CMN-GOMS CRM-GOMS	Pen and paper	Yes	1) Quick and easy to use, requiring very little training. 2) Can be used to compare task times for two or more devices. 3) Output is immediately useful.	1) Designed specifically for use in HCI. 2) Only caters for expert, error-free performance. 3) Does not take context into account.
Timeline analysis	Performance time assessment + prediction	Generic	Low	Low	KLM CPA	Pen and paper	No	1) Quick and easy to use, requiring very little training. 2) Could be used to represent team-based activity. 3) Workload can be mapped onto the timeline graph.	1) Predictive use is questionable. 2) Reliability and validity questionable. 3) Limited use.

Multimodal Critical Path Analysis (CPA)

Background and Applications

Critical Path Analysis (CPA) is a popular method in project management (Lockyer and Gordon, 1991) and is used to estimate the duration of a project in which some activities can be performed in parallel. The assumption is that a given task cannot start until all preceding tasks that contribute to it are complete. This means that some tasks might be completed and the process is waiting for other tasks before it is possible to proceed.. The tasks which are completed but waiting for others are said to be 'floating', i.e., they can shift their start times with little impact on the overall process. On the other hand, tasks that the others wait for are said to lie on the critical path, and any change to these tasks will have an impact on the overall process time. It is possible to apply these ideas to any time-based activity, including human performance.

In order to calculate CPA, one needs to know the order in which tasks are performed, their duration and their dependency. The notion of dependency is, for traditional CPA, based on the question of what tasks need to be completed before another task is allowed to commence. However, when applied to human performance models, dependency offers a richer conceptual framework in that it allows consideration of parallel activity. Traditional methods for modelling human response time are constrained because they do not represent parallelism. For example, the Keystroke Level Model (KLM) method offers a simple additive method for calculating response times in computing tasks (Card, Moran and Newell, 1983). This assumes that all tasks are performed in series and that total process time is simply the sum of all task times. However, it is apparent that people are able to perform some tasks in parallel. Models based on CPA can be constructed to represent some aspects of parallel activity, which can provide more accurate estimates of performance time (Schweickert, 1978; Gray et al., 1993; Baber and Mellor, 2001).

Describing dependency

In order to introduce the concept of dependency, it is necessary to make assumptions about the order in which tasks are performed and the nature of the tasks themselves. Clearly, some tasks need to be completed before others can start (which is central to traditional CPA modelling). This means that we can consider temporal dependency as the first stage in constructing a CPA model. However, temporal dependency tells us nothing about *why* some tasks can be performed in parallel. In order to consider this issue, we turn to notions of multiple resources.

Multiple resources

For the Human Factors community, it is convenient to assume that tasks involving different modalities, such as speaking and looking, can be performed with little interference. This assumption is not without criticism and there are several experiments that we will not consider here that suggest interference can occur at the stage of central processing of information. This means that, like many assumptions within Human Factors, what serves as a useful aid in engineering applications is not necessarily supported as a generalisable component of human cognition (although my feeling is that for many contexts, the assumption is sufficiently well supported to be treated as robust). Wickens (1992) amalgamated a considerable amount of research on multiple task performance to propose a theory of multiple attentional resources. The theory proposes a general pool (or reservoir) of attentional resources which is shared across stages of human information processing: as the demands of one stage increases, so the resource available to other stages diminishes. In order to manage this distribution of resource, the theory assumes that there are two sub-pools, one for visio-spatial resources and one for verbal-acoustic resources. Such a model would help to determine the possibility of tasks being performed in series or parallel, i.e., two 'visual' tasks would need to be performed in series (for the simple reason that one cannot look in two places at the same time), but an 'auditory' and 'visual' task could possibly be performed in parallel, e.g., the (visual) monitoring of displays could be performed in parallel with the (auditory) hearing of an alarm. The suggestion is that, as tasks draw from the same sub-pool, their interference requires serial processing, but if they use different sub-pools, they can be performed in parallel. A complication with the assumption is that the various stages of processing might draw on different versions of the sub-pool, e.g., at the input stage, the 'sub-pool' could be constrained by sensory limitations (e.g., you cannot look at two places at once, but need to move your eyes between the places), and at the output stage the 'sub-pool' would be constrained by response mechanisms, e.g., speaking or pressing buttons. Thus, at the observable stages of human response, one can make certain assumptions relating to the manner in which information is presented to the person or responses are made. However, the central processing stage is not so amenable to reductionism and it is not entirely clear what 'codes' are used to represent information. While this could be a problem for experimental psychology, Human Factors tends to stick with the observable aspects of input/output and uses these notions for characterizing tasks. So, we would consider 'input' in terms of vision or hearing, and 'output' in terms of speech or manual response (left or right hand). For the purposes of this approach, we also include a generalized 'cognition' component – it would be possible to assume that cognition is performed using different codes, and to include some additional components, but this is neither substantiated by research nor particularly necessary:

- Visual.
- Auditory.
- Spoken response.
- Manual response (left).
- Manual response (right).
- Cognition.

Domain of Application

Primarily HCI, but also generic.

Example

In order to illustrate the procedure, the following example will be used:

> A security guard is watching a bank of close-circuit television (CCTV) displays that receive images from cameras around a building. If anything suspicious occurs, the guard uses a joystick to manipulate the camera and issues a spoken notification that an intruder has been seen.

Procedure and Advice

In this chapter, construction of a CPA model is based upon a method initially developed by Gray et al. (1993) and further refined by Baber and Mellor (2001). The method may be proceduralised as follows.

Step 1: Analyse the tasks to be modelled
The tasks need to be analysed in fine detail if they are to be modelled by multimodal CPA. Hierarchical tasks analysis can be used (Figure 12.1), but it needs to be conducted down to the level of individual task units. This fine grain level of analysis is essential if reasonable predictions of response times are to be made.

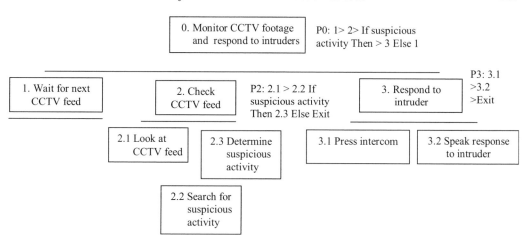

Figure 12.1   **Hierarchical Task Analysis Based on Modalities**

Step 2: Order the tasks
This requires an initial sketch (drawn as a flowchart) of the task sequences, in terms of temporal dependency (Figure 12.2). At this stage, the analyst is considering whether more than one task might feed into subsequent tasks.

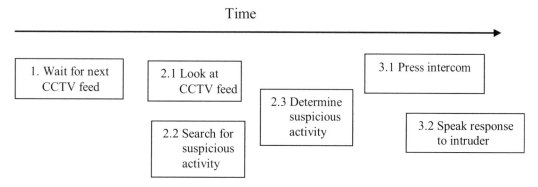

Figure 12.2   **Representation Based on Temporal Dependency**

Step 3: Allocate sub-tasks to modality
Each unit task then needs to be assigned to a modality (Table 12.2). For the purposes of control room tasks, these modalities are as follows:

- Visual tasks: for example, looking at a displays, or written notes and procedures.
- Auditory tasks: for example, listening for an auditory warning or listening to a verbal request.
- Cognition: for example, making decisions about whether or not to intervene and selecting intervention strategies.
- Manual tasks: for example, typing codes on the keyboard, pressing a button, and moving a cursor with a mouse or a tracker ball. Typically, a distinction is made between tasks performed using the left and right hand because this can be used to define the opportunity for serial or parallel performance.
- Speech tasks: for example talking to colleagues or using a speech recognition system.

Table 12.2   Defining Modalities

Visual	Auditory	Manual -L	Manual-R	Spoken	Cognition
Look at CCTV feed			Press intercom	Speak response	Determine Suspicious activity
Search for suspicious activity					

Step 4: Sequence the sub-tasks in a multimodal CPA diagram
The tasks are put into the order of occurrence, checking the logic for parallel and serial tasks. For serial tasks, the logical sequence is determined by the task analysis. For parallel tasks, the modality determines their placement in the representation (Figure 12.3).

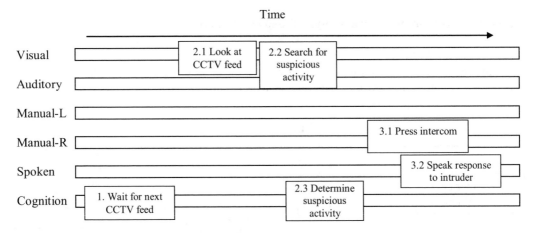

Figure 12.3   Representation Based on Modalities

Step 5: Allocate timings to the sub-tasks
Timings for the tasks are derived from a number of sources. For the purposes of this exercise the timings used are based on the human-computer interaction (HCI) literature, and are presented in Table 12.3.

Table 12.3   Estimates of Activity Times from the Literature on HCI

Activity	Activity time (ms)	Source
Read Read simple information Read short textual descriptions Recognise familiar words or objects	 340 1800 314-340	 Baber and Mellor (2001) John and Newell (1990) Olsen and Olsen (1990)
Hear (auditory warning)	300	Graham (1999)
Search Checking or monitoring or searching Scanning, storing and retrieving	 2700 2300-4600	 Baber and Mellor (2001) Olsen and Olsen (1990)
Diagnosis or decision mental preparation for response choosing between alternative responses simple problem solving	 1350 1760 990	 Card et al (1980) John and Newell (1990) Olsen and Nielson (1988)

Speak	100 per phoneme or space	Hone and Baber (2001)
Move hand to tracker ball or keyboard	214-400 320	Card et al (1980) Baber and Mellor (2001)
Move tracker ball to target item Move cursor via tracker ball 100mm	1500 1245	Olsen and Olsen (1990) Baber and Mellor (2001)
Press key (e.g., ACK or CANCEL key)	200 80-750 230	Baber and Mellor (2001) Card et al (1980) Olsen and Olsen (1990)
Type headcode Average typist (40 wpm) Typing random letters Typing complex codes	280 500 750	Card et al (1980) Card et al (1980) Card et al (1980)
Auditory processing (e.g., speech)	2300	Olsen and Olsen (1990)
Switch attention from one part of a visual display to another	320	Olsen and Olsen (1990)

Step 6: Determine the time to perform the whole task

The time that the task may be performed can be found by tracing through the CPA using the longest node-to-node values. The calculations in CPA are fairly simple, providing you follow two basic rules:

1. On the 'Forward-pass', take the longest time.
2. On the 'Backward-pass', take the shortest time.

The calculation can be most easily represented in the form of a diagram representing the tasks and their start / finish times. Each task is represented as a box containing its number and name, its time, the earliest and latest start times and float.

Step 7: Calculating the earliest start time (EST)

The EST is defined by the completion of ALL preceding tasks. This means that, on the forward-pass, all preceding tasks need to be completed and so one takes the longest time as the EST. For example, if the preceding tasks took 8 units and 10 units, then the EST would be 10 units (because both tasks need to be completed and so one takes the longer of the two tasks). The EST is calculated as the cumulative sum of preceding times.

Step 8: Calculating the latest finish time (LFT)

The LFT is the latest time that the process can support a task to complete. If the task is allowed to 'float' it can finish within an acceptable range, but if it is on the critical path, then any variation in completion time would affect the entire process. On the backward-pass, one takes the earliest of possible times.

Table 12.4   Summary Analysis

Task	Duration	EST	EFT	LST	LFT	Float
Wait for CCTV feed	5000*	0	0	5000	5000	0
Look at CCTV	280	5000	5000	5280	5280	0
Search for suspicious activity	2700	5280	5280	7980	7980	0
Decide suspicious Activity	1350	5280	6630	6630[a]	7980	1350

| Press intercom | 200 | 7980 | 7980 | 8180 | 8180 | 0 |
| Speak response | 2000** | 8180 | 8180 | 10180 | 10180 | 0 |

*Assume feed cycles every ½ second or so

**Assume the phrase "This is Security. You are under surveillance" is spoken

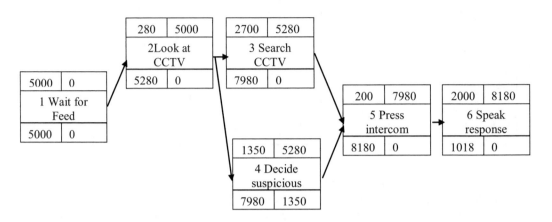

Figure 12.4   Summary Analysis

Step 9: Completing the CPA
Having established a sequence (based on temporal and modality dependency) and associated tasks with times, the final stage is to perform the calculation. In this section, the boxes defined above are presented (Figure 12.4) in conjunction with a table (Table 12.4) to illustrate the calculations.

1. Begin with an EST on 0 for the first activity.
2. Calculate EFT as the sum of EST and duration.
3. Use the EFT for one task as the EST of the next task (unless there is a choice of EFTs, in which case take the largest – see value marked [a]).
4. Continue calculating EFT until the end.
5. Set the LFT to equal the EFT of the final task.
6. Subtract duration from LFT to get LST.
7. Insert LST as EFT on previous task (unless there is a choice, in which case take the smallest - see value marked [b]).
8. Continue until first task reached.

Keystroke Level Model (KLM)

Background and Applications

The Keystroke Level model (KLM) is a very simple method that is used to predict task execution time in HCI tasks. The KLM method originates from the GOMS (Card, Moran and Newell, 1983) family of methods. KLM uses a number of pre-defined operators to predict expert error- free task execution times. KLM uses four physical motor operators, one mental operator and one system response operator. The KLM operators are presented below:

- Keystroking (K) – represents a keystroke or button press (on any button device)
- Pointing (P) – represents pointing to a target on a display with a mouse
- Homing (H) – represents the hand movement of the user when moving his hands between keys, buttons etc.
- Drawing (D) – represents the drawing of straight line segments using a mouse.
- Mental operator (M) – represents the user's mental preparation to execute a physical operation.
- System response operator (R) – represents the system response time.

Each operator has an associated execution time. Total task performance time is equal to the sum of each operator exhibited in the task. The KLM formula is presented in Figure 12.5. The KLM operator execution times are presented in Table 12. 5.

$$\textbf{Texecute} = \textbf{Tk} + \textbf{Tp} + \textbf{Th} + \textbf{Td} + \textbf{Tm} + \textbf{Tr}$$

Figure 12.5   KLM Formula

Table 12.5   KLM Operator Execution Times

Operator/Action	Execution time
K – Pressing Key or Button	
Best typist	.08
Good typist	.12
Average skilled typist	.20
Average non-secretary typist	.28
Typing random letters	.50
Typing complex codes	.75
Worst typist (unfamiliar with keyboard)	1.20
P – Pointing with mouse to a target on a display	1.10
H – Homing hands on keyboard, button etc	.40
D – Drawing straight line segments	.9nd + .16/d
M – Mental preparation	1.35
R – System response time	t

The KLM method also provides a set of heuristic rules for placing the mental operations (M). These are presented below.

Rule 0:   Insert Ms in front of all Ks that are not part of argument strings proper (e.g. text or numbers)

Rule 1:   If an operator following an M is fully anticipated in an operator previous to M, then delete the M

Rule 2:   If a string of MKs belongs to a cognitive unit (e.g. the name of a command) then delete all Ms but the first.

Rule 3:   If a K is a redundant terminator (e.g. the terminator of a command immediately following the terminator of its argument) then delete the M in front of it.

Rule 4:   If a K terminates a constant string (e.g. a command name), then delete the M in front of it; but if the K terminates a variable string (e.g. an argument string) then keep the M in front of it

Domain of Application

HCI.

Procedure and Advice

Step 1: Compile task list and determine scenario to be analysed
Firstly, the analyst should compile an exhaustive task list for the device or system under analysis. Once the task list is complete, the analyst should select the particular task or set of tasks that are to be analysed.

Step 2: Determine the component operations involved in the task
Once the task under analysis has been defined, the analyst should determine the component operations involved in the task. KLM calculates task performance time by summing the component operations involved in the task.

Step 3: Insert physical operations
Any homing or button presses involved in the task should be recorded. The time for each component should be recorded.

Step 4: Insert system response time
Next, the analyst should insert the appropriate system response time. This is normally determined from manufacturer specifications (Stanton and Young 1999). If these are not readily available a domain expert estimate is sufficient.

Step 5: Insert mental operations
Finally, the mental operation times should be inserted. The analyst should use the KLM heuristic rules to place the mental operations.

Step 6: Calculate the total task time
To calculate the total task time, the analyst should add each associated component operation time. The sum of the operation times equals the total task performance time (error-free performance). For maximum accuracy, the final sum should be multiplied by 1.755.

Advantages

1. KLM is very easy and quick to use.
2. KLM requires very little training (Stanton and Young, 1999).
3. Although the method was developed specifically for HCI, KLM has been applied successfully in alternative domains, such as driving (Stanton and Young, 1999) and also 'bank deposit reconciliation systems' (Kieras and John, 1994).
4. KLM can be used to quickly compare the task times for two different devices or systems.
5. KLM has proven to be effective at predicting transaction time, within acceptable limits of tolerance, e.g., usually within 20% of the mean time observed from human performance (Card et al., 1983; Olson and Olson, 1990).
6. Gives an immediately useful output of estimated task performance time.
7. Encouraging reliability and validity data (Stanton and Young, 1999).

Disadvantages

1. KLM was designed specifically for computer-based tasks (HCI). New operators may have to be developed for the method to be used in other domains.
2. KLM only models error-free expert performance.

3. KLM does not take context into account.
4. There is limited validation evidence associated with the use of KLM outside of HCI.
5. KLM assumes that all performance is serial and cannot deal with parallel activity.
6. KLM ignores other unit-task activity and also variation in performance.
7. KLM ignores flexible human activity (Baber and Mellor, 2001).

Related Methods

KLM is part of the GOMS (Card, Moran and Newell, 1983) family of methods developed for use in the HCI domain. These are NGOMSL, KLM, CMN-GOMS and CPM-GOMS. A HTA for the system or device under analysis is also very useful when conducting a KLM analysis.

Approximate Training and Application Times

Stanton and Young (1999) suggest that KLM is moderately time consuming to train. Execution time is dependent upon the size of the task under analysis, but is generally low. Stanton and Young also reported that KLM execution times improve considerably on the second application.

Reliability and Validity

Stanton and Young (1999) reported outstanding reliability and validity measures for KLM. Out of twelve HF methods tested, KLM was the only method to achieve acceptable levels across the three ratings of inter-rater reliability, intra-rater reliability and validity.

Tools Needed

KLM is a pen and paper method. The analyst should also have access to the device or system under analysis and also the KLM operator times.

Example (Source: Stanton and Young, 1999)

The following example is taken from a KLM analysis of a Ford in-car radio system.

When using the Ford 7000 RDS EON in-car stereo, to switch the device on the user has to push the on/off button. For the KLM analysis, this would be presented as:

Task	**Execution time(s)**
Switch on	MHKR = 2.65 + 1 = 3.65

i.e. M = the driver thinking about pressing the on/off button, H = the driver positioning his finger over the button, K = the driver actually pressing the button and R = the time it takes for the radio to turn on (system response time).

The above example is a very simple one. A more complicated one, again for the Ford 7000 RDS EON, would be to adjust the treble on the system. To do this, the driver would have to push the bass button twice and then use the volume knob. Using a KLM analysis, this would be presented as:

Task	Execution time(s)

Adjust treble   MHKKHKR = 4.15+0.3 = 4.45

i.e. M = the driver thinking about the following actions, H = the driver positioning his finger over the BASS button, KK = the driver pressing the BASS button twice, H = the driver positioning his finger over the volume button, K = the driver turning the volume button and R = the system response time.

The full KLM analysis of the Ford and Sharp in-car radios performed by Stanton and Young (1999) is presented in Table 12.6.

Table 12.6   KLM Output

Task	Time – FORD	Time - SHARP	Difference +/-
Switch unit on	MHKR = 2.65+1 = 3.65	MHKR = 2.65+1 = 3.65	0
Adjust Volume	MHKR = 2.65+0.1 = 2.75	MHKR = 2.65+0 = 2.65	+0.1
Adjust Bass	MHKHKR = 3.95+0.2 = 4.15	MHKR = 2.65+0 = 2.65	+1.5
Adjust Treble	MHKKHKR = 4.15+0.3 = 4.45	MHKR = 2.65+0 = 2.65	+1.8
Adjust Balance	MHKKHKR = 4.15+0.3 = 4.45	MHKKR = 2.85+0.1 = 2.95	+1.5
Choose new Pre-set	MHKR = 2.65+0.2 = 2.85	MHKR = 2.65+0.2 = 2.85	0
Use Seek	MHKR = 2.65+1 = 3.65	MHKR = 2.65+1 = 3.65	0
Use Manual Search	MHKHKR = 3.95+1 = 4.95	MHKR = 2.65+1 = 3.65	1.3
Store Station	MHKR = 2.65+1 = 3.65	MHKR = 2.65+3 = 5.65	-2
Insert Cassette	MHKR = 2.65+1 = 3.65	MHKR = 2.65+1 = 3.65	0
Autoreverse and FF	MHKRHKRKR = 4.15+5 = 9.15	MHKRKRK = 3.05+5 = 8.05	1.1
Eject Cassette	MHKR = 2.65+0.5 = 3.15	MHKR = 2.65+0.3 = 2.95	0.2
Switch Off	MHKR = 2.65+0.5 = 3.15	MHKR = 2.65+0.7 = 3.35	-0.2
Total time	53.65	48.35	5.3

As a result of the KLM analysis, it can be concluded that when performing the set of tasks outlined above, it takes around five seconds longer to complete them using the Ford design.

Flowchart

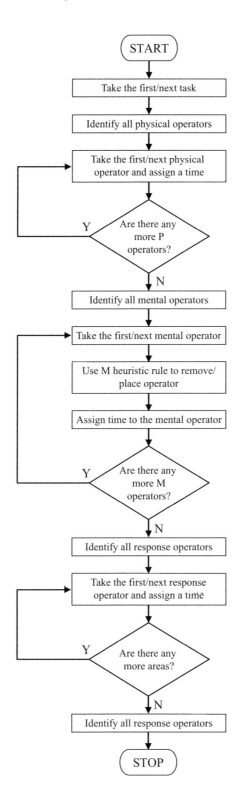

Timeline Analysis

Background and Applications

Although not a set methodology, timeline analysis is an approach that can be used in order to depict scenarios in terms of tasks and their associated task performance times. Timeline analysis can be used to display the functional and temporal requirements of a task. Timeline analysis can be used both predictively and retrospectively, and the output is typically a graph. Timeline analysis can also be combined with workload analysis to represent the workload associated with each task step (Kirwan and Ainsworth, 1992). In terms of analysing command and control and team-based tasks, the appeal of timeline analysis lies in the fact that it could potentially depict individual and team task steps over time.

Domain of Application

Generic.

Procedure and Advice

Step 1: Data collection
The first step in any timeline analysis is to collect specific data from the system under analysis. Task performance times should be recorded for all of the behaviours exhibited in the system. Typically, observational analysis is used during the data collection phase. If the method is being applied retrospectively, then the analyst(s) should observe the scenario under analysis. If a predictive timeline is required, similar scenarios in similar systems should be observed.

Step 2: HTA
Once sufficient data regarding the task under analysis is collected, a HTA should be conducted. HTA (Annett et al., 1971; Shepherd, 1989; Kirwan and Ainsworth, 1992) is based upon the notion that task performance can be expressed in terms of a hierarchy of goals (what the person is seeking to achieve), operations (the activities executed to achieve the goals) and plans (the sequence in which the operations are executed). The hierarchical structure of the analysis enables the analyst to progressively redescribe the activity in greater degrees of detail. The analysis begins with an overall goal of the task, which is then broken down into subordinate goals. At this point, plans are introduced to indicate in which sequence the sub-activities are performed. When the analyst is satisfied that this level of analysis is sufficiently comprehensive, the next level may be scrutinised. The analysis proceeds downwards until an appropriate stopping point is reached (see Annett et al, 1971; Shepherd, 1989, for a discussion of the stopping rule).

Step 3: Determine performance times
Step 3 allows the analyst(s) to create a performance time database for the analysis. Each task step in the HTA should be assigned a performance time. If the analysis is retrospective, this involves sifting through the data gathered during observations and recording the task performance times for each task. If a predictive timeline is required, then the analyst(s) should record the performance times for similar tasks to that involved in the predicted scenario.

Step 4: Construct the timeline graph
The timeline graph normally flows from left to right with the time running along the Y-axis and the tasks running up the X-axis.

Advantages

1. Timeline graphs can be used to compare the performance times associated with two different systems or designs.
2. Timeline analysis could be used to represent team-based tasks and parallel activity.
3. Timeline analysis can be used to highlight problematic tasks or task sequences in the design of systems and processes.
4. Workload analysis can be mapped directly onto a timeline graph. This makes for a very powerful analysis.
5. Timeline analysis is a simple method requiring little training.
6. Requires very few resources once data collection phase is complete.

Disadvantages

1. The reliability and validity of the method is questionable.
2. Observation data is often flawed by a number of biases.
3. When used predictively, timeline analysis can only model error-free performance.
4. Initial data collection phase is time consuming and resource intensive.

Approximate Training and Application Times

The training for timeline analysis is very low. The application time is minimal once the initial data collection is complete. The data collection involved is dependent upon the scenario under analysis. For large, complex scenarios, the data collection time associated with timeline analysis is very high.

Reliability and Validity

Kirwan and Ainsworth (1992) report that the method possesses high face validity. No data regarding the reliability and validity of the method are available in the literature.

Tools Needed

Once the data collection phase is complete, timeline analysis can be conducted using pen and paper. The data collection phase (observation) typically requires using video and audio recording devices.

Flowchart

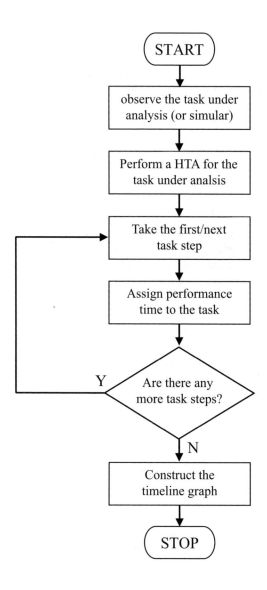

Chapter 13

Human Factors Methods Integration: A Case Study in the Railway Industry

Introduction

The aim of this concluding chapter is not just to present a comprehensive methodology for the analysis of command and control scenarios, but more importantly to show how the previous human factors methods can be combined and integrated to answer questions of direct relevance to engineers and designers. Obviously it is nearly impossible to show all the possible combinations of methods as they relate to specific practical problems. However, this chapter will succeed in its purpose if it demonstrates that with intelligent application a toolkit approach can be developed from the methods matrix and the 100 or so methods covered in this book. We illustrate the principle of the toolkit approach with reference to a case study drawn from an analysis of railway maintenance activities.

Event Analysis of Systemic Teamwork (EAST)

The EAST methodology was developed specifically to examine the work of distributed teams of people in complex socio-technical systems; so called command, control, communications, computers and intelligence (C4i) scenarios. Although militaristic in origin, the technological mediation of task success among dispersed individuals, and groups of individuals, all working towards a common goal is a feature of many contemporary analysis domains. At the most basic level the descriptive constructs to be extracted from such domains can be distilled down to simply:

- *Why* (the goals of the system, sub-system(s) and agent(s)).
- *Who* (the agents participating in a scenario are).
- *When* (tasks are performed, and which agents are associated with their performance).
- *Where* (agents are physically located).
- *How* (agents collaborate and communicate to achieve scenario aims).
- *What* (tasks are agents performing, and what knowledge is used and/or shared).

As we have seen in the previous chapters, there are well over 100 different methods available to the ergonomist covering all of these constructs and more besides. It would seem evident based on this that a high degree of circumspection is required before embarking on the development of yet more. In this concluding chapter an approach based on method integration is proposed. The aim is to show how existing methods can be combined in useful ways to analyse complex, multi-faceted scenarios. Method integration has a number of compelling advantages, because not only does the integration of existing methods bring reassurance in terms of a previous validation history, but it also enables the same data to be analysed from multiple perspectives. These multiple perspectives, as well as being inherent in the scenario that is being described and measured, also provide a form of internal validity. Assuming that the separate methods integrate on, and are compatible with a common theoretical basis, then their application to the same data set offers a form of 'analysis triangulation' (see Figure 13.1). The methods matrix in Chapter 1 enables the analyst to complete this step relatively easily, and an explanation of the EAST methodology serves to describe an example of how this can be practically achieved.

Summary of Component Methods Within EAST

Whilst the methods that comprise the full EAST analysis are tried and tested, the integration of them into one methodology is a paradigm case of the toolkit approach. EAST is an analytic method, developed out of an 'ergonomist as scientist' rather than 'practitioner' perspective, although this depends to some extent on how the method is ultimately used. EAST is grouped around three main network based approaches; task, knowledge and social networks. The network based approach is an expression of the common theoretical perspective required for method integration in this case. Each network, and the links between them, have associated methods all of which provide several insights into the main descriptive constructs identified in Figure 13.1. The task network is summed up by an HTA (Chapter 3) which identifies the actors in the scenario, the temporal structure of tasks, where tasks (and associated actors) are located geographically, and what tasks are being performed. The HTA is one of the main foundation methods within EAST, and drives a CDA analysis (Chapter 9), which provides structured insight into the general question of how team-working tasks are performed, and what team-working skills they require. A CUD (Chapter 9) is also founded on data from the HTA, it provides insight into who the actors are, the flow of tasks (i.e. when), where actors are located geographically, what items are being communicated and how (i.e. the communications technology used). The social network is embodied by a SNA (Chapter 9) which extends the analysis of communications by considering the 'links' between actors, rather than according to task flow. The propositional network (Chapter 7) represents the type and structure of knowledge existent during the scenario. In support of this is a form of content analysis (Chapter 3) performed on the outputs of the CDM method. Finally, the question of 'why' is provided by the HTA goal structure, which describes the goals of the whole system as well as individual goals of system agents. Exactly how these methods and their outputs combine are elaborated shortly. For the time being Table 13.1 is a methods matrix that relates the component methods to the descriptive constructs identified above. The overlap between methods, and the constructs they access is explained by the multiple perspectives provided on properties such as 'Who' and 'What'. For example, the HTA deals with 'what' tasks, the CDA deals with 'what' team-working skills, and the CUD deals with 'what' communications technology is used. Each being a different but complementary perspective on the same descriptive construct, and a different but complementary perspective on the same data derived from observation and interview. This is an example of analysis triangulation.

Table 13.1   Methods Matrix Mapping Descriptive C4i Constructs onto Component Methods of EAST

	HTA	CDA	CUD	SNA	Propositional Networks
Who	■		■		
When	■		■		
Where	■		■		
What				■	■
How		■	■		
Why	■				

Structure of the EAST Methodology

The internal structure of the EAST methodology can be broken down into three layers comprised of established methods covered in previous chapters:

* Layer 1 – data collection methods.
* Layer 2 – data analysis methods.
* Layer 3 – representational methods.

It is important to consider the theoretical issues surrounding the use of methods applicable to these three levels. This consideration is important from the point of view of validity in terms of the individual method, but also in terms of compatibility 'between' methods.

     The internal structure of the methodology is illustrated in Figure 13.2 below. Live observation provides input into all of the layer 2 analysis methods. An HTA serves to provide a definition of tasks and a goal structure for the remaining analysis methods. The analysis methods are then summarised and represented on an enhanced form of OSD (the SNA can also be used as a representational method). The CDM interview data collected live is represented using a propositional network, thus representing the structure of knowledge at key decision points in the scenario. The outputs of EAST, therefore, provide an integrated picture of multiple perspectives. That is, the component methods are compatible with each other to the extent that they can be summarised within a common representation (e.g. the OSD), but the individual methods, and combinations of them are also capable of generating insights into the core emergent properties of any C4i type scenario. These are the properties that relate to task success. The component methods of EAST are briefly described below, but the reader is referred to the relevant previous chapters for a complete description.

Layer 1 – Data Collection Methods

Structured data collection methodologies are required to extract meaningful data from any scenario. Annett (2003) argues that data collection should comprise of observation and interviews as a minimum, and both Annett (2003) and Kieras (2003) argue for the least intrusive method of observation that circumstances permit. Therefore a two step process of observation and interview is proposed as a means to collect key information from within live C4i scenarios, where several people are likely to be working remotely from each other.

     Observation itself takes the form of multi-site activity sampling (Stanton, Baber and Young, 2005). Activity sampling is an aid to unobtrusively recording activity (or actual behaviour) in the field. This process involves the use of pre-defined categories or classes of action, which can then be used to create a checklist. The checklist could be completed at regular time intervals, e.g., every 15 seconds (by ticking the appropriate action in the appropriate column for that observation), or could be completed whenever an action occurs (by entering the time against the action). Activity sampling provides a means of relating the timing of actions to locations, and to the decisions made by specific actors in context. It can be assumed that in a number of cases there will also be pre-existing material in the form of task analyses (or similar) that will enable task descriptions to be structured, sampled and even validated through observation.

     In basic terms, whilst observational techniques provide information on the observable inputs and outputs of human information processing, they produce limited data on the process of decision making. Interviewing people enables the analyst to capture data on these unobservable processes, particularly if the interviewee is describing a recent event and how they dealt with it. In recent years, the study of decision making in real-world situations has received a great deal of attention, and there is a growing emphasis on the use of interviews to collect such information. The Critical Decision Method (CDM) (Klein and Armstrong, 2005) is a contemporary example. According to Klein, 'The CDM is a retrospective interview strategy that applies a set of cognitive probes to actual non-routine incidents that required expert judgment or decision making' (Klein, Calderwood and MacGregor, 1989, p. 464). In this approach, the interview proceeds through a series of four stages: briefing and initial recall of incidents, identifying decision points in a specific incident, probing the decision points, and checking. A slightly modified version of the CDM probes presented in O'Hare et al (2000) are adopted within EAST and presented in Table 13.2. These permit elicitation of information on key decision points as well as non-routine 'incidents'.

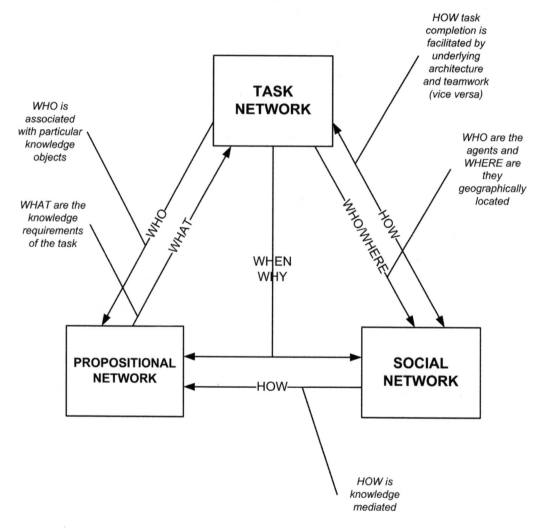

Figure 13.1 Integration and Triangulation of Analysis Methods Within EAST

The selection of data collection methods proceeds not just from the theoretical perspective, but also the practical. Given that most C4i scenarios will involve the simultaneous observation of activities distributed geographically and among individuals and teams, the proposed two-step process of activity sampling and CDM interview provide an expedient method of data capture in this context.

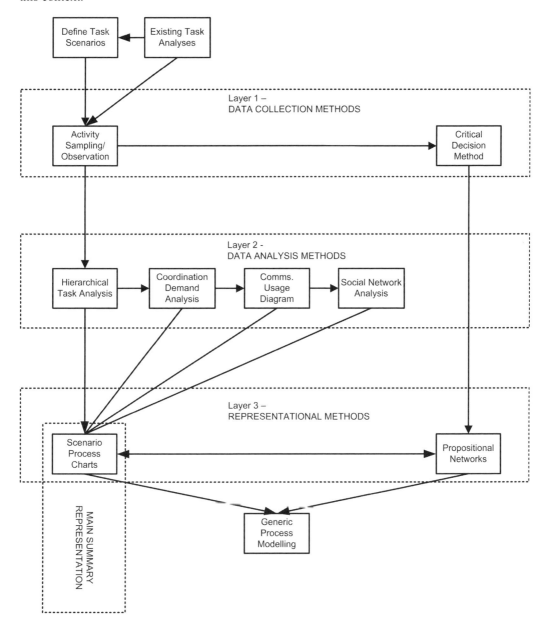

Figure 13.2   Internal Structure of EAST Methodology

Layer 2 – Analysis Methods

Structured analysis methodologies take the data extracted earlier in the data collection phase, and model it in terms of deeper, more fundamental concepts. These concepts relate ultimately to task success, but specifically to task and social structures, team working and mediating communications technology.

Hierarchical Task Analysis (HTA)

Task analysis is the activity of collecting, analysing and interpreting data on system performance and is one of the central underpinning analysis methods within EAST (Annett and Stanton, 2000; Diaper and Stanton, 2004). Hierarchical Task Analysis (HTA) is a means of describing a system in terms of goals and sub-goals, with feedback loops in a nested hierarchy (see Chapter 3).

Table 13.2   CDM Probes (O'Hare, et al., 2000)

Cognitive Cue	Sample Question
Goal specification	What were your specific goals at the various decision points?
Goal identification	What features were you looking at when you formulated your decision? How did you know that you needed to make the decision? How did you know when to make the decision?
Expectancy	Were you expecting to make this type of decision during the course of the event? Describe how this affected your decision-making process
Conceptual model	Are there situations in which your decision would have turned out differently? Describe the nature of these situations and the characteristics that would have changed the outcome of your decision
Influence of uncertainty	At any stage, were you uncertain about either the reliability or the relevance of information that you had available? At any stage, were you uncertain about the appropriateness of the decision?
Information integration	What was the most important piece of information that you used to formulate the decision?
Situation awareness	What information did you have available to you when formulating the decision?
Situation assessment	Did you use all the information available to you when formulating the decision? Was there any additional information that you might have used to assist in the formulation the decision?
Options	Were there any other alternatives available to you other than the decision that you made? Why were these alternatives considered inappropriate?
Decision blocking	Was there any stage during the decision-making process in which you found it difficult to process and integrate the information available? Describe precisely the nature of the situation.
Basis of choice	Do you think that you could develop a rule, based on your experience, which could assist another person to make the same decision successfully? Do you think that anyone else would be able to use this rule successfully? Why?/ Why not?
Generalisation	Were you at any time reminded of previous experiences in which a similar decision was made? Were you at any time reminded of previous experiences in which a different decision was made?

Its enduring popularity and indeed its appropriateness within EAST can be put down to two key points. First, it is inherently flexible: the approach can be used to describe any system, even C4i.

Second, it can be used for many ends: from person specification, to training requirements, to error prediction, to team performance assessment, and to system design. The multiple perspectives available from HTA fit well with the multiple perspectives available from C4i scenarios. HTA has additional pragmatic benefits because it already underpins a number of subsequent analysis methodologies such as Co-ordination Demand Analysis (CDA) (Burke, 2005) and Communications Usage Diagrams (CUD) (Watts and Monk, 2000), making it an ideal candidate for method integration. Task analysts applying HTA are also required to understand both the ways in which people adapt to their environment and the ways that they adapt their environment to themselves. Thus HTA has the further benefit of capturing and specifying the contextual conditions and precursors within C4i scenarios within detailed task descriptions and as 'plans' within the task hierarchy.

In its application within EAST, the definition of the HTA proceeds with reference both to what has been observed and what may have been previously defined through any pre-existing task analyses. It is possible to meaningfully integrate these information sources on goal structure to produce a task analysis that accurately describes what has been observed, is consistent with what has already been pre-defined, and also covers key decision points covered in the CDM interview.

Co-ordination Demand Analysis (CDA)

It might be assumed that C4i activity will be dominated by co-ordination activities, but this supposition needs to be checked. Individual tasks from the HTA can be assessed for the type of co-ordination that is required for successful performance using Co-ordination Demand Analysis (CDA) (Burke, 2005). The method integrates with the HTA, where the tasks identified in it are assessed according to multi-dimensional aspects of team working, presented in Table 13.3 below.

Table 13.3   Co-ordination Demand Dimensions

Co-ordination Dimension	Definition
Communication	Includes sending, receiving, and acknowledging information among crew members.
Situational Awareness (SA)	Refers to identifying the source and nature of problems, maintaining an accurate perception of the aircraft's location relative to the external environment, and detecting situations that require action.
Decision Making (DM)	Includes identifying possible solutions to problems, evaluating the consequences of each alternative, selecting the best alternative, and gathering information needed prior to arriving at a decision.
Mission analysis (MA)	Includes monitoring, allocating, and co-ordinating the resources of the crew and aircraft; prioritizing tasks; setting goals and developing plans to accomplish the goals; creating contingency plans.
Leadership	Refers to directing activities of others, monitoring and assessing the performance of crew members, motivating members, and communicating mission requirements.
Adaptability	Refers to the ability to alter one's course of action as necessary, maintain constructive behaviour under pressure, and adapt to internal or external changes.
Assertiveness	Refers to the willingness to make decisions, demonstrating initiative, and maintaining one's position until convinced otherwise by facts.
Total Co-ordination	Refers to the overall need for interaction and co-ordination among crew members.

Burke (2005) distinguishes between team working tasks (those comprised of the co-ordination dimensions in Table 13.3 above), and task work (individual tasks that are performed in isolation). For example, a teamwork task would be dealing with the issuing of an instruction to another individual, whereas a 'task work' task would be inputting data into the C4i system. It is argued by Burke that existing team-working methodologies tackle only a few of the necessary dimensions of skill; CDA aims to be more comprehensive. CDA also integrates readily within the EAST paradigm where it provides a profile of team-working skills according to the tasks identified earlier in the HTA.

Communications Usage Diagram (CUD)

The Communications Usage Diagram (CUD) (Watts and Monk, 2000) is another task analysis technique which in the current application provides an opportunity to systematically critique the communications technology in use within C4i (or indeed any scenario). The critique is based upon the task flow. It identifies actors in specific locations, the communications in use within identified tasks, and an approximate indication of the sequencing of events. The critique of communications technology currently in use is based upon this. It identifies the positive and negative points associated with a given communications media within the current context of use, and enables the analyst to propose alternative solutions. The CUD is useful as a way of drawing out practical, design related outputs as well as providing a more theoretical level of description.

Social Network Analysis (SNA)

Social network analysis is a means to present and describe, in a compact and systematic fashion, the network structure underlying individuals or teams who are linked through communications with each other (Driskell and Mullen, 2005). The relationships that are specified from this analysis can be used to determine what aspects of the network structure constrain or enhance the performance of agents in the network (Driskell and Mullen, 2005). Unlike the other analysis methods within EAST, SNA is not directly based on the task analysis. However, foundation data on actors and communications is derived from the HTA and CUD.

SNA can be used to analyse the formal and informal relationships between people in a network, but there is also no reason why they cannot show technological mediation of communication, and networks where some of the nodes are non-human. This is of particular relevance within C4i. In a practical sense the approach might reveal sub-optimal networks and bottlenecks in communication. The approach also allows a complex network to be summarised on just a small number of key metrics, and for these same metrics to permit easy comparison between different C4i scenarios. Another major advantage that Driskell and Mullen (2005) identify is that this 'network approach focuses on the relationships among actors embedded in their social context' (pg. 58-1). Again, another important consideration within socio-technical systems like C4i.

Layer 3 – Representational Methods

Representational methods take the extracted data modelled in the analysis section, and provide a means of simplifying and presenting these deeper concepts in various integrated, graphical forms.

Operation Sequence Diagram (OSD)

Process charts offer a systematic approach to describing activities. They emphasise essential features using a graphical representation that is easy to follow and understand (Kirwan and Ainsworth, 1992). Charting techniques such as this preserve the ability of preceding methods such as SNA and HTA to represent human and non-human elements of the C4i system (Drury, 1990). Charting techniques are also capable of representing one of the key contextual factors in C4i scenarios, and that is the temporal structure and interrelations between and among processes. Several enhancements to the OSD representation have been made to reflect the outputs of the supporting analysis methods. The OSD presents a temporal overview of tasks, the outputs of the CDA, comms media from the CUD, and links between agents from the SNA. The approach summarises a large amount of supporting analysis in a fashion that is graphical and relatively easy to follow, whilst also being scaleable to suit different 'sized' C4i scenarios. This enhanced version of OSD is therefore one of the key summary representations within EAST.

Two additional reasons underlie the selection of the OSD. First, OSD has long been a popular and useful tool in the Human Factors toolkit. Second, many approaches to systems analysis (such as Unified Modelling Language) make use of sequence diagrams in their representations, and so it ought to be possible to integrate a Human Factors OSD with the more technical sequence diagrams used by systems analysts. In this manner, we propose that the process-based analysis derived from EAST provides a convenient route into HFI as well as methods integration.

Propositional Network (PN)

Propositional Networks are like semantic networks in that they contain nodes (with words) and links between nodes. It is argued that the application of basic propositions and operators enables dictionary-like definitions of concepts to be derived (Ogden, 1987). Stanton et al (2005) takes this basic notion and extends it to offer a novel way of modelling knowledge in any scenario. Knowledge relates strongly to SA. A systems view of SA (and indeed an individual view as well) can be understood as 'activated knowledge' (Bell and Lyon, 2000), and therefore propositional networks offer a novel and effective means of representing the total, or 'systems level' view of SA. The theoretical background to this approach is described in Chapter 7. However, an opportunity arises within EAST to apply the DSA methodology in a practical sense to C4i scenarios.

The knowledge used in C4i activities is accessed via the CDM, where a systematic content analysis of the interview transcripts permits 'knowledge objects' to be extracted, and subsequently linked. Knowledge objects are analogous to propositions, and can be defined as an entity or phenomenon about which an individual requires information in order to act effectively. The resultant network of knowledge objects enables at least four powerful perspectives on SA.

1. Firstly, a major advantage of propositional networks is that they do not differentiate between different types of node (e.g. knowledge related to objects, people or ideas) and therefore from a design perspective, they do not constrain assessments to consideration of existing configurations of people and objects, rather to the required knowledge elements associated with a scenario.
2. Secondly, the network shows the totality of knowledge used in the scenario, at a systems level, regardless of whether agents in the scenario are human or technical.
3. Thirdly, shared SA can be accessed from the CDM, where agents can be attributed to knowledge objects within the network.
4. Fourth, Endsley (1995a) states that SA occurs within a 'volume of time and space' (pg 36), and it is possible to illustrate this key temporal aspect of SA by animating the propositional network in terms of active and non-active knowledge objects (Figure 13.10 later in this Chapter provides an illustration of the concept). To do this the scenario is divided into tasks phases according to the higher level goals of the HTA. The CDM relates to these phases, and accesses information on decision making within them, allowing active and non-active knowledge objects to be specified and represented.

Procedure and Advice

The high level procedure for applying EAST can be summarised in Table 13.4 below as involving nine key steps. Obviously, within these overall headings a degree of flexibility can be adopted to suit the particular domain or circumstances.

Table 13.4　　High Level Procedure for EAST

STAGE	ACTION	TIMING	OUTPUT
1	Organise observation. It is proposed that many of the sessions can also be undertaken in simulators or training centres, as an alternative to the field.	Prior to observation.	Stakeholder involvement. Details of scenario; number of personnel; key decision roles.
2	Conduct HTAs with SMEs Existing task analysis material would be sourced during this stage and validated by SMEs. If required, new task analyses would be undertaken with SMEs.	Prior to observation.	Definition of task scenario. Details of task structure, activities and actors.
3	Define objectives. This stage will involve checking that the proposed technique is feasible (e.g., in terms of security, access, privacy etc.). If possible define 'ideal' performance, perhaps in terms of a list of roles, responsibilities, decisions and timing of events.	Prior to observation.	List of agreed objectives; agree observation posts; If possible, description of ideal performance.
4	Brief and train observers.	Prior to observation 30 – 60 minutes.	Demonstrate sampling strategy; practice.
5	Arrive at Scenario. On arrival at 'scenario', position observers at their posts. Synchronise watches.	On-site 5 – 10 minutes.	
6	Observation. The incident is sampled using the pro-forma/ experimental materials.	During observation Duration of incident or n x 20 minute observations.	Multiple activity samples.
7	Interview. Participants interviewed by observer(s) using CDM methodology.	After observation 1 hour per interviewee.	Interview transcript containing knowledge objects.
8	Define CDA and CUD Outputs with SMEs This involves engaging SMEs to assist in the rating of tasks along teamwork dimensions, and the critique of communications technology in use during the scenario.	After observation (can be undertaken at any stage after Step 2 if required) 2 hours.	Validated CDA and CUD data.
9	Collation. The activity samples are collated to produce full EAST analysis.	After session.	Analysis and representations of C4i scenario.

Railway Maintenance Example

Three examples of complex and dynamic resource systems are taken from the UK rail industry. The scenarios serve as a source of live data to demonstrate the capability of the method. The data is sourced, in this case, from written transcripts based on communications between parties in the scenarios, and interviews with subject matter experts.

Broadly speaking the C4i activities under consideration are those involved in the setting up of safety systems required when carrying out maintenance of railway track (for example, see Figure 13.3). Safety systems are required so that workers on the track do not come into conflict with moving trains, and that trains do not travel over railway infrastructure that is rendered unsafe by the maintenance work, or the requirement for it. The strict procedures underpinning these systems are specified nationally in the UK railway industry Rule Book (RSSB, 2003).

Figure 13.3   Example of Track Maintenance Activities (RSSB)

Railway operations are an example of civilian C4i, where a 'management infrastructure' is required and in place. Maintenance activities on the railway possess all the essential ingredients of C4i including:

- A common goal;
- Individuals and teams co-ordinating to reach it;
- Geographical dispersion of people, systems and artefacts;
- The presence of numerous systems, procedures and technology to support their endeavour.

Background

Under normal conditions a signaller has the key responsibility for controlling train movements and maintaining safety for an area of railway line. This control occurs remotely from the line at a control centre (a signalbox or signalling centre). These can be located many miles from where activity could be taking place.

During maintenance, another person takes responsibility for an area of the line (sometimes referred to as a 'possession') and/or for preventing trains passing over the possession (measures referred to as 'protection'). These individuals are normally termed the person in charge of possession (PICOP) or controller of site safety (COSS). Communication and co-ordination are required to transfer responsibility between the signaller and PICOP/COSS. The PICOP/COSS also have to communicate and co-ordinate with various other personnel, such as those carrying out maintenance within their areas of control, drivers of trains and on track-plant which may be in the possession, and personnel implementing aspects of the possession (all of which may also be dispersed over a certain geographical area). Three specific maintenance scenarios are briefly described below, with Figure 13.4 providing additional clarity on the general layout and relative geographical positions of personnel.

Scenario 1 – Planned Maintenance Activities

This scenario describes the processes and activities for setting up a possession for a stretch of track so that planned maintenance can take place. This requires co-ordination between multiple parties, including; communication between the signaller and PICOP (so that appropriate 'protecting' signals are set to danger), and the provision of instructions to a 'competent person' (CP) to place a form of protection against oncoming trains at the limits of the possession (these take the form of explosive charges called detonators that emit a loud noise to alert drivers who may have just run over them). Additional complexity comes in the form of a number of engineering work sites within the possession, each of which has an engineering supervisor (ES) and COSS responsible for setting up and managing each one. The ES will also use CPs to place marker boards as a form of additional protection at the ends of the individual worksites.

Scenario 2 – Emergency Engineering Work

When railway personnel are required to carry out unplanned emergency engineering work on the line, such as when track or infrastructure has been damaged or has suddenly degraded, then the passage of trains must be stopped and an emergency protection procedure called a T2(X) applied. For this procedure, a portion of the railway which is normally under the control of a signaller working remotely from a signal box becomes the responsibility of a (COSS), who will work on the line. The workers will be protected from train movements by the signaller placing signals at the limits of the work to danger. Emergency protection can be arranged between the COSS and Signaller following discussion with the Network Rail Area Operations Manager. It can be noted in the scenario above that *non*-emergency engineering work involves greater advanced planning and protection, whereas in emergency scenarios organisation tends to occur 'on the day'.

Scenario 3 – Ending a Track Possession

When the possession is ended the 'set-up' procedure outlined in scenario 1 is largely reversed. First, the engineering supervisor (ES) of a worksite has to check that the worksite can be closed. This requires agreement between the ES and each controller of site safety (COSS) within the worksite (there is a controller of site safety responsible for each piece of work being undertaken within the worksite). Once this has been checked and the PICOP has been informed, then the ES can instruct a CP to remove the worksite marker boards. The PICOP is informed when this is completed and then, when all the worksites within a possession are closed, the possession itself can be closed. The PICOP can then instruct a CP to remove the possession protection. The PICOP will inform the signaller that lines are now safe and clear for trains to run. Control of the line is then passed from the PICOP to the signaller and normal running of trains over the lines can resume.

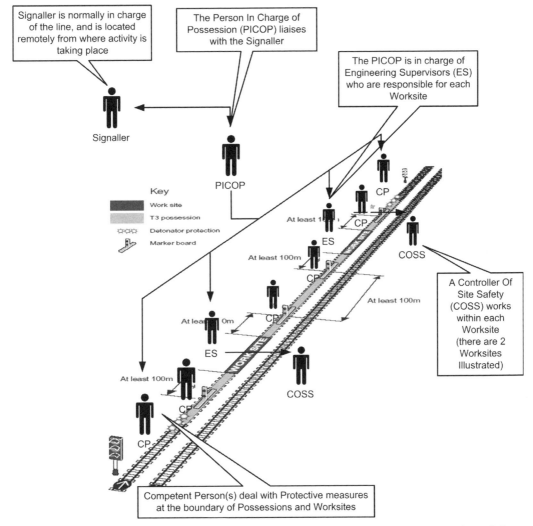

Figure 13.4 Overall Diagram of the Various Track Possession Scenarios (Adapted from RSSB, 2003)

Outputs from Component Methods

Task networks

The first step in the EAST methodology, subsequent to collecting the data, is to model the goal structure of the scenario using HTA. The outputs of this step are represented as task networks.

These are graphical representations of the 'plan 0' within the HTA, and depict the task structure in terms of how tasks relate to each other functionally and temporally. In the present case the highly proceduralised and rigid nature of the activity is seen as a more or less linear task flow assuming that no unusual circumstances bring a premature end to matters (Figure 13.5).

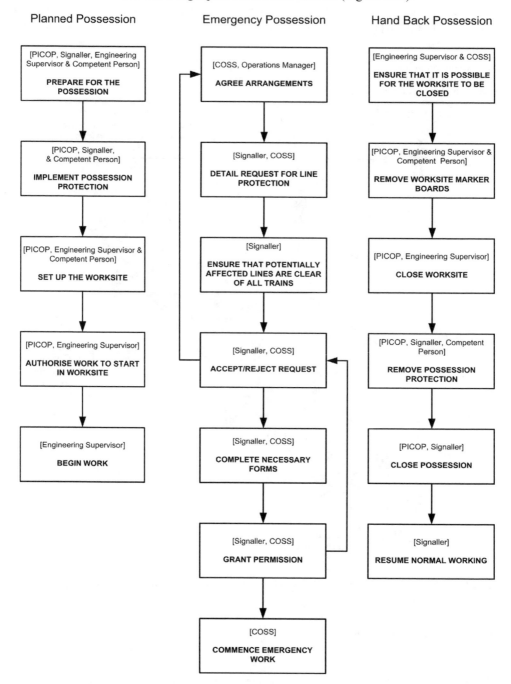

Figure 13.5   Task Networks for Each Scenario

The following is an extract from the verbal transcripts, and shows a typical communication occurring between the Signaller [S] and Person In Charge of Possession [PICOP]:

S	"Wimbledon…" [answers phone with name of signal box]
S	"…panel 1" [signalling panel, and associated geographical area being worked by the signaller]
PICOP	"Hello Wimbledon, its [name of PICOP] at Waterloo [station]
S	"…Yes…."
PICOP	"the blocks [protective measures] now been put out mate on the down main slow and the up main slow…" [referring to different lines]
S	"…right…"
PICOP	"…and it's clear of 15 64 b points and 15 12 b points."
S	"It's all yours, at, er, what we on, 9:53 then."
PICOP	"oh, 9:53, cheers mate."
S	"…ok…"
PICOP	"Can I take your name please, I forgot to write it down earlier
S	"…[provides name]."
PICOP	"[name] thanks a lot mate…."
S	"ok…"
PICOP	"…bye."

It is interesting to note the data collection transcripts which highlight that some of the required and critical steps may be implied. For example, the PICOP's closure of communication is by saying 'bye', which is implied by the Signaller to mean that there are no remaining issues or ambiguity, and that points 15 64b, and 15 12b are indeed clear. Also, the sequencing of communications is more flexible than the procedures may suggest (for example, the PICOP may only inquire in more detail as to the name of the Signaller at the stage when it is needed for the completion of documentation, rather than at the beginning of a call). However, at the level illustrated above, any informality or flexibility occurs within the confines of a well defined procedure.

CDA

Based on Figure 13.6, the supposition that C4 is dominated by co-ordination tasks appears to be justified. In the three scenarios under analysis the tasks that fall into the 'teamwork' track, and that require co-ordination, form between 66 and 72% of total tasks undertaken. Figure 13.7 below extracts the teamwork tasks for further analysis. The analysis proceeds according to seven co-ordination dimensions, and one summary total co-ordination score (based on the mean of the individual scores). This analysis reveals a broadly similar pattern of co-ordination activity within the scenarios, certainly the total co-ordination figures are comparable, falling within the mid-point of the rating scale. Of more interest is the pattern of results across the seven individual dimensions where a distinctive footprint emerges. Communication, situation awareness and decision making are prominent dimensions, and there is also a smaller 'blip' for the leadership dimension. Leadership can be taken as a further indication perhaps of some decision-making activity. It can be further noted that the larger (and more complex) the scenario, the larger the leadership blip is. Therefore in summary, not only are the majority of total tasks dominated by co-ordination activities, but those activities are dominated by communications and the creation and maintenance of SA.

CUD

General observations from the CUD analysis are that the communications are entirely verbal. Given the nature of the scenario, verbal and telephone communications appear to be appropriate in most stages of the interaction. However, possible technology options could be helpful in three respects.

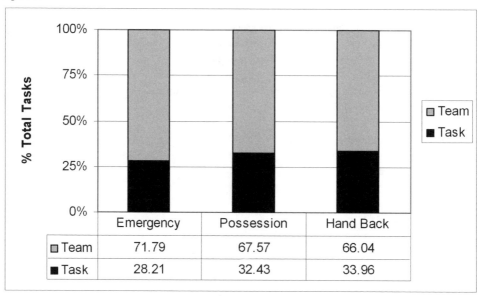

Figure 13.6   Results of CDA Analysis Showing Percentage of Task/Teamwork Activities Undertaken Within Each Scenario

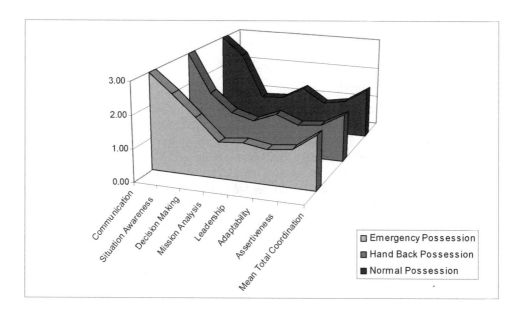

Figure 13.7   Results of CDA Analysis Showing Profile of Results on Each of the Co-ordination Dimensions

1. Firstly, removing possible sources of error inherent in verbal communications.
2. Secondly, removing the cumbersome nature of read-back procedures.
3. Thirdly, alleviating the physical disturbance to other tasks caused by the unscheduled and ad-hoc presentation of verbal communications.

Of course, any new approaches would require fuller risk justification and assessment within the wider task context before application. The key point is that the CUD method provides a systematic way of presenting the existing situation and considering alternatives to it based on data. Figure 13.8 summarises the communications technology in use within the scenarios.

Social networks
Social Network Analysis is used in the EAST method to represent and summarise the communication/ information links between agents in the scenario. Figure 13.8 presents a graphical representation of the networks derived from each of the scenarios, and is also annotated with comms information drawn from the CUD analysis.

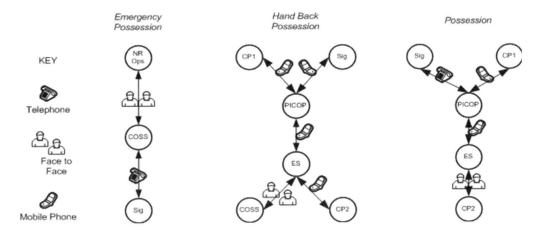

Figure 13.8   Graphical Representation of Social Networks Overlain with Comms Media Drawn from CUD Analysis

A range of mathematical metrics (derived from graph theory) can be applied. The results show that the PICOP, Signaller and Engineering supervisors have the highest levels of socio metric status and centrality. These metrics indicate that they are key agents in the scenarios. The notion of centrality is also born out when considering 'betweenness', that is the PICOP and ES fall between pairs of other positions in the network most frequently. Having identified the key agents, it is also possible to view the network as a whole using the concept of network density. Density is the degree of interconnectivity between agents, or the number of network links used compared to those that are theoretically available (the maximum being a case where all agents are linked to each other). In Table 13.5 below it can be seen that the emergency possession scenario has the densest pattern of connectivity, with the remaining two scenarios being broadly comparable.

Table 13.5   Comparison of Network Density Between Scenarios

	Possession	Emergency Possession	Hand Back Possession
Density	0.4	0.67	0.33

Although the metrics allow comparison between networks, intelligent interpretation is required. For example, a network with every agent connected to each other would permit easy dissemination of information, but might also be inefficient. Similarly, having one central node may have advantages for co-ordination but offers the potential for an information bottleneck. The main point is that the interpretation and then subsequent comparison of networks has to take into account a range of contextual factors, but the metrics can be used to gauge properties of the networks that may constrain or enhance performance. For the time being the networks derived from the scenarios above appear to be relatively well matched to the procedures being undertaken, with a mix of central agents and interconnectivity.

Representational Methods

Scenario Process Charts (OSD)
Figure 13.9 presents a sample of an enhanced OSD from scenario 1 (the planned maintenance task), and highlights how the preceding methods are integrated with it. The operations loading is presented in Table 13.6, showing the Person In Charge Of Possession (PICOP), Signaller and Competent Person (CP) as the most heavily loaded individuals in the network in terms of activity. The operations loading table provides a further level of summarisation in being able to capture, in a relatively compact manner, the process based aspects of what is often a large OSD.

Table 13.6   Task Loading Table

	OPERATIONS				
Agent	Operation	Receive	Decide	Transport	Total
PICOP	54	30	1		85
Signaller	17	16	1		34
Eng Supervisor	13	17		1	31
Competent Person 1	17	20		1	38

Propositional networks (PN)
The propositional network provides an overview, for each scenario, of all the knowledge elements and their relationships. It also allows the knowledge elements related to a specific phase in the scenario to be modelled, and the history of previously used knowledge objects to be represented. Figure 13.10 displays the network elements related to taking a possession for emergency maintenance. Shaded cells denote knowledge objects that are currently active within the task phase, faded cells indicate previously active knowledge. The main image in Figure 13.10 is intended to provide information on the specific types of knowledge objects, whereas the smaller networks alongside are merely illustrative of changing activation.

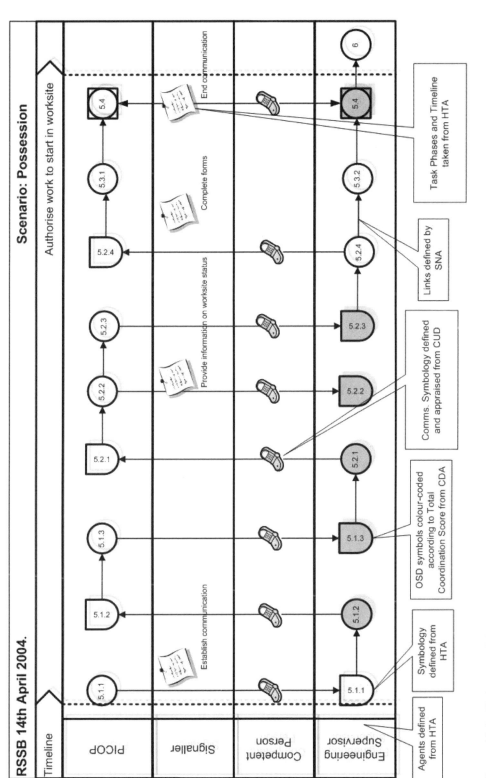

Figure 13.9 Enhanced OSD Summary Representation

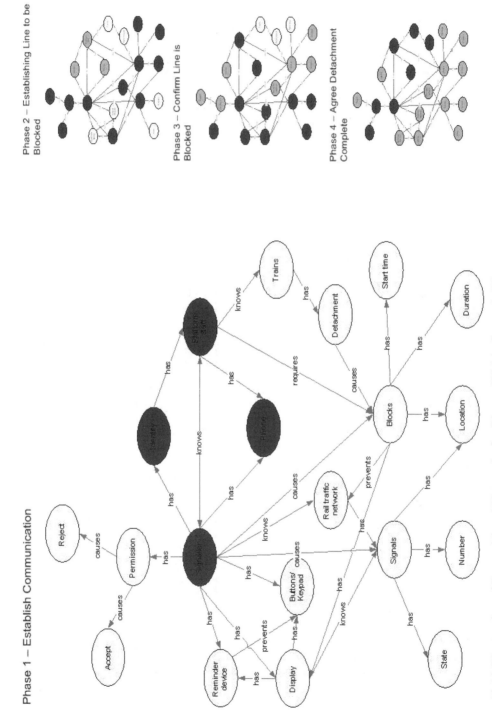

Phase 1 – Establish Communication

Phase 2 – Establishing Line to be Blocked

Phase 3 – Confirm Line is Blocked

Phase 4 – Agree Detachment Complete

Figure 13.10 Illustration of Propositional Networks for Phases Within Scenario Three

Despite the emergency procedure scenario being a relatively simple proceduralised task, the propositional network appears complex. It should be recognised that this complexity does not necessarily reflect complexity in the task itself. For example, some of the knowledge elements are internalised skills (e.g. participant knowledge of the railway rule book or a signaller's knowledge of the current status of the railway) or simple objects (e.g. telephones) which would not provide load or add to the complexity perceived by a skilled participant. It does, however, demonstrate that a large number of related objects are used to accomplish relatively straight forward tasks. In the context of task redesign, the propositional network provides a prompt which can allow system designers to question the necessity for knowledge objects, the form those objects can take and how they are communicated. This is a novel perspective. The network could also be considered as a tool for training design, which describes the knowledge elements and relationships that someone undertaking the task must have available.

Summary

The summary and individual outputs derived from EAST have been presented. It should be evident that the data generated from an EAST analysis is extensive, so in Figure 13.11 an attempt is made to convey an impression of what the total EAST representation looks like. It is from this representation that a C4 scenario can be surveyed relatively quickly according to the key constructs of why, who, when, where, how and what. In turn, areas and themes that require further detailed insights can be extracted and examined.

Conclusions

The individual outputs available from EAST present a number of distinct but overlapping perspectives on the railway maintenance scenarios. The creation and maintenance of SA based on communications between actors emerges as a key issue and can be examined further. One strategy to enable this is to extract the knowledge objects that the signaller requires, and that different actors possess. The relevant propositional networks and companion CDMs can be used for this purpose. The sharing of information can then be related to the sequence and timing of actions and actors. Where knowledge objects are shared, consideration can also be given to the means by which this sharing occurs, usually facilitated by communications technology. This particular approach enables the analyst to proceed from a theoretical level to one that is much closer to practical design outputs. Figure 13.12 below illustrates this example of an approach to a more detailed analysis. The important point to make is that further combinations and re-combinations of separate human factors methods enables insights previously generated to be explored even further.

In conclusion, the application of the EAST methodology to live railway data illustrates the design and descriptive capability of the method. The method summarises the task structure, network structure, and operational context into a form that enables ready comparisons on key metrics to be drawn between scenarios, and for individual practical themes and insights to be extracted. It is also important to note that the method is scaleable, and its application to a host of military and civil domains provides data necessary to enhance understanding, to develop generic models and theories of command and control, and ultimately to design complex systems and environments like these to better serve the human actors and task goals within them. But beyond this, the EAST method demonstrates how individual human factors methods contained in this book can be combined to fully encompass the boundaries of complex problem domains in order to better serve the wider goal of HFI.

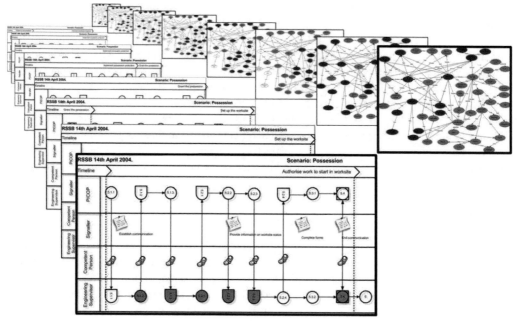

Figure 13.11 Summary of Application of EAST to Live Railway Data

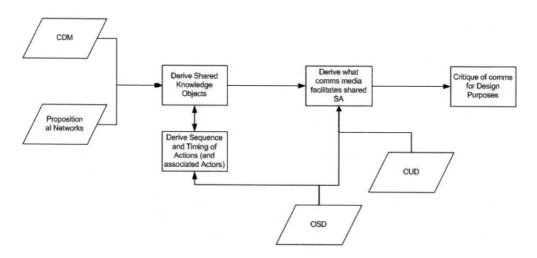

Figure 13.12 Plan for Detailed Analysis of Communications and SA Within Railway Scenarios

Acknowledgements

The findings presented in this chapter are presented here with the kind permission of the Rail Safety and Standards Board. A more detailed exposition of these rail industry related findings and the EAST methodology can be found in Walker et al. (2005).

Appendix

Human Factors Methods Database and Glossary

Table A.1 HEI/HRA Techniques

Method	Author/Source
AIPA – Accident Investigation and Progression Analysis	Fleming et al (1975)
APJ – Absolute Probability Judgement	Kirwan (1994)
ASEP – Accident Sequence Evaluation Programme	Swain (1987)
ATHEANA – A Technique for Human Error Analysis	Cooper et al (1996); Hollnagel (1998)
CADA – Critical Action Decision Approach	Gall (1990); Kirwan (1992, 1994)
CAMEO/TAT	Fujuta et al (1995); Kirwan (1988)
Confusion Matrice Analysis	Potash et al (1981)
COMET – Commission Event Trees	Blackman (1991)
COSIMO – Cognitive Simulation Model	Kirwan (1998a)
CREAM – Cognitive Reliability and Error Analysis Method	Hollnagel (1999)
DYLAM – Dynamic Logical Analysing Methodology	Kirwan (1998a)
EOCA – Error of Commission Analysis	Kirwan (1994, 1998a)
FMEA – Failure Modes and Effects Analysis	Kirwan and Ainsworth (1992)
GASET – Generic Accident Sequence Event Tree	Kirwan (1994)
GEMS – Generic Error Modelling System	Reason (1990)
HET – Human Error Template	Marshall et al (2003); Salmon et al (2002, 2003)
HAZOP – Hazard and Operability Study	Swann and Preston (1995)
HCR – Human Cognitive Reliability	Hannaman et al (1984)
HEART – Human Error Assessment Rate Technique	Williams (1986)
HECA – Human Error Criticality Analysis	Karwowski (2000)
HEIST – Human Error Identification in Systems Tool	Kirwan (1994)
HERA – Human Error and Recovery Assessment System	Kirwan (1998)
HMECA – Human Error Mode, Effect and Criticality Analysis	Kirwan (1992a)
HFAM – Human Factors Analysis Methodology	Pennycook and Embrey (1993)
Hit-Line – Human Interaction Timeline	Macwan and Mosleh (1994)
Human Error HAZOP	Whalley (1988); Kirwan and Ainsworth (1992)
HRMS – Human Reliability Management System	Kirwan (1994)
IMAS – Influence Modelling and Assessment System	Embrey (1986)
INTENT	Gertmann et al (1992)
INTEROPS – Integrated Reactor Operator System	Kirwan (1998a)
JHEDI – Justification of Human Error Data Information	Kirwan (1990b)
MAPPS – Maintenance Personnel Performance Simulation	Seigal et al (1984)
MEDA – Maintenance Error Decision Aid	Eurocontrol website
Murphy Diagrams	Pew et al (1981); Kirwan (1994)
Paired Comparisons	Kirwan (1994)

PHEA – Predictive Human Error Analysis	Embrey (1986); Stanton and Young (1999)
PHECA – Potential Human Error Cause Analysis	Whalley (1988)
SAINT – Systems Analysis of Integrated Networks of Tasks	Kirwan (1994)
SCHAZOP	Kirwan and Kennedy (1996a)
SCHEMA – Systematic Critical Human Error Management Approach	Livingston et al (1992)
SHARP – Systematic Human Action Reliability Procedure	Spurgeon et al (1987); Karwowski (2000)
SHERPA – Systematic Human Error Reduction Approach	Embrey (1986); Stanton and Young (1999)
SLIM MAUD	Embrey et al (1984); Kirwan (1992, 1994)
SNEAK	Hahn and de Vries (1991)
SPEAR – System for Predictive Error Analysis and Reduction	CCPS (1993); Karwowski (2000)
SRK Framework	Rasmussen et al (1981); Kirwan (1992a)
STAHR – Socio-Technical Assessment of Human Reliability	Hollnagel (1998); Phillips et al (1983)
TAFEI – Task Analysis for Error Identification	Baber and Stanton (1991, 1996)
TALENT – Task Analysis Linked Evaluation Technique	Kirwan (1998a); Ryan (1988)
THEA – Technique for Human Error Assessment Early in Design	Pocock, Harrison, Wright and Johnson
THERP – Technique for Human Error Rate Prediction	Swain and Guttman (1983)
TOPPE – Team Operations Performance and Procedure Evaluation	Kirwan (1998a)
TRACEr - Technique for the Retrospective and Predictive Analysis of Cognitive Errors in ATC	Kirwan and Shorrock (2002)

Table A.2   Task Analysis Techniques

Method	Author/Source
ACTA – Applied Cognitive Task Analysis	Miltello and Hutton (2000); Annett and Stanton (2000)
CPA – Critical Path Analysis	Baber (1998)
Critical Incident Technique	Flanagan (1954)
Critical Decision Method	Klein (2003)
Cognitive Task Analysis	Klein (2003)
Cognitive Work Analysis	Vicente (1999)
Cognitive Walkthrough Technique	Pocock et al (1992)
GOMS – Goals, Operators, Methods and Selection Rules	Card, Newell and Moran (1983)
HTA – Hierarchical Task Analysis	Annett and Duncan (1971); Annett, Duncan and Stammers (1971)
HTA(T)	Annett (2004)
Integrated Task Analysis	
TAKD – Task Analysis for Knowledge Descriptions	Not used anymore
TAG – Task Action Grammers	Karwowski (1999)
Tabular Scenario Analysis	
Task Decomposition	Kirwan and Ainsworth (1992)
TKS – Task Knowledge Structure	Karwowski (1999)
TTA – Tabular Task Analysis	Human Factors Integration in Future ATM systems – Methods and Tools
TTRAM – Task and Training Requirements Analysis Methodology	Swezey et al (2000)
User Needs Task Analysis	Wilson and Corlett (1999)
Work Domain Analysis	Vicente (1999)

Table A.3   Data Collection Techniques

Method	Author/Source
Interviews	Various
Questionnaires	Various
Observational analysis	Various
Talkthrough	Kirwan and Ainsworth (1992)
Verbal Protocol analysis	Walker (in press)
Walkthrough	Kirwan and Ainsworth (1992)

Table A.4   Situation Awareness Measurement Techniques

Method	Author/Source
SAGAT – Situation Awareness Global Assessment Technique	Endsley (1995)
SA-SWORD – Subjective Workload Dominance Metric	Vidulich (1989)
SARS – Situation Awareness Rating Scales	Waag and Houck (1994)
SART – Situation Awareness Rating Technique	Taylor (1990)
SALSA	Hauss and Eyferth (2002)
SABARS – Situation Awareness Behavioural Rating Scales	Endsley (2000)
PSAQ – Participant SA Questionnaire	Endsley (2000)
SPAM – Situation-Present Assessment Method	Durso et al (1998)
SACRI - Situation Awareness Control Room Inventory	Hogg et al (1995)
C-SAS – Cranfield Situation Awareness Scale	Dennehy (1997)
CARS – Crew Awareness Rating Scale	McGuinness and Foy (2000)
MARS – Mission Awareness Rating Scale	Matthews and Beal (2002)
Verbal Protocol Analysis	Walker (2004)
Process Indices	Endsley (2000)
Performance Measures	Endsley (2000)

Table A.5   Mental Workload Assessment Techniques

Method	Author/Source
Bedford Scale	Roscoe and Ellis (1990)
CNS – Cognitive Neurometric System	Dean (1997)
Cognitive Task Load Analysis	Neerincx (2002)
DRAWS – Defence Research Agency Workload Scale	Farmer et al (1995); Jordan et al (1995)
Workload Profile Technique	Tsang and Velazquez (1996)
ISA – Instantaneous Self Assessment Workload	Jordan (1992)
MACE - Malvern Capacity Estimate	Goillau and Kelly (1996)
MCH – Modified Cooper Harper Scale	Cooper and Harper (1969)
NASA TLX – NASA Task Load Index	Hart and Staveland (1988)
Objective Workload Assessment (WinCrew)	Hadley, Guttman and Stringer (1999); Coolican (1994)
Physiological Techniques (HRV, HR etc)	Various
Primary Task Performance Measures	Various
Secondary Task Performance Measures	Various
SWAT – Subjective Workload Assessment Technique	Reid and Nygeren (1998)
SWORD – Subjective WORkload Dominance Assessment Technique	Vidulich (1989)

Table A.6   Performance Time Measurement Prediction Techniques

Method	Author/Source
KLM – Keystroke Level Model	Card, Moran and Newell (1983) Stanton and Young (1999)
CPA – Critical Path Analysis	Baber (1998)
Timeline Analysis	Kirwan and Ainsworth (1992)

Table A.7   Charting Techniques

Method	Author/Source
CPA – Critical Path Analysis	Baber (1996)
DAD – Decision Action Diagrams	Kirwan and Ainsworth (1992); Kirwan (1994)
Event Tree Analysis	Kirwan and Ainsworth (1992); Kirwan (1994)
Fault Tree Analysis	Kirwan and Ainsworth (1992); Kirwan (1994)
Information Flowcharts	Various
Input-Output Diagrams	Various
Murphy Diagrams	Pew et al (1981)
Operation Sequence Diagrams	Kurke (1961); Sanders and McCormick (1992)
Operator Action Event Tree	Various
Petri Nets	Kirwan and Ainsworth (1992)
Process Charts	Kirwan and Ainsworth (1992); Marshall et al (2003)
Signal Flow Graphs	Kirwan and Ainsworth (1992)

Table A.8   Traditional Design Techniques

Method	Author/Source
Co-Design	Williams, Bound and Coleman (1999)
Conjoint techniques	Williams, Bound and Coleman (1999)
Ethnography	Williams, Bound and Coleman (1999)
Focus groups	Williams, Bound and Coleman (1999)
Immersion	Williams, Bound and Coleman (1999)
Mentoring	Williams, Bound and Coleman (1999)
Rapid prototyping	Williams, Bound and Coleman (1999)
Role play	Williams, Bound and Coleman (1999)
Scenarios	Diaper and Stanton (2003)
Shadowing	Williams, Bound and Coleman (1999)
Talkthrough analysis	Williams, Bound and Coleman (1999)
Think aloud protocols	Williams, Bound and Coleman (1999)
Time and Motion studies	Various
Walkthrough analysis	Kirwan and Ainsworth (1992)

Table A.9   Interface Analysis Techniques

Method	Author/Source
Checklists	Various
Heuristics	Stanton and Young (1999)
Interface Surveys	Kirwan and Ainsworth (1992)
Link Analysis	Drury (1990)
Layout Analysis	Stanton and Young (1999)
QUIS – Questionnaire for User Interface Satisfaction	Chin, Diehl and Norman (1988)
Repertory Grids	Kelly (1955)
SUMI – Software Usability Measurement Inventory	Kirakowski
SUS – System Usability Scale	Stanton and Young (1999)
WAMMI – Website Analysis and Measurement Inventory	Kirakowski and Claridge (2002)

Table A.10   Software Based Techniques

Technique	Author(s)
Analytica	
ATCS Performance Measurement Database	
ATLAS	
BMD-HMS – Boeing McDonnell Douglas Human Modelling System	
CASHE:PVS – Computer Aided Systems Human Engineering Performance Visualisation System	
CADA – CSERIAC Anthropometric Data Analysis files	
CSSM – Continuous Safety Sampling Methodology	
FAULTrEASE	
IPME	
FAST – Functional Analysis System Technique	
Hiser Element Toolkit	
IPME Integrated Performance Modelling Environment	
JACK	
KIT– Key Issues Tool	
MicrSaint	
MIDAS – Man-Machine Integration Design and Analysis Systems	
Observer	
PHA – Pro 5	
PUMA – Performance and Usability Modelling in ATM	
SAM 2000	
WinCrew	

Table A.11   Team Techniques

Method	Author
Team Training Methods (Various)	Salas (2003); Various
Distributed Simulation Training for Teams	Andrews (2003)
Synthetic Task Environments for Teams – CERTT's UAV-STE	Cooke and Shope (2003)
Team Building	Salas (2003)
Measuring Team Knowledge	Cooke (2003)
Team Communications Analysis	Jentsch and Bowers (2003)
Questionnaires for Distributed Assessment of Team Mutual Awareness	MacMillan et al (2003)
Team Decision Requirement Exercise	Klinger and Bianka (2003)
TARGETS – Targeted Acceptable Responses to Generated Events or Tasks	Fowlkes and Burke (2003)
BOS – Behavioural Observation Scales	Baker (2003)
Team Situation Assessment Training for Adaptive Co-ordination	Burke (2003)
Team Task Analysis	Burke (2003)
Team Training Methods (Various)	Salas (2003); Various
Social Network Analysis	Driskell and Mullen (2003)
Team Critical Decision Method	Klien (2000)
CUD – Comms Usage System	Watts and Monk (2000)
Pentanalysis	Diaper, McKearney and Hearne (2000)
TTRAM – Task and Training Requirements Methodology	Swezey et al (2000)
MUSE – Method for Usability Engineering	Lim and Long (1994); Stanton, Hedge, Brookhuis, Salas and Hendrick (2003)
CUD – Comms Usage Diagram	Annett and Stanton (2000)
Co-ordination Demands Analysis	Burke (2004)
Event Analysis of Systemic Teamwork	Baber and Stanton (2004)
Team Cognitive Task Analysis	Klien (2000); Stanton, Hedge, Brookhuis, Salas and Hendrick (2003)
Propositional Networks	Baber and Stanton (2004)

Table A.12   Other Techniques

Technique	Author(s)
EFHA – Early Human Factors Analysis	McLeod and Walters (1999)
MORT – Management Oversight Technique	Johnson (1980)
SACL – The Stress Arousal Checklist	Wilson and Corlett (1999)
SSADM – Structured Systems Analysis and Design Methodology	Weaver (1993)
MUSE – Method for Usability Engineering	Lim and Long (1994)

Bibliography and References

Ainsworth, L. and Marshall, E. (1998), 'Issues of quality and practicality in task analysis: preliminary results from two surveys', *Ergonomics* 41(11), 1604-1617, reprinted in J. Annett and N.A. Stanton (2000) *op.cit.* pp. 79-89.

Ainsworth, W. (1988), 'Optimization of string length for spoken digit input with error correction', *International Journal of Man Machine Studies*, 28 pp. 573-581

Anderson, J.R. (1980), *Cognitive Psychology and its Implications*, San Francisco, CA: Freeman.

Annett, J. and Stanton, N.A. (2000). *Task Analysis*, London: Taylor and Francis.

Annett, J. (2000), 'Theoretical and pragmatic influences on task analysis methods' in J.M. Schraagen, S.F. Chipman and V.L. Shalin (eds), *Cognitive Task Analysis*, Lawrence Erlbaum Associates, Mahwah, New Jersey pp. 25-37.

Annett, J. (2002) 'A note on the validity and reliability of ergonomics methods', *Theoretical Issues in Ergonomics Science*, 3 (2), pp. 229-232.

Annett, J. (2003), 'Hierarchical task analysis', in D. Diaper and N.A. Stanton (eds), *Handbook of Task Analysis in Human-Computer Interaction*, pp. 67-82, Mahwah, NJ: Lawrence Erlbaum Associates.

Annett, J. (2005), 'Conclusions', in J.R. Wilson and E.N. Corlett (eds), *Evaluation of Human Work*, 3rd Edition, Boca Raton, Fl: CRC Press, 1009-1013.

Annett, J. and Stanton, N.A. (eds) (2000), *Task Analysis*, London: Taylor and Francis.

Annett, J. (2004), 'Hierarchical task analysis', in N.A. Stanton, A. Hedge, K. Brookhuis, E. Salas and H. Hendrick (eds), *Handbook of Human Factors and Ergonomics Methods*, Boca Raton, FL:CRC Press.

Annett, J. (2005), 'Hierarchical Task Analysis (HTA)', in N.A. Stanton, A. Hedge, K, Brookhuis, E. Salas and H. Hendrick. (eds), *Handbook of Human Factors Methods*, London: Taylor and Francis.

Annett, J., Duncan, K.D., Stammers, R.B. and Gray, M. (1971), *Task Analysis*, London: HMSO.

Annett, J., Cunningham, D.J. and Mathias-Jones, P. (2000), 'A method for measuring team skills', *Ergonomics*, 43(8), pp. 1076-1094.

Annett, J., Duncan, K.D., Stammers, R.B. and Gray, M.J. (1971), *Task Analysis*, Training Information No.6, London: HMSO.

Annett, J., Duncan, K.D., Stammers, R.B., and Gray, M. (1971), *Task Analysis*, London: HMSO.

Astley, J.A. and Stammers, R.B. (1987), 'Adapting hierarchical task analysis for user-system interface design', in J.R. Wilson, E.N. Corlett and I. Manenica (eds), *New Methods In Applied Ergonomics*, London: Taylor and Francis, pp. 175-184.

Baber, C., Walker, G., Salmon, P. and Stanton, N.A. (2004), 'Observation study conducted at the fire service training college', *Human Factors Integration Defence Technology Report* (unpublished).

Baber, C. and Stanton, N.A. (1996), 'Human error identification techniques applied to public technology: predictions compared with observed use', *Applied Ergonomics*, 27 (2) pp. 119-131.

Baber, C. and Stanton, N.A. (1999), 'Analytical prototyping', in J.M. Noyes and M. Cook (eds), *Interface Technology: The leading edge*, Baldock: Research Studies.

Baber, C. and Stanton, N.A. (1994), 'Task analysis for error identification: a methodology for designing error-tolerant consumer products', *Ergonomics*, 37, pp. 1923-1941.

Baber, C. and Stanton, N.A. (1996), 'Observation as a technique for Usability Evaluations', in P. Jordan et al (eds), *Usability in Industry*, pp 85-94, London: Taylor and Francis.

Baber, C. (1991), Speech Technology in the Control Room Systems: A Human Factors Perspective, Chichester: Ellis Horwood.

Baber, C. (1996), 'Repertory Grid Theory and its application to product evaluation', in P. Jordan et al (eds), *Usability in Industry*, pp. 157-165, London: Taylor and Francis.

Baber, C. (2004b), 'Critical path analysis' in N.A. Stanton, A. Hedge, K. Brookhuis, E. Salas and H. Hendrick (eds), *Handbook of human factors and ergonomics methods*, Boca Raton, FL: CRC Press.

Baber, C. (2004a), 'Repertory Grid for Product Evaluation', in N.A. Stanton, A. Hedge, K. Brookhuis, E. Salas and H. Hendrick (eds) *Handbook of Human Factors and Ergonomics Methods*, Boca Raton, FL:CRC Press.

Baber, C. (2005), 'Evaluating Human-Computer Interaction', in J.R. Wilson and E.N. Corlett (eds), *Evaluation of Human Work*, 3rd Edition, Boca Raton, Fl: CRC Press, pp. 357-388.

Baber, C. and Mellor, B.A. (2001), 'Modelling multimodal human-computer interaction using critical path analysis', *International Journal of Human Computer Studies*, 54 pp. 613-636.

Baber, C. and Stanton, N.A. (2002), 'Task analysis for error identification: theory, method and validation', *Theoretical Issues in Ergonomics Science*, 3 (2), pp. 212-227.

Baber, C., and Stanton, N.A. (1996), 'Observation as a technique for usability evaluations', in P.W. Jordan, B. Thomas, B.A. Weerdmeester and I. McClelland (eds), *Usability Evaluation in Industry*, pp. 85-94, London: Taylor and Francis.

Baber, C., Walker, G., Stanton, N.S. and Salmon, P. (2004), *Report on Initial Trials of WP1.1 Methodology Conducted at Fire Service Training College*, WP1.1.1/01, 29th January 2004.

Baber, C. and Stanton, N.A. (2004), 'Methodology for DTC-HFI WP1 field trials. Defence Technology Centre for Human Factors Integration, Report 2.1.

Bainbridge, L. (1982), 'Ironies of automation', in J. Rasmussen, K. Duncan and J. Neplat (eds), *New Technology and Human Error*, New York: Wiley.

Baker, D.P., Salas, E., and Cannon-Bowers, J.A. (1998), 'Team task analysis: Lost but hopefully not forgotten', *The Industrial and Organizational Psychologist*, 35 (3), pp. 79-83.

Baker, D. (2005), 'Behavioural Observation Scales (BOS)', in N.A. Stanton, A. Hedge, K. Brookhuis, E. Salas and H. Hendrick (eds), *Handbook of Human Factors Methods*, London: Taylor and Francis.

Bartlett, F.C. (1932), *Remembering: A study in experimental and social psychology*, Cambridge: Cambridge University Press.

Bell, H.H. and Lyon, D.R. (2000), 'Using observer ratings to assess situation awareness', in M.R. Endsley (ed.,) *Situation Awareness Analysis and Measurement*, pp. 129-146, Mahwah, NJ: LEA.

Brewer, W.F. (2000), 'Bartlett's concept of the schema and its impact on theories of knowledge representation in contemporary cognitive psychology', in A. Saito (ed.) *Bartlett, Culture and Cognition*, London: Psychology Press, pp. 69-89.

Burford, B. (1993), 'Designing Adaptive ATMs', Birmingham: University of Birmingham unpublished MSc Thesis.

Burke, S.C. (2005), 'Team task analysis', in N.A. Stanton et al. (eds), *Handbook of Human Factors and Ergonomics Methods*, pp. 56.1-56.8, London: CRC.

Card, S.K.; Moran, T.P. and Newell, A. (1983), *The Psychology of Human-Computer Interaction*, Hillsdale, NJ: Lawrence Erlbaum Associates.

Card, S.K., Moran, T.P. and Newell, A. (1983) *The Psychology of Human-Computer Interaction*, Hillsdale, NJ: LEA.

Casali, J.G. and Wierwille, W.W (1983), 'A comparison of rating scale, secondary task, physiological, and primary task workload estimation techniques in a simulated flight task emphasising communications load', *Human Factors*, 25, pp. 623-641.

CCPS (Center for Chemical Process Safety) (1994), *Guidelines for Preventing Human Error in Process Safety*, New York: American Institute of Chemical Engineers. Reproduced in W. Karwowski and W.S Marras (eds) (1999), *The Occupational Ergonomics Handbook*, Florida: CRC Press LLC.

Cha, D.W (2001), 'Comparative study of subjective workload assessment techniques for the evaluation of ITS-orientated human-machine interface systems', *Journal of Korean Society of Transportation*, Vol 19 (3), pp. 450-58.

Chin, J.P., Diehl, V.A. and Norman, K.L. (1988), 'Development of an instrument measuring user satisfaction of the human-computer interface', *Human factors in computing systems (CHI '88)*, New York, Association for Computing Machinery, pp. 213-218.

Chin, M., Sanderson, P. and Watson, M. (1999), 'Cognitive work analysis of the command and control work domain', *Proceedings of the 1999 Command and Control Research and Technology Symposium* (CCRTS), June 29-July 1, Newport, RI, USA, Volume 1, pp. 233-248.

Ciavarelli, A. and Sather, T. (2002), 'Human Factors Checklist: An Aircraft Accident Investigation Tool', School of Aviation Safety, Monterey, CA. Available at: www.avsafety.nps.navy.mil/gouge/hfchklst.pdf

Collier, S.G., Folleso, K. (1995), 'SACRI: A measure of situation awareness for nuclear power control rooms', in D.J. Garland and M.R. Endsley (eds), *Experimental Analysis and Measurement of Situation Awareness*, pp. 115-122, Daytona Beach, FL: Embry-Riddle University Press.

Collins, A.M. and Loftus, E.F. (1975), 'A spreading-activation theory of semantic processing', *Psychological Review*, 82, pp. 407-428.

Cooke, N.J. (2004), 'Measuring team knowledge', in N. Stanton, A. Hedge, K. Brookhuis, E. Salas and H. Hendrick (eds), *Handbook of Human Factors and Ergonomics Methods,* Boca Raton, FL: CRC, pp. 491-496

Cooper, G.E. and Harper, R.P. (1969), 'The use of pilot rating in the evaluation of aircraft handling qualities', Report No. ASD-TR-76-19, Moffett Field, CA: National Aeronautics and Space Administration.

Crawford, J.O., Taylor, C. and Po, N.L.W. (2001), 'A case study of on-screen prototypes and usability evaluation of electronic timers and food menu systems', *International Journal of Human Computer Interaction*, 13 (2), pp. 187-201.

Dean, T.F. (1997), *Directory of Design Support Methods*, Defence Technical Information Centre, DTIC-AM. MATRIS Office, ADA 328 375, September.

Defence Technology Centre for Human Factors Integration (2003), *Methodology for DTC HFI WP1 Field Trials* (Report: Draft 2.1.), London, UK.

Dekker, S.W.A. (2002), 'Reconstructing human contributions to accidents: the new view on human error and performance', *Journal of Safety Research*, 33, pp. 371-385.

Dennehy, K. (1997), *Cranfield – Situation Awareness Scale, User Manual*, Applied Psychology unit, College of Aeronautics, Cranfield University, COA report No. 9702, Bedford, January.

Diaper, D. (1989), *Task Analysis in Human Computer Interaction*, Chichester: Ellis Horwood.

Diaper, D. and Stanton, N.A. (2004), *Handbook of Task Analysis in Human-Computer Interaction*, Mahwah, NJ: Lawrence Erlbaum Associates.

Dillon, A. and McKnight, C. (1990) 'Towards a classification of text types: a repertory grid approach', *International Journal of Man-Machine Studies,* 33, pp. 623-636.

Dinadis, N. and Vicente, K.J. (1999), 'Designing functional visualisations for aircraft systems status displays', *International Journal of Aviation Psychology*, 9, pp. 241-269.

Driskell, J.E. and Mullen, B. (2005), 'Social Network Analysis', in N.A. Stanton et al. (eds), *Handbook of Human Factors and Ergonomics Methods*, pp. 58.1-58.6, London: CRC.

Drury, C. (1990), 'Methods for direct observation of performance', in J.R. Wilson and E.N. Corlett (eds), *Evaluation of Human Work*, 2nd Edition, London: Taylor and Francis, pp. 45-68.

Durso, F.T., Hackworth, C.A., Truitt, T., Crutchfield, J., Manning, C.A. (1998), 'Situation awareness as a predictor of performance in en route air traffic controllers', *Air Traffic Quarterly*, 6, pp. 1-20.

Durso, F.T., Truitt, T.R., Hackworth, C.A., Crutchfield, J.M., Nikolic, D., Moertl, P.M., Ohrt, D. and Manning, C.A. (1995), 'Expertise and chess: A pilot study comparing situation awareness methodologies', in D.J. Garland and M. Endsley (eds), *Experimental Analysis and Measurement of Situation Awareness*, Embry-Riddle Aeronautical University Press.

Easterby, R. (1984), 'Tasks, processes and display design', in R. Easterby and H. Zwaga (eds), *Information Design*, pp. 19-36, Chichester: Whiley.

Embrey, D.E. (1986), 'SHERPA: A systematic human error reduction and prediction approach', Paper presented at the International Meeting on Advances in Nuclear Power Systems, Knoxville, Tennessee.

Embrey, D.E. (1993), *Quantitative and Qualitative Prediction of Human Error in Safety Assessments*, Institute of Chemical Engineers Symposium Series, 130, pp. 329-350.

Endsley, M.R. (1989), *Final Report: Situation awareness in an advanced strategic mission*, Northrop Document 89-32, Northrop Corporation.

Endsley, M.R. (1993), 'A survey of situation awareness requirements in air-to-air combat fighters' *The International Journal of Aviation Psychology*, 3, pp. 157-168.

Endsley, M.R. (1995a), 'Toward a theory of situation awareness in dynamic systems', *Human Factors*, 37(1), pp. 32-64.

Endsley, M.R. (1995b), 'Measurement of situation awareness in dynamic systems', *Human Factors*, 37, pp. 65-84.

Endsley, M.R., Sollenberger, R. and Stein, E. (2000), 'Situation awareness: A comparison of measures', in *Proceedings of the Human Performance, Situation Awareness and Automation: User-Centered Design for the New Millennium*, Savannah, GA: SA Technologies, Inc.

Endsley, M.R. (1995c), 'Towards a theory of situation awareness in dynamic systems', *Human Factors*, 37, pp 32-64.

Endsley, M.R. and Kiris, E.O. (1995), *Situation Awareness Global Assessment Technique (SAGAT) TRACON Air Traffic Control Version User Guide*, Lubbock TX: Texas Tech University.

Endsley, M.R. and Rogers, M.D. (1994), *Situation Awareness Information Requirements for En Route Air Traffic Control*, DOT/FAA/AM-94/27, Washington, DC: Federal Aviation Administration Office of Aviation Medicine.

Endsley, M.R. (1990), 'Predictive utility of an objective measure of situation awareness', in *Proceedings of the Human Factors Society*, 34th Annual Meeting, pp. 41-45, Santa Monica, CA: Human Factors Society.

Endsley, M.R. (2000), 'Theoretical underpinnings of situation awareness: A critical review', in M.R. Endsley and D.J. Garland (eds), *Situation Awareness Analysis and Measurement*, Lawrence Erlbaum Associates.

Endsley, M.R., Holder, C.D., Leibricht, B.C., Garland, D.C., Wampler, R.L. and Matthews, M.D. (2000), *Modelling and Measuring Situation Awareness in the Infantry Operational Environment* (1753), Alexandria, VA: Army Research Institute.

Endsley, M.R., Smolensky, M. (1998), 'Situation awareness in air traffic control: The picture', in M. Smolensky and E. Stein (eds), *Human Factors in Air Traffic Control*, pp. 115-154, New York: Academic Press.

Endsley, M.R., Sollenberger, R. and Stein, E. (2000), 'Situation awareness: A comparison of measures', in *Proceedings of the Human Performance, Situation Awareness and Automation: User-Centered Design for the New Millennium*, Savannah, GA: SA Technologies, Inc.

Endsley, M.R. and Garland, D.G. (2000), *Situation awareness analysis and measurement*, Mahwah, NJ: Lawrence Erlbaum.

Endsley, M.R. (1988), 'Situation Awareness Global Assessment Technique (SAGAT)', *Proceedings of the National Aerospace and Electronics Conference (NAECON)*, pp. 789-795, New York, IEEE.

Evans, L. (2002), 'Transportation safety', in R.W. Hall (ed.) *Handbook of Transportation Science*, 2nd Edition, Norwell, MA: Kluwar Academic Publishers, , pp. 67-112.

Eyferth, K., Niessen, C., Spath, O. (2003), 'A model of air traffic controllers conflict detection and conflict resolution', *Aerospace Science and Technology*, 3, in press.

Farmer, E.W., Jordan, C.S., Belyavin, A.J., Bunting, A.J., Tattersall, A.J. and Jones D.M. (1995), *Dimensions of operator workload*, Defence Evaluation and Research Agency, Report DRA/AS/MMI/CR95098/1.

Federal Aviation Administration (1996), *Report on the Interfaces between Flightcrews and Modern Flightdeck Systems*, Washington DC: Federal Aviation Administration.

Flanagan, J.C. (1954), 'The critical incident technique', *Psychological Bulletin*, 51, pp. 327-358.

Flin, R., Goeters, K.M., Hormann, H.J. and Martin, L. (1998), 'A generic structure of non-technical skills for training and assessment', *Proceedings of the 23rd Conference of the European Association for Aviation Psychology*, Vienna, 14-18th September 1998.

Fracker, M. (1991), *Measures of Situation Awareness: Review and Future Directions*, Report No.AL-TR-1991-0128. Wright Patterson Air Force Base, Ohio: Armstrong Laboratories.

Gertmann, D.I., Blackman, H.S. (1994), *Human Reliability and Safety Analysis Data Handbook*, New York: John Wiley and Sons, Reproduced in W. Karwowski and W.S Marras (eds) *The Occupational Ergonomics Handbook* (1999), Florida: CRC Press LLC.

Gertmann, D.I., Blackman, H.S., Haney, L.N., Seidler, K.S. and Hahn, H.A. (1992), 'INTENT: A method for estimating human error probabilities for decision based errors', *Reliability Engineering and System Safety*, 35, pp. 127-137. Reproduced in W. Karwowski and W.S Marras (eds), *The Occupational Ergonomics Handbook* (1999), Florida: CRC Press LLC.

Gilbreth, F.B. (1911), *Motion Study*, Princeton, NJ: Van Nostrand.

Gillan, D.J. and Cooke, N.J. (2001), 'Using pathfinder networks to analyze procedural knowledge in interactions with advanced technology', in E. Salas (ed.), *Advances in Human Performance and Cognitive Engineering Research*, Amsterdam: JAI, pp. 125-161.

Glendon, A.I. and McKenna, E.F. (1995), *Human Safety and Risk Management*, London: Chapman and Hall.

Go, K. and Carroll, J.M. (2003), 'Scenario-based task analysis', in D. Diaper and N. Stanton (eds), *The Handbook of Task Analysis for Human-Computer Interaction*, London: Lawrence Erlbaum Associates.

Goillau, P.J. and Kelly, C. (1996), 'Malvern Capacity Estimate (MACE) – a proposed cognitive measure for complex systems', in D. Harris (Ed) *First Int. Conf. On Engineering Psychology and Cognitive Ergonomics*. Stratford-upon-Avon: Ashgate.

Graham, R. (1999), 'Use of auditory icons as emergency warnings: evaluation within a vehicle collision avoidance application', *Ergonomics*, 42 (9), pp. 1233-1248.

Gray, W. D., John, B. E., and Atwood, M. E. (1993). 'Project Ernestine: Validating a GOMS analysis for predicting and explaining real-world performance'. *Human-Computer Interaction*, 8(3), 237-309.

Greenberg, S. (2003), 'Working through task-centred system design', in D. Diaper and N. Stanton (eds), *The Handbook of Task Analysis for Human Computer Interaction*, London: Lawrence Erlbaum Associates Inc.

Gugerty, L.J. (1997), 'Situation awareness during driving: Explicit and implicit knowledge in dynamic spatial memory', *Journal of Experimental Psychology: Applied*, 3, pp. 42-66.

Hahn, A.H. and DeVries, J.A. (1991), 'Identification of human errors of commission using SNEAK analysis', *Proceedings of the Human Factors Society 35th Annual Meeting*, pp 1080-1084, reproduced in W. Karwowski and W.S Marras (eds) (1999), *The Occupational Ergonomics Handbook*, Florida: CRC Press LLC.

Harris, C.J. and White, I. (1987), *Advances in Command, Control and Communication Systems*, London: Peregrinus.

Harris, D., Stanton, N., Marshall, A. Young, M.S., Demagalski, J. and Salmon, P. (in press), 'Using SHERPA to predict design-induced error on the flight deck', *Aerospace Science and Technology Journal*.

Harrison, A. (1997), *A Survival Guide to Critical Path Analysis*, London: Butterworth-Heinemann.

Hart, S.G. and Staveland, L.E. (1988), 'Development of a multi-dimensional workload rating scale: Results of empirical and theoretical research', in P.A. Hancock and N. Meshkati (eds), *Human Mental Workload*, Amsterdam, The Netherlands: Elsevier.

Hauss, Y. and Eyferth, K. (2003), 'Securing future ATM-concepts' safety by measuring situation awareness in ATC', *Aerospace Science and Technology*. In press

Helmreich, R.L. (2000), 'On error management: Lessons from aviation', *BMJ 2000*, 320, pp. 781-785.

Hess, B. (1999), 'Graduate student cognition during information retrieval using the world wide web: A pilot study', *Computers and Education*, 33, 1, pp. 1-13.

Hilburn, B.G. (1997), 'Free Flight and Air Traffic Controller Mental Workload', Presented at the 9th Symposium on Aviation Psychology, Columbus, Ohio, USA.

Hogg, D.N., Folleso, K., Strand-Volden, F. and Torralba, B. (1995), 'Development of a situation awareness measure to evaluate advanced alarm systems in nuclear power plant control room', *Ergonomics*, 38 (11), pp. 2394-2413.

Hollnagel, E. (1993), *Human Reliability Analysis: Context and control*, London: Academic Press.

Hollnagel, E. (1998), *Cognitive Reliability and Error Analysis Method – CREAM*, 1st Edition, Oxford: Elsevier Science.

Hollnagel, E. (2003), *Handbook of Cognitive Task Design*, USA: Lawrence Erlbaum Associates.

Hollnagel, E., Kaarstad, M. and Lee, H-C. (1999), 'Error mode prediction', *Ergonomics*, 42, pp. 1457-1471.

Hone, K.S. and Baber, C. (1999), Modelling the effect of constraint on speech-based human-computer interaction. *International Journal of Human Computer Studies*, 50(1), 85–107.

Houghton, R.J., Baber, C., McMaster, R., Stanton, Salmon, P., Stewart, R. and Walker, G. (2005), 'Command and control in emergency services operations: A social network analysis', *Ergonomics* (in press)

Hyponen, H. (1999), 'Focus Groups', in H.A. Williams, J. Bound and R. Coleman (eds), *The Methods Lab: User Research for Design*, Design for Ageing Network, Geneva: International Standards Office.

Isaac, A., Shorrick, S.T. and Kirwan, B. (2002), 'Human error in European air traffic management: The HERA project', *Reliability Engineering and System Safety*, 75, pp. 257-272.

ISO 13407 (1996), *Human-centred Design Processes for Interactive Systems*, Geneva: International Standards Office

ISO 13407 (1999), *Human-centred Design Processes for Interactive Systems*, Geneva: International Standards Office.

ISO 9126 (2000), *Software Engineering – Product Quality*, Geneva: International Standards Office.

ISO 9241 (1998), *Ergonomics of Office Work with VDTs – Guidance on Usability*, Geneva: International Standards Office.

ISO 9241:11 (1998), 'Ergonomics Requirements for Office Work with Visual Display Terminals – Part 11: Usability', Geneva: International Standards Office.

Jeannott, E., Kelly, C. and Thompson, D. (2003), *The Development of Situation Awareness Measures in ATM Systems*, EATMP report. HRS/HSP-005-REP-01.

Jensen, R. S. (1997), 'The boundaries of aviation psychology, human factors, aeronautical decision making, situation awareness, and crew resource management'. *International Journal of Aviation Psychology*, 7 (4) 259-267

Jentsch, F., and Bowers, C.A. (2005), 'Team communications analysis', in N.A. Stanton, A. Hedge, K, Brookhuis, E. Salas and H. Hendrick. (eds), *Handbook of Human Factors methods*, London: Taylor and Francis.

John, B.A. and Newell, A. (1990), 'Toward an engineering model of stimulus-response compatibility', in R.W. Proctor and T.G. Reeve (eds), *Stimulus-Response Compatibility*, North-Holland: Amsterdam, pp. 427-479.

Johnson, P., Diaper, D. and Long, J. (1984), 'Tasks, skills and knowledge: Task analysis for knowledge-based descriptions', in B. Shackel (ed.), *Interact '84 – First IFIP Conference on Human-Computer Interaction*, Amsterdam: Elsevier, pp. 23-27.

Jones, D.G., and Kaber, D.B. (2005). 'Situation awareness measurement and the situation awareness global assessment technique', in N. Stanton, Hedge, Hendrick, K. Brookhuis, E. Salas (eds), *Handbook of Human Factors and Ergonomics Methods*, London: Taylor and Francis.

Jones, D.G. and Endsley, M.R. (2000), 'Can real-time probes provide a valid measure of situation awareness?', Proceedings of the Human Performance, Situation Awareness and Automation: User Centred Design for the New Millennium Conference, October 2000.

Jones, D.G. (2000), 'Subjective measures of situation awareness', in M.R. Endsley and D.J. Garland (eds), *Situation Awareness Analysis and Measurement*, Mahwah, NJ: Lawrence Erlbaum Associates.

Jordan, C.S., Farmer, E.W. and Belyavin, A.J. (1995), 'The DRA Workload scales (DRAWS): A validated workload assessment technique', *Proceedings of the 8th international symposium on aviation psychology*, Volume 2, pp. 1013-1018.

Karwowski, W. (2001), International Encyclopedia of Ergonomics and Human Factors Vols I-III, London: Taylor and Francis.

Karwowski, W. (1998), *The Occupational Ergonomics Handbook*, New York: CRC Press.

Karwowski, W. and Marras, W.S. (1999), *The Occupational Ergonomics Handbook*, Florida: CRC Press LLC.

Kennedy, R.J. (1995), 'Can human reliability assessment (HRA) predict real accidents? A case study analysis of HRA', in A.I. Glendon and N.A Stanton (eds), *Proceedings of the Risk Assessment and Risk Reduction Conference*, 22nd March 1994, Aston University, Birmingham.

Kennedy, R. and Kirwan, B. (1998), 'Development of a hazard and operability-based method for identifying safety management vulnerabilities in high risk systems', *Safety Science*, 30, pp. 249-274.

Kieras, D. (2003), 'GOMS models for task analysis', in D. Diaper and N. Stanton (eds), *The Handbook of Task Analysis for Human-Computer Interaction*, pp. 83-117, Mahwah, NJ: Lawrence Erlbaum Associates.

Kim, I.S. (2001), 'Human reliability analysis in the man-machine interface design review', *Annals of Nuclear Energy*, 28, pp. 1069-1081.

Kirakowski, J. (1996), 'The Software usability measurement inventory: background and usage', in P. Jordan, B. Thomas and B. Weerdmeester (eds), *Usability Evaluation in Industry*, London: Taylor and Francis.

Kirwan, B. and Ainsworth, L.K. (1992), *A guide to Task Analysis*, London: Taylor and Francis.

Kirwan, B. (1990), 'Human reliability assessment', in J.R. Wilson and E.N. Corlett (eds), *Evaluation of human work: a practical ergonomics methodology*, 2nd ed., pp. 921-968, London: Taylor and Francis.

Kirwan, B. (1994), A guide to practical human reliability Assessment, London: Taylor and Francis.

Kirwan, B. (1996), *Human Error Recovery and Assessment (HERA) Guide*, Project IMC/GNSR/HF/5011, Industrial Ergonomics Group, School of Manufacturing Engineering, University of Birmingham, March.

Kirwan, B. (1996), 'The validation of three Human Reliability Quantification techniques – THERP, HEART and JHEDI: Part 1 – technique descriptions and validation issues', *Applied Ergonomics*, 27, 6, pp. 359 – 373.

Kirwan, B. (1992a) 'Human error identification in human reliability assessment. Part 1:overview of approaches', *Applied Ergonomics*, 23, pp. 299-318.

Kirwan, B. (1992b), 'Human error identification in human reliability assessment. Part 2: detailed comparison of techniques', *Applied Ergonomics*, 23, pp. 371-381.

Kirwan, B. (1998a), 'Human error identification techniques for risk assessment of high-risk systems – Part 1: Review and evaluation of techniques', *Applied Ergonomics*, 29, pp. 157-177.

Kirwan, B. (1998b), 'Human error identification techniques for risk assessment of high-risk systems – Part 2: Towards a framework approach', *Applied Ergonomics*, 5, pp. 299-319.

Kirwan, B. and Ainsworth, L.K. (1992), *A Guide to Task Analysis*, London: Taylor and Francis.

Kirwan, B., Evans, A., Donohoe, L., Kilner, A., Lamoureux, Atkinson, T. and MacKendrick, H. (1997), 'Human Factors in the ATM System Design Life Cycle', FAA/Eurocontrol ATM R&D Seminar, Paris, France, Internet source: http://atm-seminar-97.eurocontrol.fr/kirwan.htm.

Klein, G. and Armstrong, A.A. (2005), 'Critical decision method', in N.A. Stanton, A. Hedge, K. Brookhuis, E. Salas and H. Hendrick. (eds), *Handbook of Human Factors and Ergonomics Methods*, 58-1–58-6, Boca Raton, FL:CRC Press.

Klein, G. (2000), 'Cognitive task analysis of teams', in J.M. Schraagen, S.F. Chipman, V.L. Shalin (eds), *Cognitive Task Analysis*, pp. 417-431, Mahwah, NJ: Lawrence Erlbaum associates.

Klein, G.A., Calderwood, R. and MacGregor, D. (1989), 'Critical decision method for eliciting knowledge', *IEEE Transactions on Systems*, Man and Cybernetics, 19(3), pp. 462-472.

Klein, G., Schmitt, J., McCloskey, M., Heaton, J., Klinger, D. and Wolf, S. (1996), *A decision-centred study of the regimental command post*, Fairborn, OH: Klein Associates.

Kletz, T. (1991), *An Engineer's View of Human Error*, Second Edition, Rugby, Warwickshire: Institution of Chemical Engineers.

Kletz, T. (1974), 'HAZOP and HAZAN: Notes on the identification and assessment of hazards', in C.D. Swann and M.L Preston (eds), 'Twenty five years of HAZOPs', *Journal of Loss Prevention in the Process Industries*, vol 8 (6).

Klinger, D.W. and Hahn, B.B. (2005) 'Team decision requirement exercise: Making team decision requirements explicit', in N.A. Stanton, A. Hedge, K. Brookhuis, E. Salas and H. Hendrick (eds), *Handbook of Human Factors Methods*, London: Taylor and Francis.

Langford, J. and McDonagh, D. (2002), *Focus Groups: Supporting effective product development*, London: Taylor and Francis.

Lawrence, D., Atwood, M.E., Dews, S. and Turner, T. (1995), 'Social interaction in the use and design of a workstation: two contexts of interaction' In P.J. Thomas (ed), *The Social and Interactional Dimensions of Human Computer Interfaces*. Cambridge: Cambridge University Press.

Lawton, R. and Ward, N.J. (2005), 'A systems analysis of the Ladbroke Grove rail crash', *Accident Analysis & Prevention*, 37, pp. 235-244.

Lewis, C. and Reiman, J. (1993), *Task Centred User Interface Design: A practical introduction*, Boulder, CO: University of Colorado. Shareware book available from ftp.cs.colorado.edu/pub/cs/distribs/clewis/HCI-Design-Book.

Lewis, C., Polson, P., Wharton, C. and Rieman, J. (1990), 'Testing a walkthrough methodology for theory-based design of walk-up-and-use interfaces', in *Proceedings of CHI'90 conference on Human Factors in Computer Systems*, pp. 235-241, New York: Association for Computer Machinery.

Lim, K.Y. and Long, J. (1994), *The MUSE Method for Usability Engineering*, Cambridge: Cambridge University Press.

Lockyer, K. and Gordon, J. (1991), *Critical Path Analysis and Other Project Network*, Upper Saddle River, NJ: Prentice Hall.

Luximon, A. and Goonetilleke, R.S. (2001), 'A simplified subjective workload assessment technique', *Ergonomics*, 44 (3), pp. 229-243.

MacMillan, J., Paley, M.J., Entin, E.B. and Entin, E.E. (2005), 'Questionnaires for distributed assessment of team mutual awareness', in N.A. Stanton, A. Hedge, K. Brookhuis, E. Salas and H. Hendrick (eds), *Handbook of Human Factors Methods*, London: Taylor and Francis.

Marsden, P. and Kirby, M. (2005), 'Allocation of functions', in N.A. Stanton, A. Hedge, K. Brookhuis, E. Salas and H. Hendrick (eds), *Handbook of Human Factors Methods*, London: Taylor and Francis.

Marshall, A., Stanton, N., Young, M., Salmon, P., Harris, D., Demagalski, J., Waldmann, T. and Dekker, S. (2003), 'Development of the human error template – a new methodology for assessing design induced errors on aircraft flight decks', ERRORPRED Final Report E!1970, August 2003.

Matheus, C.J., Kokar, M.M. and Baclawski, K. (2003), 'A core onotology for situation awareness', *Proceedings of the 6th International Conference on Information Fusion*, pp. 545-552, Cairns, Australia.

Matthews, M.D. and Beal, S.A. (2002), 'Assessing situation awareness in field training exercises', U.S. Army Research Institute for the Behavioural and Social Sciences. Research Report 1795.

Matthews, M.D., Pleban, R.J., Endsley, M.R. and Strater, L.D. (2000), 'Measures of infantry situation awareness for a virtual MOUT environment', *Proceedings of the Human Performance, Situation Awareness and Automation Conference (HPSAA II)*, Daytona, Florida: LEA.

McFadden, K.L. and Towell, E.R. (1999), 'Aviation human factors: a framework for the new millennium', *Journal of Air Transport Management*, 5, pp. 177-184.

McGuinness, B. and Ebbage, L. (2002), 'Assessing human factors in command and control: workload and situational awareness metrics', in the proceedings of the *2002 Command and Control Research and Technology Symposium*, Monterey, CA.

McGuinness, B. and Foy, L. (2000), 'A subjective measure of SA: the Crew Awareness Rating Scale (CARS)', presented at the Human Performance, Situational Awareness and Automation Conference, Savannah, Georgia, 16-19 Oct 2000.

McGuinness, B. (1999), 'Situational Awareness and the Crew Awareness Rating Scale (CARS)', *Proceedings of the 1999 Avionics Conference*, Heathrow, London. 17-18th Nov. 1999. ERA Technology report 99-0815 paper 4.3.

Medina, A.L., Lee, S.E., Wierwille, W.W. and Hanowski, R.J. (2004), 'Relationship between infrastructure, driver error, and critical incidents', in *Proceedings of the Human Factors and Ergonomics Society 48th Annual Meeting*, pp. 2075–2080.

Megaw, E.D. (2005), 'The definition and measurement of mental workload', in J.R. Wilson and E.N. Corlett (eds), *Evaluation of Human Work*, Boca Raton, FL: CRC Press, [3rd Edition] pp. 525-552

Militello, L.G. and Hutton, J.B. (2000), 'Applied Cognitive Task Analysis (ACTA): A practitioner's toolkit for understanding cognitive task demands', in J. Annett and N.S Stanton (eds), *Task Analysis*, pp. 90-113, London: Taylor and Francis.

Militello, L.G. and Militello, J.B. (2000), 'Applied Cognitive Task Analysis (ACTA): A practitioner's toolkit for understanding cognitive task demands', in J. Annett and N.S Stanton (eds), *Task Analysis*, pp. 90-113, London: Taylor and Francis.

Miller, G.A., Galanter, E. and Pribram, K.H. (1960), *Plans and the Structure of Behaviour*, New York: Holt.

MoD (2000), *Human Factors Integration: An introductory guide*, London: HMSO.

Naikar, N. and Sanderson, P.M. (1999), 'Work domain analysis for training-system definition and acquisition', *International Journal of Aviation Psychology*, 9, pp. 271-290.

Naikar, N. and Sanderson, P.M. (2001), 'Evaluating design proposals for complex systems with work domain analysis', *Human Factors,* 43 (4), pp. 529-542.

Naikar, N. and Saunders, A. (2003), 'Crossing the boundaries of safe operation: An approach for training technical skills on error management', *Cognition Technology and Work*, 5, pp. 171-180.

Naikar, N., Lintern, G. and Sanderson, P.M. (2002), 'Cognitive work analysis for air defense applications in Australia', in M.D. McNeese and M.A. Vidulich, *Cognitive Systems Engineering in Military Aviation Environments: Avoiding cogminutia fragmentosa!*, Wright Patterson Air Force Base, Dayton, Ohio: Human Systems Information Analysis Center.

Naikar, N., Pearce, B., Drumm, D. and Sanderson, P. (2003), 'Designing teams for first-of-a-kind, complex systems using the initial phases of cognitive work analysis: case study' *Human Factors*, 45 (2), pp. 202-217.

Neerincx, M.A. (2003), 'Cognitive task load analysis: Allocating tasks and designing support', in E. Hollnagel (ed), *Handbook of Cognitive Task Design*, pp. 281-305, Mahwah, NJ: Lawrence Erlbaum Associates Inc.

Neisser, U. (1976), *Cognition and Reality: Principles and implications of cognitive psychology*, San Francisco: Freeman.

Nelson, W.R, Haney, L.N, Ostrom, L.T and Richards, R.E. (1998), 'Structured methods for identifying and correcting potential human errors in space operations', *Acta Astronautica*, 43, pp. 211-222.

Nielsen, J. and Molich, R. (1990), 'Heuristic evaluation of user interfaces', in J.C Chew and J. Whiteside (eds), *Empowering People: CHI 90 Conference Proceedings*, pp. 249-256, Monterey, CA: ACM Press.

Norman, D.A. (1988), *The Design of Everyday Things*, MIT Press, USA.

O'Hare, D., Wiggins, M., Williams, A. and Wong, W. (2000), 'Cognitive task analysis for decision centred design and training', in J. Annett and N.A. Stanton (eds), *Task Analysis*, pp. 170-190, London: Taylor and Francis.

Ogden, G.C. (1987), 'Concept, knowledge and thought', *Annual Review of Psychology*, 38, pp. 203-227.

Olson, J.R., Olson, G.M., (1990) 'The growth of cognitive modeling in human-computer interaction since GOMS', *Human-Computer Interaction*, vol 5, pp. 221-265.

Olson, J.R. and Nielsen, E. (1988), 'The growth of cognitive modelling in human-computer interaction since GOMS', *Human-Computer Interaction*, 3, pp. 309-350.

Oppenheim, A.N. (2001), *Questionnaire Design, Interviewing and Attitude Measurement*, London: Continuum.

Ormerod, T.C. (2000), 'Using task analysis as a primary design method: The SGT approach', in J.M. Schraagen, S.F. Chipman and V.L. Shalin (eds), *Cognitive Task Analysis*, pp.181-200, Mahwah, NJ: Lawrence Erlbaum associates.

Ormerod, T.C. and Shepherd, A. (2003) 'Using task analysis for information requirements specification: The sub-goal template (SGT) method', in D. Diaper and N. Stanton (eds), *The Handbook of Task Analysis for Human-Computer Interaction*, pp. 347-366, Mahwah, NJ: Lawrence Erlbaum associates, Inc.

Ormerod, T.C., Richardson, J. and Shepherd, A. (1998), 'Enhancing the usability of a task analysis method: A notation and environment for requirements', *Ergonomics*, 41(11), pp. 1642-1663, Reprinted in Annett and Stanton (2000) *op.cit.* pp. 114-135.

Patrick, J., Gregov, A. and Halliday, P. (2000), 'Analysing and training task analysis', *Instructional Science*, 28(4), pp. 51-79.

Pennycook, W.A. and Embrey, D.E. (1993), 'An operating approach to error analysis, in Proceedings of the first Biennial Canadian Conference on Process Safety and Loss Management. Edmonton, Alberta, Canada. Waterloo, Ontario, Canada: Institute for Risk Research, University of Waterloo', in W. Karwowski and W.S Marras (eds) (1999), *The Occupational Ergonomics Handbook*, Florida: CRC Press LLC.

Pocock, S., Harrison, M.D., Wright, P.C. and Johnson, P. (2001), 'THEA: a technique for human error assessment early in design', in M. Hirose (ed.), *Interact01*, Amsterdam: IOS Press, pp. 247-254

Polson, P.G., Lewis, C., Rieman, J. and Wharton, C. (1992), 'Cognitive walkthroughs: a method for theory based evaluation of user interfaces', *International Journal of Man-Machine Studies*, 36, pp. 741-773.

Quillian, R. (1969), 'The teachable language comprehender: a simulation program and theory of language', *Communications of the ACM*, 12, pp. 459-476.

Rail Safety and Standards Board (2003), *Master Rule Book*, Newark: Willsons.

Rasmussen, J. (1986), *Information Processing and Human-Machine Interaction*, Amsterdam: North-Holland.

Rasmussen, J., Pejtersen, A. and Goodstein, L.P. (1994), *Cognitive Systems Engineering*, New York: Wiley.

Ravden, S.J. and Johnson, G.I. (1989), *Evaluating Usability of Human-Computer Interfaces: A practical method*, Chichester: Ellis Horwood.

Reason, J. (1990), *Human Error*, Cambridge: Cambridge University Press.

Reason, J., Manstead, A., Stradling, S., Baxter, J. and Campbell, K. (1990), 'Errors and violations on the roads: a real distinction?', *Ergonomics*, 33, pp. 1315-1332.

Redding, R.E. (1989), 'Perspectives on cognitive task-analysis: The state of the state of the art', *Proceedings of the Human Factors Society*, 33, pp. 1353-1357, Santa Monica, CA: Human Factors Society.

Reid, G.B. and Nygren, T.E. (1988) 'The subjective workload assessment technique: A scaling procedure for measuring mental workload', in P.S. Hancock and N. Meshkati (eds), *Human Mental Workload*, Amsterdam, The Netherlands: Elsevier

Roscoe, A. and Ellis, G. (1990), *A Subjective Rating Scale for Assessing Pilot Workload in Flight* (TR90019), Farnborough, UK: RAE.

Roth, E.M., Patterson, E.S. and Mumaw, R.J. (2002), 'Cognitive engineering: Issues in user-centred system design', in J.J Marciniak (ed.), *Encyclopedia of Software Engineering*, 2nd Edition, pp. 163-179, New York: John Wiley and Sons.

Rubio, S., Diaz, E., Martin, J. and Puente, J. M. (2004), 'Evaluation of subjective mental workload: A comparison of SWAT, NASA-TLX, and workload profile methods', *Applied Psychology: An international review*, 53 (1), pp. 61-86.

Salmon, P.M., Stanton, N.A., Young, M.S, Harris, D., Demagalski, J., Marshall, A., Waldmann, T. and Dekker, S. (2003), 'Predicting design induced pilot error: A comparison of SHERPA, human error HAZOP, HEIST and HET, a newly developed aviation specific HEI method', in D. Harris, V. Duffy, M. Smith and C. Stephanidis (eds), *Human-Centred Computing – Cognitive, Social and Ergonomic Aspects*, London: Lawrence Erlbaum Associates.

Salmon, P.M., Stanton, N.A., Walker, G. and Green, D. (in press), 'Situation awareness measurement: A review of applicability for C4i environments', *Journal of Applied Ergonomics*.

Salmon, P.M., Stanton, N.A., Walker, G., McMaster, R. and Green, D. (2005), 'Command and control in the energy distribution domain',. Unpublished manuscript.

Salmon, P.M., Stanton, N.N., Walker, G. and Green, D. (2004), 'Future battlefield visualisation: Investigating data representation in a novel C4i system', in *Proceedings of the Land Warfare 2004 conference*, Defence Science & Technology Organisation, Melbourne, September 2004.

Salmon, P.M., Stanton, N.A., Young, M.S., Harris, D., Demagalski, J., Marshall, A., Waldmann, T. and Dekker, S. (2003a), 'Using existing HEI techniques to predict pilot error: A comparison of SHERPA, HAZOP and HEIST', in, S. Chatty, J. Hansman and G. Boy (eds) *Proceedings of International Conference on Human-Computer Interaction in Aeronautics - HCI-Aero 2002*, Menlo Park, CA: AAAI Press, pp. 126-130.

Salmon, P.M., Stanton, N.A., Young, M.S., Harris, D., Demagalski, J., Marshall, A., Waldmann, T. and Dekker, S. (2003b), 'Predicting design induced pilot error: A comparison of SHERPA, human error HAZOP, HEIST and HET, a newly developed aviation specific HEI method', in D. Harris, V. Duffy, M. Smith and C. Stephanidis (eds), *Human-Centred Computing – Cognitive, Social and Ergonomic Aspects*, London: Lawrence Erlbaum Associates, London.

Salmon, P., Stanton, N.A., Young, M.S., Harris, D., Demagalski, J., Marshall, A., Waldman, T., Dekker, S.W.A. (2002), 'Using existing HEI techniques to predict pilot error: A comparison of SHERPA, HAZOP, and HEIST', *Proceedings of HCI-Aero 2002*, Cambridge, MA.: MIT.

Salvendy, G. (1997), *Handbook of Human Factors and Ergonomics*, 2nd Edition, Canada: John Wiley and Sons.

Sanders, M.S. and McCormick, E.J. (1992), *Human Factors Engineering and Design*, London: McGraw-Hill International Editions.

Schaafstal, A. and Schraagen, J.M. (2000), 'Training of troubleshooting: A structured, task analytical approach', in Schraagen, J.M., Chipman, S.F. and Shalin, V.L. (eds), *Cognitive Task Analysis*, pp. 57-71. Hillsdale, NJ: Erlbaum.

Schraagen, J.M., Chipman, S.F. and Shalin, V.L. (2000), *Cognitive Task Analysis*, USA: Lawrence Erlbaum Associates.

Schweickert, R. (1978), 'A critical path generalization of the additive: factor method', *Journal of Mathematical Psychology*, 18, pp. 105-139.

Scott, J. (1991), *Social Network Analysis: A Handbook*, London: Sage.

Seamster, T.L., Redding, R.E. and Kaempf, G.L. (2000), 'A skill-based cognitive task analysis framework', in Schraagen, J.M., Chipman, S.F. and Shalin, V.L. (eds), *Cognitive Task Analysis*, pp. 135-146, Hillsdale, NJ: Erlbaum.

Seigal, A.I., Bartter, W.D., Wolf, J.J., Knee, H.E. and Haas, P.M. (1984), 'Maintenance Personnel Performance Simulation (MAPPS) Model: Summary Description', NUREG/CR-3626, U.S Nuclear Regulatory Commission, Washington, D.C.

Selcon, S.J. and Taylor, R.M. (1989), 'Evaluation of the situation awareness rating technique (SART) as a tool for aircrew system design', *Proceedings of AGARD Symposium on Situational Awareness in Aerospace operation*, Copenhagen, DK Oct.

Selcon, S.J. and Taylor, R.M. (1989), 'Evaluation of the situational awareness rating technique (SART) as a tool for aircrew system design', *Proceedings of AGARD Symposium on Situational Awareness in Aerospace Operation*, Copenhagen, DK Oct.

Shappell, S.A. and Wiegmann, D.A. (2000), 'The human factors analysis and classification system', Report Number DOT/FAA/AM-00/07, Washington DC: Federal Aviation Administration.

SHEPHERD, A. (1989), 'Analysis and training in information technology tasks', in D. Diaper (ed.), *Task Analysis for Human-Computer Interaction*, pp. 15-55, Chichester: Ellis Horwood.

Shepherd, A. (2002), *Hierarchical Task Analysis*, London: Taylor and Francis.

Shorrock, S.T., Kirwan, B. (1999), 'The development of TRACEr: a technique for the retrospective analysis of cognitive errors in ATC', in Harris, D. (ed.), *Engineering Psychology and Cognitive Ergonomics*, 3, Aldershot, UK: Ashgate Publishing.

Shorrock, S.T., Kirwan, B. (2000), 'Development and application of a human error identification tool for air traffic control', *Applied Ergonomics*, 33, pp. 319-336.

Smalley, J. (2003), 'Cognitive factors in the analysis, design, and assessment of command and control systems', in E. Hollnagel (ed.), *Handbook of Cognitive Task Design*, pp. 223-253, Mahwah, NJ: LEA.

Smith, K. and Hancock, P.A. (1995) 'Situation awareness is adaptive, externally directed consciousness', *Human Factors*, 37, 1, pp. 137-148.

Smolensky, M.W. (1993), 'Toward the physiological measurement of situation awareness: The case for eye movement measurements', in *Proceedings of the Human Factors and Ergonomics Society 37th Annual Meeting*, Santa Monica: Human Factors and Ergonomics Society.

Stanton (in press) 'Hierarchical task analysis, developments, applications and extensions', *Applied Ergonomics*.

Stanton, N.A. and Young, M.S. (1999), *A Guide to Methodology in Ergonomics: Designing for Human Use*, London: Taylor and Francis.

Stanton, N.A. (2002), 'Human error identification in human computer interaction', in J. Jacko and A. Sears (eds), *The Human Computer Interaction Handbook*, pp. 371-383, Mahwah, NJ: Lawrence Erlbaum Associates.

Stanton, N.A. (2004), 'The psychology of task analysis today', in D. Diaper and N.A. Stanton (eds), *Handbook of Task Analysis in Human-Computer Interaction*, pp. 567-584, Mahwah, NJ: Lawrence Erlbaum Associates.

Stanton, N.A. (2005), 'Human factors and ergonomics methods', in N.A. Stanton, A. Hedge, K. Brookhuis, E. Salas and H. Hendrick (eds), *Handbook of Human Factors and Ergonomics Methods*, Boca Raton, Fl: CRC Press.

Stanton, N.A. and Annett, J. (2000), 'Future directions for task analysis', in J. Annett and N.A. Stanton (eds), *Task Analysis*, pp. 229-234, London: Taylor and Francis.

Stanton, N.A. and Baber, C. (2002), 'Error by design: methods to predict device usability', *Design Studies*, 23 (4), pp. 363-384.

Stanton, N.A. and Stevenage, S.V. (1998), 'Learning to predict human error: issues of acceptability, reliability and validity', *Ergonomics*, 41(11), pp. 1737-1756.

Stanton, N.A. and Wilson, J. (2000), 'Human factors: step change improvements in effectiveness and safety', *Drilling Contractor*, Jan/Feb, pp. 46-41.

Stanton, N.A. and Young, M. (1999), *A Guide to Methodology in Ergonomics: Designing for human use*, London: Taylor and Francis.

Stanton, N.A. and Young, M.S. (1998), 'Is utility in the mind of the beholder? A review of ergonomics methods', *Applied Ergonomics*, 29 (1) pp. 41-54

Stanton, N.A. and Young, M.S. (1999), 'What price ergonomics?', *Nature*, 399, pp. 197-198.

Stanton, N.A. (1995), 'Analysing worker activity: a new approach to risk assessment?', *Health and Safety Bulletin*, 240, (December), pp. 9-11.

Stanton, N.A. (2004), 'The psychology of task analysis today', in D. Diaper and N.S. Stanton (eds), *The Handbook of Task Analysis for Human-Computer Interaction*, New Jersey: Lawrence Erlbaum Associates.

Stanton, N.A. and Baber, C. (1996a), 'A systems approach to human error identification', *Safety Science*, 22, pp. 215-228.

Stanton, N.A. and Baber, C. (1996b), 'Task analysis for error identification: applying HEI to product design and evaluation', in P.W. Jordan, B. Thomas, B.A. Weerdmeester and I.L. McClelland (eds), *Usability Evaluation in Industry*, pp. 215-224, London: Taylor and Francis.

Stanton, N.A. and Baber, C. (1998), 'A systems analysis of consumer products', in N.A. Stanton (ed.), *Human factors in consumer products*, pp. 75-90, London: Taylor and Francis.

Stanton, N.A. and Baber, C. (2002), 'Error by design: methods for predicting device usability', *Design Studies*, 23 (4), pp. 363-384.

Stanton, N.A., Baber, C. and Young, M.S. (2005), 'Observation', in N.A. Stanton et al. (eds), *Handbook of Human Factors and Ergonomics Methods*, pp. 28.1-28.7, London: CRC.

Stanton, N.A., Stewart, R., Harris, D., Houghton, R.J., Baber, C., McMaster, R., Salmon, P., Hoyle. G., Walker, G., Young. M.S., Linsell, M., Dymott, R. and Green, D. (2005), 'Distributed situation awareness in dynamic systems: theoretical development and application of an ergonomics methodology', submitted to *Ergonomics*.

Stanton, N.A., Chambers, P.R.G. and Piggott, J. (2001), 'Situational awareness and safety', *Safety Science*, 39, pp. 189-204.

Stanton, N.A., Hedge, A., Salas, E., Hendrick, H. and Brookhaus, K. (2005), *Handbook of Human Factors and Ergonomics Methods*, London: Taylor and Francis.

Stanton, N.A. (2003), 'Human error identification in human computer interaction', in J. Jacko and A. Sears (eds), *The Handbook of Human-Computer Interaction*, Mahwah, NJ: Lawrence Erlbaum Associates.

Staples, L.J. (1993), 'The task analysis process for a new reactor', *Proceedings of the Human Factors and Ergonomics Society 37th Annual Meeting - Designing for Diversity*, Seattle, Washington, October 11-15, 1993, The Human Factors and Ergonomics Society, Santa Monica, California, pp. 1024-1028.

Stoner, H.A., Wiese, E.E. and Lee, J.D. (2003), 'Applying ecological interface design to the driving domain: The results of an abstraction hierarchy analysis', in *Proceedings of the Human Factors and Ergonomics Society 47th Annual meeting*, 2003.

Swann, C.D. and Preston, M.L. (1995), 'Twenty-five years of HAZOPs', *Journal of Loss Prevention in the Process Industries*, 8, 6, 1995, pp. 349-353.

Swain, A.D. and Guttmann, H.E. (1983), 'A handbook of human reliability analysis with emphasis on nuclear power plant applications', NUREG/CR-1278, USNRC, Washington, DC-20555.

Swezey, R.W., Owens, J.M., Bergondy, M.L. and Salas, E. (2000), 'Task and training requirements analysis methodology (TTRAM): An analytic methodology for identifying potential training uses of simulator networks in teamwork-intensive task environments', in J. Annett and N. Stanton (eds), *Task Analysis*, pp. 150–169, London: Taylor and Francis.

Taylor, R.M. (1990), 'Situational Awareness Rating Technique (SART): The development of a tool for aircrew systems design', in *Situational Awareness in Aerospace Operations* (AGARD-CP-478) pp. 3/1 –3/17, Neuilly Sur Seine, France: NATO-AGARD.

Thornton, G.E. and Zorich, S. (1980), 'Training to improve observer accuracy, *Journal of Applied Psychology*, 65, 351-354

Tsang, P.S. and Velazquez, V.L. (1996), 'Diagnosticity and multidimensional subjective workload ratings', *Ergonomics*, 39, pp. 358-381.

Van Welie, M. and Van Der Veer, G. (2003), 'Groupware task analysis', in E. Hollnagel (ed.), *Handbook of Cognitive Task Design*, pp 447-477, NJ: Lawrence Erlbaum Associates Inc.

Verplank, B., Fulton, J., Black, A. and Moggridge, B. (1993), 'Observation and Invention – Use of scenarios in interaction design', Tutorial notes for InterCHI 93. Amsterdam.

Vicente, K.J. (1999), *Cognitive Work Analysis: Towards safe, productive, and healthy computer-based work*, Mahwah, NJ: Lawrence Erlbaum Associates, Inc.

Vidulich, M.A. (1989), 'The use of judgement matrices in subjective workload assessment: The subjective Workload Dominance (SWORD) technique', in *Proceedings of the Human Factors Society 33rd Annual Meeting*, pp. 1406-1410, Santa Monica, CA: Human Factors Society.

Vidulich, M.A. and Hughes, E.R. (1991), 'Testing a subjective metric of situation awareness', in *Proceedings of the Human Factors Society 35th Annual meeting*, pp. 1307–1311.

Vidulich, M.A.and Tsang, P.S. (1985), 'Assessing subjective workload assessment. A comparison of SWAT and the NASA bipolar methods', in *Proceedings of the Human Factors Society 29th Annual Meeting*, Santa Monica, CA: Human Factors Society, pp. 71-75.

Vidulich, M.A. and Tsang, P.S. (1986a), *Collecting NASA Workload Ratings*, Moffett Field, CA: NASA Ames Research Center.

Vidulich, M.A. and Tsang, P.S. (1986b), 'Technique of subjective workload assessment: A comparison of SWAT and the NASA bipolar method', *Ergonomics*, 29 (11), 1385-1398.

Vidulich, M.A., Ward, G.F. and Schueren, J. (1991), 'Using subjective workload dominance (SWORD) technique for projective workload assessment', *Human Factors*, 33, 6, pp. 677-691.

Waag, W.L. and Houck, M.R (1994), 'Tools for assessing situational awareness in an operational fighter environment', *Aviation, Space and Environmental Medicine*, 65(5) A13-A19.

Walker, G.H., Gibson, H., Stanton, N.A., Baber, C., Salmon, P. and Green, D. (2005), 'Event analysis of systemic teamwork (EAST): A novel integration of ergonomics methods to analyse C4i activity'. Submitted to a *Special Issue of Ergonomics on C4i.*

Walker, G.H., Stanton, N.A. and Young, M.S. (2001), 'Hierarchical task analysis of driving: A new research tool', in M.A. Hanson (ed.), *Contemporary Ergonomics 2001*, London: Taylor and Francis, pp. 435-440.

Walker, G.H. (2004), 'Verbal protocol analysis', in N.A. Stanton, A. Hedge, K. Brookhuis, E. Salas and H. Hendrick (eds), *Handbook of Human Factors Methods*, Boca Raton, USA: CRC Press.

Walker, G.H., Gibson, H., Baber, C., and Stanton, N. A.. (2004), Work package 1.1.3: Report on results of WP1.1 EAST methodology for railway data: possession scenario. *Defence Technology Centre for Human Factors Integration.*

Walker, G.H., Stanton, N.A. and Young, M.S. (2001), 'An on-road investigation of vehicle feedback and its role in driver cognition: Implications for cognitive ergonomics', *International Journal of Cognitive Ergonomics*, 5(4), pp. 421-444.

Walker, G.H. (2005), 'Verbal protocol analysis', in N.A. Stanton; A. Hedge, K. Brookhuis; E. Salas and H. Hendrick (eds), *The Handbook of Human Factors and Ergonomics Methods*, Boca Raton, Fl: CRC Press.

Wasserman, S. and Faust, K. (1994), *Social Network Analysis: Methods and Applications*, Cambridge University Press, Cambridge.

Watts, L.A. and Monk, A.F. (2000), 'Reasoning about tasks, activities and technology to support collaboration', in J. Annett and N. Stanton (eds), *Task Analysis*, pp. 55-78, UK, Taylor and Francis.

Weber, R.P. (1990), *Basic Content Analysis*, Sage Publications, London.

Weerdmeester B. A. and I.L. McClelland (eds), *Usability Evaluation in Industry*, pp. 215-224, London: Taylor and Francis.

Van Welie, M. and van der Veer, G.C. (2003), 'Groupware task analysis', in E. Hollnagel (ed.) *Handbook of Cognitive Task Design*, New Jersey: Lawrence Erlbaum Associates, pp. 447-476.

Whalley, S. J. (1988), 'Minimising the cause of human error', in B. Kirwan and L.K. Ainsworth (eds) *A Guide to Task Analysis*, London: Taylor and Francis.

Whalley. S.J. and Kirwan, B. (1989), 'An evaluation of five human error identification techniques', *Paper presented at the 5th International Loss Prevention Symposium*, Oslo, June.

Wickens, C.D., Gordon, S.E. and Lui, Y. (1998), *An Introduction to Human Factors Engineering*, New York: Longman.

Wickens, C.D. (1992), *Engineering Psychology and Human Performance*, New York: Harper Collins.

Wierwille, W.W. and Eggemeier, F.T. (1993), 'Recommendations for mental workload measurement in a test and evaluation environment', *Human Factors*, 35, pp. 263-282.

Wilkinson P.R. (1992), 'The Integration of Advanced Cockpit and Systems Design', AGARD Avionics Panel Symposium, May 1992 Madrid, AGARD-CP-521 Paper 26.

Williams, J.C. (1986), 'HEART – a proposed method for assessing and reducing human error', in *9th Advances in Reliability Technology Symposium*, University of Bradford.

Williams, J.C. (1989), 'Validation of human reliability assessment techniques', *Reliability Engineering*, 11, pp. 149-162.

Wilson, J.R. (1995), 'A framework and context for ergonomics methodology', in J.R. Wilson and E.N. Corlett (eds), *Evaluation of Human Work*, 2nd Edition, London: Taylor and Francis, pp. 1-39.

Wilson, J.R. and Corlett, N.E. (1995), *Evaluation of Human Work: A Practical Ergonomics Methodology*, London: Taylor and Francis.

Woodson, W., Tillmand, B., and Tillman, P. (1992), *Human Factors Design Handbook*, New York, McGraw-Hill Inc.

Yamaoka, T. and Baber, C. (2000), '3 point task analysis and human error estimation', *Proceedings of the Human Interface Symposium 2000*, Tokyo, Japan, pp. 395-398.

Young, M. and Stanton, N.A. (1997), 'Automobile automation', *International Journal of Cognitive Ergonomics*, 1 (4) pp. 325-336.

Young, M.S. and Stanton, N.A. (2001), 'Mental workload: theory, measurement and application', in W. Karwowski (ed.), *International Encyclopedia of Ergonomics and Human Factors - Volume 1*, London: Taylor and Francis.

Young, M.S. and Stanton, N.A (2004), 'Taking the load off: investigations of how Adaptive Cruise Control affects mental workload', *Ergonomics*, 47 (8), pp. 1014-1035.

Zachary, W. W., Ryder, J. M., & Hicinbothom, J. H. (1998), 'Cognitive task analysis and modeling of decision making in complex environments' in Cannon-Bowers, Janis A. (Ed); Salas, Eduardo (Ed). (1998). Making decisions under stress: Implications for individual and team training. (pp. 315-344). Washington, DC, US: American Psychological Association.

Index